TABLE OF CONTENTS

COVER — DESCRIPTION

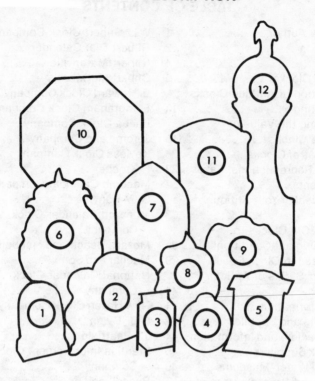

1. **TERRY CLOCK CO.**, black iron case. 8¼" x 5¼". 3½" dial. 8 Day. spring. strike. c. 1870 .... **$110.00** **$130.00**

2. **ANSONIA**, black enamel iron case. 12" x 10½". 4" paper dial. 8 Day. spring. strike. c. 1905 .... 140.00 165.00

3. **HENRY MARCH**, French carriage clock. oriental bird and bamboo motif. 8 Day. hour and half hour strike. hour repeat 2750.00 3250.00

4. **ANSONIA**, "Giant" round alarm. 8 Day. spring. strike 90.00 100.00

5. **WELCH**, miniature "Patti." the super star in minis. c. 1880 .... 3200.00 3600.00

6. **ANSONIA**, "Lydia." gold plated bronze clock. H. 19½". open escapement. 8 Day. spring. cathedral gong. half hour strike. c. 1891 ...... 1150.00 1350.00

7. **WELCH**, late J.C. Brown. fine ripple front. rosewood. behive. H. 19". cut glass tablet. c. 1860 .... 1075.00 1275.00

8. **WATERBURY**, Valhalla. Art Noveau. gold plated white metal. H. 12". 4" dial. 8 Day. spring. half hour strike. original finish. c. 1890 .... 200.00 250.00

9. **ANSONIA**, procelain. 8 Day. spring. hour and half hour strike. c. 1900 .... 300.00 400.00

10. **GILBERT**, regulator "B." oak. H. 29". 8 Day. spring. hour and half hour strike. simple calendar. c. 1900 .... 325.00 375.00

11. **ITHACA**, "Melrose." 22" x 12". 6" deep. 8 Day. spring. hour and half hour strike. 6" and 8" glass calendar dial in black and gold. cut glass pendulum bob. cherry case. ebony finish 6000.00 7000.00

12. **HOWARD**, banjo. 42" x 10". 4" deep. 8 Day. weight and pendulum. solid brass eagle. siderails and bezel. mahogany or walnut case. 7½" dial. illustrated is Mount Vernon with Washington. c. 1918 .... 2500.00 3200.00

THE OFFICIAL PRICE GUIDE TO

antique CLOCKS

BY
ROY EHRHARDT

EDITOR
THOMAS E. HUDGEONS III

FIRST EDITION

THE HOUSE OF COLLECTIBLES, INC., ORLANDO, FLORIDA 32809

ACKNOWLEDGEMENTS

The values shown in this book have been supplied by collectors and dealers from all over the United States. I'd like to take this opportunity to say thanks for the help they have given me.

Fred and Bill Andrus, Bossier City, LA; Dr. Douglas Beck, Baton Rouge, LA; Clyde and Betty Brown, Akron, OH; Mrs. William Charles Bruer, Kansas City, MO; Dr. Warner Bundens, Woodbury, NJ; Ralph Colorado, Grand Rapids, MI; Bob Coonfield, Oklahoma City, OK; Stewart Dow (deceased), Akron, OH; Sherry L. Ehrhardt, Grandview, MO; James Eller, Greensboro, NC; Ed Getman, Newton, MA; Roy Good, Memphis, TN; L.E. "Bud" Grove, Healdsburg, CA; Fred Hansen, Montgomery, NY; Robert Hansen, New Hampton, NY; Russell Henschel, Fairview Heights, IL; Tran Du Ly, Arlington, VA; Bob Mathews, Orlando, FL; Wiley McNeil, Greensboro, NC; Harry Neames, Baton Rouge, LA; Mr. and Mrs. E. H. Parkhurst, Jr., Lancaster, PA; Daryl Penniston, Lake Charles, LA; T. R. Pritts, Decatur, OL; Gregg Reddick, Dubuque, IA; Roger Rees, Rockford, IL; Shirley Shelley, Belton, MO; Royce Shepard, Battle Creek, MI; Dr. Sam Simmons, Atlanta, GA; Jim Solo, Des Moines, IA; H.A. Soper, Harrison, AR; Ron Starnes, Tulsa, OK; Douglas Thomas, Tullhoma, TN; Thomas Tognetti, San Rafael, CA; Col. George Townsend, Alma, MI; Deanna Ward, Lathrop, MO; Stacy Wood, NAWCC Museum Curator, Columbia, PA; Dick Ziebell, Ipswich, MA. Special recognition to Malvern (Red) Rabeneck, Clock Historian, a long-time collector and researcher of American Clocks. Red has worked closely with me on each of my clock books, spending many hours in consultations and pricing sessions. He is the contributor of the historical text on pages 3-41 and of the glossary.

PHOTOGRAPHIC RECOGNITION

Cover and Color Section Photographs: Photographer — Bernie Markell, Orlando, FL 32806; Location — Courtesy of NAWCC, The National Association of Watch and Clock Collectors, Inc., Columbia, PA 17512.

Color Separations: World Color, Ormond Beach, FL 32074.

IMPORTANT NOTICE. All of the information, including valuations, in this book has been compiled from the most reliable sources, and every effort has been made to eliminate errors and questionable data. Nevertheless the possibility of error, in a work of such immense scope, always exists. The publisher will not be held responsible for losses which may occur, in the purchase, sale, or other transaction of items, because of information contained herein. Readers who feel they have discovered errors are invited to WRITE and inform us, so they may be corrected in subsequent editions. Those seeking further information on the topics covered in this book, are advised to refer to the complete line of Official Price Guides published by The House of Collectibles.

Published by: The House of Collectibles, Inc.
Orlando Central Park
1900 Premier Row
Orlando, FL 32809
Phone: (305) 857-9095

Printed in the United States of America

Library of Congress Catalog Card Number: 82-82663

ISBN: 0-87637-364-3 / Paperback

ABOUT THE AUTHOR

The author is a long-time member of the National Association of Watch and Clock collectors, attending many Regional and Chapter meetings in order to keep in close contact with the "heartbeat" of clock and watch collectors and dealers. He travels extensively each year attending NAWCC Marts, antique shows, gun shows, flea markets, etc., buying, selling and trading clocks and watches.

He was awarded an NAWCC Fellowship in 1977 in recognition of his contribution to his fellow collectors, and in 1981 was elected a Director of that Association. He receives many requests from various Regionals and Chapters to participate in their meetings as a guest speaker, and is internationally known as an authority in the field of clocks and watches.

ROY EHRHARDT

INTRODUCTION

Clocks appear to be a very practical collectible until the collector looks around the room one day and realizes that he does not need 20 or 30 faces to tell the time. Fascination with sizes, shapes, mechanisms and cases is what attracts the clock collector.

Early American clocks are generally "grandfather" or "grandmother" clocks and are seven to nine feet tall and three to five feet tall respectively. They were hand-crafted in a few Eastern cities and were too expensive, even when new, for anyone but the wealthy to afford. Near the end of the 18th century, Eli Terry, a Connecticut clockmaker, improved and miniaturized the movements of these tall clocks into models about two feet tall that were priced at about $15, well within the budget of many families. Terry was assisted by his apprentice, Seth Thomas, which later became the best known New England clockmaker. These clocks had internal movements mass produced of wood to keep the price low. In 1839, brass movements were first mass produced for clocks by Chauncey Jerome. Cheap, accurate shelf clocks were then available to nearly everyone.

Most of the appeal of the 19th century clocks can be attributed to their imaginative and sometimes elaborate cases. Engraved brass faces and scene painted below the face are also attractive to some collectors. Other clocks may be decorated with fancy wooden scrolls, ornate arches, steeples or pillars made of wood, iron or even marble. Shapes and case materials are almost limitless.

Many clocks of the 19th century are extremely expensive when found in perfect condition. The same clocks needing some minor mechanical repair or case refinishing may be purchased much more reasonably. Some collectors run newspaper ads offering to buy any clock, regardless of condition. Unexpected bargains may be obtained in this manner, especially if the collector is able to do his own repairs.

Only the buyer can determine the price of an article. The price he pays is determined by his need and desire. For a clock collector, a price guide is valuable because it will modulate his desire with the price that other collectors are willing to pay. It will also temper his judgment with knowledge. Collectors' aspirations towards a clock stems from an appreciation of its' beauty, but since beauty is in the eye of the beholder, only he can place a price on what he sees. Age and rarity are desired by many collectors, and this price guide will help in judging these qualities. Many clocks that have neither great age nor rarity, command good prices simply because all collectors like to have one in their collection.

Except in rare cases, American clocks were never given serial numbers, and subsequent production figures are rarely known. The question of age is answered by a combination of factors, and rarity becomes a matter of judgment and experience. The age of a clock can often be determined by checking the label, especially on the earlier clocks. The exact form of the manufacturer's name or the address as given on the label, or the printer's name and address, will often tell the knowledgeable collector the date the clock was manufactured. Often the style of the clock will indicate within a 20 year period, when it was manufactured. Sometimes certain construction features will indicate the latest time that it was likely to have been made. Many of these features will be pointed out in this book, and a detailed study of this and following price guides will give the serious collector much of the information he needs to judge the age and rarity of clocks.

This book is designed to answer the most important questions asked by anyone looking at a clock they have not seen before. The first question, naturally, is; "How much is it worth?" And next; "How old is it?" "When and by whom was it made?" And finally; "Is it original?" "Is it rare?" The answers to the latter questions have much to do with the answer to the first, and when you become adept at answering all of these questions about clocks, you will find that you have become a knowledgeable collector.

Throughout the world there is an active interest in old clocks. Out of necessity, the collector often finds himself involved in their repair and restoration, in need of advice, and the unique expertise that binds antique clock collectors together. Today, over 30,000 people enjoy a world wide membership in a common pursuit. The National Association of Watch and Clock Collectors, Inc., begun in 1943, brings people who are interested in all phases of time-keeping in touch with each other. As a means of the enriching the horological experience, this-non profit, scientific, and educational corporation maintains a museum and library for its' members situated in the Borough of Columbia, on the eastern bank of the Susquehanna River, "within historic Lancaster County, Pennsylvania, where a continuous heritage of clock and watchmaking, spans two and one quarter centuries."

The Museum offers glimpses of rare watches, clocks, and time-keeping tools, for the collectors' leisurely perusal. These items range from scarce collectibles to modern acquisitions as sophisticated as the famed "Atomic Clock."

The Association's library houses valuable horological information in the form of records, patents, photographs, manufacturers' catalogues, and slide/tape programs. Most of the recommended readings suggested in this book, were endorsed by the National Association of Watch and Clock Collectors.

In addition the NAWCC publishes a bi-monthly magazine called the Bulletin. It is an international publication devoted to technical and historical information and problem solving. Each issue explores a specific theme, such as chime or musical clocks, chronometer manufacturing, etc. The Bulletin maintains a panel of fifty authorities, to dig up even the most elusive aspects of horology. The activities (including regional meets, conventions, and seminars) of more than one hundred world wide chapters are outlined here also.

The Mart, another bi-monthly publication, is an informal listing, in which members post items they wish to trade, sell, or buy. The Mart maintains an impressive circulation of over 30,000, as does the Bulletin. A roster of members is available upon request, and a listing of books available in the lending library will serve to further broaden the antique clock and watch collectors educational horizons.

The above listed benefits are available only to members, and your dues are tax deductible. For further information write: NAWCC, Box 33, Columbia, Pennsylvania, 17512.

Another national association, devoted to horology, repairs and providing information for their members (as well as information to inquirers) is: American Watchmakers Institute, Inc., P.O. Box 11011, Cincinnati, Ohio, 45211.

Whether you are an amateur or professional antique watch and clock collector, membership in a professional organization will keep you up to date, knowledgeable, and in good professional standing with your colleagues. It is also an enjoyable way to meet and socialize with people who have something in common. Clocks and more clocks!

HOROLOGY

A discussion of antique watch and clock collecting, seems incomplete without a short discussion of horology, the science of timekeeping. In actuality timekeeping in itself, is not a science. Foreign tribes measured time by the intervals expended in cooking a pot of rice. The early Moslems distinguished night and day through a pile of mixed, black and white thread filaments; day began when the colors of the threads could be determined in the natural light. A popular contemporary novelist, fictionalizes at length about a reclusive band of native Americans living in the caves of California and devoting their lives to a unique system of timekeeping that measured intervals by falling rocks, weather variations, or disruptions such as earthquakes. Actually this notion of clockworks is not at all far fetched, as the effects of tides, the melting of snow every year at polar ice caps, and even the sap rising or falling in the trees affects the regularity of the earth's rotation. It is an awareness of these variations in timekeeping, and an interest in accuracy, that comprise the science of horology.

The sun is not a very precise timekeeper. It's path tilts and falls somewhat short of a complete circle, making the solar days different in length. The Earth itself does not turn evenly on its axis, because the axis is constantly changing. Meanwhile, clocks behave as if these irregularities do not exist, and continue giving equal hours. The Earth actually loses a day every twelve months or so, by going around the sun and turning on its own axis. This does not seem like much, unless you begin to take decades and centuries into account. Then the implications of accuracy tend to take on a much greater importance.

Astronomers compensated for time losses, by identifying fixed celestial signposts in the sky, otherwise known as "clock stars," which, trail across the sky as the Earth rotates. Using a telescope, astronomers jot down the time the clock star intersects with a straight line across the eyepiece. The next time the apparent passage takes place marks the interval of 24 "sidereal" hours, or the equivalent of the sidereal day. Observatory clocks in astronomers' laboratories often keep track of sidereal time.

In terms of accuracy, the invention of the atomic clock, is by far the most reliable of all timekeeping instruments. Changes in the core of the Earth cause it to gain time in the summer, and lose time in the winter. Every 5000 million years we lose about one year, due to this slow but progressive loss of momentum. When atomic time superseded astronomical time, adjustments had to be made continuously, to keep atomic clocks synchronized with Earth. Since then, leap seconds have been applied simultaneously in several countries, to compensate for time deficits, based on a coordinated universal time, set precisely ten seconds behind international atomic time.

For most of the Earth, an atomic clock would be a great boon to a more precise time service, particularly, if it were to be positioned in a satellite. Space travel too suffers from time lags which have to be carefully determined to account for millions of miles of distance. Accuracy of time can make a difference in life or death situations.

The passage of time itself cannot be influenced, however. Realities or visions of life outside a time order, are beyond the power of the clockmaker. Like a still life encased within a glass bubble, our moments follow each other sequentially. Horology, and its multifaceted symbol, the clock, form the basis of our touch with reality. The time is always "now."

HISTORY OF CLOCKS

INDUSTRIAL REVOLUTION

By far the most interesting "invention" in the field of horology, belongs to the undocumented case of a former fifteenth century Earl, who allegedly invented a water clock that operated solely on the sketchily refined beverage of the time-namely mead. His drawbridge was always lowered to the local population, helpfully attempting to dispose of the "used clock water."

At any rate, the Industrial Revolution, begun in Britain (where paradoxically it had the least influence on well known clockmakers), spread to America, making certain that miraculous inventions such as the one outlined above, would not be lost for posterity.

An Englishman, named Thomas Harland is credited with making the first clocks in America, in quantity, from interchangeable parts. Eli Terry, at the age of fourteen was apprenticed to a man who had picked up Harland's skill. Terry was subsequently the recipient of the first clock patent issued by that United States Office in the late eighteenth century. The patent concerned an equation clock, with two minute hands having a center in common, each of dissimilar hue and form, one showing mean time of day and the other apparent or sundial time.

Terry's first factory in 1802 was little more than a small workshop built over a running stream, with a water-wheel to operate the machinery.

After four years, he was making two hundred clocks a year.

Eventually many old and respected clockmakers were put out of business by machine made clocks, but there was obviously no turning back. The conversion of fossil fuels into energy further hurried along the principles of automation, as did mass production.

Today, the field of electronics comprise the "new" industrial revolution, replacing more than man's muscles (as the first did) but also his brain power, skills, and decision making process. An example reflecting this shift in the public's imagination, are the popular quartz watches, as accurate as the best precision clocks of the previous century.

This trend has resulted in a fluctuating international watch market, with the Americans, Swiss and Japanese, as the main manufacturers. The newest technological discoveries have been, and will continue to be applied to the watch and clock industry.

PERIODS IN CLOCK PRODUCTION

A convenient and easy to remember classification of the periods in clock production are as follows:

COLONIAL - up to 1800: Tall case and hangups or wags on the wall.

EMPIRE - 1800 to 1840: Mostly wood works, shelf and tall case, 8 Day and 30 Hour.

VICTORIAN - 1840 to 1890: Period of greatest production and greatest variety.

MODERN - 1890 to 1940: Period of change to electric clocks operated by synchronous motors.

CONTEMPORARY - World War II to present: Period of change to electronic timekeepers.

The exact years of the various periods are unimportant, as change is usually gradual and production of various types overlaps the periods.

In the 1950's, when the National Association of Watch and Clock Collectors was growing nicely (but no one yet dreamed of the explosion of collectors of the 60's and 70's), the most eminent collectors decreed that a clock was not an antique unless it was at least 100 years old. Newer clocks were neo-antiques — collectible but not too important. That put the dividing line at 1850, and surprisingly (to many of the newer collectors) it has remained there. Today as you check the old and new articles, books, booklets, monographs, etc., you become well acquainted with the early individual makers and the partnerships that produced the distinctive Pillar & Scrolls, Triple Deckers, Weight Banjos, Carved Column and Splat, etc. — the museum pieces that we would all like to own but can't afford even if there were enough to go around.

The march of time continues; the Colonial Tall Case that could sometimes be obtained for $200, in the 50's now costs as much as $10,000.00. The 100-year-old criteria now includes a large part of the mass production era, and in not much over a quarter of a century hence will include electric clocks. To a 20-year-old, a clock a quarter of a century old may appear to be an antique, and not too many years later it certainly is an antique. The new collector entering the hobby may start out with 50-year-old alarms or kitchen clocks, and soon progress to the extremely attractive clocks of the Victorian era, 1850 to 1890.

If the old, or long time experienced collector feels that the hundred year limit is a legitimate criteria, at least let us admit that interesting collector items have been produced throughout the history of clock production.

AMERICAN CLOCKS

An American Clock Price Guide should properly start about 1850. Clocks made before that time, i.e. the tall case, the Pillar and Scroll, the wood movement clocks, etc., not made in extremely large quantities, survive in small quantities, and are usually called museum pieces. After 1800, Eli Terry started the development of mass production techniques in making clock works, and clock works became the first CIVILIAN product to be mass produced. These techniques were further refined and developed by Chauncey Jerome to produce both the works and the cases; however, production before 1850 was still small compared to that indicted by Henry Terry's estimate in 1870 of one to one and half million annually. Therefore, prices paid for these early clocks are a highly individual matter, depending on the buyer's desire and finances. If you find a tall case by Daniel Burnap, whose production during his lifetime was said to be 51 clocks, or a Pillar and Scroll by Eli Terry, Jr., are not likely to have another opportunity to purchase one of these. The same may be said of many other clocks made before 1850.

After 1840, many changes came about that resulted in the later great production of clocks. Wood works were abandoned, the 30 hr. brass works lowered the prices of clocks dramatically, then the development of the spring works paved the way for a variety of new case designs. The development of the Balance Wheel movement allowed a still greater variation in case design, and the clock industry saw the development of novelties, marines, regulators, calendars, and "Parlor Clocks", which were designed to compete with French clocks. The variety of designs became so profuse that in 1892 Hiram Camp wrote that the dealers had become amazed and bewildered to such an existent as to paralyze the Trade, the expectation of something new preventing the sale of the old. After 1840 the character of the manufacturers also began to change.

Before this time the manufacturers were mostly individual clockmakers, or family companies. In 1840 the largest factory was the Jerome Company, which was owned by Chauncey Jerome. In 1842 export of clocks to England by Jerome started the exportation of clocks to all parts of the world. In 1844 he built a new factory in New Haven, but lost his factory in Bristol by fire in 1845. In 1855 the Jerome Manufacturing Company, as it was known then, failed. The one of the first to be a corporation with a group of unrelated (by blood) stockholders. This company bought Jerome's property after the failure, and became one of the larger companies. C. Jerome was said to have influenced the organizing of the Ansonia Clock Company and the Waterbury Clock Company. These three companies, plus Seth Thomas, E. N. Welch, Ingraham Clock Company, and Gilbert Clock Company became the major producers.

Around 1850 Jerome began issuing catalogs. This practice was adopted by all clock manufacturers, and gave us some of our best records of the clocks produced. The great number of clocks produced in the great variety of designs after 1850, resulting in the survival of sufficient quantities for extensive collector trading, makes these clocks the proper subject for a price guide to help a collector identify an price the clocks that he finds in his searches.

The Victorian period in clock production may be said to encompass the years 1840-1890. Millions of clocks were produced in this period, but the survival rate is small. In 1851 there were 31 clock factories in operation. In 1853 and 1854, Jerome Mfg. Co. produced about 444,000 per year, while J. C. Brown produced 100,000, and a little later Ansonia Clock Company was producing 150,000. The attrition rate of the factories was high. In the ten years ending in 1856, four factories burned, nine failed and five closed because of low prices, leaving 13 factories with an annual production of 143,000. In 1867 New Haven Clock Company was the largest factory, with Seth Thomas second in size. New Haven was producing 200,000 annually, while Seth Thomas, William L. Gilbert, E. N. Welch and Benedict & Burham combined, had a production of 300,000.

The case styles of clocks produced during the Victorian period and the approximate period of greatest production by the entire industry is indicated by the following table:

O.G., Brass Works	1838-1918
Steeple	1843-on
Acorn	1847-1850
Banjo	1842-on
Gallery	1845-on
Iron Front	1850-1870
Connecticut Shelf	1860-1890

These were 30 Hour and 8 Day spring driven brass works in wood cases 10 to 20 inches high with 5 to 6 inch dials, Moon, Spade, or Maltese Hands, with tablet printed or mirrored, usually time and strike, sometime with alarm.

Cottage	1875-1890
Walnut Parlor	1875-1900

Includes both those called shelf clocks and kitchen clocks.

Oak Kitchen	1880-1915

Black Mantel 1880–1920
Round or Drum Alarms 1880–present
Novelties 1875–1900
Drop Octagon 1875–on
Regulators 1860–present

Parlor Regulators: Usually dead beat escapement, small wood pendulum rod, sometimes covered with gold leaf, with retaining power. Good time keepers.

Jewelers Regulators: Often with Swiss or other imported pin wheel movements, usually mercurial or gridiron compensating pendulums. These were often elaborate, probably because the jeweler considered them good advertising fixtures.

Balance Wheel Clocks 1850–present

Earliest patent to Ely Terry in 1845. Earliest produced were in wood Octagon cases, later in round brass cases, and by 1885 the brass cases were often nickel plated.

Papier-mâché Clocks . . . . 1850–prob. 1858?

Also used during WWII as alarm clock cases.

Calendars 1862–present
Simple Calendar.
Double Dial in both Simple and Perpetual.

It will be noted that many of the above styles were produced long after the Victorian period. The period after the Victorian may be called the "new" or perhaps even the modern period. It has seen the introduction of the following styles:

Art Nouveau 1890–1910
Mission 1900–1930

This plain, black-finished style is felt by some to have been a reaction to the elaborate styles of the Victorian period.

China or Porcelain 1890–present
Imitation French 1890–1920

Swinging, Statues, Cast. Usually gold or silver plated, as best exemplified by the Jennings Bros. Manufacturing Company's clocks.

Tambours (Humpbacks) 1900–present
Electric 1916–present

Many collectors use common construction features to determine quickly if a clock is likely to be old. An example is the lantern pinion pioneered by Chauncey Jerome, and once described by Henry Terry as a cheap wire pinion. It had become almost standard by 1870, and a clock with these pinions was almost certain to have been made after 1850. Another is the plate posts, with many collectors using the date of 1885 as the cutoff date for the use of pins to retain the plates. Therefore, if the works have pinned plates, it was most likely made before 1885. Hand nuts are also watched by some, believing that their use was rare in the Victorian period, and became common after the turn of the century. The style of the hands and dial would be an indication of the age if they could be depended on to be the originals. An original tablet can give an indication, as the reverse paintings of the early Empire period gave way to decals and etched glass tablets in the Victorian period.

Nickel plating was well established by 1875 but was not often used before approximately 1870, and bells were rarely used after the turn of the century, with wire gongs as the standard. Until about 1850, American clocks struck hours only.

While the construction features and the type and style of the clock will give you an idea of the probable age of the clock, the label will usually be the one thing that will determine the age and maker faster and easier than any other feature; therefore, it follows that the condition of the label has a definite effect upon the value of the clock.

The plates of the brass works usually have some identifying mark, symbol, or name stamped on them, and if this does not agree with the label it is important to ask "Why?" Was the maker on the label a case maker who purchased his movements, as did Florence Kroeber? Is the name on the label a sales agent? Have the works been changed, destroying the originality of the clock? Is it a fake?

THE VICTORIAN PERIOD OF CLOCK PRODUCTION

There has been so much written about the Colonial Period of clock production, there is no point in discussing it in this book. Clocks produced by the craftsmen of that age are now so rare and expensive that the average collector will see one only in a museum. The same is rapidly becoming true with the Empire Period, which stretched roughly from 1800 to 1840. These periods are not absolute and clear cut, but have a tendency to overlap into the years that we have selected as the beginning and end of certain periods.

The Empire Period actually represents a type of transition in which the production of clocks was developed from the work of the individual craftsman (who built not only his product but also his tools to make that product) to mass production. During the Empire Period. Eli Terry and Chauncey Jerome developed the mass production method that was used and improved upon during the Victorian Period.

The period immediately before and during the Victorian Period was probably one of the most inventive times of human history, not in terms of world-shaking inventions but rather in terms of small inventions, that had a profound effect upon human life.

To reach a true understanding of the Victorian Period it is necessary to take a look and see what else was going on around the country and the world.

We begin our discussion of the events leading up to the Victorian Period by first mentioning a little about some of the early clock makers, i.e., Thomas Harland, who apprenticed Daniel Burnap, who apprenticed Eli Terry, who apprenticed Seth Thomas; happening from around 1780 to perhaps 1795. Around 1812 we find Chauncey Jerome working for Eli Terry, and just before that, Terry, Thomas and Hoadley working together.

Here is a rough presentation of some of the important events that led up to the beginning of the Victorian Period of clock production.

Starting back in the later years of the Colonial Period we find that in 1790 the first U.S. Patent was issued, and in 1793 Eli Whitney invented the Cotton Gin. In 1807, Fulton's steamboat, the Cleremont, is finished and launched, and Eli Terry is mass producing clocks.

It was during the Empire Period that the Hartford Fire Insurance Company came into being. Their development helped ward off what seemed to be the greatest risk of the early clock factory-fire. Since history records that so many of the factories and shops were destroyed by fire, it helped the development of these factories to have a source of insurance.

In 1813, Seth Thomas was at Plymouth Hollow, busily making clocks. In 1825 the Erie Canal was opened, and that year also saw the introduction of iron frames for pianos. In 1826 John Stevens made the first successful run of an American railroad locomotive in the United States. The Spring Balance was invented in England for weighing, and mass production of firearms was begun.

The year 1836 saw the fall of the Alamo, and that same year Samuel Colt patented his revolver. The following year of 1837 was in a panic (depression). In 1839 the Insurance Company of North America got its permanent and so-called Perpetual Charter. The same year photography got off the ground with the first daguerreotypes.

1840 is the beginning of the Victorian Period of clock production. In the year following, the so-called Mercantile Agency was established. This was the first credit reporting company, which later was to develop into the well-known Dunn & Bradstreet. It was said that if a businessman desired to open an account with another business, he obtained letters of introduction from both customers of the other business and from his own creditors and customers. With this and other claims as to the type and extent of his business (as well as his earnings and capital backing), he applied for credit, and on this basis it was either granted or denied. A few of the larger companies employed traveling agents to check on the reputations of such applicants but this method proved unreliable. This is the reason that in so many of the papers of the old clock companies, we have seen letters describing various people as being very reliable; in other words, letters of recommendation. That was the only type of credit reporting in use at that time.

In 1842 we find Howard & Davis making clocks together. In 1844 the New York Life Insurance Company was founded, and Samuel B. Morse sent his first telegraph message. In 1845 the first sewing machine was completed by Elias Howe, Sr. The Mexican War lasted from 1845 to 1848. In 1849 the California Gold Rush began; and a year later the Ansonia Clock Company was in its infancy.

TIME LINE OF IMPORTANT EVENTS
AFFECTING AMERICAN CLOCKS

1780 **Daniel Burnap.**
1790 First U.S. Patent issued.
1793 Eli Whitney Cotton Gin.
1800 **COLONIAL PERIOD ENDS.**
     EMPIRE PERIOD BEGINS.
1807 Fulton's Steamboat.
     Eli Terry mass produces clocks.
1810 Hartford Fire Insurance
     Company.
1812 War of 1812.
     Eli Terry – Chauncey Jerome.
1813 **Seth Thomas at Plymouth**
     Hollow.
1825 Erie Canal opens.
     Iron frames for pianos.

1826 John Stevens' RR
     Locomotive Run.
1830 **Spring Balance (Weighing)**
     invented.
     Mass Production of firearms.
1836 Fall of the Alamo.
     Samuel Colt patents revolver.
1837 Panic (Depression).
1839 **Insurance Company of**
     North America.
     First Daguerreotypes.
1840 **EMPIRE PERIOD ENDS.**
     VICTORIAN PERIOD BEGINS.
1841 Mercantile Agency started.

1842	**Howard & Davis making clocks.**
1844	New York Life Insurance founded.
	Morse sent telegraph message.
1845	Mexican War started.
	Elias Howe's sewing machine.
1849	California Gold Rush.
1850	**Ansonia Clock Company begins.**
1851	**Wm. L. Gilbert Clock Company.**
1853	**New Haven Clock Company begins.**
	Seth Thomas Clock Company begins.
1856	Western Union.
	Bessemer Process for steel.
1857	Glass photograph negative.
	757 River Steamboats.
	Waterbury Clock Company begins.
	Ingraham Clock Company begins.
1858	First Atlantic cable.
	Mason fruit jar patented.
1859	Massachusetts Institute of Technology founded.
	Oil well, Titusville, Pa.
1861	Civil War begins.
1864	**E. N. Welch Clock Company.**
1865	Civil War ends.
1865	Chicago Union Stockyards.
1867	Buffalo Bill hired by Union Pacific RR.
	Typewriter invented.
1869	Golden Spike driven at Promontory Point.
1870	Celluloid invented.
1871	Chicago Fire.
1872	First Montgomery Ward Catalog.
	Boston Fire.
	Gatling gun patented.
1873	Panic (Depression).
1876	General Custer killed.
	Alexander Graham Bell patents the telephone.

1882	Thomas Edison's Pearl St. Station.
1883	Brooklyn Bridge opens.
1890	**VICTORIAN PERIOD ENDS.** **MODERN PERIOD BEGINS.**
1892	Oklahoma Sooners – Cherokee Strip.
1893	Moving Pictures patented.
1900	4,000 Automobiles.
1901	Marconi sends wireless message.
1903	Wright Bros. airplane flight.
	E.N. Welch becomes Sessions.
	Ford Motor Company organized.
1906	San Francisco Earthquake & Fire.
1907	Panic (Depression).
	Federal Reserve Act.
1912	Titanic sinks.
1914	Panama Canal opens.
1917	U.S. into World War I.
1918	End of World War I.
1920	First U.S. Radio Broadcast.
1927	Lindbergh flies Atlantic.
1929	Stock Market Crash.
	Ansonia Clock Co. sold to Russia.
	First television transmission.
1932	Banks close.
1937	Zepplin Hindenberg crash.
1938	Dupont markets nylon.
1939	Depression ending.
1940	**MODERN PERIOD ENDS.** **CONTEMPORARY PERIOD BEGINS.**
1941	U.S. enters World War II.
1944	**Waterbury Clock Company fails.**
1945	World War II ends.
1964	**Gilbert–Spartus Corporation.**
1967	**Ingraham — McGraw-Edison.**
1970	**Sessions failed.**
	Set Thomas — Talley Industries.

In 1851 the predecessors of the William L. Gilbert Clock Company were building clocks. In 1853 the New Haven and Seth Thomas Clock Companies began under the names that we have recognized for long. In 1857 the Waterbury and Ingraham Clock Companies started production, and the last of the seven big giants of the industry, The E. N. Welch Clock Company, got into full swing in 1864.

Going back to 1856 we find Western Union just beginning, and the invention of the Bessemer Process of making steel. A year later the glass photo negative is invented, and there are 757 river steamboats operating in the United States. In 1858 the first Atlantic cable was laid. A year later the Massachusetts Institute of Technology was founded, and the Mason fruit jar was patented. In 1859 the first oil well in the United States was opened at Titusville, Pennsylvania, and in 1861 the Civil War began. In that same year, the Chicago Union Stockyards opened, and by this time the seven giants of the clock industry were getting into gear and beginning to make an abundance of clocks.

In 1870 the first plastic was invented, called Celluloid. Even though it was not satisfactory and had a short life (particularly in the production of clocks cases), it did start the trend towards plastics that we have seen almost universally used in the Contemporary Period.

All during this time and for the rest of the Victorian Period the seven giants of the clock industry were putting out their hundreds and thousands of clocks in all sizes, shapes, kinds and colors. The Modern Period started about 1890 and we began to see the beginning of the end of the clock companies.

In 1901, Marconi sends his first wireless message. In 1903, the first airplane flight by the Wright Brothers; and that same year the Ford Motor Company was organized. The San Francisco Earthquake and Fire occurred in 1906. We saw another panic and depression in 1907. The Titanic sinks in 1912, and about this time the Federal Reserve Act was passed. The Panama Canal was completed in 1914. That same year — the beginning of the first World War. The United States enters the War in 1917, with the War ending in 1918. The seven giants of the clock industry are still producing their clocks.

In 1920, the first scheduled United States radio broadcast, followed by Lindbergh flying the Atlantic in 1927. The Stock Market Crash came in 1929, and in that same year we saw the failure of the first of the seven giants. The Ansonia Clock Company discontinued operations, and the factory and all the equipment was sold and shipped to Russia. In 1930 the old Seth Thomas Clock Company became a division of the General Time Instrument Company, again foretelling the end of the seven giants.

From the Bank Closure in 1932, and for a number of years thereafter, we had the Great Depression, which began to ease up in 1938. At this time DuPont first marketed nylon.

We end the Modern Period somewhere around 1940 or 1941, as World War II began and lasted until the latter part of 1945. During that period, in 1944, the Waterbury Company ceased to exist.

The Contemporary Period stretches from about 1940 until the present. During this time we have seen the end of the Sessions Company, the successors to E. N. Welch, and the end of the New Haven Clock Company. Of the seven giants of the clock industry, only three can be said to exist today. All three of these are now divisions of larger companies or conglomerates. Seth Thomas is a division of Talley Industries, the Ingraham Company a division of McGraw-Edison, and Gilbert has been supplanted by the Sparta Corporation. We can still see some imported spring-driven clocks with the name of some of these seven giants in our stores today. No spring-driven clocks or watches are currently being mass produced in the United States.

IDENTIFICATION OF ANTIQUE CLOCKS AND DATING

For proper identification and dating of clocks it is necessary to know something of the different names used by the companies. When a company purchased another company or factory they often used cases, movements, and lables acquired. It is necessary to know the lines of succession of the companies, especially those resulting in formation of our largest companies. The early clockmakers worked alone at times, but also made and dissolved partnerships seemingly at the drop of a hat. Factory buildings and equipment were rarely abandoned or destroyed (except by the disastrous fires that occurred so often), and when one company quit business by failure or otherwise, either a new company was formed or an existing one absorbed the remaining physical assets of the former one.

The accompanying charts in many cases will date the clocks simply by the form of the company name. You will find this same information from many sources, sometimes with slight variations in dates, but the chart form is easiest to use. For practical purposes, i.e. dating and pricing, we need not worry about the arguments over very precise dates. Some of the gaps in the dates are due to the factory laying idle or the particular clockmaker taking some time off, or getting involved in another enterprise.

In many cases, the only connections of succeeding companies with preceding ones, was the purchase of factories, either real estate or equipment or both.

Some of the companies formed to be sales outlets are shown to help identify the actual maker of the clock. There are many more sales companies that are not shown. Many, were actually assembly plants, usually for tax purposes, and assembled the finished clocks from parts shipped to them.

These charts show the development of a few companies, but to keep perspective, remember that the 1850 census showed the following numbers of clockmakers in various states:

Connecticut	582	In the same	New York	3883
New York	173	census, the	Pennsylvania	1317
Pennsylvania	105	number of	Ohio	1155
Ohio	46	Clock	Connecticut	336
Illinois	13	Peddlers	Indiana	209
Kentucky	9	were:	Illinois	194
Virginia	8		Virginia	150

To further illustrate the development of the clock industry consider this; in the Colonial period a clockmaker made all his own tools and all parts of the clock. By the beginning of the Empire period, in 1800, all clockmakers' tools could be bought and clock dealing was a separate trade. By 1870, in the Victorian period, almost all clocks were produced by mass production. Dials, bells, keys, mainsprings and other fittings were made by separate and independent factories. By the beginning of the Modern period the major producers had shrunk to slightly over a half-dozen giant corporations and a few smaller companies. At the end of the Victorian period, giants of the clock industry were: Seth Thomas Clock Company, New Haven Clock Company, Ansonia Clock Company, Waterbury Clock Company, E. Ingraham Company, William L. Gilbert Clock Company and E. N. Welch Mfg. Company.

The history of the clock industry is an important part of our country, and when you collect a clock you are doing your part to preserve that history.

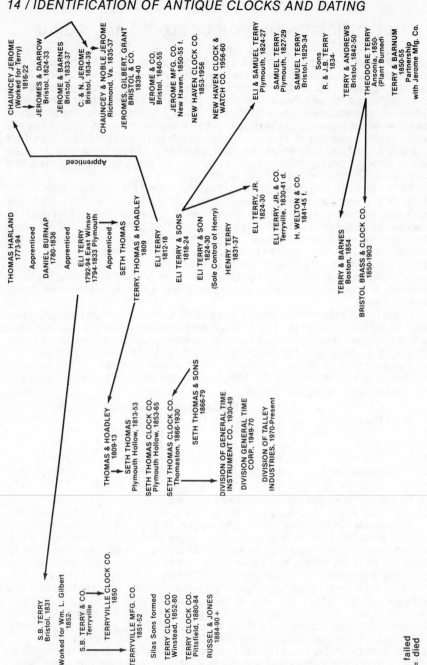

THOMAS HARLAND
1773-94

Apprenticed

DANIEL BURNAP
1780-1836

Apprenticed

ELI TERRY
1792-94 East Winsor
1794-1833 Plymouth

Apprenticed

SETH THOMAS

TERRY, THOMAS & HOADLEY
1809

ELI TERRY
1812-18

ELI TERRY & SONS
1818-24

ELI TERRY & SON
1824-30
(Sole Control of Henry)

HENRY TERRY
1831-37

ELI TERRY, JR.
1824-30

ELI TERRY, JR. & CO.
Terryville, 1830-41 d.

H. WELTON & CO.
1841-45 f.

CHAUNCEY JEROME
(Worked for Terry)
1816-22

JEROMES & DARROW
Bristol, 1824-33

JEROME & BARNES
Bristol, 1833-37

C. & N. JEROME
Bristol, 1834-39

CHAUNCEY & NOBLE JEROME
Richmond, Va. 1835-37

JEROMES, GILBERT, GRANT
BRISTOL & CO.
1839-40

JEROME & CO.
Bristol, 1840-55

JEROME MFG. CO.
New Haven, 1850-55 f.

NEW HAVEN CLOCK CO.
1853-1956

NEW HAVEN CLOCK &
WATCH CO. 1956-60

ELI & SAMUEL TERRY
Plymouth, 1824-27

SAMUEL TERRY
Plymouth, 1827-29

SAMUEL TERRY
Bristol, 1829-34

Sons
R. & J.B. TERRY
1834-

TERRY & ANDREWS
Bristol, 1842-50

THEODORE TERRY
Ansonia, 1850-
(Plant Burned)

TERRY & BARNUM
1850-55
Partnership
with Jerome Mfg. Co.

Apprenticed

THOMAS & HOADLEY
1809-13

SETH THOMAS
Plymouth Hollow, 1813-53

SETH THOMAS CLOCK CO.
Plymouth Hollow, 1853-65

SETH THOMAS CLOCK CO.
Thomaston, 1866-1930

SETH THOMAS & SONS
1866-79

DIVISION OF GENERAL TIME
INSTRUMENT CO. 1930-49

DIVISION GENERAL TIME
CORP. 1949-70

DIVISION OF TALLEY
INDUSTRIES, 1970-Present

TERRY & BARNES
Boston, 1854

BRISTOL BRASS & CLOCK CO.
1850-1903

S.B. TERRY
Bristol, 1831

Worked for Wm. L. Gilbert
1852-

S.B. TERRY & CO.
Terryville

TERRYVILLE CLOCK CO.
1850

TERRYVILLE MFG. CO.
1851-52

Silas Sons formed

TERRY CLOCK CO.
Winstead, 1852-80

TERRY CLOCK CO.
Pittsfield, 1880-84

RUSSEL & JONES
1884-90 +

f. = failed
d. = died

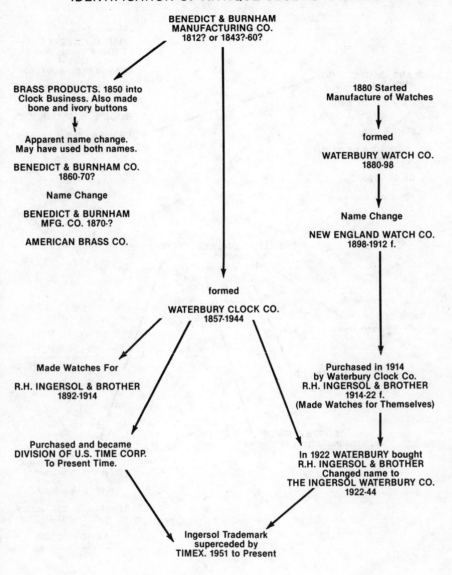

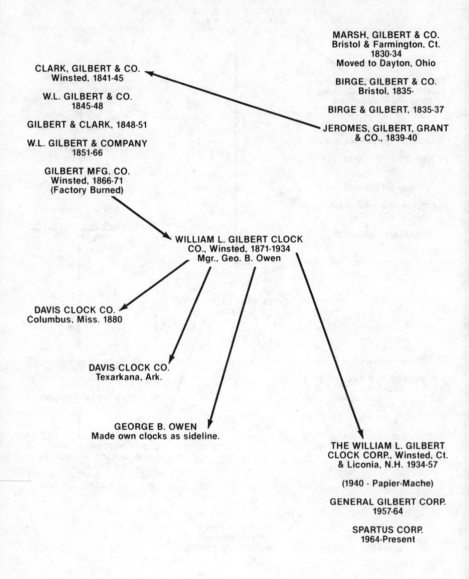

MARSH, GILBERT & CO.
Bristol & Farmington, Ct.
1830-34
Moved to Dayton, Ohio

BIRGE, GILBERT & CO.
Bristol, 1835-

BIRGE & GILBERT, 1835-37

JEROMES, GILBERT, GRANT
& CO., 1839-40

CLARK, GILBERT & CO.
Winsted, 1841-45

W.L. GILBERT & CO.
1845-48

GILBERT & CLARK, 1848-51

W.L. GILBERT & COMPANY
1851-66

GILBERT MFG. CO.
Winsted, 1866-71
(Factory Burned)

WILLIAM L. GILBERT CLOCK
CO., Winsted, 1871-1934
Mgr., Geo. B. Owen

DAVIS CLOCK CO.
Columbus, Miss. 1880

DAVIS CLOCK CO.
Texarkana, Ark.

GEORGE B. OWEN
Made own clocks as sideline.

THE WILLIAM L. GILBERT
CLOCK CORP., Winsted, Ct.
& Liconia, N.H. 1934-57

(1940 - Papier-Mache)

GENERAL GILBERT CORP.
1957-64

SPARTUS CORP.
1964-Present

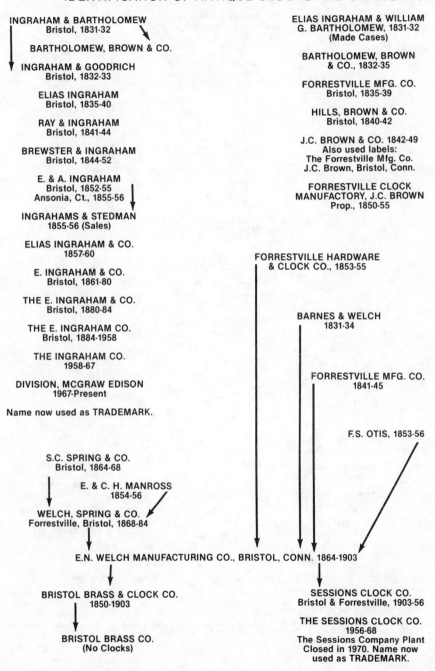

INGRAHAM & BARTHOLOMEW
Bristol, 1831-32

BARTHOLOMEW, BROWN & CO.

INGRAHAM & GOODRICH
Bristol, 1832-33

ELIAS INGRAHAM
Bristol, 1835-40

RAY & INGRAHAM
Bristol, 1841-44

BREWSTER & INGRAHAM
Bristol, 1844-52

E. & A. INGRAHAM
Bristol, 1852-55
Ansonia, Ct., 1855-56

INGRAHAMS & STEDMAN
1855-56 (Sales)

ELIAS INGRAHAM & CO.
1857-60

E. INGRAHAM & CO.
Bristol, 1861-80

THE E. INGRAHAM & CO.
Bristol, 1880-84

THE E. INGRAHAM CO.
Bristol, 1884-1958

THE INGRAHAM CO.
1958-67

DIVISION, MCGRAW EDISON
1967-Present

Name now used as TRADEMARK.

S.C. SPRING & CO.
Bristol, 1864-68

E. & C. H. MANROSS
1854-56

WELCH, SPRING & CO.
Forrestville, Bristol, 1868-84

**ELIAS INGRAHAM & WILLIAM
G. BARTHOLOMEW**, 1831-32
(Made Cases)

**BARTHOLOMEW, BROWN
& CO.**, 1832-35

FORRESTVILLE MFG. CO.
Bristol, 1835-39

HILLS, BROWN & CO.
Bristol, 1840-42

J.C. BROWN & CO. 1842-49
Also used labels:
The Forrestville Mfg. Co.
J.C. Brown, Bristol, Conn.

**FORRESTVILLE CLOCK
MANUFACTORY, J.C. BROWN**
Prop., 1850-55

**FORRESTVILLE HARDWARE
& CLOCK CO.**, 1853-55

BARNES & WELCH
1831-34

FORRESTVILLE MFG. CO.
1841-45

F.S. OTIS, 1853-56

E.N. WELCH MANUFACTURING CO., BRISTOL, CONN. 1864-1903

BRISTOL BRASS & CLOCK CO.
1850-1903

BRISTOL BRASS CO.
(No Clocks)

SESSIONS CLOCK CO.
Bristol & Forrestville, 1903-56

THE SESSIONS CLOCK CO.
1956-68
The Sessions Company Plant
Closed in 1970. Name now
used as TRADEMARK.

ANSONIA BRASS CO.
Ansonia, Ct. Anson G. Phelps
Importer of tin, brass, copper.
Built rolling mill for sheet brass.

ANSONIA CLOCK CO.
Ansonia, Ct., 1850-54
(Factory Burned)

Stockholders
Phelps
Theodore Terry
F.C. Andrews
Samual Steele Terry

ANSONIA CLOCK CO., Ansonia
ANSONIA BRASS & COPPER
COMPANY, 1854-78

ANSONIA CLOCK CO.
Ansonia, 1878-79

ANSONIA CLOCK CO.
Brooklyn, N.Y., 1879-1929
(Burned 1880)

Sold and moved factory
to Russia.

HOWARD & DAVIS
1842-59

BOSTON WATCH CO.
Roxbury, Ma. 1853-57

E. HOWARD & CO.
1859-61

THE HOWARD LOCK &
WATCH CO., 1861-63

THE HOWARD WATCH &
CLOCK CO., 1863-81

E. HOWARD WATCH &
CLOCK CO., 1881-1903

E. HOWARD CLOCK CO.
1903-34

HOWARD CLOCK PRODUCTS
INC., 1934-Present

NOTE: E. HOWARD & CO. used
on clocks from 1850 to present.
Most movements numbered.

OFFICERS
Edward Howard
George P. Reed
David P. Davis
Aaron L. Dennison
Horatio Adams

E. HOWARD & CO.

E. HOWARD & CO.
Roxbury, Ma. 1857-61

Sold Watch Company
to
KEYSTONE WATCH CASE CO.

DETERMINING THE VALUES OF ANTIQUE CLOCKS

The prices given in this book are not necessarily the prices at which any one collector would, in all instances, be willing to buy or sell, but are rather a composite of prices observed at sales by collectors, dealers, and other knowledgeable persons at shows, flea markets, marts, auctions, and private sales. The values given will be a convenient reference not only for present values, but as an indicator of the models most desired by collectors.

The prices shown herein have been analyzed by twelve of the major clock dealers located in different parts of the United States. Each of these individuals has expressed his idea of the clock values and I have made the final decision based on my knowledge of the overall market. As you know, we are in a recession and antique clock prices, along with all other collectibles, have been affected adversely by this situation. It is very difficult to know exactly what a specific clock will bring, mainly because there is not a competitive market. The asking prices I have observed during the past few months are about the same as they have been during the past couple of years, but the actual sales price is sometimes less. There are buyers for clocks but usually at a lower price level than before.

All the values given in this book are for mint original clocks and are retail. Definition of Retail Value: The price a serious collector investor, or housewife will pay another who knows the value of the clock. All other transactions will be, in most cases, below this so-called *"top price"*.

Reported in this book are some actual recent sales of rare or expensive clocks and averaged top values for the more common types. No attempt has been made to predict the future values. It has always been my policy to report only what is currently happening in the marketplace among knowledgeable collectors and dealers. This book is not a price list but an indication of value. It does not tell the buyer what he or she should pay for a particular clock but what they might expect to buy or sell for at the retail or top price level. Prices shown are based on the above definition of "retail value". Consequently, no clock sales have been recorded that occur among individuals or dealers who have no market information or the perception of actual supply and demand. As always, use the value given in this book as a guide but more importantly, use your own judgment based on your knowledge of your particular collection area and circumstances. Remember, *"the price you pay must ultimately be your own and is the value of the clock to you at that particular moment."*

Despite the fact that the values shown are based on sales between knowledgeable persons, there are still many clocks for sale at bargain prices. In other words, many clocks have been "discovered" by collectors and consequently are available at prices far below those that are sold when their real importance becomes generally known. This seeming paradox of two equally high-quality and equally rare clocks bringing widely different prices affords many excellent opportunities for the collector who is willing to take the time to educate himself.

As an example, you have identified your clock to be an Ansonia kitchen clock in near mint condition. The book says the top retail value is $175-200. This is the price you could expect to get if you can find a top buyer in your area or through the mail. For a number of reasons you have not been able to find anyone who thinks it is worth $200. All you have been offered is $125 and it looks like that is all you can get — you want to sell it now, then the $125 is what you will have to settle for.

The Ansonia kitchen clock "example" is easy compared to finding a buyer for a clock with a book value of over $1,000. There are thousands of collectors ready to pay up to $100 for a clock but only hundreds ready to pay up to $1,000, and far less who are willing to pay over $1,000. Consequently, the more your clock is worth the harder it will be to find a ready buyer. If you can afford to wait (time is on your side) sooner or later a top price buyer will come along. If you are in a hurry, though, you will likely have to settle for a lower price — perhaps as low as wholesale. Clock dealers are your best source of quick cash but seldom will they pay more than wholesale. Some, however, will sell the clock for you on consignment for a commission of 10% to 25% and this may be more advantageous to you. Otherwise, local NAWCC Chapter Marts or Regional Marts are the best opportunity to locate a retail buyer, or, if you are willing to go to the effort, an advertisement in the NAWCC Mart publication often will bring forth a top buyer.

Don't overlook the possibility of trading either. Very often two collectors can make a trade that leaves both in a much better position that could have been accomplished by the exchange of money.

If your circumstances permit you more time than money then, you can do considerably better at NAWCC Chapter or Regional Marts, flea markets, and gun, coin, and antique shows. All-line dealers at flea markets and antique shows seldom know much about clocks. Consequently, they may ask a lot more or a lot less for a clock than it is actually worth to a knowledgeable buyer. Finding an underpriced clock is rare and you will have to look through a lot of worthless or overpriced clocks to find these bargains, but when you do, the time will have been well spent.

Each issue of the NAWCC Mart publication contains offerings of clocks for sale. These are of two types: offerings of a list or offerings of specific clocks. Sometimes you can find a bargain here, too, but you will have to act fast if you want to get there before the knowledgeable dealer does. Sometimes an ad of your own for a particular clock that you want will produce good results.

Remember, no one can know everything about clocks. New information is continually being reported. Most of the time it increases the value of clocks. Knowledge is your most potent weapon in your efforts to build your collection. "The only substitute for knowledge is money."

NAWCC regionals or chapter meetings with a mart are held throughout the United States on a regular basis and it is an absolute necessity that you attend one or more, to get a better perspective on the availability of old clocks for your collection. You can acquire a distorted view of the actual amount of clocks and watches that are available by attending only local flea markets, antiques shops and shows.

The National Convention is held once a year, usually in June, at a pre-selected city. The sites for the convention are determined five years in advance. Philadelphia, Indianapolis, Atlanta and Cleveland will fill the following four years.

The National Association now has numerous U.S. and foreign chapters, and one may be near you. These chapter meetings are especially important to you as a beginning or advanced, collector or dealer. It gives you the opportunity to meet with other collectors, who sometimes have a good number of clocks for sale or trade. You can also find competent and trustworthy repairmen, sources of parts, and book dealers. It is very difficult to get a good education easily and quickly without putting all of these aspects together. Local chapters usually hold meetings every four to six weeks.

SUGGESTED METHOD FOR SELLING A CLOCK

If you have a low quality, mass-produced clock that has little collector interest, try to sell it among people who know nothing about clocks (flea markets, etc), and ask maybe two times what the book says and take what you can get. If you have a rare and/or high quality collectible piece, then look for a buyer among knowledgeable collectors or dealers.

VALUES FOR CLOCKS BY COMPANIES NOT LISTED IN THIS BOOK

There has been over the past 150 years probably no more than 12 to 15 major manufacturers of clocks. Yet, you are constantly running into clocks with names on them that you cannot find listed anywhere. The reason is that many have "private label" names on them, such as Montgomery Ward or Sears Roebuck. Many have their own brand name (private label) placed on clocks by the manufacturers. I have shown clocks in this book only by major manufacturers.

One thing to remember is that all companies made the same style clock at the same time. There was wide-spread copying of designs, if a certain kind sold well. If you have a clock, no matter what the name and you can find a similar clock in this book, the value would be about the same because of the private label or lesser known name.

There are literally hundreds and hundreds of reproduction antique American and foreign clocks, on the market now, and have been for many years. If you are buying a reproduction then pay the price for a reproduction. Do not pay the price for an antique. Some dealers take recent clocks and alter them to make them look old. A knowledgeable collector or dealer will not pay much for this clock. Also, since nice old clocks have gotten so valuable and hard to find, elaborate restoration has been undertaken on many pieces that you will find offered for sale.

CONDITIONS OR CONSIDERATIONS AS THEY AFFECT VALUE

CONDITION:

Mint original condition — 100%.

Paper dial replacing painted dial — deduct 10%. New paper dial replacing original paper dial or old paper dial in poor condition — deduct 5%.

Replacement hands or pendulum ball, if reproductions of original — deduct 2%. If not reproductions of original — deduct 5%.

Old and original works not of correct type for particular model of clock — deduct 20%.

New calendar works, reproduction of original — deduct 20%

New time works, reproduction of original — deduct 30%. New works, not reproduction of original — deduct 50-80%, or figure value of case only plus value of works.

LABELS:

Clocks that were originally produced with labels should have legible labels in fair condition. For a mint original label, add 10%. Always make sure that the label, the works and the case are consistent, matching and original. If the label is a replacement, but is a duplicate of the original that should be there, deduct 10%. No label, deduct 15-20% except on kitchen clocks, where it doesn't make as much difference.

If the works, label and the case are not consistent and matching, it is usually not a collector's item. Remember — in clocks, condition, originality and rarity are most important.

CASE:

Refinished like original, or original finish fair — deduct 5%. Good refinish, not like original, or original in poor condition — deduct 15%. Poor refinish, not of original type — deduct 25%. Missing minor unnoticeable parts, or minor damage — deduct 5%. Missing noticeable small parts, or noticeable damage — deduct 10%. Missing part of base or top, or more major damage — deduct 25%. Missing most of top or base, or more major damage — deduct 50-75%.

Many clocks were originally offered with alarm, strike, and driving power options. Some collectors feel these options enhance the value of a clock as follows:

Operating Alarm — add $10.00-$20.00. If weight operated — add $50.00-$75.00.

Hour strike — add $5.00. Hour and one-half hour strike — add $10.00; Gong — $5.00.

Beware — Many times these options are added to a clock of a model that did not have them offered as an option originally. In this case, they detract from the value of a clock.

If a clock is a rare model, these options do not affect the value nearly as much as on the common models.

BLACK ONYX

These clocks should go much higher in price. They are sleepers and are sold low because most collectors do not know what it is. Imitation marble should go lower, but sells well. Marble has always had a following but black onyx clocks are just starting to be collected. Look for sharp upward price trends here. Black wood will have its day later.

CAR CLOCKS

Car clocks probably present one of the greatest short-term investment opportunities that the clock collector can find today. Consider the following:

1. Car clocks are collected by clock collectors.
2. Car clocks are collected by watch collectors.
3. Car clocks are collected by antique car buffs.

Considering this, how long will the present bountiful supply last? Car clocks were produced by both the clock companies and the watch companies. They represent most of the 8-day movements produced by the watch companies, and these all have serial numbers. Most car clocks produced by watch companies were jeweled movements, from 4 to 15 jewels. Some clock companies produced both jeweled and non-jeweled movements. There seems to have been no serious research to determine the types or quantities manufactured; therefore, you must rely on experience and price books to help recognize the rare models.

Car clocks are priced at probably the lowest multiple of original price of any clock available today. In this category the Swiss movements are selling at prices comparable to the American, but will probably not increase as much in the future unless they have a well-known American name on the dial, such as Bailey, Banks & Biddle.

The antique car buffs particularly look for the car clocks that have auto names on the dial, such as Hudson, Oldsmobile, Ford, etc. Therefore, these original dials often double or triple the value. These collectors also desire the large, heavy, brass cases, and the mounting accessories. They also look for the bezel wind and the pull cord wind, and also the mirror mounted clocks. The watch collectors seem to prefer the higher jeweled and short run movements. The clock collectors seem to prefer the models produced by the well-known clock manufacturers, such as Seth Thomas, Waterbury, New Haven, Ingraham, etc.

All collectors seem to prefer the 8-Day models. Features such as alarms, winding indicators, sweep second hands and small second hands, unusual winding, setting or mounting, or other unusual features, all seem to increase the value.

A winding indicator is rare and will double or triple the value.

CRYSTAL REGULATORS

If glass is not beveled, subtract $50.00 to $75.00. If the glass is not mint and matched in color and thickness, the value is reduced accordingly.

For original real mercury pendulum, add $20.00 to $25.00.

If priced with visible escapement, subtract $50.00 if without. If priced without visible escapement, add $50.00 if the clock has this feature.

Dials must be mint. Reduce value if porcelain is cracked, chipped, or numbers faded.

Note gold plating on many models. Value is reduced if plating is worn or peeling.

Many of these were supplied with jewelers' or sales company names on the dial. Some of these companies became as famous and well-known as the manufacturers, and their names increase the value of the clock. This is especially true with imported clocks that have an American name on the dial. (Example: Bailey, Banks & Biddle.)

Unusual wood, stone, or pewter trim adds considerably to the value.

There are a few rare crystal regulators in existence that were manufactured by companies that were in business only a short time. These command premium prices from the collectors when they appear. (Example: Jennings Bros.)

STATUE CLOCKS

Production figures for statue clocks are unknown; therefore, the only criterion for rarity is experience, which varies with each collector. The price collectors will pay for a certain statue will sometimes vary considerably, however, certain preferences are evident. The double statue clocks are the most desired. Standing statue clocks are sought ahead of the sitting statue. The visible escapement and fancy dials certainly increase the value. Generally, the larger the size the greater the price. Condition is everything. Prices given are for mint clocks. Broken or missing parts of trim or statues drop the price drastically.

Certain Ansonia statues are very well-known, and although not as rare as others, command higher prices since every collector wants one.

Some collectors desire the three piece sets and will pay a premium for the complete set.

The price trend for all statues has been a sharp rise for the last four years.

DECORATED PORCELAIN CLOCKS

Must be mint and original. Value is reduced if porcelain is cracked, chipped, or retouched. Beware of reproductions.

Three piece sets consisting of clock and candelabrum or vases command the highest prices. Some of the vases were reverse painted from the inside. These are rare and good collector items.

Most dials were porcelain. Subtract $25.00 to $50.00 normally if dial is paper. Reduce the value if dial is cracked, chipped, or faded. If priced with plain porcelain dial, add $50.00 for visible escapement or $15.00 for fancy dial. Porcelain clocks designated as Royal Bonn usually command somewhat higher prices. Subtract $15.00 if bezel does not have beveled glass.

ALARMS

About five years ago, alarms suddenly jumped in price from the $2.00 to $5.00 range to the $15.00 range. Since then they have slowly crept up to the $20.00 to $25.00 range. They are a good bet for investment, since beginning clock collectors are likely to start with alarms. They are readily salable to most antique dealers. They are easier to work on than watches. The loud tick of the old ones, the names on most models, and the varied case designs all seem to attract collectors.

Considering the millions produced, not a very great percentage survived. This percentage will decrease as they become popular, as many will be dismantled for parts. Yet, there are undoubtedly many thousands lying around in attics, basements, and packed in old trunks waiting to be discovered, probably at reasonable prices.

Remember the following points that affect the value of alarms.

Condition is everything. Prices are predicated on mint condition. Deduct for flaws in condition. New, old stock in original boxes will usually double the value. Finding any in the original box increases value.

Prices given are for the particular make and model. Any variation changes the value.

Eight day models are the most sought after.

Other features collectors look for: calendars, striking models, solid brass cases, external bells on top, fancy cases, sweep second hands, second hands, well-known model names, beveled glass, jeweled works, single spring alarms, extra large or extra small cases, automated dials (especially popular), unusual sound, shape, size, or type of bell, bezel winding (or other unusual winding) combinations of several of these features.

Most collectors avoid foreign alarms (unless they are automated or very unusual), primarily because it is almost impossible to determine their age. If you cannot identify an alarm as American, be warned.

American alarms are more desirable if the maker's name is on the dial, but in the case of certain well-known model names, it is not necessary. Beware of any alarm that does not have the original dial.

The old alarms manufactured before 1900 bring a higher price than the later models. Some model names were used continuously over many years, such as the Waterbury Sunrise, but may be identified by the catalog pictures.

Many model names such as Sentry, were used by several manufacturers on very different types. Even the same manufacturers used the same model name for very different alarms over the years. It takes careful checking to know exactly what you have.

CUCKOO CLOCKS

The imported cuckoo clocks have not been extremely popular due to the difficulty of identifying and determining the age of these clocks. These prices are based on the approximate age as shown by the date of the catalog.

American clocks are approximately twice the value of the imported ones, and are much desired by collectors.

The very small, so-called cuckoo clocks without the bellows, do not sell well, and usually go under $10.00. The 3-Weight clocks are the most desired by collectors, and the fancier the animation the higher the price. The quarter-hour strike and the musical clocks are also much desired, and go at higher prices.

The 8-Day versions are rare, but are easily identified by the large weights. These are the most sought after. An 8-Day, 3-Weight, fancy carving with animation brings a high price.

Remember, many of these models are still made today. If you cannot verify the age of the clock, reduce the price accordingly.

Modern cuckoo clocks can be purchased at discount houses from $30.00 to $150.00 and used ones are worth somewhat less. If you cannot verify that it is more than 50 years old, buy or sell it as a used modern clock.

If you find an early cuckoo made before 1800, it is a real collector's item (maybe a museum piece), and will be valued accordingly.

Age and complexity are the greatest value-producing elements in that order, with fancy carvings and size being the next most important elements.

SCHOOL HOUSE, ROUND DROP, DROP OCTAGON

Prices have accelerated over the years rather rapidly until they exceed the amount people are willing to pay. Clock dealers are not quite ready to reduce to a point where they will sell readily. At the present time not many of these clocks are moving among knowledgeable buyers at the values shown in this book.

Two other factors causing the value to drop, may be the importing of old Japanese clocks and prolific current reproduction.

DECORATOR CLOCKS (Office or Museum)

Beautiful hanging wall or standing clocks will occasionally bring enormous prices, far exceeding the ones shown in this book. Here are some of the reasons. An important businessman may want a certain clock for his home or office. His time being very important to him, he will not want to wait and search for a good buy. The purchase price usually can be written off his taxes, therefore allowing him to pay much more than a collector would pay.

Museums, who charge admissions and whose purchases are tax deductible can pay more for the same reasons. Examples would be most of the E. Howard Banjos and Regulators and the more ornate Jeweler's and Parlor Regulators of all makes. Dealers and collectors should be watching for these situations because a few extra dollars can be picked up this way.

DECORATOR CLOCKS (Housewife)

Clocks offered for sale by the antique shops will usually be priced higher and will bring more money here than they will anywhere else. Buyers of these clocks are not usually collectors but only want one or two for use as decorator items and conversation pieces and will pay according to their desire. Some of the most common (and a lot of times very recently made clocks) will bring very high prices. Almost no type of clock escapes this kind of buyer. This is one of the reasons the beautiful statue clocks of French and American make are now bringing in so much money.

CHOKING LEVEL

Here is a very interesting situation that affects all clocks and other antiques as well. As the price of a clock increases, the number of ready buyers decreases. In simpler terms, there are many times as many buyers for $100.00

clocks as there are $1,000.00 clocks. About $300.00 to $400.00 is a level where this is most apparent. It seems here is where a lot of people choke off. If you take the original cost of a clock, which is a direct indication of the quality of the materials and workmanship, and the number of man hours it cost to produce it, you will find, for example, the cheap kitchen clocks bringing 50 times what they sold for new. On the other hand, a Jeweler's or Parlor Regulator may not bring more than 10 times its original cost. Some clocks that have not come to the attention of collectors hardly bring their original cost, an example being car clocks. As a buyer becomes more knowledgeable he usually advances to the better clocks.

CLOCK FUTURES

Factors such as choking level, dollar depreciation, and nostalgia, coupled with buyers becoming more knowledgeable, will surely cause the higher quality clocks to increase in value rapidly.

Another thing to keep in mind is that there are (and the number is increasing every day) more buyers than there are clocks. Market pressure or demand is what sets the price of any clock more than anything else, and with a steadily decreasing supply, there is nowhere to go but up. Since we have been working on this book, some of the clocks have doubled in price in a relatively short period of time. I would say that you can buy a clock or clocks at the current market value, keep and enjoy them as long as you like, and then resell them at a profit, or hand them down as family heirlooms.

OTHER TYPES OF CLOCKS

ANSONIA SWING CLOCKS

The Swing Clocks were originally designed as "attention getters" for store window displays. Today, they are very desirable collector pieces. The clocks with square gilt and nickel cases were of an early make, probably originating around the late 19th century. The round cases were made later. Beautifully made, these exquisite decorator or conversation pieces, are either in collections, destroyed, or lost, because you will seldom see one for sale.

The French also made swingers, but they were usually bigger, and more expensive.

Be careful of a reproduction of the German Junghans, a small swinger. They are not worth very much, and any time a clock is reproduced, it hurts the value of the original model.

BANJO CLOCKS

Similar to a banjo in shape, the clock's sloping sides and rectangular base offer symmetrical and visually pleasing lines. An American clock maker, Simon Willard, created the banjo design around 1800, calling it his "improved clock." Extremely American in its' design, it was made in large numbers and became popular with railway companies as station timekeepers.

Willard's design was copied by several other clockmakers, not all of them licensed, and the situation became worse after his patent ran out. The Banjo Clock is much sought after by collectors today, but buyers must be cautioned of discrepancies in determining the actual origin of the manufacturer.

CALENDAR CLOCK

A Calendar Clock shows the date, occasionally the month, and even the day of the week. Many have to be adjusted at the end of the months with fewer than 31 days. The perpetual calendar clock will make this correction itself. At midnight, every 24 hours, a pin on a wheel turns once, putting the mechanism into operation.

GRANDFATHER CLOCK

Once called "Long, Tall Case," or even "Coffin Clocks," the Grandfather Clock is probably the most well known of timekeeping collectibles. Invented in London around 1660, the Long Case or Grandfather Clock was the first household item to be successfully mass produced by an American clock-maker, (Eli Terry). The earliest surviving model, however, was made by Abel Cottey in the early 18th century.

It is reputed that the name "grandfather" originated for the tall case clock from a song written by Henry Clay in 1876 which began with the lyrics, "My grandfather's clock was too tall for the shelf . . ." Grandmother clocks are of similar design, but stand under six feet in height.

CARRIAGE CLOCKS

Carriage clocks have become extremely collectible. The value of these clocks depend on so many intricate details it would be impossible to include them in this section of the book. For example, a Grand Sonnerie (full quarter striking and repeating) carriage clock in a very simple case would be priced between $1400.00 to $1800.00, but the very same movement in a very ornate case with enamel work or porcelain panels could sell for $3000.00 to $6000.00. There are also miniature carriage clocks that sell for $300.00 for a simple timepiece up to several thousand dollars for a miniature ornate repeater.

When purchasing carriage clocks, you should seek the advice of dealers who specialize not only in the sale of such clocks but are also experts in the repair and restoration because they will be able to judge the authenticity of the item. It should also be noted that there are excellent reproductions being reproduced in Europe including repeaters, and miniatures. I have also come across old carriage clocks with reproduction porcelain panels that are very well done and could fool the average collector.

DRUM CLOCK

Used in several French clocks, the movement came outfitted in a brass container that was drum shaped. It was then placed in the clock case.

HOWARD HALL CLOCKS

These clocks are very scarce, if not downright rare. For this reason there are not enough sales to establish any kind of a price range. A good rule of thumb, in determining the value of a Howard Hall Clock, is to multiply their original cost 10 to 12 times.

The clocks of this type, are rarely shown publicly, because of the difficulty in transporting them, and also because they are rarely for sale. The clocks were, for the most part, custom made with variants as to case, style, wood, dial, and most importantly, movement. I have never talked to anyone who has seen any hall clocks of an identical, or even very similar make.

Due to their size, not many modern houses will accommodate them, and this factor limits the market somewhat. On the other hand, they are so desirable to many collectors that, if given a chance to buy one, they would — putting it in storage until they could alter their home or office.

IRON CLOCKS

The first generally known household timekeepers, iron clocks were originally made by blacksmiths and locksmiths. In some geographic areas it became popular to fit unusual wooded cases around the clocks, and to place them on wooden wall fixtures.

LANTERN CLOCK

A weight driven clock, with a lantern shaped brass case, the lantern clock originated in England, and was made for about 100 years after the early part of the 17th century. The name of the clock may originate from a mispronunciation of "latten" meaning brass, although the earliest clocks of this design sold during or before 1600 were made of iron.

LIGHTHOUSE CLOCK

The American inventor of the popular Banjo Clock, Simon Willard, is also responsible for the ornate, tall, table clock shaped like a lighthouse with a wooden base and glass shade on top. Some of these lighthouse or "lamphouse" clocks were made in France during the 19th century. Willards' version was unique in that he designed his as an alarm, where a special device tapped the top of the wooden case, instead of ringing an alarm. Sales were not too successful at the time.

The French have some models with a clock dial that turns underneath the rounded glass arch.

MANTEL CLOCKS

It is said that the smaller "grandmother" clock, inspired the trend towards the handy, easily transportable mantel clocks. As their name implies, they are intended for the mantelpiece.

MUSICAL CLOCKS

A revolving pin barrel operates the bell hammers, affecting this magnificent clock to play tunes at the hour, or at any one time. One of the earliest late 16th century British designs had 13 bells. In the 18th century, David Rittenhouse made a musical clock in Philadelphia that played ten tunes on 15 bells. It sold at the time for under $700.00.

REGULATOR CLOCKS

Generally refers to a very precise, plain cased clock, with a long pendulum and no strike. A regulator made in the mid 18th century was utilized by Captain Cook on two of his sea voyages, but was used on land with other instruments to check their current longitude.

REPLICAS, REPRODUCTIONS AND FAKES

A clock collector (and probably any collector of a valuable item) does not pursue the hobby for long, before he has an encounter with a seemingly desirable item that is not exactly what it seems. He may be lucky and have a fellow collector or an honest dealer point out the disturbing features that indicate that the clock is not what it appears to be. He may also be unlucky and purchase and carry home what he felt was a real sleeper, only to find that he was the sleeper. That rude awakening is the beginning of a rather intensive and extensive education. The acquisition of this book is one of the steps in that education.

To properly discuss the subject of clocks as related to their value, the following definitions are necessary and desirable.

ORIGINAL: A clock that is exactly as it was made, with no changes, alterations or restorations; may show all the results of age and use.

MINT ORIGINAL: An original clock that is in perfect condition, with no great signs of wear and tear except yellowing of dial and label. If the finish is dull it can be brought out by a good lemon oil or tung oil polish. If the clock originally had a label, it must still be complete and perfect except for the yellowing or browning of age. If the clock is mint original, its condition can make you imagine that it was stored since manufacture.

RESTORED: A clock that with replacement of parts and repair has been brought back to as near original as possible.

MINT RESTORED: A clock in perfect condition that has been restored to exactly original condition. This means that the restoration would be considered minor, such as refinished case, dial restored to original, or minor parts of case replaced.

REPLICA: An exact copy of an older clock. Replicas are usually manufactured by the same company that made the original, and the label will so indicate. Occasionally, a replica will be produced by another company, but again the label will so state. More on this later.

REPRODUCTION: A clock that is made to reproduce as closely as possible, the appearance of an antique clock. Reproductions fall into several classes:

    a. Old clocks that have had such an extensive restoration that over 50% of the clock has been replaced with new parts.

    b. New clocks that have been made from old wood.

    c. New clocks made from new wood.

FAKE: Any clock that is made to appear to be older than its actual age, or original when it is not, or otherwise contrived to fool the purchaser. Fakes have only one purpose — to cause the purchaser to pay a higher price.

Very experienced collectors will tell you that they can detect a fake by sight, feel and smell. They say that the smell of old age is detectable and distinctive, and cannot be duplicated or faked. The main factors in detecting fakes (which they modestly may not mention), are experience and knowledge. Knowledge of the original design and appearance of a clock is necessary to detect any deviation. Experience tells you what to look for when inspecting a possible fake.

Knowledge of clocks is obtained through visits to NAWCC marts, to museums, to collectors, and through study of books that show original pictures of the clocks. A detailed study of the pictures in this book and in catalog reprints, will allow you to detect the slight deviations that occur in many fakes. The experience that you obtain from examining many clocks and talking to many collectors is necessary to detect the fakes.

Logically, the more valuable a clock, the more likely it is to be faked. It has been said that the most faked clocks in America are the Weight Banjos and the Pillar and Scrolls. The fact that several of the major companies reproduced the Willard Banjo in the Victorian period has made it easy for the unscrupulous to represent some of these as original, either with or without some judicious faking. It has been cynically remarked that there are more Willard Banjos and Eli Terry Pillar & Scrolls existing today than ever came out of the markers' shops. The same has been said of Howard Banjos. To be more accurate, we should not call a clock, but rather the one who misrepresents the clock a fake. All clocks have value. A clock has value based on its own merits, regardless of whether we call it a fake, or a "fake dealer" calls it something else.

Since replicas are represented to be such, no discussion of these are necessary, except to advise the beginning collector that they are considered collectible and there is a market for them. Many collectors feel if they can't afford an original, the replica or a reproduction is the next best thing.

Reproductions do warrant some discussion, since there is a considerable variation in opinion among collectors as to the standing of reproductions. Reproductions made from new materials, represented as such, and exact copies of the original are sometimes collected exactly as the replicas. Reproductions made from old wood are more exact copies of the original as the original appears today, and are more desired by some collectors. Any reproduction becomes a fake when it is represented as original, and the beginning collector will gain valuable knowledge by spending time studying reproductions so that he can recognize them later when they may not be shown as such.

It is in the area of restorations that the most divergent opinions exist among collectors. How far may you go in bringing a clock to a mint restored condition? Some say that only the appearance should be worked on to achieve that mint condition. Others believe that as long as original parts are used, there is no limit to the work that may be done. Many clocks now in collections have been assembled from the original parts of several clocks. Most collectors believe that the label should not be replaced, preferring part of the original label to a whole reproduction. However, some collectors argue that the label is an essential part of a clock, and as long as there is no attempt to use the label to misrepresent a clock, a missing or destroyed label should be replaced with a reproduction as part of the restoration. Everyone seems to agree that the works should be restored to running order, and as long as the works are original, considerable restoration may be done. Replacement trim parts on the case, such as finials, moulding parts and metal parts, lower the value of the clock but are generally accepted. All collectors do not agree with the 50% replacement figure that transforms the object of a repair job from a restoration to a reproduction. Some feel the figure should be higher and some feel it should be lower. Most collectors simply adjust the price for which they will buy or sell the clock, to reflect the originality and condition.

For the beginning collector the best advice is to examine a clock carefully before you buy. It is not always prudent to refuse to buy a clock that is not mint — simply adjust the price accordingly.

References to fakes are found in clock literature in the late Victorian period, which indicates that reproductions represented to be authentic products of the master clock makers were very common.

In 1916 the Philadelphia Museum commented in its bulletin, "The commerce of superious antiquities has reached such proportions that in every museum there should be a chance for the collector to test his judgment with regards to the real value of objects offered him." The museum had a display of fakes and reproductions so that the collector could educate himself in order to be able to recognize these fakes and reproductions when he saw them. The hobby has expanded to the point where some people even make collections of fakes.

In the hobby of watch collecting, there are many collectors who have either a part of their collection or an entire collection of the Swiss fakes, the watches that were put out by the Swiss and other foreign countries to imitate the well-thought-of American watches.

Certain clock makers had such good reputations that the fakers sought to represent their products as those of the master clock maker. Even when the faker was a very good clock maker and put out very good products, he felt they would sell better, and bring a higher price, if they were represented to be a product of one of the master makers.

How many times today do you hear a collector say, "Well, I'm sure this Banjo is a Willard. It's not marked but I've looked it over and it is exactly like a Willard so it must be one of those he put out that either had the name removed or was never marked." There is a good chance that many of the clocks were put out to trade on the reputation of one of the masters.

Time has a way of taking care of almost any problem. In the case of the fakes put out in the late Victorian period, they are now antiques also and have a value of their own. If a clock is not authenticated, however, do not feel that it has the value of a clock that has a good label, or name you can judge to be authentic.

WORKS

In this book we will not attempt to expand into discussing the original works that appear in various clocks. This is a complete science in itself and will be subject to much more research in the future. When you are restoring a clock, however, and particularly when buying a clock that has been restored, make sure it has the original works for that clock. Just having an old works is not enough. It must be a works that was used in the particular case you have. A clock case with a non-original works becomes a compromise (if it's an old works or misrepresented) and so loses a great part of its antique value. If the clock does not have the original works, it cannot be considered a *mint, original* clock in the sense in which that definition is used in this book. Look for extra screw holes that have been filled, mounting brackets or blocks that have been added or moved to identify tampering with the works.

REPLICAS

A phase that has been growing in popularity is the collection of replicas of famous expensive clocks. A look at any of the NAWCC Marts will show you that this has become quite an important phase of the hobby. Some of these replicas are even put out by the same company that put out the original. They are reported to be limited in production, usually to how many they can sell. The price is very reasonable compared to the original. While you can't say this is collecting antique clocks, it's still collecting clocks.

The collector who cannot afford an original clock because it sells for thousands of dollars, feels as though it is very worthwhile to collect an exact replica that is selling for hundreds of dollars. This type of collecting cannot be criticized because it still educates the collector and the public as to what the original clocks were like. In the future this will probably become even more important. It is possible to have an entire collection of clocks with nothing but replicas.

Looking back at the history of clocks we find that in the late 1800's there were many replicas (sometimes called outright fakes) of the earlier clocks sold at that time. Those replicas sold in 1890 are now sold as antiques, hence, the replicas that are being sold today will in 50 years or so, be considered antiques. It is certainly a part of the hobby for each collector to keep himself posted on the replicas so he can recognize when they are offered for sale, whether they are represented to be replicas or not.

A few of the replicas presented here in this book are worthy of collector interest, and if you watch the advertisements in the Mart and check the replicas at the Regional conventions, you can keep yourself educated on the progress of this particular phase of the hobby.

ESCAPEMENTS

The concept of the escapement is believed to be attributed to an ancient Eastern monk, who was trying to control the rate of a water clock.

The earliest mechanical escapement device was the verge and the foliot, originating somewhere around the 14th century. The verge is a straight supporting bar, with the two escapement pawls and the balance wheel on top. It is called a verge, because it is like the pole that was carried in church processions by the verger.

The foliot is a French derivitive, from the word "folier," meaning to dance about wildly.

Many thousands of escapements have been invented since then, although the early clockmakers gave up the original verge only with the greatest persuasion. The most common escapement devices we are familiar with are: the lever for clocks and watches with balances, the anchor for pendulum clocks, and the detent escapement for marine chronometers. Some other escapement devices are illustrated on the escapement chart.

Recoil Anchor

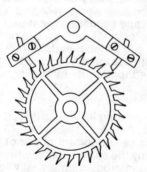

Vulliamy Dead Beat

American Anchor

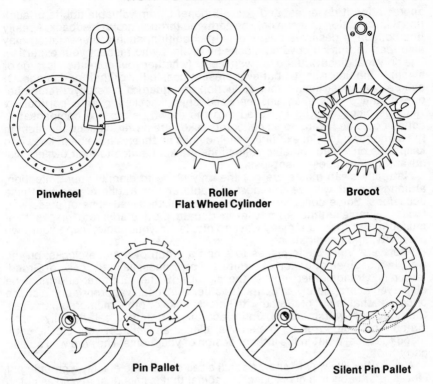

Pinwheel

**Roller
Flat Wheel Cylinder**

Brocot

Pin Pallet

Silent Pin Pallet

HOW TO DISPLAY YOUR ANTIQUE CLOCKS

Why collect beautiful and rare antique clocks, if not to display them for the enjoyment of other collectors? To edify your friends and family? The answer is fairly obvious. While it is unlikely that any serious collector of rare timepieces, stashes their bounty solely in storage, the clock collector does have unique challenges in arranging their possessions that collectors of, say, miniature dolls have never had to consider.

A Howard Longcase for example, may barely scrape into todays' low ceilinged homes. Transportation of unwieldy timepieces should be figured into the overall cost of a clock investment, as help will surely be required. By the same token, a delicate porcelain clock, displayed in a heavy traffic area of your home, is equivalent to throwing your money and the pride of horological ownership, away.

Some clock collectors solve this problem by emerging in the full flush of acquisitive pride, only at swap meets sponsored by the NAWCC. Since these horological exchanges occur only a few times every year (depending on your ability to travel), many collectors look forward to a "wall to wall" clock experience, trotting out many old and valuable clocks they may not be able to display to their fullest advantage at any other time. The merit of your collection, particularly specific collectors' series of antique clocks, will receive the appreciation it deserves, and you will benefit from valuable tidbits of additional information that can only be garnered through group feedback. A really fine collection deserves this special recognition; such a presentation may also lead to tips on coveted clocks by dealers who respect your expertise. The only real disadvantage to swap meets (whether your collection is large or small) is the unfortunate, but ever present possibility of theft or damage. Of course, you must insure your collection and guard it carefully. I remember one instance where an unsupervised child knocked over a particularly valuable piece, and disappeared into the crowd before any compensative action could be taken. Some collectors take care never to spend the night in the same town they're exhibiting their clocks in; thieves have been known to keep tabs on where valuable collections are kept, much to their owners disadvantage and subsequent loss.

Naturally swap meets are not the only place to display your collection, although you may save the most valuable and/or fragile pieces for these occasions. Some collectors, concerned about the aesthetics of preserving these valuable antiques, may even donate particularly rare pieces to a museum. But there are many ways to display in your home, using your own creativity, and imagination.

There are three basic places to stand a group of antique clocks: on the wall, in a cabinet, or on top of furniture. Sometimes, as in the case of Grandfather or Grandmother clocks, the antique IS the furniture, and must be displayed appropriately as befits its value. This means appropriating a space or corner, that is not cluttered with knickknacks or other memorabilia; where the fine lines, workmanship, and grace of your antique can be fully appreciated. This holds true for the smaller pieces as well. Let your clocks command the focal point in the interior design of your home. They are well able to carry it off.

A very effective way to show a small sized series is to display a grouping of clocks; preferably in a glass paneled cabinet that is kept dust free so as not to distract from the impact of your collection. In this manner you have a distinct advantage over an open display; the clocks themselves will take much longer to collect dust. Novelty clocks in particular tend to accummulate dust and grit within the elaborate grooves and scrollwork that embellish the design.

Metal or wooden stands can also be used to place specimens on top of tables, mantles, or any flat surface. They can be very decorative and add to the style of the clock, or plain to avoid detracting from it. Displayed in this manner they are, however, susceptible to damage from children or accidents. This holds true for direct placement on television surfaces, bureaus, bookshelves, and coffee tables.

When displaying wall clocks, the question is not so much how to display as where. You must use your own judgement and the overall design of your home to decide the most appropriate room for your antique clock. A pendulum clock may be a bit to "weighty" for the kitchen — then again if you have a breakfast nook or overall dark wooded ambiance, it may be just the thing. Check the manufacturers label in a catalogue for your hanging clocks; often this ascertains exactly where it was intended to be placed. Parlor Wall, or Kitchen Hanging is self explanatory. You are not bound by these designations, but they may provide a clue in the right direction of the room your clock will serve its decorative and functional purpose best.

Once you've figured out the practical aspects of where to display your collection, you must examine possibilities for combinations of displays. These potentialities are endless, and you will have fun experimenting and revising; you may even change it every few months! You can group your clocks according to size, whether it is all of one stature or gradations from largest to smallest. You may want to accent your collection with other items of the same basic design, or from the same era, such as music boxes, wall plaques, paintings, or china.

A topical arrangement can also work, if not carried to excess. Cherubs, gold filigree, a particular type of wood, can be carefully matched in one grouping. Beware of allowing the items to overlap or merge together; a walnut cased clock against a wood paneled wall can lose its effect. The eye must follow an interesting variation of like items, and not pass over it entirely.

If you have tried to specialize in a particular clock manufacturer, by all means try a grouping of this nature, perhaps sequencing the arrangement from earliest models to latest jeweled and non-jeweled variations, etc. This can result in an eclectic display, that will delight you, and fellow collectors.

If you only have two or three clocks instead of a substantial quantity, (as many beginners do) the style, period and condition of these items will determine whether or not you choose to group them together for a certain impact, or allow them to grace a solitary position in your home. Owners of large collections may choose a scattered tactic also, providing they have the space. Some antique clocks do best when displayed in their unique glory; you will also avoid a cluttered appearance as can happen with a group display of too many elaborate pieces.

There is alot more to antique clock collecting than the mere acquistion of valued items. Get started coordinating and placing your pieces to their best advantage. It may not add to their monetary value, but your personal satisfaction, and pride of ownership will increase by leaps and bounds.

RESTORING OLD CLOCKS TO "MINT, ORIGINAL CONDITION"

"Mint, Original Condidion" is a phrase used constantly inconnection with antiques. The term is defined in detail earlier in this text, but the implications of the term go somewhat deeper than a cursory perusal of the definitions would lead you to believe.

In antique furniture and violins, with pieces that have reached astronomical values, chemical analyses to determine if the finishes and glues are original are not unknown. In the future, as antique clock prices soar, such analyses may be used with a subsequent greater value being placed on original.

Due in part to the fact that many antique clock collections are considered as part of the furnishings of the home of the collector, some collectors have been more concerned with a "nice" appearance than with originality. This attitude may change as the hobby becomes more sophisticated, with much greater values being placed on originality and rarity.

The original factory catalogs show the pictures of the clocks as they were produced, and are the best means of checking a clock for originality. Actual photos of clocks as they exist today may show some alterations that the clock has accumulated over the years, and collectors should view such photos with caution until they are compared with the original catalog picture and description.

To give a more practical understanding of the term, "restored to mint, original condition", herewith is presented a brief discussion of some of the facets of this term as applied to clock cases.

When acquiring a new clock, my personal preference is to leave it as I get it, and simply protect it to keep it in the same condition. However, quite often the only chance you have to acquire a particular model, is in less than ideal condition. If it has been stored in an attic or shed, it is usually covered with dirt and must be carefully cleaned before you can determine its condition. Here is a reprint of the instructions for cleaning, taken from a 1926 Furniture Dealers Reference Book. (It goes without saying that the works should be removed before working on the case.)

HOW TO KEEP CLOCKS CLEAN

When wood furniture or clocks are finger marked, a trifle oiled, smoky, or carrying a bit of gloom due to the rubbing oil, try asking your druggist for a pound of USP Green soap. Take no subsitute. This will come in a tin can or a jar, and looks very much like vaseline. Then pick out the oiliest and dirtiest table top or clock. On a 6-foot table top, put a heaping tablespoonful of this soap, then take a few yards of absolutely clean, soft cheese cloth, soak it in water and wring it out. Begin spreading soap over the entire piece. Have enough in the cloth so that it spreads with a smear, and then add a little more water until you can freely rub with the grain and the sliding is easy. Then rinse out the cloth and follow each stroke with the grain, until you know you are wiping it with absolutely clear water. This may take several rinsings of the cheese cloth, and it must be continued until you are absolutely positive that every bit of soap has been removed. What has happened? We all know that the evaporation of any liquid causes a reduction of temperature. Besides this, the process contracts and hardens the finished film so that it is forced to exude any small particles of oil that may remain there. When the top is absolutely clean, take a clean piece of cheese cloth and wipe up the surface until it is absolutely dry and clear. It will be found that a surface of this kind can be kept in condition for months without a repetition of the process. The dust that may settle will not stick, and when the dust becomes noticeable pass over the article with a vacuum cleaner. Avoid dusters. They often scratch the fine finishes, which the vacuum will not do. The same process may be employed on enamels.

In a case where Green Soap is not obtainable, obtain a cake of Ivory Soap or Ivory Chips, and melt them by heating with sufficient water to obtain a consistency of vaseline. This will also do the trick.

In repair work, when it becomes necessary to give a coat of varnish or shellac or wood lacquer, (which is best applied by the spray or a brushing lacquer), try this: Reduce the soap with water to the consistency of rubbing oil. Use the finest pumice stone that can be obtained, and proceed to rub just as though it were oil. You will immediately notice that the pumice stone "bites" or cuts quicker than when rubbing with oil and, therefore, the process may be likened very much to steel wooling. You take the gloss off quickly being careful not to cut through, and you have the advantage that after you have cleaned off the pumice stone your piece is ready for delivery.

You will not receive a telephone call from the customer telling you that the finish is greasy. The finish will have such a smooth, clean feeling, that it is accepted in a final manner. Those who have not tried any of these recommendations may have their doubts. If their pieces do not turn out clear enough it will be the result of not using sufficient elbow grease when drying off the last wash water. This must be rubbed, so that there is a friction sufficient to bring out the life of the finish.

REPARING AND RESTORING OLD FINISHES

If the clock case has been refinished with a modern synthetic varnish or lacquer, this must be carefully removed in order to replace it with an original type finish. A modern finish remover usually works best on a modern finish, so choose and use carefully.

Once the case has been cleaned and/or the finish removed, the case should be very carefully examined. Be careful of comparing with a photograph of a clock. It may not be all original. If there are ANY missing parts, now is the time to replace them. If no original parts are available, have an accurate copy made by a skilled workman. Be sure that it is made of the correct wood. If the old finish is in reasonably good condition, it may be repaired or restored.

In repairing an old finish that is merely chipped or has places where the case has been rubbed enough to remove the old finish, the principle thing is, to match the color of the case at the point where the finish has been removed. Make sure that you replace the old finish with one that matches the original. If you use the same type of finish for touchup, the solvents will blend the two together. If you have a chipped spot and want to fill it with the same type of varnish thin the varnish slightly so there is an excess of solvent, and then very gently work it into the edges. It will tend to dissolve the edges of the old finish and blend the two together. By very careful workmanship you can hide a chip with this technique. Always stain the varnish to match the old varnish, but keep it on the light side. The new varnish will darken with time and may end up too dark.

A small dent in the wood may be filled by applying layers of stained varnish with a camel hair brush. This takes patience and skill.

Larger holes and dents may be filled with shellac sticks. Pick a shellac stick colored to match the wood. Make a small spatula from an old hack saw blade, with the teeth ground off. The blade should be about the width of the blemish you are going to fill. Heat the blade over a small alcohol burner, apply to the shellac stick to melt a small amount on the blade, and carefully apply to the hole or dent, reheating the blade as necessary to keep the shellac plastic. When the shellac has hardened, carefully sand it smooth.

On a rubbed spot, you have to stain the spot, if it has been rubbed enough to take off part of the color. After you have used the stain to get the same color, replace the varnish or other exterior finish. A stain can be applied to the varnish or mixed with the varnish to match the color of the old finish. Since the old varnish has become darkened with age, you will find it necessary to mix some form of stain into the varnish until you get the same color as the finish on the clock. This takes a little bit of experience. Take some scrap pieces of wood and practice staining until you can match the color of the old wood. Don't try it the first time on a very valuable clock.

Most finishes run to the brown tones. These may be matched by mixing black with Bismark Brown. Remember that when Bismark Brown is dissolved in alcohol, it produces a reddish mahogany shade. When this and black are mixed, a series of brown shades are produced proportionately to the relative amount of each. By adding a little orange, you throw the cast into the black-brown shades, so with these three colors you can match most of the cases you may be restoring.

In restoring an old finish that is still complete but lacks the original factory appearance a technique that has been used on antique furniture is effective. Rub it down with the solvent so that you actually dissolve the old finish, and let it redeposit. In this manner you maintain the color and patina of the case so that it still shows the age and beauty of the original wood, but at the same time is restored so that it appears to be many years younger than it actually is.

This technique has been used on restoring antique furniture for many years, and you can use an old-time method to make the finish look even better. Mix a little bit of beeswax, linseed oil, and pumice stone together with some stain to match the color of the case. Get the entire mixture into a very thin paste of almost creamy texture, same color of the case, then take a soft cloth and rub the case down with this mixture. If you use enough time and loving care you can eventually get the case to look as though it came out the factory door, perhaps even better than it looked originally.

GLUING THE CASE

After cleaning the case and removing the old finish (if it's necessary), you may find that the various portions of the case have become loose over the years — the glue has loosened and the case could very easily fall apart after it has spent a winter in a dry room. In this situation you may find it necessary to reglue portions of the case together. In regluing the case, please don't use an epoxy or some modern glue that was not invented back when the case was made. This may be the easy way out, and gives you an absolutely waterproof glue but it still destroys the originality of the clock. In order to preserve the originality, try to use a glue that was in general use at the time the clock was made.

The old gluepot was a fixture of factories and repair shops almost since time began, and if you are going to do extensive repairing perhaps it should be in your shop. The old hide glue, smelly, not waterproof, very subject to loosening when exposed to changing humidity and temperatures, was still the glue used in making much of our antique furniture, as well as clock cases. This glue has the advantage of setting very hard in 24 to 48 hours, depending on temperature and humidity.

If you obtain a package of hide glue flakes, you may store them indefinitely in a dry place. The old timers said the glue became better with age, and the hotter the glue when used, the stronger the bond. Do not keep the glue in your gluepot and remelt it the next day. When you turn off the pot, pour out the remaining glue and make a new batch the next time you are gluing. Be sure and keep your joints clamped together at least 12 hours, preferably 24 hours, to allow the glue to set.

If you dislike the gluepot, you can make what was called "Office Glue" according to this old recipe: Melt one pound of fish glue in two quarts of water by boiling, add eight ounces sugar, take it off the fire, and add one ounce acetic acid, let cool, then add eight ounces alcohol.

To cement marble case parts: Mix five parts Plaster of Paris, one part fresh powdered lime, and enough white of egg to make a creamy paste. Apply cement and press parts together as quickly as possible, as the cement thickens very fast. (1880 formula).

To polish a marble case: One part beeswax dissolved in ten parts turpentine. Apply liberally, rub for a long time with flannel or chamois skin, then gradually rub the marble dry. (1891).

To refinish a black enamel case: Curpic oxide two parts, cobalt oxide two parts, crystal glass 15 parts, borax four parts, manganic oxide two parts, ferric oxide 1½ parts. (1880).

Natural shellac, lacquer, and linseed oil varnish were all in use during the Victorian Period and can be used to refinish your clock case.

This brief section will not teach you to restore clocks. It, hopefully, will make you aware of some of the aspects of "restoring to original".

WOODS USED IN CLOCK CASES

The woods used in clock cases should become familiar to every collector. Certain models were put out on special order in different woods, and may be extremely rare in one of the woods.

BLACK WALNUT OR AMERICAN WALNUT

Probably the most common case wood, and certainly its beauty leaves nothing to be desired. Familiar to everyone. *Cherry* is similar.

MAHOGANY

Probably the second most common case wood. However, recognition is complicated by three distinct varieties of mahogany: (a) Cuban Mahogany, the original mahogany. The hardest and most dense of the mahoganies, it is close grained and figured; (b) Honduras or Central American Mahogany, lighter and softer than the Cuban variety, with a great variety of color and figure. (c) Phillipine Mahogany, the softest, lightest, cheapest variety, with practically no figure. Commonly seen today as the cheapest plywood and almost caused mahogany to lose its standing as a fine wood. Many young people today have only seen this type, and do not realize the great difference in the varieties.

ROSEWOOD

A hard wood, much heavier than American Walnut. Has a distinctive grain structure that finishes into a dark brown, chesnut color with darker, almost black streaks of grain. Takes a good polish; used solid or as veneer. Sometimes faked with mahogany by the casemakers, as mahogany was cheaper.

AMERICAN WHITE OAK

Hard and dense. Color varies from pale yellow to pale reddish-brown. Very well known wood.

AMERICAN RED OAK

Redder in color than the white.

CHESTNUT

Hard and dense. When finished light, chestnut becomes similar to Oak in appearance, but sometimes slightly redder and closer grained. When finished darker, it is sometimes mistaken for Walnut. When highly polished, resembles Sycamore. Watch for this wood! You will find some cases made of it that will usually be mistakenly indicated as Oak or Walnut.

AMERICAN RED GUM

Hard, not quite as dense as Walnut and Chestnut. Reddish brown in color with some dark streaks. Good grain figure.

This covers most of the woods used in clock cases during and after the Victorian Period. It seems that a majority of the wood clock cases were veneered. In the late Colonial and early Empire periods the wood was hand sawed and hand planed to make the veneer they used. The next time you look at a chip in the veneer of a clock from this period, look at it closely and imagine the hours spent by a "joiner" to get this veneer. Not many people would care to do this job today.

COLLECTORS' SERIES OF ANTIQUE CLOCKS

Most collectors have been in the habit of collecting all the clocks they could, but some have specialized in collecting one particular type of clock, i.e. wall regulators, double dial calendars, walnut shelves, triple deckers (among the older), transition types, or even pillar and scrolls. A few have specialized in one maker's clocks, although the general customary tendency is to not specialize but to collect a hodge-podge of clocks. Some collectors attempt to get one of each type, or one of each make, or some other category, which would indicate a small amount of specialization. With continued inflation, not only collectors but also investors and decorators are buying clocks and other antiques. Collectors have seen a rapid rise in the prices of clocks and suddenly find they can no longer afford the luxury of collecting multitudes of a semi-specialized category. A collector that formerly specialized in wall regulators when they were selling for about a hundred dollars apiece could get a collection for about $10,000. Now, when they are selling for $1,000 up, the minimum investment for 100 wall regulators might be $100,000. Very few collectors can afford this type of investment. In the future, rather than seeing large collections of two to three hundred various clocks, you can expect many serious collectors to show you a collection of maybe 20 or 30 clocks that are specialized in some specific category; Seth Thomas numbered regulators, a series of numbered calendars, Welchs with Patti movements, a particular group of kitchen clocks, or similar categories. In order to help collectors who may be contemplating some type of specialization, we will include information on the various collectors' series of clocks.

Many of the clocks manufactured in the United States since 1840 were listed by the manufacturers as one of a series, probably for convenience in the placing of orders. These series designations are still the most convenient way of identifying a particular clock. Collectors can be sure that everyone knows which clock they mean when they speak of a manufacturer's "Regulator No.2".

Probably the first series in which collectors began to specialize were the Seth Thomas City Series and the various series of double dial calendar clocks. It is very doubtful that any collector has ever succeeded in collecting this entire series, or even a complete series of numbered regulators. Indeed, it is even somewhat doubtful that the manufacturers ever put out all the regulators for which they had a number. During the Victorian Period the customer was still boss and could obtain almost anything he wanted and was willing to pay for. So, it is suspected that some of the numbered regulators and other models shown in the old catalogs may never have been produced except on special order. There are certain numbered regulators that to our knowledge, have never been seen. Whether they existed at that time or survive today are both subjects of speculation. The collector that manages to collect a complete series of wall regulators, or a complete Seth Thomas City Series, or any of the other series mentioned here, can be assured that he has done something that has very rarely been accomplished in the collection of clocks.

PRICING INFORMATION

The prices in this book are a composite of the opinions of dealers over the country, blended and averaged with known sales to obtain a high mean price, which must sometimes be compensated to provide a true RETAIL value for a MINT, ORIGINAL clock. All of which means that many people in the country DO NOT AGREE with all of the prices in the book. Therein lies the great opportunity presented by this book: the chance to get help in the poker game of buying and selling.

The fact that a clock is listed here at a certain price means that somewhere in the coutry is a dealer who believes that this is a fair market price. If you feel the price is extremely low, find that dealer and buy that clock. Take the book with you and show the dealers who have priced above it. Many times they will sell for the book price. If you feel the price is extremely high and you have one of those clocks for sale — lucky you. Somewhere there is a dealer or collector who will pay that price. Find him, but remember — the price is for a MINT ORIGINAL clock. Don't expect to get the price if your clock is NOT mint, original.

There are several instances where similar models of the same clock are shown with the same price, although we know that very knowledgable collectors will buy and sell the rarer model at a somewhat higher price. However, most dealers do not differentiate to this extent. This will change in future years, but at present, the book prices reflect the dealers' opinion.

This same lack of differentiation is particularly evident in the lower priced parlor "novelty" clocks, the car clocks, and the alarm clocks. If you are collecting with a long range investment objective and like the smaller, cheaper clocks, here are your great opportunity — but only if you educate yourself in the areas of rarity and originality. Historically, the clocks that increase in value the greatest amount are the most attractive clocks (in appearance) that are known to be RARE and are advertise the facts as you know them as they establish the rarity. Then watch the price climb.

Most knowledgeable collectors would be willing to pay more for an Ansonia No.8 than for No.9. However, the average collector probably would not be able to put No.8 in any room in his house due to the physical size. The dealers feel that the No.9 would go for a higher price because there are more buyers for the smaller clock.

These examples are given simply to show that this book actually creates opportunities for the collector. The book will show you the original appearance of the clock, and in some cases, indicates the rare models. Experience will teach that many other models are rare.

Only the buyer can set the final price, for if he has the money to buy and the desire for the clock but does not buy the price at this time is too high. If he buys, the price he pays sets the market value at that moment, and no price book in the world can change these facts. Therefore, arm yourself with all the knowledge possible, and GOOD HUNTING! Old saying: "It is naught, it is naught, saith the buyer; but when he is gone his way, then he boasteth."

CLOCK PARTS AND SUPPLIES

Most of the following suppliers have catalogs available illustrating their complete line. Some are free and some make a small charge that is refunded on the first order.

To assure getting a response to any type of inquiry from any service or supply company, it is absolutely necessary to include a SASE (Self-addressed, stamped envelope). Do not write to anyone requesting information without enclosing a SASE if you expect a response.

Note: Displays large assortments of clock parts and supplies at the NAWCC Regionals.

Antique Clocks
Briscoe Road
Rt. 1, Box 242-C
Swan Lake, NY 12783
(914) 292-7287

Aguilar Jewelers' Supply
520-C "E" Street
Robinson Bldg., Room 408
San Diego, CA 92101
(714) 232-2993

M. Beresh, Inc.
21700-C Greenfield Suite No.353
Oak Park, MI 48237
(313) 968-2930

Otto Frei – Jules Borel
Box 796-C
Oakland, CA 94604
(415) 832-0355

Borel & Frei
315-C West 5th St.
Los Angeles, CA 90013
(213) 689-4630

Jules Borel & Co.
121-C S.E. First St.
Miami, FL 33131
(816) 421-6100

Jules Borel & Co.,
1110-C Grand
Kansas City, MO 64106
(816) 421-6110

D.R.S. Borel
15-C West 57th St.
New York, NY 10036
(212) 757-7370

Colmans-Borel
648-C Huron Road
Cleveland, OH 44115
(216) 771-2342

California Time Service, Inc.,
3210-C Airport Way
Long Beach, CA 90806
(213) 595-5415

The Cas-Ker Company
P.O. Box 2347-C
128 E. 6th Street
Cincinnati, OH 45201
(513) 241-7076

*Bernard Edwards Dial Co.
Specializing in Clock Dials Only
1331-C Southwind Drive
Northbrook, IL 60062
(312) 272-2563

Empire Clock Inc.
1295-C Rice Street
St. Paul, MN 55117
(612) 487-2885

Esslinger & Co.
1165-C Medallion Drive
St. Paul, MN 55120
(612) 452-7180

Ewing Bros.
P.O. Box 445-C
Tucker, GA 30084
(404) 938-0115

Florida Watch & Jewelers Supply, Inc.
P.O. Box 14533-C
2828 Central Avenue
St. Petersburg, FL 33712
(813) 327-1100

Fried & Field Company
Watch Materials — Tools
657-C Mission St.
San Francisco, CA 94105

The Gould Co.
13750-C Neutron Rd.
Dallas, TX 75234
(214) 233-7725

Herr & Kline Inc.
1914-C Granby St.
Norfolk, VA 23517
(804) 623-0714
(800) 446-8094

Kilb & Company
219-C N. Milwaukee St.
P.O. Drawer 8-A
Milwaukee, WI 53201
(414) 272-6250

Langert Bros.
P.O. Box 27487-C
1620 W. Camelback Rd.
Phoenix, AZ 85061
(602) 264-1620

*S. LaRose, Inc.
234-C Commerce Place
Greensboro, NC 27420

Livesay's Inc.
2942-C W. Columbus Drive
Suite 203
Tampa, FL 33607

Marshall-Swartchild Co.,
2040-C N. Milwaukee Ave.
Chicago, IL 60647
(312) 278-2300
IL (800) 972-3776
Other (800) 621-4767

Mason and Sullivan Co.
39-C Blossom Ave.
Osterville, MA 02655
(617) 428-6993
(617) 428-5726

Mayer Bros., Inc.
P.O. Box 750
4th & Pike Bldg.
Seattle, WA 98111
(206) 682-1525

Merritt's Antiques, Inc.
RD 2-C
Douglasville, PA 19518
(800) 345-4101

Michigan Jewelers Supply Co.
Troy Commerce Center
1116-C E. Big Beaver Rd.
P.O. Box 412
Troy, MI 48084
(313) 689-9100

The Nest Co.
915-C Olive St.
St. Louis, MO 63101
(314) 241-0770

*Southwest Clock Supply
2442-C Walnut Ridge
Dallas, TX 75229
(214) 241-3570

E & J Swigart Co.
34-West Sixth St.
Cincinnati, OH 45202
(513) 721-1427

Tani Engineering
6226 Waterloo
Box 338-C
Atwater, OH 44201
(216) 947-2268

*Timesavers (Steve Berger)
P.O. Box 171-C
Wheeling, IL 6000
(312) 394-4818

Tiny Clock Shop
1378-C Old Northern Blvd.
Roslyn, NY 11576

Turncraft Clock Imports Co.
611-615-C Winnetka Avenue No.
Golden Valley, MN 55427
(612) 544-1711

FINDING DEALERS AND INFORMATION

To find local dealers check the yellow pages under "Antiques." You may also visit antiques shows, flea markets, auctions and conventions, or you can enjoy the thrill of detection by attending yard or tag sales, and by going to thrift and second-hand stores.

The following publications not only are sources of information on the history of various antiques and collectibles and trends in the field, they also contain dealer ads and ads of private individuals who either want to sell or want to buy. You can place your own want ads in many of them for a reasonable fee.

AMERICAN ART AND ANTIQUES
1515 Broadway
NYC, NY 10036

AMERICAN COLLECTOR
P.O. Box A
Reno, NV 89506

THE MAGAZINE ANTIQUES
551 Fifth Avenue
NYC, NY 10017

ANTIQUES AND THE ARTS WEEKLY
Newtown Bee
Bee Publishing Co.
Newtown, CT 06470

ANTIQUES AND COLLECTIBLES
525 N. Barry Ave.
Mamaroneck, NY 10543

ANTIQUE COLLECTING
(American Antique Collector)
P.O. Box 327
Ephrata, PA 17522

ANTIQUE COLLECTOR
Chestergate House
Vauxhall Bridge Road
London SW1V 1HF

ANTIQUES JOURNAL
P.O. Box 1046
Dubuque, IA 52001

ANTIQUE MONTHLY
P.O. Drawer 2
Tuscaloosa, AL 35401

ANTIQUE TRADER
P.O. Box 1050
Dubuque, IA 52001

ANTIQUES WORLD
P.O. Box 990
Farmingdale, NY 11737

BULLETIN OF THE NATIONAL ASSOCIATION OF WATCH AND CLOCK COLLECTORS, INC.
514 Poplar St.
Columbia, PA 17512
(Bi-montly publication Membership in the NAWCC required)

THE CLARION
AMERICA'S FOLK ART MAGAZINE
49 West 53rd St.
NYC. NY 10019

CLOCKWISE MAGAZINE
1235 E. Main Street
Ventura, CA 93001

COLLECTIBLES MONTHLY
P.O. Box 2023
York, PA 17405

COLLECTOR EDITIONS QUARTERLY
170 Fifth Ave.
NYC, NY 10010

HOBBIES
1006 S. Michigan Avenue
Chicago, IL 60605

HOROLOGICAL TIMES
P.O. Box 11011
Cincinnati, OH 45211

MAINE ANTIQUES DIGEST
P.O. Box 358
Waldoboro, ME 04572

THE MART OF THE NATIONAL ASSOCIATION OF WATCH AND CLOCK COLLECTORS, INC.
514 Poplar St.
Columbia, PA 17512
(Bi-Monthly publication. Membership in the NAWCC required)

MODERN JEWELER MAGAZINE
15 W. 10th St.
Kansas City, MO 64105

NATIONAL ANTIQUES COURIER
P.O. Box 500
Warwick, MD 21912

THE NEW YORK-PENNSYLVANIA COLLECTOR
c/o Wolfe Publications
4 S. Main Street
Pittsford, NY 14534

NINETEENTH CENTURY (FORBES)
60 Fifth Avenue
NYC, NY 10011

OHIO ANTIQUE REVIEW
72 North St.
P.O. Box 538
Worthington, OH 43085

POLITICAL COLLECTOR
503 Madison Avenue
York, PA 17404

JOEL SATER'S ANTIQUES NEWS
P.O. Box B
Marietta, PA 17547

SPINNING WHEEL
Fame Avenue
Hanover, PA 17331

THE TICK-TOCK TIMES
P.O. Box 7443
Salem, OR 97303

TRI-STATE TRADER
P.O. Box 90-CS
Knightstown, IN 46148

WATCH AND CLOCK REVIEW
2403 Champa St.
Denver, CO 80205

Y-NOT
P.O. Box 8561
Ft. Lauderdale, FL 33310

NEW CLOCK SUPPLIERS
REPRODUCTIONS OF ANTIQUE CLOCKS

The following clock dealers offer new clocks for sale with emphasis on reproduction of American antique clocks. Some issue catalogues and are free for the asking. Be sure to send a self-addressed, stamped envelope (SASE) when writing an inquiry or requesting a catalog.
Note: Displays large assortments of new clocks at the NAWCC Regionals.

Alpine Import & Export
230-C Fifth Avenue
New York, NY 10001
(212) 686-4646

*Aubrey A. Aramaki
331-C N.W. Gilman Blvd.
Issaquah, WA 98027
(206) 392-5200

*Foster Campos
213-C Schoosett St., Route 139
Pembroke, MA 02359
(617) 826-8577

Clocks, Ltd.
P.O. Box 66106-C
5256 North Rose St.
Rosemont, IL 60018
(312) 678-0988

Empire Clock, Inc.
1295-C Rice Street
St. Paul, MN 55117
(612) 487-2885

Houseman & Spong Clocks
11829-C Rockinghorse Road
Rockville, MD 20852

*Ken Kyckelhahn
252-C California Ave.
Oakdale, CA 95361
(209) 847-1337

*S. Larose, Inc.
234-C Commerce Place
Greensboro, NC 27420
(919) 275-0462

Mason & Sullivan Co.
39-C Blossom Ave.
Osterville, MA 02655
(617) 428-6993

*Merritt's Antiques, Inc.
RD 2-C
Douglassville, PA 19518
(800) 345-4101

*Timesavers
P.O. Box 171-C
Wheeling, IL 60090
(312) 394-4818

Turncraft Clock Imports Co.
611-C Winnetaka Ave.
Golden Valley, MN 55427
(612) 544-1711

CLOCK AND WATCH MUSEUMS

This list includes only museums who have a substantial collection of clocks or watches, or both. Some museums, because of limited space, do not always have their clocks and watches on display. If clocks and watches are your main interest, I would suggest you make an inquiry as to what they currently have on exhibit. An asterisk (*) indicates that these museums will always have a good exhibit of clocks or watches.

ARIZONA
Arizona Pioneers Historial Society
949 E. Second St.
Tucson
(602) 628-5774

CALIFORNIA
California Academy of Science
Golden Gate Park
San Francisco
(415) 752-8268

Los Angeles County Museum
900 Exposition Blvd.
Los Angeles
(213) 744-3411

Oakland Public Museum
1426 Oak St.
Oakland
(415) 834-2413

CONNECTICUT
*American Clock & Watch Museum
100 Maple Street
Bristol
(203) 583-6070

P.T. Barnum Museum
804 Main Street
Bridgeport
(203) 576-7320

The Marine Historical
  Association, Inc.
Mystic Seaport
Mystic
(203) 536-2631

Wethersfield Historical Society
150 Main St.
Wethersfield
(203) 529-7656

DELAWARE
*Henry Francis DuPont
Winterthur Museum
Winterthur
(302) 656-8591

DISTRICT OF COLUMBIA
*Smithsonian Institution
National Museum of American
  History
Washington
(202) 357-1300

United States Naval Observatory
Massachusetts Ave. at 34th St. NW
Washington
(202) 254-4569

FLORIDA
Lightner Museum of Hobbies
St. Augustine
(904) 824-2874 or
(904) 829-9677

Martin County Historial Society
Box 1497
Stuart
(305) 225-1961

HAWAII
Bernice P. Bishop Musuem
1355 Kalihi St.
Honolulu
(808) 847-1443

ILLINOIS
Chicago Museum of Science & Industry
5700 S. Lakeshore Dr.
Chicago
(312) 684-1414

Illinois State Museum of Natural History & Art
Spring & Edwards Sts.
Springfield
(217) 782-7386

*Time Museum
7801 E. State St.
Rockford
(815) 398-6000

INDIANA
Bartholomew County Historical Society
Court House - Washington St.
Columbus
(812) 372-3541

IOWA
*The Bily Clock Exhibit Horology Museum
Spillville
(319) 562-3569

KANSAS
Wichita Historical Museum
3751 E. Douglas Ave.
Wichita
(316) 265-9314

MAINE
Jonathan Fisher Memorial Museum
Blue Hill
(207) 374-2454

Portland Museum of Art
Portland
(207) 775-6148

MARYLAND
Maryland Historical Society
210 W. Monument St.
Baltimore
(301) 685-3750

The Walters Art Gallery
N. Charles at Centre Sts.
Baltimore
(301) 547-9000

MASSACHUSETTS
Brandeis University Library
Waltham
(617) 647-2000

Essex Institute
132 Essex St.
Salem
(617) 744-3390

Harvard University, Fogg Art Museum
Quincy St.
Cambridge
(617) 495-2387

Museum of Fine Arts
Boston
(617) 267-9300

Old Colony Historical Society
66 Church Green
Tauton
(617) 822-1622

Old Deerfield
Deerfield
(413) 774-5581

*Old Sturbridge Village
Sturbridge
(617) 347-3362

*Willard House
Grafton
(617) 839-3500

MICHIGAN
*Henry Ford Museum and
  Greenfield Village
Dearborn
(313) 271-1620

Michigan State University
East Lansing
(517) 355-2370

MINNESOTA
Lake County Historical Society
Two Harbors
(218) 834-4898

MISSISSIPPI
Old Spanish Fort Museum
200 Fort St.
Pascagoula
(601) 769-1505

Russel C. Davis Plantation
201 E. Pascagoula St.
Jackson
(601) 960-1550

MONTANA
Montana State University Museum
M.S.U. Campus Fine Arts Bldg.
Missoula
(406) 243-0211

NEVADA
Nevada Historical Society
P.O. Box 1129
Reno
(702) 784-6397

NEW YORK
The Brooklyn Museum
Brooklyn
(212) 638-5000

Buffalo & Erie County
  Historical Society
25Nottingham Court
Buffalo
(716) 873-9644

Buffalo Museum of Science
Humboldt Park
Buffalo
(716) 896-5200

*Hoffman Foundation
Newark Public Library
Newark
(315) 331-4370

Metropolitan Museum
New York
(212) 535-7710

New York State Historical
  Association
Cooperstown
(607) 547-2533

*New York University Museum
  of Clocks & Watches
Albany
(518) 457-3300

*New York University Museum
  of Clocks & Watches
University Ave. at 181st St.
Bronx
(212) 295-1630

Franklin D. Roosevelt Library
Hyde Park
(914) 229-8114

The Shaker Museum
Old Chatham
(518) 794-9100

NORTH CAROLINA
*Greensboro Clock Museum
300 Bellemeade St.
Greensboro
(919) 275-0462

*Old Salem, Inc.
614 Main St.
Winston-Salem
(919) 723-3688

OHIO
Cleveland Museum of Art
11150 East Blvd.
Cleveland
(216) 421-7340

Licking County Historical Society
6th Street Park
Newark
(614) 345-4898

Warren County Museum
S. Broadway
Lebanon
(513) 932-1817

Western Reserve Historical Society
10825 East Blvd.
Cleveland
(216) 721-5722

PENNSYLVANIA
Museum of Art Carnegie Institute
4400 Forbes Ave.
Pittsburgh
(412) 622-3270

The Ephrata Colister
632 W. Main
Ephrata
(717) 733-6600

Franklin Institute Museum
Ben Franklin Pkwy.
Philadelphia
(215) 448-1000

Hershey Museum
Park Avenue & Derry Road
Hershey
(717) 534-3439

Heritage Center of Lancaster County
Center Square
Box 997
Lancaster
(717) 299-6440

*National Museum of Clocks & Watches
514 Poplar St.
Box 33
Columbia
(717) 684-8261
Note: Headquarters of the National Association of Watch and Clock Collectors. Write for membership application.)

Old Economy Village
Ambridge
(412) 266-4500

Philadelphia Museum of Art
Philadelphia
(215) 763-8100

William Penn Memorial Museum
3rd & North Streets
Harrisburg
(717) 787-4980

SOUTH DAKOTA
South Dakota Historial Society
Memorial Bldg.
Pierre
(605) 773-3615

TEXAS
Bosque Memorial Museum
Avenue Q
Clifton
(817) 675-3845

*Old Clock Museum
929 E. Preston
Pharr
(512) 787-1923

VIRGINIA
Colonial Williamsburg Foundation
Williamsburg
(804) 229-1000

The Mariner's Museum
Newport News
(804) 595-0368

WASHINGTON
Bellingham Public Museum
121 Prospect St.
Bellingham
(206) 676-6981

Seattle Art Museum
Seattle
(206) 447-4670

CANADA
Fort George Restoration
Niagara-on-the-Lake, Ontario
(416) 468-4257

Huron County Pioneer Museum
Central Public School
North Street
Goderich, Ontario
(519) 524-9610

Robert Phillip Museum of Time
RR 1
Cookstown, Ontario
(705) 458-9221

LIBRARIES AND OTHER SOURCES OF INFORMATION

During the past ten years a number of books have been published on clocks; some as price guides, others as general information only. Go to your library and check with the Lending and Research Department to see what books they have on clocks. If you know the name and author of a particular book and it is still in print, the library will usually order it if a request is made. There are mail order book companies who specialize in books on clocks and watches. A request in writing or a phone call will result in your receiving a book catalog and you can order what you want.

SOURCES OF HOROLOGICAL BOOKS AND LITERATURE

The following companies issue catalogs. Call or write for catalog.
Note: Visa and Master Card telephone orders are accepted.

*Adams Brown Company
P.O. Box 357
Cranbury, NJ 08512
(800) 257-5378
In New Jersey
(609) 799-2125

*American Reprints
111 W. Dent
Ironton, MO 63650
Bob Spence
(314) 546-7251

Arlington Book Co.
2025 Eye St., NW
Suite 102
Washington, DC 20006
Tran Du Ly
(202) 296-6750
(202) 524-1931

Books of All Time
P.O. Box 604
Brockville, Ontario
Canada 56V 5V8
Marion Parker
(613) 345-2702

Century Editions
1440 S. Greenbrier St.
Arlington, VA 22206
Phyllis Miller
(703) 671-0770

*Heart of America Press
P.O. Box 9808
10101 Blue Ridge
Kansas City, MO 64134
Shirley Shelley
(816) 761-0080

*S. Larose, Inc.
234 Commerce Place
Greensboro, NC 27420
(919) 275-0462

Movements in Time
*Specializing in out-of-print
horological books*
Box 6629, Station A
Toronto M5W 1X4 Canada
Carol Hayter
(416) 883-1924
(416) 895-1439

LIST OF RECOMMENDED CLOCK BOOKS

Most of these books cannot be found in your local book store and must be ordered from one of the horological book dealers listed under *Sources of Horological Books and Literature.*

Abbott, Henry G. (pseud. for Hazlitt, George Henry A.), *The American Watchmaker and Jeweler,* Chicago, Hazlitt and Walker, 1910.

Abbott, Henry George (pseud.), *Antique Watches and How to Establish Their Age,* Chicago, G.K. Hazlitt, 1897.

Allix, Charles, *Carriage Clocks, Their History and Development,* Woodbridge, Suffolk, Baron, Antique Collectors Club, 1974.

American Waltham Watch Company, Bristol, CT; London, Ken Roberts, 1972.

Asprey And Co., *The Cockwork of the Heavens,* London, Asprey.

Avery, Amos Geer, *New England Clocks at Old Sturbridge Village, the Cheney Wills collection,* second edition Sturbridge, MA, 1966.

A.W.I. (Baier, Tigner and Whitney), *Question And Answers Of And For The Clockmaking Profession,* 1981.

A.W.I. *The Watchmakers And Clockmakers Buying Guide,* a where-to-buy-it directory for watch and clock repairmen, collectors, users and suppliers, edition of 1980.

Bailey, Chris H., comp., *Seth Thomas Clock Company,* reprint, Bristol CT, Ken Roberts, 1973.

200 Years of American Clocks and Watches, Englewood Cliffs, NJ, Prentice-Hall, 1975.

Bailey, Roy Rutherford, *Romance and History of Time,* Chicago, Elgin National Watch Co., 2 vol., 1922.

Baillie, G.H., *Watchmakers And Clockmakers Of The World,* 36,000 makers, necessary for the collector, Vol. 1.

Balm, Alexander, *Short History of Electric Clocks,* London, Turner and Devereux, 1973.

Barr, Lockwood Anderson, *Eli Terry Pillar and Scroll Shelf Clocks,* National Association of Watch and Clock Collectors, 1952; reprint, Exeter, NH, Adams Brown, 1956.

Barr, Lockwood Anderson, *The Origin of the Clock Label,* reprint from the *Bulletin of the National Association of Watch and Clock Collectors,* December 1955, Vol.7, no.61, Columbia, PA, 1955.

Basserman-Jordon, Ernst Von, *The Book of Old Clocks and Watches,* London, Allen and Unwin; New York, Crown, 1964, (Essential, standard work.)

Beckett, Sir Edmund, *Clock and Watch Work,* from the 8th edition of the *Encyclopaedia Britannica,* Edinburgh, A. and C. Black, 1855.

Beckman, E. D., *Cincinnati Silversmiths, Jewelers, Watch and Clock Makers,* Harrison, NY, R. A. Green, 1975.

Booth, Mary Louise, comp., *New and Complete Watchmaker's Manual with an Appendix Containing a History of Clock and Watch Making in America,* New York, J. Wiley, 1860, 1863, 1869, 1872, 1889.

Borland, Kathryn Kilby, and Helen Ross Speicher, *Clocks, from Shadow to Atom,* Chicago, Follett, 1969.

Boston Clock Company, Illustrated Catalogue, 1881, reprint, Exeter, NH, Adams Brown, 1970's.

Brearley, Harry Chase, *Time Telling Through the Ages,* New York, Doubleday, Page, for Robert H. Ingersoll Co., 1919.

Britten, F.J., *Old Clocks And Watches And their Makers,* contains comprehensive list of former clock and watchmakers. Republished from 1932 edition. Contains 12,000 names. 1977 printing.

Britten, F.J., *The Watch And Clockmakers' Handbook Dictionary And Guide,* 11th edition, definitions, illustrations. If the practical horologist, to say nothing of the collector or dealer were allowed one book, this would be the one. Contains wealth of now almost forgotten information some of which was omitted from later revised editions. Indexed.

Camp, Hiram, 1811-1893. *A Sketch of the Clock Making Business, 1792-1892,* New Haven, CT.

Carlisle, Lilian Baker, *Vermont Clock and Watchmakers, Silversmiths, and Jewelers, 1778-1878.* Shelburne, VT, Shelburne Museum, 1970, Burlington, VT. *Catalogue of Timepieces,* Exeter, NH, Adams Brown, 1969, (Tools, music boxes, clocks, watches, barometers.)

Chamberlain, Paul Mellen, *It's About Time,* New York, Richard R. Smith, 1941; reprint. London, Holland Pr, 1964.

Chandlee, Edward E., *Six Quaker Clockmakers,* Philadelphia The Historical Society of Pennsylvania, 1943.

Cipolla, Carlo Maria, *Clocks and Culture, 1300-1700,* London, Collins; New York, Walker, 1967.

Clock Makers of Concord, Massachusetts, as gathered at the Concord Antiquarian Museum, April-May 1966, Concord, MA, 1966.

Clocks and Watches, Garden City, NY, Doubleday, 1968.

Collectors Guide to Clocks, Price Guide, Gas City, IN, L. W. Promotions, 1973. (Schiller, Welch, Ansonia, Gilbert, Lasallita, Seth Thomas, Tiger, Waterbury, Ironclad, Ingraham, Ithaca.)

Conrad, Henry Clay, *Duncan Beard, Clockmaker; an address delivered at Old Drawyers Meeting House, in St. George's Hundred, New Castle County, Delaware,* June, 3 1928.

Old Delaware Clock-Makers. Wilmington, DE, The Historical Society, 1898. Primarily biographies.

Crossman, Charles S., *A Complete History of Watch and Clock Making in America,* Exeter, NH, Adams Brown, 1970.

Cumhaill, P. W., *Investing in Clocks and Watches,* New York, Potter, 1967; London, Corgi, 1971.

Cumming, Alexander, 1733-1814. *The Elements of Clock and Watch Work, adapted to practice, in two essays,* London, Author, 1766.

Cunynghame, Sir Henry Hardinge Samuel, *Time and Clocks,* ancient and modern methods of measuring time, Detroit, Singing Tree Pr, 1970.

De Carle, Donald, *Clocks and Their Value, Illustrated guide to ancient and modern clocks with a unique chart of all known Tompion clocks,* London, N. A. G. Pr, 1968, second edition 1971.

De Carle, D., *Practical Clock Repairing,* 1977. Deals with the most common repair problems. Tools and equipment discussed and construction of parts.

Dent, Edward John, 1790-1835, *On the Construction and Management of Chronometers, clocks and watches,* 1951, reprint of 1844 edition Exeter, NH, Adams Brown, 1970's.

Drepperd, Carl William, *American Clocks and Clockmakers,* Bailey and Swinfen, 1958.

Drost, William E., *Clocks and Watches of New Jersey,* Elizabeth, NJ, Engineering Pub, 1966, (Last 250 years.)

Dworetsky, Lester, and Robert Dickstein, *Horology Americana,* Roslyn Heights, NY, Horology Americana, 1972.

Eckhardt, George H. *Early Pennsylvania Clocks,* Lancaster, North Museum Commission, 1938.

Pennsylvania Clocks and Clockmakers; an epic on early American science, industry and craftmanship, New York, Devin-Adair, Bonanza, 1955.

United States Clock and Watch Patents, 1790-1890; the Record of a century of American horology and enterprise, New York, 1960.

Edwardes, Ernest Lawrence, *Weight-Driven Chamber Clocks of the Middle Ages and Renaissance 1350-1680; with some observations concerning certain larger clocks of medieval time,* Vol. 1, of *Old Weight-Driven Chamber Clocks, 1350-1850 series,* Altrincham, Eng. J. Sherratt, 1965.

Ehrhardt, Roy, *Clock Identification And Price Guide, Book I.* Carefully selected actual pages from original factory sales catalogs, factory advertisements, supply house catalogs and sales brochures. Covers American and imported clocks from 1850 to the 1940's. Notes year clock offered for sale. Original prices, 1979 retail value, 3,880 clocks pictured or described.

Ehrhardt, Roy, *Clock Identification And Price Guide, Book 2,* A continuation of Book 1 shown above, with an additional 3,257 clocks pictured or described showing 1979 retail values.

Ehrhardt, Roy, *The Pocket Watch Guide,* Kansas City, Heart of America Pr, 1972; *Book 2,* 1974, (2,600 watches and prices.)

The Timekeeper, Kansas City, Heart of America Pr, 1972.

Trade Marks on Watch Cases, Pocket Watches, Gold Rings, Kansas City, Heart of America Pr, 1975.

Electric Clocks and Chimes; a practical handbook giving complete instructions for the making of successful electrical timepieces, synchronised clock systems, and chiming mechanisms, London, P. Marshall, 1921; rev. ed. 1929.

Fennelly, Catherine, *New England Clocks, The J. Cheney Wells Collection,* Sturbridge, MA, Old Sturbridge Village, 1955.

Ferguson, James, 1710-1776, *Select Mechanical Exercises: shewing how to construct different clocks, orreries, and sun-dials, on plain and easy principles . . . with tables . . .* London, printed for W. Strahan; and T. Cadell, 1773; second edition London, 1778; third edition London, for Strahan and Cadell (?), 1790.

Fleet, Simon, *Clocks,* London, Weidenfeld and Nicolson; New York, Putnam, 1961; London, Octopus, 1972.

Fredyma, James P. *A Directory of Maine Silversmiths and Watch and Clock Makers,* Hanover, NH, Marie-Louise Antiques, 1972.

Fredyma, John J., *A Directory of Connecticut Silversmiths and Watch and Clock Makers,* Hanover, NH, P.J. and M-L Fredyma, 1973.

Fredyma, Paul J., and Marie-Louise Fredyma, *A Directory of Boston Silversmiths and Watch and Clock Makers,* Hanover, NH, M-L Fredyma, 1975.

A Directory of Vermont Silversmiths and Watch and Clock Makers, Hanover, NH, M-L Fredyma, 1975.

Fried, H.B., *Bench Practices For Watch and Clockmakers,* revised in 1974.

Fried, Henry B, *Calvacade of Time; a visual history of watches. From the private collection of the Zale Corporation,* Dallas, 1968.

The James W. Packard Collection of Unusual and Complicated Watches, owned and presented by the Horological Institute of America, Indianapolis?, the Institute, 1959.

Gazeley, William John, *Clock and Watch Escapements,* London, Heywood, 1956.

Gibbs, James W., *Buckeye Horology. A Review of Ohio clock and watchmakers,* Columbia, PA, Art Crafters, 1971.

Gilbert, (William L.,) Clock Company. Illustrated Catalogue 1901-02, reprint, Exeter, NH, Adams Brown, 1970's.

Goodrich, Ward L., *The Modern Clock. A Study of time keeping mechanism; its construction, regulation and repair,* 9th printing, Chicago, 1970.

Hagans, Orville, (compiler,) *The Best Of J.E. Coleman, 1979.* From his "Question and Answers" and "Clockwise and Otherwise" columns over the past 40 years. One of America's foremost horological authorities.

Hagans, Orville Roberts, *Horological Collection, Clock Manor Museum, Evergreen, Colorado,* Denver, Golden Bell Pr, 1964.

Hatton, Thomas, watchmaker, *An Introduction to the Mechanical Part of Clock and Watch Work* . . . London, T. Longman and G. Robinson, P. Law, and Co., 1773.

Hering, Daniel Webster, *Key to the Watches in the James Arthur Collection of Clocks and Watches. Addendum to the Lure of the Clock,* New York, NY U. Pr, 1934.

The Lure of the Clock; an account of the James Arthur Collection of Clocks and Watches at New York University, New York, Crown, 1963.

Hoopes, Penrose Robinson, *Connecticut Clockmakers of the 18th Century,* New York, Dodd Mead, Hartford, CT, E. V. Mitchell, 1930.

Early Clockmaking in Connecticut, New Haven, Tercentenary Commission, 1934.

Shop Records of Daniel Burnap, clockmaker, Hartford, Connecticut Historical Society, 1958.

Howard, (Edward), and Co. Illustrated Catalogue of Clocks Manufactured by the Howard Watch and Clock Company, Boston, 1874, Facsim., reprint, Bristol, CT; London, Ken Roberts.

1889 Catalogue of Fine Regulators, bank and office clocks, Reprint, Exeter, NH, Adams Brown, 1966.

Ingraham, (E.), and Co. Illustrated Catalogue and Price List of Clocks Manufactured by E. Ingraham and Co., Bristol, Connecticut, 1880. Introductory historical sketch of Elias Ingraham . . . Bristol; London, Ken Roberts, 1972.

James, Arthur Edwin, *Chester County Clocks and Their Makers,* West Chester, PA, Chester County Historical Society, 1947.

Jerome, Chauncey, *History of the American Clock Business for the Past 60 Years, and life of Chauncey Jerome, written by himself,* New Haven, CT, F. C. Dayton, Jr., 1860; reprint, Exeter, NH, Adams Brown, 1970's.

Jerome And Co., Philadelphia, manufacturers and wholesale clock dealers, Catalogue, Philadelphia, Young and Duross, 1852; reprint, Bristol, CT, American Clock and Watch Museum, 1964.

Johnson, Chester, *Clocks and Watches,* New York, Odyssey Pr, 1964; London, Hamlyn, 1965.

Johnson, Marilyn Ann, *Clockmakers and Cabinetmakers of Elizabethtown, New Jersey, in the Federal Period,* 1963.

Kendal, James Francis, *A History of Watches and Other Timekeepers,* London, C. Lockwood, 1892.

Lloyd, Herbert Alan, *Chats on Old Clocks,* First written by Arthur Hayden in 1917, London, Benn. 1951; second edition New York, Wyn, 1952; second edition rev. and reset as *Old Clocks,* London, Benn, 1958; Fair Lawn, NJ, Essential Books, 1959; third edition rev. London, 1964; fourth edition rev. and enl. London, Benn; New York, Dover 1970.

The Collector's Dictionary of Clocks, London Country Life, 1964; South Brunswick, NJ; A.S. Barnes, 1965.

The Complete Book of Old Clocks, New York, Putnam, 1965.

Some Outstanding Clocks Over 700 Years. 1250-1950, London, L. Hill, 1958.

Loomes, Brian, *The White Dial Clock,* New York, Drake 1975.

Lyon and Scott, *Evolution of the Timepiece,* Ottumwa, Iowa, Lyon and Scott, 1895.

Maloney, Terry, *The Story of Clocks,* N.Y., Sterling, 1960; London, Oak Tree Pr, 1962, (Juvenile Literature.)

Marshall, P., *Electric Clocks and Chimes,* Complete instructions for making successful electric timepieces. A practical handbook.Synchronized clock systems, and chiming mechanism.

Maust, Don, comp. *Early American Clocks. A collection of essays on early American clocks and their makers, a practical reference,* 2 vol. Uniontown, PA, E.G. Warman, 1971, 1973.

Milham, Willis Isbister, *The Columbus Clock,* Williamstown, MA, 1945.

Milham, Willis I., *Time and Timekeepers, including the history, construction, care, and accuracy of clocks and watches, New York, Macmillan, 1923, reprint.*

Miller, Andrew and Dalia, *Survey of American Calendar Clocks,* 1972, (Available from S. LaRose, Inc., 234 Commerce Place, Greensboro, NC).

Miller, R., *Clock Identification With Prices #2,* clocks and prices in addition to Book #1, more foreign clocks, German, Japanese, French and English, collectible and rare clocks.

Naylor, Arthur Henry, *The Study Book of Time and Clocks,* London, Bodley Head, 1959, 1965, (Juvenile Literature.)

Nelthropp, Henry Leonard, *Treatise on Watchwork, past and present,* London; New York, E. and F. N. Spon, 1873.

New Haven Clock Company, 1886 Catalog, Reprint with 1887 price list supplement, Bloomsburg, PA, G. and G.

1889-90 Catalogue, Reprint, Exeter, NH, Adams Brown, 1974.

Nicholls, Andrew, *Clocks in Color,* New York, Macmillan, 1976.

Nutting, Wallace, *The Clock Book; being a description of foreign and American clocks,* Framingham, MA, Old America Co., 1924; expanded edition as *The Complete Clock Book,* by William B. Jacobs, Jr., and John E. Edwards, Stratford, CT, Edmund-Bradley, 1970's; facsim. reprint, Greens Farms, CT, Modern Farms and Crafts, 1975.

Overton, George Leonard, *Clocks and Watches,* London; New York, Pitman, 1922.

Palmer, Brooks, *The Book Of American Clocks,* 12th printing, 318 pages, 310 illustrations, extensive list of American clockmakers, good for identification.

Palmer, Brooks, *The Romance of Time,* New Haven, C. Schaffner Advertising Agency, 1954.

Palmer, Brooks, *A Treasury Of American Clocks,* 9th printing.

Pertuch, Walter Albert Richard, and Emerson W. Hilker, comps., *Horological Books and Pamphlets in the Franklin Institute Library,* Philadelphia, the Institute, 1956; second edition Philadelphia, 1968; 19 ?.

Pocket Timepieces of New York Chapter Members, New York, National Association of Watch and Clock Collectors, 1968.

Prentiss Clock Improvement Company, 1897 catalogue, Reprint, St. Louis, American Reprints, 1969; 1972.

Proctor, (Frederick T.), Collection of Antique Watches and Table Clocks, Utica, NY, 1913.

Richardson, Albert Deane, 1833-69, *Ancient and Modern Time-Keepers, containing . . . notice of works of the National Watch Company, Elgin, Illinois, Reprint from Harper's Monthly Magazine, 1869,* New York, 1870.

Roberts, Kenneth D., *Contributions of Joseph Ives to Connecticut Clock Technology, 1810-62, Bristol, CT, Ken Roberts, 1970.*

Eli Terry and the Connecticut Shelf Clock, Bristol, CT, Ken Roberts, 1973.

Robertson, John Drummond, 1857, *The Evolution of Clockwork, with a special section on the clocks of Japan. With a comprehensive bibliography of horology,* London, Cassell, 1931; facsim. reprint, Wakefield, Eng. S.R.

Royer-Collard, Frederick Bernard, *Skeleton Clocks,* London, N.A.G. Pr, 1969.

Sanderson, R. L., *Waltham Industries,* Waltham MA, 1957, American Waltham Watch Co., U.S.

Sands, Anna B., *Time Pieces of Old and New Connecticut,* Hartford, CT, Manufacturers Association, 1926.

Schwartz, Marvin D., *Collector's Guide to Antique American Clocks, history, style, identification,* Garden City, NY, Doubleday, 1975.

Seth Thomas Clock Co. Illustrated Catalogue of Clocks, 1892-93, Reprint, Exeter, NH, Adams Brown, 1970's.

Factory List of Seth Thomas Clock Movements, 1907 Catalogue, Reprint, Exeter, NH, Adams Brown, 1970's.

Smith, Alan, *Clocks and Watches,* London, Connoisseur, 1975; New York, Hearst, 1976.

Smith, Eric, *Repairing Antique Clocks: a guide for amateurs,* Newton Abbott, David and Charles, 1973.

Sobol, Ken, *The Clock Museum,* New York, McGraw-Hill, 1967.

St. Louis Clock and Silver Ware Co., 1904 catalog, St. Louis, American Reprints, 1975, (Ansonia, Sempire, Waterbury, Gilbert, Ingraham, Newman.)

The Story of Edward Howard and the First American Watch, Boston, E. Howard Watch Works, 1910.

Terwilliger, Charles, *The Horolovar Collection, a comprehensive history and catalogue of 400-day clocks, 1880-1912,* Bronxville, NY, Horolovar Co., 1962.

Thomson, Richard, *Antique American Clocks and Watches,* Princeton, NJ; London, Van Nostrand, 1968.

Tyler, Eric John, *The Craft of the Clockmaker,* London, Ward Lock, 1973; New York, Crown, 1974, (14th century to present, includes tools.)

Ullyett, Kenneth, *Clocks and Watches,* Feltham, Hamlyn, 1971.

The Plain Man's Guide to Antique Clocks, by W. J. Bentley; London, M. Joseph, 1963.

In Quest of Clocks, Feltham, Spring Books, 1968.

Vulliamy, Benjamin Lewis, 1780-1854, *On the Construction and Regulation of Clocks for Railway Stations,* London, W. Clowes, 1845.

Some Considerations on Public Clocks, Particularly Church Clocks, London, priv. printed, 1831.

Ward, Francis Alan Burnett, *Clocks and Watches, Vol.I.*

Warman, Edwin G., *Early American Clocks,* 3 vol., Uniontown, PA, Warman Pub. Co., 1970's.

Watch-making in America. Embodying the history of watchmaking as an invention, and as an industry, Reprint from Appleton's Journal, July, 2, 1870, Boston, Appleton, 1870.

Waterbury Clock Company, 1867 Catalog, Reprint, St. Louis, American Reprints, 1973.

Way, Robert Barnard, and Noel D. Green, *Time and Its Reckoning,* New York, Chemical Pub. Co., 1940.

Weight-Driven Clocks; Vol. II. Spring-Driven Clocks, 2 vol., London, Science Museum, 1973, 1972.

Welch, (E. N.), Manufacturing Co. Catalogue 1885, Reprint, Exeter, NH, Adams Brown, 1970, (Regulators, calendars, alarms, ship bell, cottage, etc.)

Welch, Kenneth Frederick, *Time Measurement: An Introductory History*, London, David and Charles, 1972; as *The History of Clocks and Watches*, New York, Drake, 1972.

Wells, Joel Cheney, 1874, *New England Clocks at Old Sturbridge Village, the J. Cheney Wells Collection*, Sturbridge Village, MA, 1955.

Willard, John Ware, *A History of Simon Willard, inventer and clockmaker, together with some account of his sons — his apprentices — and the workmen associated with him*, Boston, E. O. Cockayne, 1911; reprint, New York, 1968.

Willsberger, Johann, *Clocks and Watches*, New York, Dial Pr, 1975.

Wood, Edward J., *Curiosities of Clocks and Watches from the Earliest Times*, London, Richard Bentley, 1866, reprint of 1866 edition, Detroit, Gale, 1975.

Wright, Lawrence, *Clockwork Man: the story of time, its origins, its uses, its tyranny*, New York, Horizon, 1969.

Wyatt, Sir Matthew Digby, 1820-77, *The History of the Manufacture of Clocks*, reprints from the *Clerkenwell News*, London, 1870.

CALENDAR EVENTS

As of this writing, the 1983 dates for regional meetings, conventions, and seminars are as follows:

February 18-20	Pacific-Northwest Regional, Seattle, Washington
March 17-19	Southern Regional, Memphis, Tennessee
April 8-9	Southern Ohio Regional, Ft. Mitchell, Kentucky
April 22-24	Greater New York Regional, Hauppauge, New York
May 13-15	St. Louis Regional, St. Louis, Montana
May 20-22	Great Plains Regional, Omaha, Nebraska
June 9-12	Western Regional, Anaheim, California
June 29-July 3	NAWCC National Convention, Philadelphia, Pennsylvania
July 15-16	Midwest Regional, Des Plaines, Illinois
August 5-7	Missouri Regional, Columbia, Montana
September 2-4	Great Lakes Regional, Dearborn, Michigan
September 23-24	Kentucky Blue-Grass Regional, Lousiville, Kentucky
September 30-October 2	M-K-O Regional, Wichita, Kansas
October 20-23	Great Southwestern Regional, Houston, Texas
October 28-29	NAWCC Council Seminar, Lancaster, Pennsylvania

The above information was gathered from the December 1982 issue of the *Bulletin of the National Association of Watch and Clock Collectors, Inc.*

GLOSSARY
Courtesy of Malvern "Red" Rabeneck

ABRASIVE

A substance used for grinding and polishing. These are generally oilstone, emery, carborundum, lavigated aluminum oxide; any substance gritty enough to wear the surface of another material.

ACETONE

A chemical liquid used to dissolve celluloids; used in crystal cement and as a dehydrator after cleaning watch parts although not well recommended as a rinse because of its violent inflammability.

ACORN CLOCK

Called this because of the shape of the case.

ADJUSTED

Term applied to watch movements and some small clock movements to indicate that they have been corrected for various errors, such as isochronism, temperature, and positions.

ADVERTISING CLOCK

Any clock used with advertising. This advertising could be on the clock dial, tablet, or case, or the clock could be part of the advertising.

ALARM

An attachment to a clock whereby, at a predetermined time, a bell is sounded.

ALARM CLOCK

A clock which is primarily used for an alarm.

AMMONIA

A sharp smelling liquid used in practically all watch and clock cleaning solutions.

ANIMATED CLOCK

A clock with a visible life-like motion imitating, among many other things, a pecking bird, dancing ballerina, spinning wheel, etc.

ANNIVERSARY CLOCK

So called because it needs winding only once a year on the "anniversary" of the previous winding. Also known as a 400 day clock.

ANCHOR ESCAPEMENT

Resembles a ship's anchor in appearance. Invented about 1671, and enabled the clockmaker to use a long pendulum. Also called recoil escapement.

ANCHOR (VERGE)

A device that regulates the speed of rotation of the escape wheel.

APPARENT SOLAR DAY

The interval between successive sun crossings of the local meridian by the sun as indicated by a sundial.

ARABIC FIGURES

Figures on a dial, such as 1, 2, 3, as opposed to *Roman Numerals,* such as I, II, V, IX.

ARBOR

The axle of a wheel (gear) or a shaft that turns in a bearing; commonly referred to as the barrel arbor, pallet arbor, winding arbor, etc.

ARC

The angle through which the balance wheel or pendulum swings.

ARCH

The curved part of any clock case that resembles a door arch.

ARKANSAS STONE

A white marble-like silicon stone used in various shapes and sizes as a grinding stone to sharpen gravers and tools. Used in powdered form as an abrasive with grinding laps. So called because the highest grade stones were found in Arkansas.

ATMOS CLOCK

A clock operated by a bellows-like mechanism that operates the clock because of changes in atmospheric temperature and pressure. Changes in temperature provide most of the power. The first Atmos clock used a tube of mercury rather than an aneroid. All use a torsion pendulum.

AUTO CLOCK

A timepiece designed to be mounted in an automobile, usually on the instrument panel, but may be mounted in other places.

BACK PLATE

The arbors of a clock train are supported by two plates; the one farthest from the dial is known as the back plate. Also called Top Plate and Upper Plate.

BARN CLOCK

Very early electric clock.

BALANCE

The oscillating wheel of a clock or watch, which in conjunction with the hairspring (balance spring) regulates the speed of a clock or watch. May be made of bi-metal to compensate for temperature changes and may be studded with screws for regulation.

BALANCE COCK

The support for the upper pivot of the balance staff.

BALANCE SPRING

A long fine spring that regulates the vibration of the balance. Also known as a hairspring.

BALANCE STAFF

The axis of the balance. (Axle shaft)

BALANCE WHEEL

Coloquial term for the balance.

BALLOON CLOCK

Shaped like hot-air balloons of the late 18th century; these were bracket (table or shelf) clocks.

BANJO CLOCK

A clock vaguely resembling a banjo, an American design. Simon Willard introduced these in 1802 as a new, improved timepiece. Because of the shape of the cases, they are called Banjos today.

BARREL

The round container or housing that holds the mainspring. This was eliminated on most American clocks.

BARREL ARBOR

The axle of the barrel around which the mainspring is coiled.

BARREL HOOK

A hook or slot in the inside of the barrel wall upon which the end of the last coil of mainspring is attached.

BEAT

The sound of the ticking of a clock, caused by the teeth of the escape wheel striking the pallets or arms of the escapement. A clock is said to be "in beat" if the ticks are very evenly spaced.

BEARING

The support for a pivot or arbor. Jeweled bearings are used where there is danger of rapid wear on the pivots of fast moving parts such as the balance staff and also train wheel pivots. In clocks, the bearings are usually brass, but wood, ivory and various jewels have also been used.

BEEHIVE CLOCK

Clock with a rounded Gothic case.

BEESWAX

A tough, yellowish-brown wax used as a temporary adhesive by watchmakers. Also was often used to polish the wooden clock cases.

BEETLE HAND

The hour hand, shaped like a stag beetle, frequently found on early Massachusetts shelf clocks and other early clocks. Generally used with a poker or straight minute hand.

BELL TOP

The rounded top of a bracket clock, resembling a bell, popular in England in the late 17th century.

BENZENE

A coal tar product used as a cleaner and rinse in watch and clock cleaning. Highly volatile and inflammable. (Benzol) (C_6H_6). More expensive than *benzine.*

BERYLLIUM

A metal used in minute quantities with nickel and steel to produce non-magnetic, noncorrosive balances and springs capable of good temperature adjustments.

BEZEL

The metal or wood ring that holds the glass over the dial.

BIMETALLIC

Made up of two metals. In watchmaking, this refers to the split balance having a brass rim and steel frame.

BLACK FOREST CLOCK

Term now used to mean any clock made in the Black Forest area of Germany.

BLACK MANTEL CLOCK

Shelf clock with a case, generally a horizontal rectangle in shape, but made in all possible variations of shape and trim but predominantly black in color. Very popular from 1890 to 1930.

BLIND MAN'S CLOCK

Colloquial usage — applies the term to a braille clock which has the numbers in braille; and also applies the term to a quarter-hour repeater in which the strike may be activated at will.

BLINKING EYE (WINKER)

Iron statue clock with winking eye.

BLOWPIPE

A thin, tapered tube made of copper, used to force a jet of blown air through a flame and directed at an object. The jet of air directs the flame to a point and raises the heat of the flame. Usually the blowpipe is held in the mouth.

BLUING

To change the color of polished steel by heating it to approximately 540°F.

BOB

The weighted end of a pendulum. Usually held on the threaded rod by a nut, thus enabling it to be raised or lowered for time adjustment.

BOSS

The round disk applied to the arch of a dial on which is usually recorded the maker's name. Usually used on early brass dials.

BOX REGULATOR

A very plain rectangular wall clock, usually with trim on the top and bottom but none on the sides, sometimes with advertising on the tablet.

BRACE

The hook or connection attached to the outer end of the mainspring.

BRACKET CLOCK

Term used by British to indicate a shelf clock.

BRASS WORKS

Clock works with brass plates and brass wheels.

BREGUET

A horological genius of the late 18th and early 19th century. The name applied to the type of hairspring which has its last outer coil raised above the body of the spring and curved inwards.

BRIDGE

Upper plates in a plate watch for the support of the wheels. Always has at least two feet or supports.

BROACH

A tapered steel tool, with flat cutting edges used to enlarge holes already drilled.

BROCOT ESCAPEMENT

Trade term for visible escapement (wheel and pallets) on the clock dial.

BROKEN ARCH

An arch that has a short, horizontal, straight section outward from each bottom end of the arch.

BUSHING

The bearing that supports the end or pivot of the arbor. Called a bushing because it is usually made of a brass bushing or tube inserted into a hole in the plate. May be bradded in place. (Term not in common usage except by clockmakers and watchmakers.) In a watch, bushings are known as jewels.

BUTTING

The action of two wheels or a wheel and pinion improperly matched or distorted wherein their teeth butt each other instead of enmeshing perfectly.

CABINET CLOCK

Trade term for a small 12″ to 24″ shelf or table clock without visible pendulum (a vague term).

CALENDAR CLOCK

Any clock that indicates the date. A simple calendar clock usually has a single, extra hand pointing to a day of the month number outside the chapter ring. A perpetual calendar shows the month, date, and day of the week, and automatically compensates for the number of days in the month and leap year. (See also Double Dial Calendar)

CAMEL BACK

Trade term for clock resembling the shape of Napoleon's hat; also called Hump Back or Tambour.

CAM

A small flat piece used to transfer circular motion into back-and-forth motion to a lever or other contacted piece.

CANNON PINION

A thin, steel tube with pinion leaves at its lower end and carrying the minute hand on its upper end.

CANNON TUBES

A misnomer applied to the hour pipe which carries the hour hand.

CAP JEWEL

The flat solid jewel upon which rests the pivot end. Also called the *endstone*.

CARRIAGE CLOCK

Small portable clock, usually with a brass case with glass sides and top. Spring driven with a balance wheel escapement.

CASE

That which contains the clock or watch; the housing or containment for the works.

CASTLE WHEEL

The clutch wheel.

CENTER OF GRAVITY

That point in a body around which the mass is evenly balanced.

CENTER-SECONDS HAND

Sometimes called sweep-seconds hand. Mounted on the center post of clocks and watches.

CENTER WHEEL

The wheel in a watch the axis of which usually carries the minute hand.

CHAIN (FUSEE)

A miniature "bicycle" chain connecting the barrel and fusee of English watches and chronometers.

CHAMFER

To remove a sharp edge from a hole or drilled surface.

CHAPTER RING

The circle on the dial that contains the numbers for the hours and minutes. So called because in early clocks it was a separate ring attached to the dial.

CHRONOGRAPH

A watch that has a center-seconds hand driven from the fourth wheel which can be started, stopped, and caused to fly back to zero by pressing on a knob or lever.

CHRONOMETER

A clock which has passed strict observatory tests; a very accurate time-keeper; term also used for watches, particularly mounted, boxed watches with spring detent escapements, for use on ships at sea.

CHRONOMETER ESCAPEMENT
A detent escapement used in chronometers.

CHINA OR PORCELAIN CLOCK
Entire case of glazed porcelain. (Very fragile and easily broken.)

CIRCULAR ESCAPEMENT
The lever escapement wherein the center of the pallets lifting surface is planted on a circle whose center is the pallet arbor. Found mostly in American watches.

CIRCULAR PITCH
The pitch circle divided into as many spaces as there are teeth on the wheel or pinion.

CLEPSAMMIA
An hour glass filled with sand; also called a "sand thief."

CLEPSYDRA
A form of clock using water, instead of sand, that falls from one container to another at a given rate.

CLICK
A spring-tensioned pawl holding the ratchet wheel against the tension of the mainspring, enabling the spring to be wound, usually making the clicking noise as the clock is wound.

CLOCK
A machine that records the passing of time and also strikes at least the hours — differing from a "timepiece," which keeps time only.

CLOCKWISE
The direction of circular motion going in the same direction as the hands of a clock, circling from horizontal left, upward around and down toward lower right.

CLUB-TOOTH WHEEL
That type of wheel which has a lifting face off the end of the teeth.

CLUTCH PINION
The pinion surrounding the square of the stem. Serves alternately to wind and set the watch.

COCK
An overhanging support for a bearing such as the balance cock; a bridge having a support at one end only.

COLLET

A collar, usually brass, that holds a wheel on an arbor.

COMPENSATING BALANCE

A balance with a bi-metallic rim made of brass and steel. The diameter increases or decreases with changes in temperature to compensate for these changes.

COMPENSATING PENDULUM

A pendulum that maintains a constant distance between the center of gravity of the pendulum and the suspension point, thus compensating for changes in temperature and keeping much more accurate time. The two principle forms are the Harrison or grid pendulum and the Graham or mercury pendulum.

CONICAL PIVOT

A pivot which curves back into the main body of its arbor, such as those used with cap jewels. (Balance staff pivots.)

CONNECTICUT SHELF

Any shelf clock manufactured in Connecticut. Some common styles are: Beehive, Column, Cottage, Octagon Top, OG & OOG, Round Top (Venetian), Split Top, Steeple.

CORDLESS CLOCK

Slang term for a battery-operated clock.

COUNT WHEEL

The clock wheel that regulates the "count" of the striking by means of slots on the circumference.

CROWN

A grooved circular piece fastened to the stem for winding the watch. (Slang winding knob or button)

CROWN WHEEL

A wheel that drives the ratchet wheel.

CROWN WHEEL ESCAPEMENT

So called because of its resemblance to a crown. Another name for verge escapement.

CRUTCH

The arm from the pallet arbor which connects the escapement to the pendulum, thus regulating the escapement with the motion of the pendulum and giving the pendulum the impulse or power to keep it swinging.

CRUTCH WIRE
A wire that carries the impulse from the escapement to the pendulum.

CRYSTAL REGULATOR (FOUR GLASS REGULATOR)
Shelf clock with glass panels on each side, completely exposing the interior.

CRYSTAL PALACE CLOCK
Made by Ansonia.

CURB PINS
The two regulator pins almost pinching the hairspring.

CYANIDE (POTASSIUM)
A poisonous, white crystalline substance dissolved in water to brighten tarnished metals. Very, very poisonous. Can kill by inhalation of fumes, absorption through the skin, or by ingestion. Not recommended for use.

CYLINDER ESCAPEMENT
A frictional escapement patented by Thomas Tompion 1695.

DATE DIAL
An accessory dial marked with the dates of the month. Usually moved twice every 24 hours.

DEAD BEAT ESCAPEMENT
So called because when the pallets engage the escape wheel, there is no further movement of the escapement — the mechanism was "dead." Generally considered to be the most accurate type.

DEDENDUM
The portion of a wheel tooth or pinion leaf that is below the pitch circle. In a watch wheel (train) the dedendum would be the portion of the tooth that is below the curved top of the tooth.

DENNISON GAUGE
A mainspring gauge composed of a thick strip of brass with numbered and graduated notches or slots used to designate the width of a mainspring. The system uses the millimeter as its unit. 1.00 mm equals No. 1 Dennison; 1.10 mm equal No. 2 Dennison, etc.

DEPTHING TOOL
A tool which will accommodate two wheels or a wheel and pinion between their centers and, by means of a screw, bring them into correct pitch; this distance may then be transferred to the plates for comparison or verification.

DETENT

The setting lever. Also that part of the chronometer escapement that locks the escape wheel. A detainer or pawl.

DIAL

The face of a clock.

DIAL TRAIN

The train of wheels under the dial which moves the hands. The cannon pinion, hour wheel, minute wheel and pinion.

DIAL ARCH

The arched portion at the top of some dials. It usually contains a Boss, moon dial or fancy decoration.

DIAL FOOT

A post or pillar on the back of a dial for attaching the dial to the front or false plate.

DIE

A plate with cutting edges normally used to thread screws and stems. A steel plate used to shape objects forced into them.

DISCHARGING PALLET

The exit pallet jewel. The pallet jewel from which an escape tooth drops as it leaves the pallet.

DOLLAR WATCH

A practical timepiece with a non-jeweled movement. The case and movement an integral unit with a dial of paper on brass or other inexpensive material. Ingersoll sold his first Dollar watch for $1.00 in 1892. (Taken from *The Watch That Made the Dollar Famous* by George E. Townsend.)

DOUBLE-ROLLER ESCAPEMENT

A form of lever escapement in which a separate roller is used for the safety action.

DOUBLE WIND

Nickname for a clock with two springs (therefore two winding arbors) geared together to drive the time train. Used in many 15 day and 30 day clocks.

DOUBLE DIAL CALENDAR

Calendar dial is usually round and is separate, and usually under the time dial.

DRAW

The force which keeps the pallet against the banking pins. The result of the combined angles of the escape teeth and the pallet locking surface.

DROP

The free, unrestrained motion of the escape wheel as it leaves one pallet jewel before it drops upon the locking surface of another pallet jewel.

DROP LOCK

The extent of the lock on the pallets after an escapement has been banked to the drop.

DRUM

In a weight-driven clock, the round barrel on which the weight gut or cord is wound.

DRUM CLOCK

A clock whose case is round metal, resembling a drum or tin can.

DUMB REPEATER

Where the hammer strikes a fixed metal block instead of a bell or gong.

DUPLEX ESCAPEMENT

A watch escapement in which the escape wheel has two sets of teeth. One set locks the wheel by pressing on the balance staff. The other set gives impulse to the balance. The balance receives impulse at every other vibration.

EBAUCHE

A term used by Swiss watch manufacturers to denote the raw movement without jewels, escapement, plating, engraving. The ebauche manufacturers supply their ebauches to trade name importers in the U.S.A. and other countries who have them finished, jeweled, dialed, cased, etc., and engraved with their own (advertised) name brands.

EIGHT DAY CLOCK

Will run eight days on one winding.

ELECTRIC CLOCK

General term for clock powered by electricity. In this country, usually used to indicate a clock powered by AC.

ELINVAR

A nonrusting, nonmagnetizing alloy containing iron, nickel, chromium, tungsten, silicon and carbon. Used for balance and balance spring. (Hamilton)

ENGINE CLOCK

A small, usually round metal cased, balance wheel clock that could be used in any position without affecting its rate. (A slang term for any clock that could have been used in the engine room of a ship.)

ENAMEL (SOFT)

A soluble paint used in dials.

ENAMEL (HARD)

A porcelain-like paint, acid-resisting and durable. A baked enamel.

ENDSHAKE

The free up and down space of pivoted wheels or arbors in their bearings. (End play.)

ENTRANCE JEWEL

The jewel first contacted by an escape tooth before it enters between the pallets. Also called the *right jewel.* Also called *stone.*

EPICYCLOID

A curve generated by a point in the circumference of a circle as it rolls upon another circle. It forms the kind of tooth used in watch wheels.

EQUATION CLOCK

A type of clock that shows the difference between solar time and mean time.

EQUIDISTANT ESCAPEMENT

The lever escapement whose pallet jewels have their entrance corners equally distant from the center of the pallet. Used more often in Swiss watches.

EPHEMERIS TIME (ET)

Is based on the revolution of the earth around the sun. The ephemeris second is defined as 1/31,556,925.9747 of the tropical year for 1900.

ESCAPE

The method of regulating the release of power.

ESCAPE WHEEL

Regulator of the running of the clock.

ESCAPEMENT

A means by which the pendulum allows the going train to operate at a regular interval, thus controlling the passage of time. It usually consists of anchor and escape wheel.

ESCUTCHEON

The trim around a keyhole.

EUREKA CLOCK

A clock whose movement has a large balance wheel, driven by a battery-powered electromagnet. Invented 1906.

FALSE PLATE

A plate between the front plate of the movement and the dial on some clocks to make it easier to fit the dial to the movement.

FINIAL

The spires, or turnings, or finishing points, on top of a clock case. May be wood or metal. Various types, according to their shapes and appearance, are called "ball and spike", "urn", "acorn", "pineapple", "flower basket", "eagle", etc. Sometimes removable.

FLASHPOINT

The point at which the vapor of heated oil will explode or ignite at the approach of a spark or flame.

FLAT HAIRSPRING

A hairspring whose spirals develop on a flat surface. As opposed to the overcoil (Breguet) hairspring.

FLAT OGEE

A clock whose appearance closely resembles an Ogee, except that the front surface is flat rather than having the S-curve of a typical Ogee.

FLOATING BARREL

A barrel whose arbor has only one bearing surface. One attached only to the barrel bridge with no support from the lower plate.

FLUTED COLUMNS

Columns with grooves running the length of the turning.

FLY

A fan or type of air brake used to regulate or slow the speed of a strike train. Usually a thin, flat plate set in a slot in the arbor so that it provides maximum air resistance when rotating.

FLYING PENDULUM CLOCK (Also called Ignatz)

Novelty clock invented in 1883 with a small ball on a thread hung from an arm which swings in a horizontal circle, regulated by twisting and untwisting a round vertical rod. Famous for lack of accuracy. Reproduced in 1959.

FOLIOT

An early type of pendulum used in verge escapements; later used on the Columbus clock. It has two arms with adjustable weights on the ends and swings in a horizontal plane.

FORK

A two-pronged rod sometimes used to engage the verge or pallet with the pendulum; the end of the pallet containing the slot, horns and guard finger.

FOUR HUNDRED DAY CLOCK

See Anniversary Clock.

FOURTH WHEEL

Usually the wheel which carries the second hand and drives the escape wheel; it is the fourth wheel from the great wheel in the going train of a clock.

FREE PENDULUM CLOCK

Most accurate pendulum clock ever made.

FRET

Lattice-type or other fancy decoration across the top of some wood tall cases or mantel clocks, usually between finials.

FRICTION ROLLER

As a bearing for pivots, it needs no lubrication.

FRONT PLATE

Two plates hold the arbor's of a clock train; the front plate is nearest to the dial, also called Pillar Plate, Dial Plate and Lower Plate.

FRONT WIND

Clock wound through the dial.

FULL PLATE

Top plate of a watch in full round diameter. Clocks are also referred to as "full plate" when the plates are not pierced or otherwise cut out.

FUZEE

A grooved, cone-shaped pulley with a spiral track cut around it, which the mainspring barrel drives by a chain or cord (usually gut). As the spring runs down, it preserves, more or less, a constant torque on the train as long as the clock is running. The word "fuzee" means thread.

GALLERY CLOCK

Usually 8″ dial or larger, either eight day or electric, with a simple case of various configuration for use on walls of public places; i.e. in galleries.

GATHERING PALLET

A part of the rack-and-snail strike train. A small metal bar that rotates once for each strike and gathers one tooth of the rack until the striking is completed.

GILT

As applied to clock cases, meant gold-leafed. In modern times the term is sometimes used to mean gold-colored.

GIMBAL

A device, similar to a universal joint, that keeps a clock level. Usually used in ships' chronometers.

GINGERBREAD

Nickname for a kitchen clock with very elaborate designs pressed into the wood of the case.

GIRANDOLE CLOCK

A variant of the banjo clock. Invented by Lemuel Curtis and, as far as can be determined, made only by him in Concord, Massachusetts. Usually considered to be the most beautiful wall clock ever built. (Many reproductions)

GOLD FILLED

Another name for rolled gold.

GOLD PLATED

Electro-plated a few thousandths of an inch thick with pure or alloyed gold.

GOLD LEAF

Very, very thin sheet of solid gold. Was applied to clock cases, columns, and tablets for decoration; the term "Gold Leaf" was also used to mean the act of applying the gold.

GOTHIC CASE

Case that resembles Gothic architecture, having a pointed top like the end of a gabled roof.

GRANDE SONNIERIE

A quarter hour repeater; a type of striking in which the last hour struck is repeated at each quarter. Present day usage sometimes applies the term to a quarter hour repeater which can be made to strike at will..

GRANDFATHER CLOCK

The popular name for a long-case clock. Today's height is usually 7' plus or minus one foot.

GRANDMOTHER CLOCK

Popular name for the dwarf or miniature tall case clock. Today the height is usually 66" plus or minus 6".

GRANDDAUGHTER CLOCK

Popular name for the dwarf or miniature tall case clock. Today the height is usually 48" plus or minus 6".

GRAVITY CLOCK

A clock driven by its own weight.

GRAVITY ESCAPEMENT

A type of escapement used on tower clocks. The impulse is given to the pendulum directly by a small falling weight that is raised by the going train after each beat of the pendulum.

GREAT WHEEL

The first wheel in the train. On the drum, it is weight-driven; on the going barrel or on the fuzee, it is spring-driven, depending upon which type is used.

GREENWICH CIVIL TIME

Also called Universal Time (UT). It is Local mean time as measured at Greenwich, England.

GRIDIRON PENDULUM

A series of steel and brass rods in the pendulum to counteract the heat and cold to which it is subjected. By this means the pendulum length is kept constant. Invented by John Harrison of London.

GROANER MOVEMENT

A wood works with a distinctive appearance, so called because of the distinctive noise usually made by these movements.

GUARD PIN

A thin finger emerging from a boss below the slot in the pallet fork and working in conjunction with the safety roller to aid in preventing "over-banking."

HAIRSPRING

The spiraled spring attached to the balance to govern the speed of the balance oscillations.

HALLMARK

A mark or design stamped on gold, silver or platinum objects, such as watch and clock cases, to indicate the quality of the objects. Marks were used to indicate the assayor, the location purity of metal, the maker, and the date.

HAMMER

The part of a clock that strikes the bell, gong, rod, tube, etc. in striking, chiming and alarm mechanisms.

HANDS

Used to mark hours, minutes, or seconds on a clock dial.

HAND SET CLOCKS

A clock which is set by pushing against the hands to move them.

HANGING BARREL
Same as floating barrel.

HEEL OF TOOTH
Letting-off corner of a tooth of the escape wheel.

HELICAL HAIRSPRING
The spiraled cylindrical spring used in marine chronometer balances.

HOLLOW-COLUMN CLOCKS
A type of shelf clock in which the weights fall through a hollow column situated on either side of the case.

HOOD
The top part of a tall clock that covers the dial and works.

HOOK (Pendulum hook)
The hook at the top of the pendulum which engages the suspension spring. Not used in all clocks.

HOROLOGY
The science of measuring time, or the principles and art of constructing instruments for measuring and indicating portions of time.

HOURGLASS
An early form of timekeeper in which sand falls at a given rate from one container to another through a slender glass neck.

HOUR WHEEL
A flat, brass, toothed wheel mounted on a tube which fits over the cannon pinion and supports the hour hand.

HUMP BACK
See Camel Back.

HYPOCYCLOIDAL
A path or curve generated by a point on the circumference of a circle rolling within another circle. Generally, flanks of pinion leaves have this form.

IMPULSE CLOCK
A slave clock driven by electrical impulses from the master clock.

IMPULSE PIN
Roller jewel.

IMPULSE AND LOCKING

Dead-beat escapements have two actions: impulse is the period during which the train imparts impulse to the balance or pendulum; during the rest of the time the train is locked.

INCABLOC

Trade name for a shock-resisting arrangement of balance jewels and staff design. Mostly used in watches.

INCLINED PLANE CLOCK

A form of gravity clock consisting of a drum clock which was powered by a weight attached to the center wheel arbor which turned the arbor as the clock rolled down the inclined plane.

INDEX

The regulator scale. Used to help in adjusting the regulation. Some pendulums had indexes. Many later mantel clocks that adjusted regulator through a hole in the dial with the small end of the key had indexes. Most balance wheel clocks and watches had indexes.

INVAR

A steel alloy containing about 36 per cent nickel that remains the same length at different temperatures. Used in the making of balance wheels. Also used for pendulum rods in clocks for temperature compensation. Similar to Elinvar.

INVOLUTE

A curve traced by the end of a string as it is unwound from a spool. The shape of wheel teeth used in gears where great strength is needed.

IRON-FRONT CLOCK

Connecticut Shelf Clock with cast-iron front.

ISOCHRONISM

Quality of keeping equal time during the normal run of the mainspring, usually the qualitites of a well-formed overcoil hairspring.

JACK

A moving figure turned by a clock mechanism. In very clocks, the Jack struck the bell.

JACOT TOOL

A tool used for burnishing or polishing pivots.

JEWEL

Synthetic or semiprecious stones used for bearings in watches and precision clocks.

JEWELER'S REGULATOR CLOCK

A high grade, accurate, compensated clock used by a jeweler as a time standard for regulating timepeices.

KEY, BENCH

A tool with varied size prongs capable of fitting into all sizes of winding arbors.

KIDNEY DIAL

So called because of its shape. Usually used on the Massachusetts shelf clock.

LUNETTE

The half circle above the dial. Usually contains a phase of the moon or ornamentation.

LYRE CLOCK

A variation of the banjo, usually attributed to Aaron Willard, Jr., of Boston.

MAINSPRING

The flat, ribbon-like tempered steel spring wound inside the barrel and used to drive the train wheels. Most American clocks eliminated the barrel.

MAINTAINING POWER

A device in a clock that provides sufficient power to keep it going while being wound.

MAIN TRAIN

The toothed wheels in a watch that connect the barrel with the escapement.

MAIN WHEEL

An ambiguous term applied occasionally to the crown wheel, the center wheel, and sometimes to the barrel.

MALTESE CROSS

The cross-like part of the stop works attached to the barrels of fine watches.

MANTEL CLOCK

Name later used for Shelf Clock.

MARINE CHRONOMETER

A boxed watch clock set in gimbals utilizing the spring detent escapement; used on shipboard to determine longitude.

MARQUETRY

A type of decoration on wood made by inlaying wood veneer in elaborate designs.

MASSACHUSETTS SHELF CLOCK

Style of clock sometimes called Half Clock, or Box on Box Clock.

MASTER CLOCK

A clock which can control slave clocks by various methods.

MEAN SOLAR TIME

The time used in everyday life, the time shown by clocks, obtained by averaging solar time into equal periods (hours, days).

MEAN TIME

Where all days and hours are of equal length. This is opposed to Solar Time where all days are not of equal length.

MEANTIME SCREWS

The adjustable screws in a better grade balance used to bring the watch to close time without the use of the regulator. Sometimes called *timing screws.*

MIDDLE-TEMPERATURE ERROR

The temperature error between the extremes of heat and cold characteristic of a compensating balance and steel balance spring.

MILLIMETERS

The smallest unit in the metric linear system. One millimeter equals 0.03937 of an inch.

MINUTE REPEATER

A striking watch that will ring the time to the minute by a series of gongs activated by a plunger or push piece. A watch striking the hours, quarter hours, and additional minutes.

MINUTE WHEEL

The wheel in the dial train that connects the cannon pinion with the hour wheel.

MISSION STYLE

A trade term used for an American clock case of very plain design, usually of dark oak. Became popular in 1900 to 1930, usually as a reaction to the earlier Victorian style.

MOON DIAL

Usually at the top in the arch portion of a clock dial that indicates the phases of the moon.

MOTION TRAIN

A series of wheels and pinions that allows the rotation of the hour and minute hands.

MOVEMENT

The assembly of gears between two plates in such a fashion as to provide the transmitting of power from either the weights or the springs. Sometimes called "works."

MOVING EYE CLOCK

A clock with a case shaped like a figure of man or animal, with the eyeballs connected to the escapement, giving them movement.

MUSICAL ALARM

An alarm that activates a music box instead of a bell.

MYSTERY CLOCK

A clock which appears to work without any power or wheels.

NEW HAMPSHIRE MIRROR CLOCK

A type of clock thought to have originated in New Hampshire and attributed to Benjamin Morrill of Boscawen.

NONMAGNETIC

A balance and spring composed of alloys that will not retain magnetism after being put through a magnetic field.

NOVELTY CLOCK

Trade term for a variety of small clocks, usually in the shape of a familiar object or idea, sometimes animated. A vague term used for many variants of clocks.

OG Or Ogee

A wave-like molding, one side convex, the other concave, shaped like the letter "S." From 1825 to 1915, six or more sizes were used.

OILSTONE

Generally, the Arkansas white stone used with oil.

ONE DAY CLOCK OR WATCH

Will run usually 30 hours on one winding.

OPEN FACE

A watch dial with the figure "12" at the winding stem.

ORMOULU

Sometimes mistakenly spelled "Ormolu." Refers to brass castings that have gilt or gold plating for clock cases or parts of cases.

ORRERY

A machine in a planetarium that shows the relative positions of the planets.

OIL SINK

An indentation at the pivot hole of a clock used for the retention of oil.

OVERBANKING

The malfunction of the pallet fork in which it shifts from one banking pin to another without being released by the roller jewel.

OVERCOIL

The last coil of the Breguet spring that is bent up and over the body of the spring.

OVER-COMPENSATION

When the temperature rises, a clock pendulum becomes longer due to expansion and the clock slows down and loses time. The compensation pendulum was developed to correct this defect. Then, if a clock gained time with increasing temperature, it was said to have "over-compensation."

PATTI MOVEMENT

Made by E.N. Welsh and Co., is a good collector piece and has a distinctive plate design and enclosed mainsprings.

PALLET

The part through which the escape wheel gives the impulse to the pendulum or balance wheel. The jeweled lever working in conjunction with the escape wheel; the frame containing the pallet jewels.

PALLET ARMS

The metal body which contains the pallet stones.

PALLET ARBOR

The axis of the pallets.

PALLETS

The two projections from the ends of the anchor that engage with the escape wheel teeth and allow one tooth to pass with each swing of the pendulum.

PALLET STONES

Jewels or stones inserted in the pallet arms.

PATINA

The distinctive appearance of old wood after years of TLC. Constant polishing for many years enhances this appearance.

PEDOMETER

A watch with a delicately tripped pendulum and ratchet attached used to tell walking-distances covered by the wearer. The jogging motion moves the pendulum which advances a set of gears attached to an indicator. Later this principle was used to wind a watch called the "self-winding watch."

PEGWOOD

Small wood stick about ⅛" thick and 6" long whose sharpened end is used to clean or "peg" jewel holes or bushings.

PENDULUM

A weight swinging under the influence of gravity. In clocks, the time controlling element is usually a pendulum, consisting of a pendulum rod (of wood or metal) with a weight (called a "bob") at the bottom end, which swings to time the release of energy from the springs, or falling weights. Since a pendulum swings in a circular arc rather than the desired cycloidal arc, in practice, the shorter the swing the more accurate.

PETITE SONNERIE CLOCK

Strikes the quarters and half hour but does not strike the hours at each quarter as does Grand Sonnerie.

PHILLIPS' SPRING

A balance spring with terminal curves formed on lines laid down by M. Phillips. The term "Phillips' curve" is rarely used.

PILLAR

A rod or post of metal or wood that connects to the front and back plates holds them a fixed distance apart in both clocks and watches.

PILLAR CLOCK

A French clock with a case consisting of a drum clock mounted on two or four pillars standing on a base. The pendulum hangs in the middle of the pillars.

PILLAR PLATE

The lower or dial plate of the watch; also called front plate.

PILLAR AND SCROLL

Shelf clock design attributed to Eli Terry. Has columns on each side of the case and a splat cut in a double scroll design. Usually has three finials.

PINION

The smaller wheel with teeth called leaves, working in connection with a larger wheel. See Lantern Pinion.

PIN PALLET

The lever escapement wherein the pallet has upright pins instead of horizontally set jewels. Used in alarm clocks and nonjeweled watches.

PIN-WHEEL CLOCK

A pendulum-type clock movement using a pin-wheel escapement.

PIN-WHEEL ESCAPEMENT

Where the locking and impulse is affected by pins mounted near the rim of the escape wheel, at right angles to the plane of the wheel. Considered very accurate, usually made by the Swiss, and used in many high-grade Jeweler's Regulator clocks.

PITCH CIRCLE

A circle concentric with the circumference of a toothed wheel and cutting its teeth at such a distance from their points as to touch the corresponding circle of a pinion working with it and having with that circle a common velocity, as in a rolling contact.

PITCH DIAMETER

The diameter of the pitch circle.

PIVOT

The end of a rotating arbor; the ends of the shafts in a clockworks; the tips that run in the jewels or bushings or other bearings.

PLATE

Discs of brass or nickel which form the foundation of a movement. The pillar or lower plate lies next to the dial. The upper pieces supporting one, two, or three wheels are generally referred to as bridges. In the full-plate watch the upper piece is called the top plate or back plate.

PLATES

The front and back of the clock movement, between which the wheels, pinions and arbors are fitted.

PLATFORM ESCAPEMENT

A balance wheel escapement mounted on a separate self-contained plate so that it can be removed and replaced as a unit. Often used on carriage clocks.

PLATO CLOCK

Small carriage size clock with flipping cards or panels to indicate the hours and minutes.

POISING

An operation to adjust the balance so that all weights are counterpoised. In other words, statically balancing a wheel or balance in a clock or watch.

POSITION CLOCK

A regulator.

POSITION REGULATOR

A regulator.

POSITION TIMING

Adjusting a watch so that it keeps precise time when the watch is placed in a given position. Adjusted to three, four, five, or six positions.

POTENCE

Supporting one pivot of an arbor, a cock or bracket fixed to the plate of a clock or watch.

PULL REPEATER

A device whereby the striking mechanism of a clock is set in motion between the hours.

QUAIL CLOCK

Essentially a cuckoo clock, but with bellows that give sounds imitating the call of a quail.

QUARTER REPEATER

A repeater which strikes the hours and quarter hours.

QUARTER SCREWS

Four screws used in timing.

QUARTER STRIKE

A clock that strikes the quarter hours, usually on two bells.

QUARTZ CLOCK

An accurate electronic clock invented in 1929, which has a quartz crystal controlled oscillator followed by frequency dividers controlling a phonic motor that drives the clock.

QUICK TRAIN

A watch movement beating five times per second, or 18,000 per hour.

"R·A" REGULATOR

Slang term for wall regulator with "R-A" on pendulum, which probably actually means: R = retard by turning the adjusting nut toward R to lower the pendulum; A = advance by turning the adjusting nut toward A to raise the pendulum.

RACK CLOCK

A gravity clock consisting of a rack or straight toothed bar mounted vertically so that the clock slides down the rack with a pinion engaging the rack to drive the clock.

RACK AND SNAIL

The rack is a bar with teeth on one edge; the snail is a snail-shaped cam. Simply, a striking mechanism which allows the strike to be repeated, by setting itself for correct striking shortly before striking begins.

RATCHET

A wheel usually placed over a mainspring arbor and working with a retaining click or pawl.

RATCHET TOOTH WHEEL

The name given to the English type escape wheel which has pointed teeth.

RATE

A "good rate" is a good timekeeper; if it gains or loses, it is said to have a gaining or losing rate.

RECEIVING PALLET

The pallet stone over which a tooth of the escape wheel slides in order to enter between the pallet stones.

RECOIL CLICK

A click designed so that it will not permit the mainspring to be wound dead tight, recoiling a bit after any winding.

RECOIL ESCAPEMENT

An escapement whose escape wheel recoils when the pallets become more deeply locked or push back the escape wheel during the unlocking action. Results in the second hand backing up slightly before advancing.

REGULATOR

Part of the balance bridge which resembles a racquette (racket) and contains vertical pins which straddle the hairspring. When the regulator moves towards the stud, the effective length of the hairspring is made longer and the balance slows in speed; when the pins are moved farther from the stud, the hairspring is made shorter and the watch goes faster.

REGULATOR CLOCK

Any accurate wall clock in the early days; later the term was applied to many Connecticut wall clocks, becoming merely an advertising term, a sales pitch.

REGULATOR CLOCK TRADE AND SLANG TERMS

A. **Octagon Top Long Drop:** eight, ten, 12″ dial with case, approximately 36″ high.
B. **Octagon Top Short Drop:** Same as above except 25″ high.
C. **Round Top Long Drop:** eight, ten, 12″ dial with case approximately 36″ high.
D. **Round Top Short Drop:** Same as above except approximately 25″ high.
E. **Square Top:** Same as above.
F. **Wall Seconds Bit:** Usually 40″ to 84″ long with seconds bit.
G. **Parlor (Shelf):** Usually 26″ to 34″ high.
H. **Parlor (Wall Hanging):** Usually 30″ to 60″.
J. **Jewelers (Sweep second):** Largest type, up to eight feet long.

REPEATER

In clock parlance, a clock that can be triggered to repeat the last strike. A watch that strikes, having two hammers and two gongs. A lever is provided to set the striking mechanism into action. A quarter repeater strikes the hour and the last quarter hour. A minute repeater, in addition, strikes the number of minutes since the last quarter.

REPEATER ALARM

An alarm that rings in short bursts and keeps repeating the ringing at regular intervals.

REVERSE PAINTING

Painting of a picture or design on glass, painted on the back side of the glass. Since the painting is done in reverse order of a normal painting (background is put on last), this gives it the name. Used on clock tablets since the painting is protected, being inside the case, and it can also be painted over with a layer of protective paint.

RIGHT-ANGLED ESCAPEMENT

An escapement in which the line of centers of the escape wheel and pallets are at right angles to pallets and balance.

RIPPLE FRONT

The wavy part of the clock case, usually applied. Commonly used on the beehive and steeple cases.

ROCOCO

A term used in several ways to indicate ornamentation in clocks, sometimes used to mean an over-supply of ornamentation.

ROLLED GOLD

A metal plate formed by bonding a thin sheet of gold to one or both sides of a backing metal. Made by rolling the sandwich until the gold is at the desired thinness.

ROLLER JEWEL

A long, thin jewel inserted in the roller table; sometimes called impulse pin.

ROLLER TABLE

A circular disc attached to the balance staff in which is fitted the roller jewel.

ROLLING CLOCK

See Inclined Plane Clock.

ROMAN STRIKE

Instead of one bell, two-bells of different tone were used for striking the hours, a "one" bell and a "five" bell. Hours one, two , and three were struck on the "one" bell. Six was struck by one strike on the "five" bell, and one on the "one", thus following the Roman numerals which appear on the clock dial as VI. Four was struck by one strike on the "one" bell and one on the "five" bell, since "four" appears on these dials as IV, instead of the usual IIII.

ROSKOPF WATCH

A watch with the barrel encroaching upon the center of the movement; hence no center wheel. The dial train is activated through the minute wheel which is set clutch tight on the barrel cover. Usually employing the pin pallet escapement. (First dollar watch)

ROUND TOP

Nickname for a clock case with a top in the shape of a full semi-circle. (Venetian)

RUBY PIN

The upright roller jewel set into the impulse roller.

RUN

A term applied to the action of slide caused by draw. The action of the pallet toward the banking pin after lock takes place.

SAFETY ROLLER

The small, crescented roller disc planted above the impulse roller. The upper part of the double roller.

SCHOOLHOUSE CLOCK

Nickname usually applied to an octagon top short drop, but sometimes also used for the long drop.

SCREWPLATE

A steel plate with holes of many sizes threaded with cutting edges for the forming of watch screws.

SEAT BOARD

Short board upon which movement is mounted.

SECONDS PENDULUM

A pendulum that has a one-second swing. Theoretically has to be 39.14″ long.

SELF WINDING CLOCK

A spring driven clock with a mechanism for automatic winding, usually powered by batteries.

SETTING LEVER

The detent which fits into the slot of the stem and pushes down the clutch lever.

SHAKE

The distance the escape wheel can be moved backward (manually) before the back of a tooth contacts a pallet jewel when the opposite jewel is at the very moment of unlocking. Shake is always less than drop.

SHEEP'S-HEAD CLOCK

A lantern clock in which the chapter ring is wider than the rest of the clock.

SHELF CLOCK

A type of case designed to sit on a shelf as opposite to a tall clock.

SHIP'S BELL COLCK

A clock that strikes on the ship's bell system.

SIDEREAL DAY

Duration of the earth's rotation with respect to the stars. The calculated relation between sidereal time and mean time is tabulated for each day in the Nautical Almanac. Mean sidereal day is twenty-three hours, fifty-six minutes, 4.091 seconds of mean solar time.

SIMPLE CALENDAR

Trade term for days of the month indicated by an extra hand pointing to the day of the month number around the outside of the chapter ring.

SINGLE ROLLER ESCAPEMENT

A form of lever escapement in which one roller performs the functions of both impulse and safety actions.

SKELETON CLOCK

Clock that had the plates cut out so that only a "skeleton" remained. This allowed a good view of the wheel, and the clock was usually placed under a glass dome for better viewing.

SLAVE CLOCK

A clock that did not keep time on its own, but was slaved to a master clock.

SLIDE

The opening of the banking pins beyond that of drop lock.

SOLAR TIME

Time as indicated by a sundial.

SONORA CHIME CLOCK

A Seth Thomas clock that used turned cupped bells to play the Westminster chimes.

SPANDREL

The four corners of a square clock dial in which designs are painted or fancy metalwork is applied.

SPLAT

The decorator piece at the top of a clock case.

SPIRIT LEVEL

A small sealed disc with a liquid bubble used on poising tools to determine when the jaws are level.

SPRING BARREL

The barrel containing the mainspring.

SPRING CLOCK

Springs rather than weights are the motive power.

SPRINGING

The act of co-ordinating a hairspring with a balance so that the vibrations will equal a given number per hour; also called vibrating.

STAFF

A pivoted arbor or axle usually referred to the axle of the balance; as the "balance staff".

STAR WHEEL

A steel wheel used in chronographs to lift levers.

STEADY PINS

Pins used to secure the perfect alignment of two pieces of metal.

STEEPLE CLOCK

Clock with a sharp gothic case with finials on each side.

STEM

The squared shaft going through the winding pinion and clutch wheel.

STENCILED

Decoration applied to splats, columns, and other areas of the clock cases.

STOPWATCH

A simple form of chronograph with controlled starting and stopping of the hands; sometimes also stopping the balance wheel. A timer in pocket watch form.

STOPWORK

The mechanism on a barrel of a watch or clock that permits only the central portion of the mainspring to be wound, thus utilizing that portion of the spring whose power is less erratic.

STORE CLOCK

Nickname for the box reguator.

STRAIGHT LINE ESCAPEMENT

An escapement in which the centers of the escape wheel, pallets, and balance are planted in a straight line.

STRIKE LEVER

The lever that strikes the gong, bell, or chimes.

STRIKE TRAIN

The added gears used to operate the striking mechanism of a clock.

STUD

The metal piece anchored to the balance bridge into which the outer end of the hairspring is attached.

SUNK SECONDS

The small second dial which is depressed to avoid the second hand from interfering with the progress of the hour and minute hand.

SUSPENSION SPRING

The straight, flat spring at the top of the pendulum, from which the pendulum hangs and which allows the pendulum to swing.

SWEEP SECONDS

Mounted in the center of the clock dial, this hand sweeps the full area of the dial. Also called "center seconds".

SWINGING ARM

Clock takes the form of a pendulum, usually supported by an arm of a statue. Most common seen are made by Ansonia, German Junghams and French. (The Japanese are now reproducing the German version.)

SYNCHRONOUS CLOCK

A clock driven by an alternating current (AC) synchronous electric motor whose speed was regulated by the frequency of the AC. The name was derived from the speed of the motor being sychronized with the frequency of the alternating current. Naturally, the accuracy of the clock was dependent on the accuracy of the frequency of the AC.

TABLET

The front lower glass of a clock case.

TALL CLOCK

Long-case, floor or hall clock, nicknamed Grandfather.

TAMBOUR

See Camel Back.

TAPE CLOCK

A round clock that lay horizontally on a table, with the hours and fractions of hours shown on a "tape" dial wrapped around the case. This portion of the case revolved with a single pointer showing the time. This rather rare clock was usually operated by an alarm clock type movement, and sometimes had an alarm.

TAVERN CLOCK

Also generally known as an Act of Parliament Clock; usually an English clock.

TEAR DROP

A shelf clock with rounded top and hanging finials, usually out of walnut.

THIRD WHEEL

The wheel of a watch that drives the fourth pinion.

TIME AND STRIKE

Any clock that strikes as well as telling the time.

TIMEPIECE

Any clock that does not strike or chime.

TIMER

A timepiece that does not show the time of day, but shows elapsed time, used to time any event or operation, hence the name. See Stop Watch.

TIME RECORDER

A clock that, by imprinting or punching paper, records the time it is activated.

TIME STAMP

A date stamp which incorporates a timepiece to also stamp the time.

TIMING SCREWS

Screws used to bring a watch to time, sometimes called the mean-time screws.

TOE OF TOOTH

Locking corner of a tooth of the escape wheel.

TORSION PENDULUM

A pendulum that hangs from a suspension spring and rotates in a horizontal plane, twisting and untwisting the suspension spring. Very roughly analogous to the operation of a balance wheel. Has a very long period, therefore, generally used in 400-day clocks.

TOTAL LOCK

The distance of lock upon the pallet jewel after slide when the pallet rests against the banking pin.

TOURBILLION

A watch in which the escapement, mounted on a cage attached to the fourth pinion, revolves around the mounted and stationary fourth wheel.

TOWER OR TURRET CLOCK

A steeple, church or public clock in a tower.

TRAIN

A combination of two or more wheels and pinions, geared together and transmitting power from one part of a mechanism to another, usually from the power source (weight or spring) to the escapement.

TRIPPING

A malfunction caused by the failure of the escape tooth to lock upon the locking surface of the pallet jewel. Instead, the tooth enters directly upon the lifting surface with the result that the pallet may have an action like an alarm clock hammer.

TROPICAL YEAR (or Mean Solar Year)

The time it takes the earth to revolve about the sun, as reckoned from the vernal equinox, or first point of Aries.

UNIVERSAL TIME (UT)

This is also known as Greenwich Civil Time. A corrected value of Universal Time (UT) to account for observed motion of the geographic poles and for the projected annual variation in the earth's rate of rotation is called UT-2.

UP-AND-DOWN INDICATOR

The semi-circular dial on chronometers that tells how much the mainspring has been unwound and thus indicates when the spring should be wound.

VENETIAN

Trade name of a clock case with the top in the shape of a full semi-circle.

VERGE

A recoil frictional escapement with a crown escape wheel and pallets set at right angles to the axis of the escape wheel.

VERGE STAFF

The arbor upon which the pendulum, crutch or balance is mounted is the verge or verge staff.

VIBRATING TOOL

A master balance of certified accuracy as to vibrations per hour which is mounted in a box with glass top. The box may be swiveled to set the balance into its vibratory arcs. The balance to be compared or vibrated is suspended by its hairspring attached to a scaffold and when the box is twisted on its platform both balances will start vibrating. Thus the suspended balance may be compared (in speed) with the master balance and its hairspring lengthened or shortened until both balances swing in unison.

VISIBLE ESCAPEMENT

Trade term when wheel and pallet are visible on the clock dial.

V.P.

Trade abbreviation for Visible Pendulum.

WAGON-THE-WALL-CLOCK

Slang name for a wall clock on which the weights and pendulum are exposed.

WAGON SPRING CLOCK

A clock whose spring is a flat-leaved arched semi-elliptical spring, resembling a wagon spring (or early auto spring). Invented by J. Ives, it is now a rare clock because of the tendency to self-destruct if the cable connecting the spring to the winding drum would break.

WALL CLOCK

Any type of clock that hangs on the wall.

WARNING

In striking clocks, the strike train is set in motion to strike a few minutes before the hour but is stopped short until released by the minute hand.

WATCHMAN'S CLOCK

A portable time recorder, usually in a carrying case, with provisions for a key to be inserted and turned which prints the time. Thus, the keys were placed at points on a watchman's rounds so that it would show the time he passed each station.

WEIGHTS

A source of power for the movement in clocks, as opposed to springs.

WHEEL

Any circular piece of metal on the periphery of which teeth may be cut of various forms and numbers.

WINDING DRUM (Barrel)

The cylinder onto which the wire or cord supporting the weight is wound.

WINDING PINION

The first winding wheel through which the stem enters. A wheel with two sets of teeth. One is set radial to its center and the other is set upright, crown style with ratchet teeth. The wheel above the clutch wheel.

WINDING SQUARE

The square end of the arbor on which the key is placed for winding the clock.

WINKER (Blinking Eye)

Iron statue clock with moving eyes.

YEAR CLOCK

See Anniversary Clock.

HOW TO USE THIS BOOK

The Official 1983 Price Guide to Antique Clocks is arranged in alphabetical order. Headings refer to manufacturers and clocks designs. Within the printed listing you will find technical information, further designed to help in identifying YOUR particular clock. Information listed will include: the name of the clock (if it was not named by the manufacturer, then the name it most commonly goes under in horological circles), metal, wood (these are broken into specific listings and corresponding price differences), color, parts of the movement (pendulums, spring wound, etc.), any other visual characteristics, dimensions in inches, approximate date (if known), and individual characteristics such as day, strike, alarm, calendar, etc. A glossary of terms is provided for identification of these features.

You will also find a price RANGE beside each listing description. These listings are current and as accurate as possible. Remember that these price ranges listed do *not* represent the highest and lowest prices the clock has ever sold for. Rather, it represents an average RANGE for that particular clock value.

The information contained in parenthesis after each listing, refers to additional references. The (E) picture references alluded to in parenthesis, refer to CLOCK BOOK I AND II by the author of this book, Roy Ehrhardt. The (M) picture references, refer to *Survey of American Calendar Clocks,* by Andrew and Dalia Miller, 1972.

Both of these books are listed in the bibliography. They can easily be ordered through one or more of the preceeding horological book sources. Inquire by phone or mail. As with most of the pictures in this book, (and since there are over one thousand illustrations you may very well find what you're looking for right here), the Ehrhardt and Miller volumes, feature line drawings culled from the pages of old clock manufacturers catalogues. Wide and subtle differences are apparent. You could not ask for a more accurate representation of your antique clock.

Once you have located a picture and/or printed listing that seems to resemble the clock YOU own, you must deduce the following items of information by examining your clock thusly: First, look for the name of the manufacturer if the clock is all original. The name can be found in a number of places; on the dial (sometimes out near the edge under the bezel), on the back of the movement; on a paper label inside; on the back or bottom of the clock; and sometimes, though rarely on large clocks, underneath the dial. Second, measure both the height, and width, and dial size of the clock you are trying to identify. Compare your clock's size, with the size in the listings. Third, check the movement to see whether it has a calendar, alarm, etc. This information will also be included in the listings.

If you cannot find a picture of your clock in the section under the manufacturer, look under the other manufacturers as well. Clocks that were good sellers (shelf, swing, kitchen, etc.) were sold by all of the major makers with only slight variations. Fortunately in most instances, the makers name will not affect the actual value of your antique clock. What it DOES do is make the identification of a clock much easier to ascertain. There should be enough information in *The Official Price Guide to Antique Clocks,* to make up the missing pieces in your clock identification puzzle.

ANSONIA CLOCK COMPANY

The Ansonia Company was best known for its decorative imitation gold, and ornate novelty clocks. Petulant cupids and angels, deep thinkers, athletes, babies, and languid ladies drape and adorn the ornamental designs, that characterize the name and products of Ansonia.

Anson Phelps founded the Company in Derby, Connecticut. An importer of tin, brass, and copper in the Eastern section of the states, he already owned a copper mill (hence the ormolu). Phelps maintained considerable financial backing, as well as contacts and knowledgeable business associates in his venture. From such formidable beginnings he suffered two serious setbacks. In 1854 the factory burned at a loss of several thousand dollars. At this time the Ansonia Clock Company became the Ansonia Brass and Copper Company, as Phelps had little choice but to move the clock facilities into the standing copper mill. By 1879, or thereabouts, the clock company was reformed, and manufacturing operations were moved to the Brooklyn section of New York. Unfortunately this factory also burned, after a scant few months in its new location of operation.

By the late 19th and early 20th century, Phelps had reestablished his name in the clock industry as one of the major manufacturers. The factory was rebuilt and expanded. Ansonia sales officers and agents could be found all over the world. It was during this time also, that many different designs of clocks were included in the manufacturing process: alarms, cabinet, carriage, crystal regulators, galley, kitchen, mantel or shelf, onyx and marble, porcelain and china, statue, etc. Ansonia was in its heyday, at the height of its productivity, fame, and power.

Any type of business enterprise is vulnerable to some extent or another; changing tides in the publics' imagination, world events and crisis, new inventions, world leaders, even literature and art can spell success or eventual failure in a business or industry. The events leading up to these financial difficulties are not always completely fair insofar as the amount of effort or expertise expended by the company, may be completely professional.

We have already discussed some of the elemental threats to business in those days. Fire was the greatest hazard. Ansonia had already weathered two severe setbacks for this reason, and recovered admirably. Their next major problem was not as obvious although just as dehabilitating.

Just before World War I Ansonia's strongest selling point, the novelty clock, became subject to fierce competition. Rather than maintain competitive realistic prices for their clocks, they attempted to cut their losses, offering clocks at, "old pricing." This tactic failed, and Ansonia began a downward spiral in the clock industry, that resulted in heavy losses. By 1929 the majority of the timekeeping machinery and some tools and dies, were sold to the Russian government and shipped out of the country. This formulated the basis (along with the remains of a watch company purchased a year later) of the clock and watch industry in Moscow.

None of the major clock industries survived the Depression and subsequent Second World War, intact. Ansonia was the first to go under. In 1904 the company had attempted to jump on "the dollar watch" bandwagon, perhaps as an ineffectual guard against the first hints of potential financial difficulties. (Ansonia clocks were not cheap.)

The idea behind the dollar watch was to make it in the same manner as a cheap clock. This concept bore little resemblance to the traditional, intricate style that went into the handcrafted watch. It did not pan out. Instead designers turned to the tourbillon watch, concocted by the French genius Breguet.

Watches are difficult timekeepers due to the unstable positions they are likely to fall into. Breguet's watch had a turning escapement which minimized these errors in accuracy. American designers went one step further, allowing the entire movement to rotate inside the cast. The Ansonia Company produced a similar non jeweled model. They sold millions of these inexpensive watches in the two and a half decades before they went out of business; an interesting comparison to the scrolled elaborate clockwork the Ansonia collector is familiar with.

ADVERTISING

☐ **Correct Time.** *dial 10", spring, c. 1890, 8 Day (E2-29).*
.... **260.00**   **285.00**

☐ **Our Advertiser.** *Silver or Gold Plate, height 7½", dial 2", spring, c. 1890, 1 Day (E2-31).*
.... **100.00**   **125.00**

☐ **Window Clock,** *dial 20", spring, c. 1890, 8 Day, Standard Time (E2-29).*
.... **350.00**   **385.00**

☐ **Window Clock,** *plate glass, embossed gilt figures, dial 20", spring, c. 1890, 8 Day (E2-29).*
.... **375.00**   **425.00**

ALARM

DRUM

☐ **The Ansonia Watch,** *Roman or Arabic dial, small seconds dial at bottom, stem wind, nickel plated, spring, c. 1898, 1 Day (E1-161).*
.... **35.00**   **50.00**

☐ **Bee,** *nickel, dial 2", spring, c. 1898, 1 Day (E1-161).*
.... **40.00**   **50.00**

☐ **Bee,** *nickel, dial 2", spring, c. 1898, 1 Day, alarm (E1-161).*
.... **55.00**   **65.00**

☐ **Bee,** *nickel, dial 2", winds without key, spring, c. 1890, 1 Day (E2-10).*
.... **40.00**   **50.00**

☐ **Bee,** *nickel, stem-winding alarm, no key for winding, dial 2", spring, c. 1890, 1 Day (E2-10).*
.... **45.00** **55.00**

☐ **Bee Time,** *nickel, dial 2", spring, c. 1917, (E1-179).*
.... **50.00** **60.00**

☐ **As above,** *dial 12", 1 Day, alarm.*
.... **110.00** **125.00**
☐ **As above,** *dial 12", 8 Day.*
.... **100.00** **110.00**

☐ **Dandy,** *nickel, dial 3", spring, c. 1890, 1 Day, (E2-10).*
.... **25.00** **35.00**
☐ **As above,** *1 Day, alarm.*
.... **30.00** **40.00**

☐ **Electric clock,** *dry cell battery enclosed in polished oak case, 10" x 8¾", c. 1898, 1 Day, alarm (E1-161).*
.... **95.00** **115.00**

☐ **Improved Bee,** *seamless brass case, nickel plated, dial 2", spring, c. 1917, 1 Day, alarm (E1-179).*
.... **55.00** **65.00**

☐ **Midget,** *nickel, dial 8", spring, c. 1883, 1 Day, alarm (E2-9).*
.... **75.00** **85.00**
☐ **As above,** *dial 8 ", 8 Day.*
.... **65.00** **75.00**

☐ **Peep-O-Day,** *nickel, sunken center, dial 6", spring, c. 1883, 1 Day, alarm (E2-9).*
.... 25.00   30.00

☐ **Peep-O-Day,** *nickel, dial 4", spring, c. 1883, 1 Day, alarm (E2-9).*
.... 25.00   30.00

☐ **As above,** *1 Day, alarm, calendar.*
.... 65.00   75.00

☐ **As above,** *1 Day, strike.*
.... 70.00   85.00

☐ **Peep-O-Day,** *nickel, dial 5", spring, c. 1898, 1 Day, alarm (E1-161).*
.... 40.00   50.00

☐ **Peep-O-Day,** *nickel, dial 6", spring, c. 1898, 1 Day, alarm (E1-161).*
.... 40.00   50.00

☐ **Peep-O-Day,** *nickel, dial 4", repeating strike, spring, c. 1890, 1 Day (E2-10).*
.... 85.00   95.00

☐ **As above,** *dial 6", 1 Day.*
.... 35.00   45.00

☐ **Racket,** *nickel, dial 5", spring, c. 1898, 1 Day, strike, alarm (E1-161).*
.... 45.00   55.00

☐ **Simplex,** *seamless brass case, nickel plated, spring, c. 1917, 8 Day, alarm (E1-179).*
.... 45.00   55.00

☐ **Six-Inch Peep-O-Day,** *fancy, nickel, dial 6", spring, c. 1890, 1 Day, alarm (E2-10).*
.... 45.00   55.00

☐ **Standard,** *nickel, dial 4", spring, c. 1890, 1 Day (E2-10).*
.... 40.00   50.00

FANCY

☐ **Bee,** *nickel, leather case, height 4", spring, c. 1890, 1 Day, alarm (E2-10).*
.... 50.00   60.00

☐ **Pirate,** *nickel, dial 4", spring, c. 1890, 1 Day, alarm (E2-10).*
.... 40.00   50.00

☐ **Planet,** *nickel, dial 4", spring, c. 1883, 1 Day (E2-9).*
.... 110.00   115.00

☐ **Princess,** *nickel, spring, c. 1883, 1 Day (E2-9).*
.... 30.00   40.00

☐ **As above,** *dial 5", 8 Day.*
.... 45.00   55.00

☐ **Bella,** *height 9", dial 4", spring, c. 1890, 1 Day (E2-30).*
.... 90.00   110.00

☐ **As above,** *1 Day, alarm.*
.... 100.00   120.00

☐ **Dauntless,** *bronze and nickel finish, height 18", dial 4", spring, c. 1883, 1 Day, alarm.*
.... 150.00   170.00
☐ **As above,** *dial 4", 8 Day.*
.... 170.00   190.00
☐ **As above,** *dial 5", 8 Day, alarm.*
.... 150.00   170.00
☐ **As above,** *dial 5", 8 Day.*
.... 170.00   190.00

☐ **Charmer,** *bronze finish, height 15", dial 4", spring, c. 1883, 1 Day, alarm (E2-8).*
.... 90.00   110.00
☐ **Cupid's Dart,** *bronze and nickel finish, height 16", dial 4", spring, c. 1883, 1 Day, alarm, (E2-9).*
.... 135.00   155.00
☐ **As above,** *8 Day, alarm.*
.... 155.00   175.00

☐ **Domestic,** *bronze and nickel finish, height 15", dial 6", spring, c. 1883, 1 Day, alarm (E2-9).*
.... 130.00   150.00
☐ **As above,** *8 Day, strike.*
.... 150.00   170.00

☐ **Jewel Case,** *bronze finish, height 16", dial 4", spring, c. 1883, 1 Day, alarm (E2-8).*
.... **130.00   150.00**
☐ **As above,** *8 Day, alarm.*
.... **150.00   170.00**

☐ **Echo,** *bronze and nickel finish, hand moves automatically and rings bell, height 7½", dial 4", spring, c. 1883, 1 Day, alarm (E2-9).*
.... **165.00   185.00**
☐ **As above,** *1 Day, strike.*
.... **170.00   205.00**

☐ **Good Luck,** *bronze finish, dial 4", spring, c. 1883, 1 Day (E2-9).*
.... **60.00   70.00**
☐ **As above,** *1 Day, alarm.*
.... **80.00   90.00**

☐ **Grandfather,** *bronze and nickel finish, height 8", dial 4", spring, c. 1883, 1 Day, calendar (E2-8).*
.... **170.00   200.00**

☐ **Little Dorrit,** *black enamel case, height 12", dial 4", spring, c. 1883, 1 Day, alarm (E2-9).*
.... **150.00   170.00**

☐ **Nightingale,** *bronze and nickel finish, height 10", dial 4", spring, c. 1883, 1 Day, alarm (E2-8).*
.... 80.00   90.00
☐ **As above,** *8 Day, alarm.*
.... 90.00   110.00

☐ **Octagon Peep-O-Day,** *nickel, dial 4", spring, c. 1890, 1 Day (E2-10).*
.... 25.00   35.00

☐ **Octagon Peep-O-Day,** *nickel, dial 4", spring, c. 1890, 1 Day, alarm, calendar (E2-10).*
.... 90.00   110.00

☐ **Octagon Princess,** *nickel, dial 4", spring, c. 1890, 1 Day (E2-10).*
.... 25.00   35.00

☐ **Pagoda,** *bronze and nickel finish, height 15", dial 4", spring, c. 1883, 1 Day, alarm (E2-9).*
.... 140.00   160.00
☐ **As above,** *dial 4", 8 Day.*
.... 160.00   180.00
☐ **As above,** *dial 5", 1 Day, alarm.*
.... 160.00   180.00
☐ **As above,** *dial 5", 8 Day.*
.... 170.00   200.00

☐ **Pride,** *bronze and nickel finish, height 10", dial 4", spring, c. 1883, 1 Day, alarm (E2-8).*
.... 90.00   110.00

☐ **Tally-Ho,** *bronze and nickel finish, height 10", dial 4", c. 1883, 1 Day, alarm (E2-9).*
.... 80.00   100.00
☐ **As above,** *8 Day.*
.... 80.00   110.00

☐ **Twins No.1,** *bronze and nickel finish, height 12", dial 4", spring, c. 1883, 1 Day (E2-8).*
.... 115.00   135.00
☐ **As above,** *1 Day, alarm.*
.... 125.00   145.00

☐ **Twins No. 2,** *bronze and nickel finish, height 10", dial 4", spring, c. 1883, 1 Day (E2-8).*
.... 130.00   150.00
☐ **As above,** *1 Day, alarm.*
.... 150.00   170.00

☐ **Woodbine,** *bronze finish, height 13", dial 4", spring, c. 1883, 1 Day, alarm (E2-8).*
.... 115.00   135.00
☐ **As above,** *8 Day, alarm.*
.... 125.00   145.00

CABINET

☐ **Cabinet Antique,** *polished oak or mahogany, with antique brass trimmings, French sash, porcelain dial, ½ hour old English bell strike, bell on top, 18¾" x 11½", dial 4¾", spring, c. 1896, 8 Day (E2-13).*
. . . . 850.00 1000.00

☐ **Cabinet Antique,** *polished mahogany or oak, with antique brass trimmings, French sash, porcelain dial, ½ hour gong strike, 20" x 9¼", dial 4¾" spring, c. 1896, 8 Day (E2-13).*
. . . . 600.00 850.00

☐ **Cabinet A,** *antique oak, with antique brass lacquered trimmings, 19" x 10¼", sash and dial 5¾", ½ hour slow strike movement, cathedral gongs on sounding boards, French sash and metal dials, spring, c. 1896, 8 Day (E2-13).*
. . . . 230.00 260.00

☐ **Cabinet B,** *antique oak, with antique brass lacquered trimmings, 18" x 11½", sash and dial 5¾", ½ hour slow strike movement, cathedral gongs on sounding boards, French sash and metal dial, spring, c. 1896, 8 Day (E2-13).*
. . . . 230.00 260.00

☐ **Cabinet C,** *antique oak, with antique brass lacquered trimmings, 18½" x 11½", sash and dial 5¾", ½ hour slow strike movement, cathedral gongs on sounding boards, French sash and metal dial, spring, c. 1896, 8 Day (E2-13).*
.... **250.00 280.00**

☐ **Cabinet E,** *antique oak, with antique brass lacquered trimmings, 18" x 12", sash and dial 5¾", ½ hour slow strike movement, cathedral gongs on sounding boards, French sash and metal dial, spring, c. 1896, 8 Day (E2-13).*
.... **230.00 260.00**

☐ **Idaho,** *oak, 15½" x 11¼", dial 6", spring, c. 1910, 8 Day, strike (E2-12).*
.... **120.00 140.00**

☐ **Ilion,** *oak, 13" x 9½", dial 6", spring, c. 1910, 8 Day, strike (E2-12).*
.... **115.00 135.00**

☐ **Inca,** *oak, 13" x 9½", dial 6", spring, c. 1910, 8 Day, strike (E2-12).*
.... **110.00 130.00**

☐ **India,** *oak, 15¾" x 11¼", dial 6", spring, c. 1910, 8 Day, strike (E2-12).*
.... **120.00 140.00**

☐ **Ipswich,** *oak, 15¼" x 11¾", dial 6", spring, c. 1910, 8 Day, strike (E2-12).*
.... **120.00 140.00**

☐ **Island,** *oak, 13" x 9½", dial 6", spring, c. 1910, 8 Day, strike (E2-12).*
.... **115.00 135.00**

☐ **Plymouth,** *oak, 10½″ x 8½″, dial 4¼″, spring, c. 1883, 8 Day, strike (E2-11).*
.... **140.00   160.00**

☐ **Ramsgate,** *oak, 16¼″ x 11¾″, dial 6″, spring, c. 1910, 8 Day, strike (E2-12).*
.... **135.00   155.00**

☐ **Leeds,** *oak, 11½″ x 8⅓″, dial 4¼″, c. 1883, 8 Day, strike (E2-11).*
.... **140.00   160.00**

☐ **Rialto,** *oak, 16″ x 10¼″, dial 6″, c. 1910, 8 Day, strike (E2-12).*
.... **135.00   155.00**

☐ **Riverdale,** *oak, 16½″ x 11½″, dial 6″, c. 1910, 8 Day, strike (E2-12).*
.... **135.00   155.00**

☐ **Rockland,** *oak, 16¼″ x 10¾″, dial 6″, spring, c. 1910, 8 Day, strike (E2-12).*
.... **135.00   155.00**

☐ **Rockwood,** *oak, 16″ x 10¾″, dial 6″, c. 1910, 8 Day, strike (E2-12).*
.... **135.00   155.00**

☐ **Roxbury,** *oak, 16¼" x 10¾", dial 6", spring, c. 1910, 8 Day, strike (E2-12).*
.... 135.00   155.00

☐ **Salem,** *oak, 14¾" x 10¾", dial 5", spring, c. 1883, 8 Day, strike (E2-11).*
.... 155.00   175.00

☐ **Summit,** *oak, 14¾" x 10¾", dial 5", spring, c. 1883, 8 Day, strike (E2-11).*
.... 165.00   185.00

☐ **Tivoli,** *oak, 15" x 11½", dial 5", spring, c. 1883, 8 Day, strike (E2-11).*
.... 155.00   175.00

☐ **As above,** *walnut.*
.... 180.00   200.00

☐ **As above,** *mahogany.*
.... 180.00   200.00

☐ **Toronto,** *oak, 16¾" x 11¼", dial 5", spring, c. 1883, 8 Day, strike (E2-11).*
.... 155.00   175.00

☐ **As above,** *mahogany.*
.... 180.00   200.00

☐ **Trieste,** *oak, 14¾" x 11½", dial 5", spring, c. 1883, 8 Day, strike (E2-11).*
.... 150.00   170.00

☐ **As above,** *mahogany.*
.... 180.00   200.00

☐ **Troy,** *oak, height 15¼", base 10¾", dial 5", spring, ½ hour gong, c. 1890, 8 Day, strike (E2-21).*
.... 100.00   120.00

☐ **As above,** *walnut.*
.... 125.00   145.00

☐ **As above,** *mahogany.*
.... 125.00   145.00

☐ **Tunis,** *oak, height 14", base
11½", dial 5", spring, ½ hour
gong, c. 1890, 8 Day, strike
(E2-21).*
.... 90.00   110.00
☐ **As above,** *walnut.*
.... 115.00   135.00
☐ **As above,** *mahogany.*
.... 115.00   135.00

☐ **Turkey,** *oak, 15¾" x 10", dial 5",
spring, c. 1883, 8 Day, strike
(E2-11).*
.... 150.00   170.00
☐ **As above,** *walnut.*
.... 175.00   195.00
☐ **As above,** *mahogany*
.... 175.00   195.00

CALENDAR

☐ **Adelaide,** *walnut parlor, height
24", dial 6", spring, 8 Day, strike,
simple calendar (E2-25).*
.... 250.00   275.00

☐ **Bankers Ink Stand,** *height 12",
dial 4", 1 Day, simple calendar
(E2-8).*
.... 250.00   325.00

☐ **Carlos,** *walnut parlor, height
24½", dial 6", spring, 8 Day,
strike, simple calendar (E2-25).*
.... 250.00   275.00

☐ **Gem Ink,** *height 8¾", dial 4",
spring, 1 Day, simple calendar
(E2-8, M258-88).*
.... 275.00   325.00

☐ **Grandfather,** *height 8", dial 4", spring, 1 Day, simple calendar (E2-8).*
.... **175.00   200.00**

☐ **Lily Ink,** *height 7", dial 4", spring, 1 Day, simple calendar (E2-8, M256-87).*
.... **250.00   300.00**

☐ **Novelty Calendar,** *Ansonia Brass and Copper Co., Connecticut, height 26", dial 10½", spring, 8 Day (M263-90).*
.... **800.00 1000.00**

☐ **Octagon Peep-O-Day,** *dial 4", spring, 1 Day, alarm, simple calendar (E2-10, M260-88).*
.... **100.00   125.00**

☐ **Octagon Top,** *gilt short drop, 19½" x 12", dial 8", spring, 8 Day, strike, simple calendar (E1-177, E2-39, M253-86).*
.... **225.00   250.00**

☐ **Octagon Top,** *gilt short drop, height 21½", dial 10", spring, 8 Day, strike, simple calendar (E2-39).*
.... **250.00   275.00**

☐ **Octagon Top,** *gilt short drop, height 24", dial 12", spring, 8 Day, strike, simple calendar (E2-39).*
.... **275.00   300.00**

☐ **Octagon Top,** *long drop, height 32", dial 12", spring, 8 Day, strike, simple calendar (M247-85).*
.... **350.00   400.00**

☐ **Octagon Top,** *long drop, regulator A, height 32", dial 12", spring, 8 Day, strike, simple calendar (E1-177, E2-39, M248-85).*
.... **400.00   425.00**

☐ **Office Ink Stand,** *height 13", dial 4", 1 Day, simple calendar (E2-8).*
.... 250.00   300.00

☐ **Para Parlor,** *wall regulator, height 39", dial 8", spring, 8 Day, strike, simple calendar (E2-40).*
.... 550.00   625.00

☐ **Parlor Ink Stand No.1,** *height 9", dial 2", 1 Day, simple calendar (E2-27).*
.... 200.00   250.00

☐ **Parlor Ink Stand No.2,** *height 8", dial 2", 1 Day, simple calendar (E2-27).*
.... 250.00   300.00

☐ **Parlor Ink Stand No.3,** *height 11", dial 4", 1 Day, simple calendar (E2-27).*
.... 300.00   350.00

☐ **Peep-O-Day,** *round alarm, dial 4", spring, 1 Day, alarm, simple calendar (E2-9).*
.... 75.00   100.00

☐ **Planet,** *round alarm, dial 4", spring, 1 Day, simple calendar (E2-9).*
.... 100.00   125.00

☐ **R.C. Octagon Top,** *short drop, height 19½", dial 8", spring, 8 Day, strike, simple calendar (E2-39).*
.... 225.00   250.00

☐ **R.C. Octagon Top,** *short drop, height 21½", dial 10", spring, 8 Day, strike, simple calendar (E2-39).*
.... 250.00   275.00

☐ **R.C. Octagon Top,** *short drop, height 24", dial 12", spring, 8 Day, strike, simple calendar (E2-39).*
.... 275.00   300.00

☐ **Regulator Octagon Top,** *height 32", dial 12", spring, 8 Day, strike, simple calendar (E2-39).*
.... 400.00   450.00

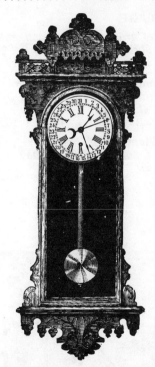

☐ **Rio Parlor,** *wall regulator, height 39", dial 8", spring, 8 Day, strike, simple calendar (E2-40).*
.... 550.00   625.00

☐ **Round Alarm,** *lion's head on each side, dial 4", spring, 1 Day, strike, simple calendar (M254-87).*
.... 75.00   100.00

☐ **Round Top,** *long drop, height 32", dial 12", spring, 8 Day, strike, simple calendar (E2-39).*
.... 350.00   400.00

☐ **Study Ink Stand,** *height 9½",
dial 4", 1 Day, simple calendar
(E2-27).*
.... **250.00   300.00**

☐ **Victorian Kitchen,** *23" x 14½",
barometer and thermometer, dial
5", spring, 8 Day, strike, simple
calendar (M251-86).*
.... **135.00   150.00**

CARRIAGE

☐ **Bee Carriage,** *brass finish, height
6", spring, c. 1890, 8 Day (E2-22).*
.... **105.00   125.00**

☐ **Bonnibel,** *polished brass, height
55", dial 1½", spring, c. 1910, 8
Day (E2-36).*
.... **140.00   160.00**

☐ **Brilliant,** *nickel, height 7½", dial
2½", spring, c. 1883, 1 Day
(E2-8).*
.... **105.00   125.00**

☐ **Companion,** *nickel, height 8",
dial 2", spring, c. 1883, 1 Day,
alarm (E2-8).*
.... **105.00   125.00**

☐ **Dora,** *black enameled case, hand
painted decorations, French
sash, gilt finish, height 10", dial
4", spring, c. 1883, 1 Day, strike
(E2-9).*
.... **105.00   125.00**

☐ **As above,** *8 Day, strike.*
.... **130.00   150.00**

☐ **Elliptical Carriage,** *nickel, height
6", spring, c. 1883, 1 Day, alarm
(E2-8).*
.... **105.00   125.00**

☐ **Gem,** *rich burnished silver or
gold, fancy, height 4½", dial
1½", spring, c. 1898, 1 Day
(E1-161).*
.... **55.00   75.00**

☐ **Comet,** *silver plated, height 7⅞",
dial 2½", spring, c. 1910, 1 Day,
strike, alarm (E2-36).*
.... **180.00   200.00**

☐ **Oriole,** *brass finish, enameled in
fancy colors, height 7", dial 3",
spring, c. 1890, 1 Day, alarm
(E2-10).*
.... **80.00   100.00**

☐ **As above,** *1 Day, strike.*
.... **105.00   125.00**

☐ **As above,** *1 Day, musical alarm.*
.... **130.00   150.00**

☐ **Ornamental Carriage,** *black enameled panels, embossed with gilt ornamentation, height 7", dial 3", spring, c. 1890, 1 Day, alarm (E2-10).*
.... **135.00   155.00**

☐ **Pearl,** *rich burnished gold, fancy, height 5", dial 1½", c. 1898, 1 Day (E1-161).*
.... **70.00   90.00**

☐ **Peep-O-Day,** *nickel, black enameled panels, hand painted decorations, height 7", dial 3", spring, c. 1883, 1 Day, alarm (E2-8).*
.... **130.00   150.00**

☐ **Pert,** *nickel, height 5", dial 5¾", spring, c. 1910, 1 Day, alarm (E2-36).*
.... **115.00   135.00**

☐ **Pert,** *nickel, height 5", dial 1¾", spring, c. 1898, 1 Day, alarm (E1-161).*
.... **95.00   115.00**

☐ **Satellite,** *rich gold, height 5⅝", dial 1½", spring, c. 1910, 8 Day (E2-36).*
.... **200.00   220.00**

☐ **Tally-Ho Carriage,** *nickel, repeating strike, height 8½", dial 3", spring, c. 1883, 8 Day, strike (E2-8).*
.... **260.00   300.00**

☐ **Peep-O-Day Carriage,** *nickel, height 7", dial 3", spring, c. 1890, 1 Day, alarm (E2-10).*
.... **115.00   135.00**

☐ **Tourist,** *nickel, height 7⅛", dial 2½", spring, c. 1910, 1 Day, strike, alarm (E2-36).*
. . . . **115.00   135.00**

☐ **Vida,** *rich burnished gold, fancy, height 5¼", dial 2", spring, c. 1898, 1 Day (E1-161).*
. . . . **50.00   70.00**

CHINA OR PORCELAIN
LARGE CASE

☐ **Accomac,** *painted and decorated porcelain, 11½" x 9¾", spring, c. 1898, 8 Day, strike with gong (E1-157).*
. . . . **165.00   185.00**

☐ **Chemung,** *hand painted and gold decorated cases, ½ hour strike, cathedral gong on sounding board, round polished brass escapement movement, ruby pallets, rack strike, with patent regulator and striking parts, cream porcelain dial, Rococo sash, 10½" x 8", spring, c. 1898, 8 Day (E1-158).*
. . . . **160.00   180.00**

☐ **Kennebeck,** *hand painted and gold decorated cases, ½ hour strike, cathedral gong on sounding board, round polised brass escapement movement, ruby pallets, rack strike, with patent regulator and striking parts, cream porcelain dial, Rococo sash, 11" x 10½", spring, c. 1898, 8 Day (E1-158).*
. . . . **245.00   275.00**

☐ **La Bretagne,** *15" x 12½", spring, c. 1910, 8 Day, strike (E2-38).*
. . . . **310.00   350.00**

☐ **La Calle,** *hand painted and gold decorated cases, ½ hour strike, cathedral gong on sounding board, round polished brass escapement movement, ruby pallets, rack strike, with patent regulator and striking parts, cream porcelain dial, Rococo sash, 14½" x 10", spring, c. 1898, 8 Day (E1-158).*
. . . . **270.00   300.00**

☐ **La Cannes,** *11¾" x 11¼", dial 4", spring, c. 1890, 8 Day, strike (E2-37).*
. . . . **270.00   300.00**

☐ **La Cette,** *12" x 12", dial 4", spring, c. 1890, 8 Day, strike (E2-37).*
. . . . **270.00   300.00**

☐ **La Chapelle,** *12" x 12", dial 4", spring, c. 1890, 8 Day, strike (E2-37).*
. . . . **295.00   325.00**

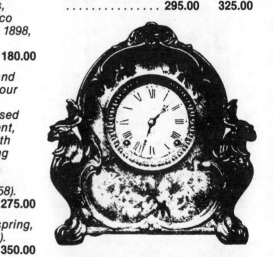

☐ **La Charny,** *11½" x 11", dial 4", spring, c. 1890, 8 Day, strike (E2-37).*
. . . . **270.00   300.00**

☐ **La Chartres,** *11¾" x 11¼", dial 4", spring, c. 1890, 8 Day, strike (E2-37).*
. . . . 270.00   300.00

☐ **La Clair,** *hand painted and gold decorated cases, ½ hour strike, cathedral gong on sounding board, round polished brass escapement movement, ruby pallets, rack strike, with patent regulator and striking parts, cream porcelain dial, Rococo sash, 13" x 9¾", spring, c. 1898, 8 Day (E1-158).*
. . . . 270.00   300.00

☐ **La Clairmont,** *11¾" x 10¾", dial 4", spring, c. 1890, 8 Day, strike (E2-37).*
. . . . 250.00   280.00

☐ **La Cruz,** *11½" x 8½", dial 4", spring, c. 1910, 8 Day, strike (E2-36).*
. . . . 230.00   260.00

☐ **La Fleur,** *14" x 12¾", dial 4", spring, c. 1890, 8 Day, strike (E2-37).*
. . . . 295.00   325.00

☐ **La Floride,** *14½" x 12½", dial 4", spring, c. 1910, 8 Day, strike (E2-38).*
. . . . 260.00   300.00

☐ **La Formose,** *12¾" x 13½", dial 4", spring, c. 1890, 8 Day, strike (E2-37).*
. . . . 310.00   350.00

☐ **La Flandre,** *14¾" x 12½", dial 4", c. 1910, 8 day, strike (E2-38).*
. . . . 310.00   350.00

☐ **La France,** *12¾" x 9½", dial 4", spring, c. 1890, 8 Day, strike (E2-37).*
. . . . 260.00   300.00

□ **La Friese,** *10¾" x 12½", dial 4",
spring, c. 1890, 8 Day, strike
(E2-37).*
.... 260.00   300.00

□ **La Gironde,** *13¾" x 11", dial 4",
spring, c. 1910, 8 Day, strike
(E2-38).*
.... 250.00   280.00

□ **La Isere,** *11¾" x 12½", dial 4",
spring, c. 1910, 8 Day, strike
(E2-38).*
.... 295.00   325.00

□ **La Layon,** *14½" x 15", dial 4",
spring, c. 1910, 8 Day, strike
(E2-38).*
.... 345.00   375.00

□ **La Manche,** *13¾" x 14", dial 4",
spring, c. 1890, 8 Day, strike
(E2-37).*
.... 295.00   325.00

□ **La Mayenne,** *13½" x 9½", dial
4", spring, c. 1890, 8 Day, strike
(E2-37).*
.... 240.00   280.00

□ **La Meuse,** *14" x 10½", dial 4",
c. 1910, 8 day, strike (E2-38).*
.... 240.00   280.00

□ **La Mine,** *14½" x 11¼", dial 4",
spring, c. 1910, 8 Day, strike
(E2-38).*
.... 295.00   325.00

□ **La Moselle,** *14½" x 9", dial 4",
spring, c. 1910, 8 Day, strike
(E2-38).*
.... 240.00   280.00

□ **La Nord,** *11¾" x 14½", dial 4",
spring, c. 1910, 8 Day, strike
(E2-38).*
.... 295.00   325.00

□ **La Orb,** *13" x 14½", dial 4",
c. 1890, 8 Day, strike (E2-37).*
.... 310.00   350.00

□ **La Palma,** *11⅞" x 14¼", dial 4",
spring, c. 1910, 8 Day, strike
(E2-38).*
.... 310.00   350.00

□ **La Plaine,** *11½" x 8½", dial 4",
spring, c. 1910, 8 Day, strike
(E2-36).*
.... 210.00   240.00

□ **La Plata,** *13" x 14", dial 4",
spring, c. 1890, 8 Day, strike
(E2-37).*
.... 310.00   350.00

☐ **La Rambla,** *12" x 10", dial 4", spring, c. 1890, 8 Day, strike (E2-37).*
.... 300.00   315.00

☐ **La Riviere,** *12½" x 14½", dial 4", spring, c. 1910, 8 Day, strike (E2-38).*
.... 295.00   325.00

☐ **La Savoie,** *11¼" x 9", dial 4", spring, c. 1910, 8 Day, strike (E2-36).*
.... 230.00   260.00

☐ **La Scarpe,** *11¼" x 9¼", dial 4", spring, c. 1910, 8 Day, strike (E2-36).*
.... 230.00   260.00

☐ **La Sedan,** *11¼" x 9¼", dial 4", spring, c. 1910, 8 Day, strike (E2-36).*
.... 230.00   260.00

☐ **La Seine,** *11½" x 9¾", dial 4", spring, c. 1910, 8 Day, strike (E2-36).*
.... 230.00   260.00

☐ **La Tosca,** *14½" x 10", dial 4", spring, c. 1910, 8 Day, strike (E2-38).*
.... 310.00   350.00

☐ **La Vendee,** *hand painted and gold decorated cases, ½ hour strike, cathedral gong on sounding board, round polished brass escapement movement, ruby pallets, rack strike, with patent regulator and striking parts, cream porcelain dial, Rococo sash, 14½" x 13", spring, c. 1898, 8 Day (E1-158).*
.... 345.00   375.00

☐ **La Verdon,** *hand painted and gold decorated cases, ½ hour strike, cathedral gong on sounding board, round polished brass escapement movement, ruby pallets, rack strike, with patent regulator and striking parts, cream porcelain dial, Rococo sash, 14½" x 13½", spring, c. 1898, 8 Day (E1-158).*
.... 300.00   340.00

☐ **La Vergne,** *11¾" x 14¼", dial 4", c. 1910, 8 day, strike (E2-38).*
.... 310.00   350.00

☐ **La Vogue,** *hand painted and gold decorated cases, ½ hour strike, cathedral gong on sounding board, round polished brass escapement movement, ruby pallets, rack strike, with patent regulator and striking parts, cream porcelain dial, Rococo sash, 12¾" x 11¼", spring, c. 1898, 8 Day (E1-158).*
.... 310.00   350.00

☐ **Osceola,** *hand painted and gold decorated cases, ½ hour strike, cathedral gong on sounding board, round polished brass escapement movement, ruby pallets, rack strike, with patent regulator and striking parts, cream porcelain dial, Rococo sash, 11¾" x 13½", spring, c. 1898, 8 Day (E1-158).*
.... 310.00   350.00

☐ **Ossipee,** *decorated porcelain, 11¾" x 12½", spring, c. 1898, 8 Day, strike (E1-137).*
.... 240.00   280.00

SMALL CASE

☐ **Acme,** *decorated porcelain, height 4½", dial 2", spring, c. 1898, 1 Day, strike (E1-156).*
.... 35.00   40.00

☐ **Crescent,** *decorated porcelain, height 5¼", dial 2", spring, c. 1898, 1 Day (E1-157).*
.... 35.00   40.00

☐ **Cuckoo,** *decorated porcelain, height 6", dial 2", spring, c. 1898, 1 Day (E1-157).*
.... 35.00   40.00

☐ **Flora,** *decorated porcelain, height 4½", dial 2", spring, c. 1898, 1 Day (E1-157).*
. . . . **30.00**   **35.00**

☐ **Gannet,** *decorated or delft porcelain, height 6⅞", spring, c. 1898, 1 Day, strike (E1-155).*
. . . . **65.00**   **75.00**

☐ **Helena,** *decorated porcelain, height 5¼", dial 2", spring, c. 1898, 1 Day, strike (E1-157).*
. . . . **35.00**   **40.00**

CONNECTICUT SHELF

BEE HIVE

☐ **Tudor, V.P.,** *veneered wood, height 19", dial 6", spring, c. 1890, 1 Day, strike (E2-15).*
. . . . **105.00**   **135.00**

☐ **As above,** *8 Day, strike.*
. . . . **165.00**   **185.00**

O.G.

☐ **O.G.** *weight, veneered, height 26", c. 1890, 1 Day (E2-20).*
. . . . **135.00**   **155.00**

☐ **As above,** *1 Day, alarm.*
. . . . **180.00**   **200.00**

☐ **O.G.,** *weight, polished and veneered oak, height 30", dial 9", c. 1898, 1 Day, strike, with weights (E1-155).*
. . . . **195.00**   **225.00**

☐ **As above,** *1 Day, strike, spring.*
. . . . **135.00**   **155.00**

ROUND TOP

☐ **Arab,** *veneered wood, height 14", spring, c. 1890, 1 Day (E2-15).*
. . . . **65.00**   **85.00**

☐ **As above,** *1 Day, strike.*
. . . . **85.00**   **105.00**

☐ **As above,** *8 Day, strike.*
. . . . **130.00**   **150.00**

☐ **As above,** *8 Day, strike.*
.... 80.00   100.00

☐ **Cottage Extra,** *veneered, height 13", spring, c. 1890, 1 Day, strike (E2-20).*
.... 70.00   90.00
☐ **As above,** *1 Day, strike, alarm.*
.... 90.00   110.00

☐ **Arcadian,** *veneered wood, height 18", dial 6", spring, c. 1890, 1 Day, strike (E2-15).*
.... 125.00   145.00
☐ **As above,** *8 Day, strike.*
.... 165.00   185.00

☐ **Cottage,** *polished and veneered oak, height 12", dial 5", spring, c. 1898, 1 Day (E1-155).*
.... 50.00   70.00
☐ **As above,** *1 Day, strike.*
.... 70.00   90.00

☐ **Cottage,** *veneered, height 12", spring, c. 1890, 1 Day (E2-20).*
.... 70.00   90.00
☐ **As above,** *1 Day, alarm.*
.... 90.00   110.00

☐ **Cottage Extra,** *polished and veneered oak, height 12", dial 6", spring, c. 1898, 1 Day, strike (E-155).*
.... 60.00   80.00

☐ **Flint,** *wood, height 19½", dial 5½", spring, c. 1890, 1 Day, strike (E2-15).*
.... 115.00   135.00
☐ **As above,** *8 Day, strike.*
.... 165.00   185.00

☐ **Standard,** *veneered wood, height 18½", dial 6", spring, c. 1890, 1 Day, strike (E2-15).*
.... 115.00   135.00
☐ **As above,** *8 Day, strike.*
.... 165.00   185.00

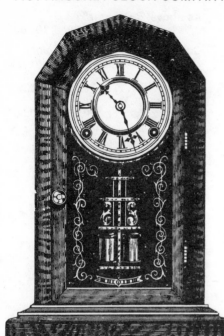

☐ **Neptune,** *walnut, height 15",
spring, c. 1890, 1 Day, strike or
alarm (E2-20).*
.... **115.00   135.00**

☐ **Pansy,** *wood, height 15", dial 5",
spring, c. 1890, 1 Day, strike
(E2-15).*
.... **115.00   135.00**
☐ **As above,** *8 Day, strike.*
.... **145.00   165.00**

☐ **Spartan,** *walnut veneered, height
18½", dial 6", spring, c. 1891, 1
Day, strike (E2-21).*
.... **110.00   130.00**
☐ **As above,** *1 Day, strike, alarm.*
.... **130.00   150.00**

☐ **Theban,** *veneered wood, height
18½", dial 6", spring, c. 1890, 1
Day, strike (E2-15).*
.... **115.00   135.00**
☐ **As above,** *8 Day, strike.*
.... **165.00   185.00**

SPLIT TOP
☐ **Maud,** *veneered wood, height
19", dial 6", spring, c. 1890, 1
Day, strike (E2-15).*
.... **105.00   125.00**
☐ **As above,** *8 Day, strike.*
.... **155.00   175.00**

☐ **Neptune,** *veneered wood, height
15", dial 5", c. 1890, 1 Day, strike
(E2-15).*
.... **115.00   135.00**
☐ **As above,** *8 Day, strike.*
.... **145.00   165.00**

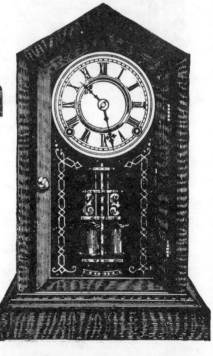

☐ **Spartan,** *veneered wood, height
18½", dial 6", spring, c. 1890, 1
Day, strike (E2-15).*
.... **95.00   125.00**
☐ **As above,** *8 Day, strike.*
.... **145.00   165.00**

STEEPLE

- [ ] **Decorated Gothic,** *veneered wood, bronze ornaments, height 20", dial 6", spring, c. 1890, 1 Day, strike (E2-15).*
  .... 130.00   150.00
- [ ] **As above,** *8 Day, strike.*
  .... 180.00   200.00

- [ ] **Sharp Gothic,** *V. P., polished and veneered oak, height 19½", dial 6", spring, c. 1898, 1 Day, strike (E1-155).*
  .... 130.00   150.00
- [ ] **As above,** *8 Day, strike.*
  .... 180.00   200.00

- [ ] **Sharp Gothic,** *V.P., veneered, spring, c. 1890, 1 Day, strike, or 1 Day, alarm (E2-20).*
  .... 130.00   150.00

- [ ] **Sharp Gothic,** *V.P., veneered wood, height 19½", dial 6", spring, c. 1890, 1 Day, strike (E2-15).*
  .... 130.00   150.00
- [ ] **As above,** *8 Day, strike*
  .... 180.00   200.00

- [ ] **Small Sharp Gothic,** *veneered wood, height 15", dial 4½", spring, c. 1890, 1 Day (E2-15).*
  .... 105.00   135.00
- [ ] **As above,** *1 Day, alarm.*
  .... 105.00   135.00
- [ ] **As above,** *1 Day, strike.*
  .... 145.00   165.00

- [ ] **Small Sharp Gothic,** *polished and veneered oak, height 16", dial 4½", spring, c. 1898, 1 Day (E1-155).*
  .... 80.00   100.00
- [ ] **As above,** *1 Day, strike.*
  .... 100.00   120.00

CRYSTAL PALACE

- [ ] **Crystal Palace No.1,** *extra, glass covered, height 18½", spring, c. 1890, 8 Day, strike (E2-22).*
  .... 540.00   600.00

☐ **Crystal Palace No.2,** *extra, glass covered, height 20", dial 6", spring, c. 1896, 8 Day, hour and ½ hour strike, cathedral gong movement (E2-14).*
.... **540.00   600.00**

CRYSTAL REGULATOR

☐ **Acme,** *porcelain dial, white beveled plate glass front, back and sides, 10¾" x 6⅞", dial 4", c. 1910, 8 Day, strike, polished brass (E1-134).*
.... **165.00   190.00**
☐ **As above,** *gold plated.*
.... **195.00   215.00**

☐ **Admiral,** *visible escapement, porcelain dial, white beveled plate glass front, back and sides, green onyx top and base, 18" x 10", dial 4", c. 1910, 8 Day, strike (E1-133).*
.... **950.00   1200.00**

☐ **Ambassador,** *visible escapement, porcelain dial, white beveled plate glass front, back and sides, green onyx top and base, 11½" x 7¼", dial 4", c. 1910, 8 Day, strike (E1-133).*
.... **310.00   350.00**

☐ **Apex,** *rich gold, visible escapement, porcelain dial, white beveled plate glass front, back and sides, 18½" x 10½", dial 4", c. 1910, 8 Day, strike (E1-138).*
.... **2350.00   2500.00**

☐ **Aquitaine,** *rich gold plated, beveled white plate glass back door, pendulum visible through beveled white plate glass panel, 11¾" x 6¼", dial 4", c. 1917, 8 Day, strike (E1-180).*
.... **265.00   305.00**

☐ **Baronet,** *polished brass, rich gold ornaments, visible escapement, porcelain dial, white beveled plate glass front, back and sides, 12½" x 7½", dial 4", c. 1910, 8 Day, strike (E1-138).*
.... **360.00   400.00**

☐ **Blazon,** *visible escapement, porcelain dial, white beveled plate glass front, back and sides, green onyx top and base, 13¼" x 8", dial 4", c. 1910, 8 Day, strike (E1-133).*
.... **460.00   520.00**

☐ **Carlton,** *visible escapement, porcelain dial, white beveled plate glass front, back and sides, 10½" x 7", dial 4", c. 1910, 8 Day, strike , polished brass (E1-134).*
.... 160.00   185.00
☐ **As above,** *gold plated.*
.... 190.00   210.00

☐ **Cavalier,** *visible escapement, porcelain dial, white beveled plate glass front, back and sides, green onyx top and base, 12" x 8", dial 4", c. 1910, 8 Day, strike (E1-135).*
.... 410.00   460.00

☐ **Cetus,** *visible escapement, porcelain dial, white beveled plate glass front, back and sides, 11" x 6⅝", dial 4", c. 1910, 8 Day, strike, polished brass (E1-134).*
.... 190.00   210.00
☐ **As above,** *gold plated.*
.... 205.00   235.00

☐ **Chancellor,** *visible escapement, porcelain dial, white beveled plate glass front, back and sides, green onyx top and base, 13" x 7½", dial 4", c. 1910, 8 Day, strike (E1-133).*
.... 425.00   475.00

☐ **Claudius,** *porcelain dial, white beveled plate glass front, back and sides, 11¼" x 7", dial 4", c. 1910, 8 Day, strike, gold plated (E1-134).*
.... 190.00   210.00

☐ **Clifton,** *visible escapement, porcelain dial, white beleved plate glass front, back and sides, 10¼" x 6½", dial 4", c. 1910, 8 Day, strike, polished brass (E1-134).*
.... 190.00   210.00
☐ **As above,** *gold plated.*
.... 205.00   235.00

☐ **Colby,** *porcelain dial, white beveled plate glass front, back and sides, 10¾" x 6¾", dial 4", c. 1910, 8 Day, strike, polished brass (E1-134).*
.... 195.00   225.00
☐ **As above,** *gold plated.*
.... 220.00   250.00

☐ **Consort,** *visible escapement, porcelain dial, white beveled plate glass front, back and sides, green onyx top and base, 16" x 8", dial 4", c. 1910, 8 Day, strike (E1-133).*
.... 540.00   600.00

☐ **Consul,** *visible escapement, porcelain dial, white beveled plate glass front, back and sides, green onyx top and base, 13" x 7¾", dial 4", c. 1910, 8 Day, strike, polished brass (E1-138).*
.... 270.00   310.00

☐ **Coral,** *porcelain dial, white beveled plate glass front, back and sides, 9¾" x 6⅜", dial 4", c. 1910, 8 Day, strike, polished brass (E1-134).*
.... 140.00   165.00
☐ **As above,** *gold plated.*
.... 165.00   190.00

☐ **Corona,** *visible escapement, porcelain dial, white beveled plate glass front, back and sides, 11½" x 6⅞", dial 4", c. 1910, 8 Day, strike, polished brass (E1-134).*
.... **175.00   205.00**

☐ **As above,** *gold plated.*
.... **200.00   230.00**

☐ **Cosmo,** *visible escapement, porcelain dial, white beveled plate glass front, back and sides, green onyx top and base, 15¼" x 8", dial 4", c. 1910, 8 Day, strike (E1-135).*
.... **610.00   685.00**

☐ **Count,** *visible escapement, porcelain dial, white beveled plate glass front, back and sides, 16½" x 8", dial 4", c. 1910, 8 Day, strike (E1-133).*
.... **515.00   575.00**

☐ **Danube,** *rich gold plate, beveled plate glass front, back and sides, porcelain dial, 9" x 7¾", dial 3", c. 1917, 8 Day, strike (E1-180).*
.... **190.00   210.00**

☐ **Dawson,** *porcelain dial, white beveled plate glass front, back and sides, 9¼" x 5⅞", dial 3", c. 1910, 8 Day, strike, polished brass (E1-135).*
.... **145.00   170.00**

☐ **As above,** *gold plated.*
.... **165.00   190.00**

☐ **Delta,** *porcelain dial, white beveled plate glass front, back and sides, 9¼" x 5⅝", dial 3", c. 1910, 8 Day, strike, polished brass (E1-135).*
.... **135.00   160.00**

☐ **As above,** *gold plated.*
.... **155.00   180.00**

☐ **Deputy,** *visible escapement, porcelain dial, white beveled plate glass front, back and sides, green onyx top and base,*

13¼" x 7¾", dial 4", c. 1910, 8 Day, strike (E1-133).
.... **490.00   550.00**

☐ **Diplomat,** *polished brass, rich gold ornaments, visible escapement, porcelain dial, white beveled plate glass front, back and sides, 18¼" x 7¾", dial 4½", c. 1910, 8 Day, strike (E1-138).*
.... **450.00   500.00**

☐ **Dolphin,** *porcelain dial, white beveled plate glass front, back and sides, 9¼" x 5⅝", dial 3", c. 1910, 8 Day, strike, polished brass (E1-133).*
.... **135.00   160.00**

☐ **As above,** *gold plated.*
.... **155.00   180.00**

☐ **Doria,** *rich gold plate, convex glass front, beveled plate glass sides and back, plain porcelain dial, 8⅞" x 6", dial 3", c. 1917, 8 Day, strike (E1-180).*
.... **165.00   190.00**

☐ **Dorval,** *porcelain dial, white beveled plate glass front, back and sides, 8⅞" x 5⅝", dial 3", c. 1910, 8 Day, strike, polished brass (E1-135).*
.... **130.00   155.00**

☐ **As above,** *gold plated.*
.... **150.00   175.00**

☐ **Duchess,** *visible escapement, porcelain dial, white beveled plate glass front, back and sides, green onyx top and base, 11" x 7¼", dial 4", c. 1910, 8 Day, strike (E1-133).*
.... **310.00   350.00**

☐ **Dunbar,** *porcelain dial, white beveled plate glass front, back and sides, 9⅛" x 5⅝", dial 3", c. 1910, 8 Day, strike, polished brass (E1-135).*
.... **135.00   160.00**

☐ **As above,** *gold plated.*
.... **155.00   180.00**

☐ **Envoy,** *polished brass, rich gold ornaments, visible escapement, porcelain dial, white beveled plate glass front, back and sides, 19" x 9¾", dial 4", c. 1910, 8 Day, strike (E1-138).*
. . . . 535.00   610.00

☐ **Escutcheon,** *visible escapement, porcelain dial, white beveled plate glass front, back and sides, green onyx top and base, 13¾" x 8⅛", dial 4", c. 1910, 8 Day, strike (E1-133).*
. . . . 400.00   450.00

☐ **Eulogy,** *rich gold, visible escapement, porcelain dial, white beveled plate glass front, back and sides, 19½" x 9¼", dial 4", c. 1910, 8 Day, strike (E1-138).*
. . . . 675.00   750.00

☐ **Excelsior,** *gilt or silver finish, height 20½", dial 5½", hour and ½ hour strike, cathedral gong movement, c. 1896, 8 Day (E2-14).*
. . . . 850.00   1100.00

☐ **Floral,** *rich gold, visible escapement, porcelain dial, white beveled plate glass front, back and sides, 16½" x 8¾", dial 4", c. 1910, 8 Day, strike (E1-138).*
. . . . 900.00   1000.00

☐ **Gardant,** *visible escapement, porcelain dial, white beveled plate glass front, back and sides, green onyx top and base, 16¼" x 9", dial 4", c. 1910, 8 Day, strike (E1-133).*
. . . . 625.00   700.00

☐ **Griffin,** *visible escapement, porcelain dial, white beveled plate glass front, back and sides, green onyx top and base, 13" x 8¾", dial 4", c. 1910, 8 Day, strike (E1-135).*
. . . . 450.00   500.00

☐ **Khedive,** *visible escapement, porcelain dial, white beveled plate glass front, back and sides, green onyx top and base, 14¼" x 8⅛", dial 4", c. 1910, 8 Day, strike (E1-135).*
. . . . 565.00   640.00

☐ **Laureate,** *visible escapement, porcelain dial, white beveled plate glass front, back and sides, green onyx top and base, 16" x 8", dial 4", c. 1910, 8 Day, strike (E1-135).*
. . . . 625.00   700.00

☐ **Legate,** *polished brass, rich gold ornaments, visible escapement, porcelain dial, white beveled plate glass front, back and sides, 14¼" x 9¾", dial 4½", c. 1910, 8 Day, strike (E1-138).*
. . . . 425.00   475.00

☐ **Marchioness,** *polished brass, rich gold ornaments, visible escapement, porcelain dial, white beveled plate glass front, back and sides, 15¾" x 8¼", dial 4", c. 1910, 8 Day, strike (E1-136).*
.... **725.00   800.00**

☐ **Marquis,** *polished brass, rich gold ornaments, visible escapement, porcelain dial, white beveled plate glass front, back and sides, 15½" x 7½", dial 4", c. 1910, 8 Day, strike (E1-136).*
.... **625.00   700.00**

☐ **Octavia,** *porcelain dial, white beveled plate glass front, back and sides, 12¼" x 7⅝", dial 4", c. 1910, 8 Day, strike, gold plated (E1-138).*
.... **295.00   335.00**

☐ **Oriel,** *visible escapement, porcelain dial, white beveled plate glass front, back and sides, 13¾" x 6⅞", dial 4", c. 1910, 8 Day, strike, polished brass (E1-134).*
.... **210.00   240.00**

☐ **As above,** *gold plated.*
.... **235.00   265.00**

☐ **Premier,** *visible escapement, porcelain dial, white beveled plate glass front, back and sides, green onyx top and base, 13¾" x 8", dial 4", c. 1910, 8 Day, strike (E1-133).*
.... **440.00   490.00**

☐ **Prince,** *visible escapement, porcelain dial, white beveled plate glass front, back and sides, green onyx top and base, 15" x 8½", dial 4", c. 1910, 8 Day, strike (E1-135).*
.... **635.00   710.00**

☐ **Prism,** *visible escapement, porcelain dial, white beveled plate glass front, back and sides, green onyx top and base, 10¾" x 6⅜", dial 4", c. 1910, 8 Day, strike, polished brass (E1-134).*
.... **160.00   185.00**
☐ **As above,** *gold plated.*
.... **180.00   210.00**

☐ **Provence,** *visible escapement, porcelain dial, white beveled plate glass front, back and sides, 11" x 6½", dial 4", c. 1910, 8 Day, strike, polished brass (E1-134).*
.... **195.00   225.00**
☐ **As above,** *gold plated.*
.... **220.00   250.00**

☐ **Queen,** *visible escapement, porcelain dial, white beveled plate glass front, back and sides, green onyx top and base, 13½" x 8⅛", dial 4", c. 1910, 8 Day, strike (E1-135).*
.... **430.00   480.00**

☐ **Radiant,** *visible escapement, porcelain dial, white beveled plate glass front, back and sides, green onyx top and base, 17" x 9¼", dial 4", c. 1910, 8 Day, strike (E1-133).*
.... **645.00   720.00**

☐ **Rampant,** *visible escapement, porcelain dial, white beveled plate glass front, back and sides, 13¾" x 9", dial 4", c. 1910, 8 Day, strike (E1-135).*
.... 540.00   600.00

☐ **Regis,** *visible escapement, porcelain dial, white beveled plate glass front, back and sides, 11½" x 8", dial 4", convex front and sides, c. 1910, 8 Day, strike, gold plated (E1-138).*
.... 270.00   310.00

☐ **Renaissance,** *visible escapement, porcelain dial, white beveled plate glass front, back and sides, 16½" x 8", dial 4", c. 1910, 8 Day, strike, rich gold (E1-138).*
.... 665.00   740.00

☐ **Rouen,** *porcelain dial, white beveled plate glass front, back and sides, 11" x 6¾", dial 4", c. 1910, 8 Day, strike, polished brass (E1-134).*
.... 190.00   220.00
☐ **As above,** *gold plated.*
.... 215.00   245.00

☐ **Roy,** *porcelain dial, white beveled plate glass front, back and sides, convex front, 11⅛" x 7¼", dial 4", c. 1910, 8 Day, strike, polished brass (E1-134).*
.... 195.00   225.00
☐ **As above,** *gold plated.*
.... 220.00   250.00

☐ **Sirius,** *visible escapement, porcelain dial, white beveled plate glass front, back and sides, 13" x 9", dial 4", polished brass, rich gold ornaments, c. 1910, 8 Day, strike (E1-138).*
.... 900.00   1000.00

☐ **Symbol,** *gilt or silver finish, height 20", dial 6", hour and ½ hour strike, cathedral gong movement, c. 1896, 8 Day (E2-14).*
.... 400.00   450.00

☐ **Symbol Extra,** *gilt or silver finish, height 15¼", dial 5½", hour and ½ hour strike, cathedral gong movement, c. 1896, 8 Day (E2-14).*
.... 465.00   525.00

☐ **Symbol No.1,** *gilt or silver finish, height 22", dial 6", hour and ½ hour strike, cathedral gong movement, c. 1896, 8 Day (E2-14).*
.... 465.00   525.00

☐ **Symbol No.2,** *gilt or silver finish, height 15½", dial 5", hour and ½ hour strike, cathedral gong movement, c. 1896, 8 Day (E2-14).*
. . . . **425.00   475.00**

☐ **Touraine,** *rich gold plated, beveled white plate glass back door, pendulum visible through beveled white plate glass panel, 11" x 6¼", dial 4", c. 1917, 8 Day, strike (E1-180).*
. . . . **260.00   295.00**

☐ **Viceroy,** *polished brass, rich gold ornaments, visible escapement, porcelain dial, white beveled plate glass front, back and sides, 16" x 8¼", dial 4", c. 1910, 8 Day, strike (E1-136).*
. . . . **625.00   700.00**

☐ **Viscount,** *polished brass, rich gold ornaments, visible escapement, porcelain dial, white beveled plate glass front, back and sides, 16" x 8¼", dial 4", c. 1910, 8 Day, strike (E1-136).*
. . . . **645.00   720.00**

☐ **Vulcan,** *porcelain dial, white beveled plate glass front, back and sides, 12¼" x 7½", dial 4", c. 1910, 8 Day, strike, rich gold (E1-134).*
. . . . **205.00   235.00**

☐ **Wanda,** *visible escapement, porcelain dial, white beveled plate glass front, back and sides, 11¼" x 6⅝", dial 4", c. 1910, 8 Day, strike, polished brass (E1-134).*
. . . . **180.00   210.00**

☐ **As above,** *gold plated.*
. . . . **205.00   235.00**

GALLERY

☐ **Ansonia Lever,** *walnut, dial 12", spring, c. 1900, 8 Day (E2-24).*
. . . . **135.00   160.00**

☐ **As above,** *8 Day, strike.*
. . . . **155.00   180.00**

☐ **Foyer No.1,** *antique oak or oak, height 39", dial 18", pendulum, c. 1890, 8 Day (E2-28).*
. . . . **220.00   250.00**

☐ **As above,** *8 Day, strike.*
. . . . **245.00   275.00**

☐ **As above,** *30 Day.*
. . . . 360.00   400.00

☐ **Foyer No.2,** *antique oak or oak,*
height 32½ ", dial 14", pendulum,
c. 1890, 8 Day (E2-28).
. . . . 175.00   200.00
☐ **As above,** *8 Day, strike.*
. . . . 195.00   225.00
☐ **As above,** *30 Day.*
. . . . 270.00   300.00

☐ **Foyer No.3,** *antique oak or oak,*
height 25½ ", dial 12", pendulum,
c. 1890, 8 Day (E2-28).
. . . . 155.00   180.00
☐ **As above,** *8 Day, strike.*
. . . . 175.00   200.00

GRANDFATHER

☐ **Foyer No.4,** *dark wood, oak,*
height 23", dial 12", pendulum,
c. 1890, 8 Day (E2-28).
. . . . 150.00   175.00
☐ **As above,** *8 Day, strike.*
. . . . 175.00   200.00

☐ **Antique Standing,** *mahogany,*
oak, antique brass trimming,
weight, height 94", gilt and
silvered dial 10", c. 1910, 8 Day,
strike (E2-42).
. . . . 5400.00   6000.00

☐ **Antique Standing No.2,**
*mahogany, oak, heavy brass,
with raised numerals on raised
silvered circle, gilt center,
pierced corners, moon disk,
showing moon changes, weight,
antique brass trimmings, height
104", dial 12", c. 1910, 8 Day,
strike (E2-42).*
. . . . **5000.00   5500.00**

☐ **Antique Standing No.3,**
*mahogany, oak, heavy brass,
with raised numerals on raised
silvered circle, gilt center,
pierced corners, moon disk,
showing moon changes, antique
brass trimmings, weight, height
100", dial 12", c. 1910, 8 Day,
strike (E2-42).*
. . . . **5000.00   5500.00**

☐ **Antique Standing No.5,**
*mahogany, oak, brass
ornaments, weight, height 93",
gilt and silvered dial 12", c. 1910,
8 Day, strike (E2-42).*
. . . . **3150.00   3500.00**

KITCHEN

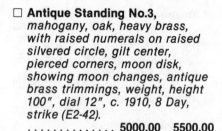

☐ **Aspen,** *walnut, 22" x 14¼", dial
6", spring wound, c. 1900, 8 Day,
strike (E2-24).*
. . . . **165.00   190.00**
☐ **As above,** *Arlington.*
. . . . **165.00   190.00**
☐ **As above,** *Arden.*
. . . . **165.00   190.00**

☐ **As above,** *Antler.*
.... 165.00   190.00
☐ **As above,** *Arctic.*
.... 165.00   190.00
☐ **As above,** *Andes.*
.... 165.00   190.00

☐ **Aspen,** *oak, 22" x 14¼", dial 6",
spring wound, c. 1900, 8 Day,
strike (E2-24).*
.... 140.00   165.00
☐ **As above,** *Arlington.*
.... 140.00   165.00
☐ **As above,** *Arden.*
.... 140.00   165.00
☐ **As above,** *Antler.*
.... 140.00   165.00
☐ **As above,** *Arctic.*
.... 140.00   165.00
☐ **As above,** *Andes.*
.... 140.00   165.00

☐ **Ada,** *dark wood or oak, height
22½", dial 5", c. 1890, 8 Day
hour and ½ hour strike (E2-16).*
.... 175.00   200.00

☐ **Adelaide,** *dark wood or oak,
height 24", dial 6", spring
wound, c. 1900, 8 Day, strike,
calendar (E2-25).*
.... 250.00   280.00

☐ **Aden,** *walnut, height 21", dial 6",
spring wound, c. 1890, 8 Day,
strike, spring alarm (E2-20).*
.... 150.00   175.00

Africa

☐ **Africa,** *walnut, height 21", dial 6", spring wound, c. 1890, 8 Day, strike, spring alarm (E2-20).*
.... 145.00   170.00

☐ **Agnes,** *dark wood or oak, height 21", dial 5", spring wound, c. 1890, 8 Day, hour and ½ hour strike (E2-16).*
.... 175.00   200.00

☐ **Alaska,** *walnut, height 21", dial 6", spring wound, c. 1890, 8 Day, strike, spring, alarm (E2-20).*
.... 145.00   175.00

☐ **Amazon,** *antique oak, height 19", spring wound, c. 1890, 8 Day, strike (E2-22).*
.... 115.00   140.00

☐ **As above,** *8 Day, strike, spring alarm.*
.... 135.00   160.00

☐ **America,** *walnut, height 21", dial 6", spring wound, c. 1890, 8 Day, strike, spring alarm (E2-20).*
.... 160.00   185.00

☐ **Amy,** *dark wood or oak, height 21½", dial 5", spring wound, c. 1890, 8 Day, hour and ½ hour strike (E2-16).*
.... 160.00   185.00

☐ **Arabia,** *walnut, height 21", dial 6", spring wound, c. 1890, 8 Day, strike (E2-19).*
.... 150.00   175.00

☐ **Atlas,** *walnut, height 21", dial 6", spring wound, c. 1890, 8 Day, strike (E2-19).*
.... 165.00   190.00

☐ **Aurania,** *walnut, height 20", dial 6", spring wound, c. 1890, 8 Day, strike (E2-19).*
.... 115.00   140.00

☐ **Austria,** *walnut, height 21", dial 6", spring wound, c. 1890, 8 Day, strike, alarm (E2-20).*
.... 150.00   175.00

☐ **Australia,** *dark wood or oak, height 21", dial 6", spring wound, c. 1890, 8 Day, strike (E2-18).*
.... 150.00   175.00

☐ **Baltic,** *walnut, height 19", dial 6", spring wound, c. 1890, 1 Day, strike (E2-19).*
.... 110.00   135.00

☐ **Blackbird,** *ebonized case, spring wound, c. 1890, 1 Day, strike, spring, and 8 Day, strike (E2-17).*
.... 165.00   190.00

☐ **Blanche,** *dark wood or oak, height 23", dial 6", spring wound, c. 1890, 8 Day, hour and ½ hour strike (E2-16).*
.... 175.00   200.00

☐ **Britannic,** *walnut, height 20", dial 6", spring wound, c. 1890, 1 Day, strike, spring (E2-21).*
.... 105.00   130.00

☐ **As above,** *1 Day, strike, alarm.*
.... 125.00   150.00

☐ **Belgrade,** *dark wood or oak, height 24", dial 6", spring wound, c. 1900, 8 Day, hour and ½ hour strike (E2-25).*
.... 230.00   260.00

☐ **Canada,** *walnut, height 21", dial 5½", spring wound, c. 1891, 1 Day, strike, spring (E2-21).*
.... 105.00   130.00

☐ **As above,** *1 Day, strike, spring, alarm.*
.... 125.00   150.00

☐ **Carlos,** *dark wood or oak, height 24½", dial 6", spring wound, c. 1900, 8 Day, strike, calendar (E2-25).*
.... 250.00   280.00

☐ **Celtic,** *walnut, height 19", dial 6", spring wound, c. 1890, 1 Day, strike (E2-19).*
.... 110.00   135.00

☐ **Chicago,** *antique oak, height 21¼", spring wound, c. 1890, 8 Day, strike, spring (E2-22).*
.... 165.00   190.00

☐ **As above,** *8 Day, strike, spring alarm.*
.... 180.00   210.00

☐ **Clara,** *dark wood or oak, height 23", dial 6", spring wound, c. 1890, 8 Day, hour and ½ hour strike (E2-17).*
.... 160.00   185.00

☐ **Colon,** *walnut, height 24", dial 6", spring wound, c. 1890, 8 Day, strike (E2-19).*
.... 190.00   220.00

☐ **Colorado,** *walnut, height 25", dial 6", spring wound, c. 1890, 8 Day, strike (E2-22).*
.... 165.00   180.00

☐ **As above,** *8 Day, strike, alarm.*
.... 180.00   210.00

☐ **Cuba,** *black walnut, height 24½", dial 6", spring wound, c. 1890, 8 Day, strike (E2-17).*
.... 175.00   200.00

☐ **Epsom,** *dark wood or oak, height 19", dial 5", spring wound, c. 1890, 8 Day, hour and ½ hour strike (E2-17).*
.... 165.00   190.00

☐ **Ranger,** *dark wood or oak, height 19", dial 5", spring wound, c. 1890, 8 Day, hour and ½ hour strike (E2-17).*
.... 160.00   185.00

☐ **Embossed,** *dark wood or oak, height 21", dial 5", spring wound, c. 1890, 8 Day, hour and ½ hour strike (E2-17).*
.... 160.00   185.00

☐ **Express,** *walnut, height 21", dial 6", spring wound, c. 1890, 8 Day, strike (E2-18).*
.... 165.00   190.00

☐ **Farragut,** *dark wood or oak, height 22", dial 6", spring wound, c. 1890, 8 Day, strike (E2-18).*
.... 155.00   180.00

☐ **Fulda,** *walnut, height 21", dial 6", spring wound, c. 1890, 1 Day, strike (E2-19).*
.... 115.00   140.00

☐ **Fulda,** *walnut, height 21", dial 6", spring wound, c. 1891, 8 Day, strike, spring (E2-21).*
.... 105.00   130.00
☐ **As above,** *1 Day, strike, spring, alarm.*
.... 125.00   150.00

☐ **Fulton,** *walnut, height 21", dial 6", spring wound, c. 1890, 8 Day, strike (E2-18).*
.... 165.00   190.00

☐ **Galena,** *walnut, height 21", dial 6", spring wound, c. 1890, 8 Day, strike (E2-18).*
.... 165.00   190.00

☐ **Gallant,** *black walnut, height 22½", dial 6", spring wound, c. 1890, 8 Day, strike (E2-18).*
.... 155.00   180.00

☐ **Globe,** *walnut, height 19", dial 6", spring wound, c. 1890, 1 Day, strike (E2-18).*
.... 155.00   180.00
☐ **As above,** *8 Day, strike.*
.... 200.00   230.00

☐ **Hampshire,** *walnut, height 23", dial 6", spring wound, c. 1890, 8 Day, strike (E2-21).*
.... 145.00   170.00
☐ **As above,** *8 Day, strike, alarm.*
.... 165.00   190.00

☐ **Herald,** *hand painted decoration, height 16½", dial 5", spring wound, c. 1890, 1 Day, strike and 8 Day, strike (E2-19).*
.... 125.00   150.00

☐ **Hudson,** *antique oak, height 21½", spring wound, c. 1890, 8 Day, strike, spring (E2-22).*
.... 125.00   150.00
☐ **As above,** *8 Day, strike, spring, alarm.*
.... 145.00   170.00

☐ **Idaho,** *walnut, height 22¼", dial 6", spring wound, c. 1890, 8 Day, strike (E2-22).*
.... 135.00   160.00
☐ **As above,** *8 Day, strike, alarm.*
.... 155.00   180.00

☐ **Illinois,** *walnut, height 22", dial 6", spring wound, c. 1890, 8 Day, strike (E2-22).*
.... 135.00   155.00
☐ **As above,** *8 Day, strike, alarm.*
.... 155.00   180.00

☐ **Ingomar,** *walnut, height 22", dial 6", spring wound, c. 1890, 8 Day, strike (E2-18).*
.... 170.00   195.00
☐ **As above,** *ash.*
.... 220.00   245.00

□ **Iowa,** *walnut, height 22¼", dial 6", spring wound, c. 1890, 8 Day, strike (E2-22).*
. . . . **135.00   160.00**
□ **As above,** *8 Day, strike, alarm.*
. . . . **155.00   180.00**

□ **Japan,** *walnut, height 19", dial 6", spring wound, c. 1890, 1 Day, strike and 8 Day, strike (E2-19).*
. . . . **115.00   140.00**

□ **Julia,** *dark wood, height 19", dial 5", spring wound, c. 1890, 8 Day, hour and ½ hour strike (E2-16).*
. . . . **160.00   185.00**

□ **"K" Assortment,** *Kenmore, oak, height 22½" x 14½", dial 6", spring wound, c. 1900, 8 Day, strike (E2-24).*
. . . . **145.00   170.00**
□ **As above,** *Kinsico.*
. . . . **145.00   170.00**
□ **As above,** *Kirkwood.*
. . . . **145.00   170.00**

□ **Kentucky,** *black walnut, with rosewood trimmings, height 22", dial 6", spring wound, c. 1890, 8 Day, strike (E2-18).*
. . . . **160.00   185.00**
□ **As above,** *ash.*
. . . . **210.00   235.00**

□ **Lima,** *black walnut, height 24", dial 6", spring wound, c. 1890, 8 Day, strike (E2-18).*
. . . . **170.00   195.00**

□ **Louise,** *dark wood or oak, height 21", dial 5", c. 1890, 8 Day hour and ½ hour strike (E2-16).*
. . . . **160.00   185.00**

☐ **Louisiana,** *walnut, height 22¾″, dial 6″, c. 1890, 8 Day, strike (E2-21).*
. . . . 135.00   160.00
☐ **As above,** *8 Day, strike, alarm.*
. . . . 155.00   180.00

☐ **Lowell,** *black walnut with rosewood trimmings, height 23½″, dial 6″, c. 1890, 8 Day, strike (E2-18).*
. . . . 155.00   180.00
☐ **As above,** *ash.*
. . . . 180.00   205.00

☐ **Madison,** *black walnut, rosewood trimmings, height 22½″, dial 6″, spring wound, c. 1890, 8 Day, strike (E2-18).*
. . . . 165.00   190.00
☐ **As above,** *ash.*
. . . . 185.00   210.00

☐ **Maryland,** *walnut, height 23″, dial 6″, spring wound, c. 1890, 8 Day, strike (E2-21).*
. . . . 135.00   160.00
☐ **As above,** *8 Day, strike, alarm.*
. . . . 155.00   180.00

☐ **Metropolis,** *walnut, height 24″, dial 6″, spring wound, c. 1890, 8 Day, gong, strike (E2-22).*
. . . . 165.00   190.00
☐ **As above,** *8 Day, strike, alarm.*
. . . . 180.00   210.00

☐ **Michigan,** *walnut, height 24″, dial 6″, spring wound, c. 1890, 8 Day, gong, strike (E2-22).*
. . . . 165.00   190.00
☐ **As above,** *8 Day, strike, alarm.*
. . . . 180.00   210.00

☐ **Mobile,** *walnut, height 20″, dial 6″, spring wound, c. 1890, 8 Day, strike (E2-19).*
. . . . 170.00   195.00
☐ **As above,** *ash.*
. . . . 200.00   225.00

☐ **Mosel,** *walnut, height 23″, dial 6″, spring wound, c. 1891, 1 Day, strike (E2-21).*
. . . . 105.00   130.00
☐ **As above,** *1 Day, strike, alarm.*
. . . . 125.00   150.00

☐ **Oder,** *walnut, height 19″, dial 6″, spring wound, c. 1890, 1 Day, strike (E2-19).*
. . . . 110.00   135.00

☐ **Oder,** *walnut, height 19″, dial 6″, spring wound, c. 1891, 1 Day, strike, spring (E2-21).*
. . . . 105.00   130.00
☐ **As above,** *1 Day, strike, spring, alarm.*
. . . . 125.00   150.00

☐ **Ohio,** *walnut, height 22″, dial 6″, spring wound, c. 1890, 8 Day, strike (E2-21).*
. . . . 135.00   160.00
☐ **As above,** *8 Day, strike, alarm.*
. . . . 155.00   180.00

☐ **Oregon,** *walnut, height 19″, dial 6″, spring wound, c. 1890, 1 Day, strike (E2-19).*
. . . . 110.00   135.00

☐ **Pauline,** *dark wood or oak, height 22", dial 5", spring wound, c. 1890, 8 Day, hour and ½ hour strike (E2-17).*
.... **160.00   185.00**

☐ **Peru,** *walnut, height 21¼", dial 6", spring wound, c. 1890, 8 Day, strike (E2-19).*
.... **160.00   185.00**

☐ **Plebeian,** *dark wood or oak, height 20½", dial 6", spring wound, c. 1890, 8 Day, hour and ½ hour strike (E2-17).*
.... **140.00   165.00**

☐ **Post,** *walnut, height 20", dial 6", spring wound, c. 1890, 1 Day, strike (E2-18).*
.... **155.00   180.00**

☐ **Primrose,** *dark wood or oak, height 16", dial 4", spring wound, c. 1890, 8 Day, strike (E2-17).*
.... **155.00   180.00**

☐ **Quality,** *dark wood or oak, height 17", dial 5", spring wound, c. 1890, 8 Day, hour and ½ hour strike (E2-17).*
.... **155.00   180.00**

☐ **Quebec,** *antique oak, height 21¼", spring wound, c. 1890, 8 Day, strike, spring (E2-22).*
.... **145.00   170.00**
☐ **As above,** *8 Day, strike, spring, alarm.*
.... **165.00   190.00**

☐ **Ranger,** *walnut, height 20", dial 5", spring wound, c. 1890, 8 Day, strike (E2-19).*
.... **170.00   195.00**

☐ **Ringgold,** *dark wood or oak, height 24¾", dial 6", spring wound, c. 1890, 8 Day, strike (E2-17).*
.... **155.00   180.00**

☐ **Steel,** *bronze ornaments, height 16½", dial 6", spring wound, c. 1890, 1 Day, strike (E2-19).*
.... **110.00   135.00**
☐ **As above,** *8 Day, strike.*
.... **140.00   165.00**

☐ **Sun,** *hand painted decoration, height 16", dial 6", spring wound, c. 1890, 1 Day, strike and 8 Day, strike (E2-19).*
.... **130.00   155.00**

☐ **Sydney,** *ash with black trimmings, height 22", dial 6", spring wound, c. 1890, 8 Day, strike (E2-19).*
.... **165.00   190.00**

☐ **Tantivy,** *walnut, height 23", dial 6", spring wound, c. 1890, 8 Day, strike (E2-19).*
.... **170.00   195.00**

☐ **Tribune,** *hand painted decoration, height 18", dial 6", spring wound, c. 1890, 1 Day, strike (E2-18).*
.... **110.00   135.00**
☐ **As above,** *8 Day, strike.*
.... **165.00   190.00**

☐ **Umbria,** *walnut, height 22", dial 6", spring wound, c. 1891, 1 Day, strike (E2-21).*
.... 105.00   130.00
☐ **As above,** *1 Day, strike, alarm.*
.... 125.00   150.00

☐ **Werra,** *walnut, height 20", dial 5", spring wound, c. 1891, 1 Day, strike, spring (E2-21).*
.... 105.00   130.00
☐ **As above,** *1 Day, strike, spring, alarm.*
.... 125.00   150.00

EBONY

☐ **Greek,** *walnut, ebonized case, height 17", dial 5", spring wound, c. 1900, 1 Day, strike, spring (E2-24).*
.... 165.00   190.00
☐ **As above,** *1 Day, strike, spring.*
.... 210.00   240.00

HANGING

☐ **Carlos No.1,** *oak and dark wood, height 24½", dial 6", spring wound, c. 1910, 8 Day, strike (E2-41).*
.... 375.00   425.00
☐ **As above,** *No.2.*
.... 375.00   425.00
☐ **As above,** *No.3.*
.... 375.00   425.00
☐ **As above,** *No.4.*
.... 375.00   425.00
☐ **As above,** *No.5.*
.... 375.00   425.00
☐ **As above,** *No.6.*
.... 375.00   425.00

☐ **Gomez,** *oak, , height 24", dial 6½", spring wound, c. 1910, 8 Day, strike (E2-41).*
.... 310.00   350.00
☐ **As above,** *mahogany.*
.... 335.00   375.00
☐ **As above,** *walnut.*
.... 360.00   400.00

□ **Habana,** *dark wood or oak, height 25", dial 6", spring wound, c. 1890, 8 Day, hour and ½ hour strike (E2-16).*
. . . . **230.00** **260.00**

□ **Hanging Assortment No.3-A,** *walnut, height 26", dial 6", spring wound, c. 1900, 8 Day, hour and ½ hour strike (E2-23).*
. . . . **210.00** **240.00**
□ **As above,** *No.3-B.*
. . . . **210.00** **240.00**
□ **As above,** *No.3-C.*
. . . . **210.00** **240.00**
□ **As above,** *No.3-D.*
. . . . **210.00** **240.00**
□ **As above,** *No.3-E.*
. . . . **210.00** **240.00**
□ **As above,** *No.3-F.*
. . . . **210.00** **240.00**

□ **Hanging Assortment No.4,** *Cardenas, walnut, height 26", dial 6", spring wound, c. 1900, 8 Day, strike (E2-24).*
. . . . **260.00** **290.00**
□ **As above,** *Canada.*
. . . . **260.00** **290.00**
□ **As above,** *Colon.*
. . . . **260.00** **290.00**
□ **As above,** *Chile.*
. . . . **260.00** **290.00**
□ **As above,** *Caldera.*
. . . . **260.00** **290.00**
□ **As above,** *Cuba.*
. . . . **260.00** **290.00**

□ **Hanging Assortment No.4,** *Cardenas, oak, height 26", dial 6", spring wound, c. 1900, 8 Day, strike (E2-24).*
. . . . **210.00** **240.00**
□ **As above,** *Canada.*
. . . . **210.00** **240.00**
□ **As above,** *Colon.*
. . . . **210.00** **240.00**
□ **As above,** *Chile.*
. . . . **210.00** **240.00**
□ **As above,** *Caldera.*
. . . . **210.00** **240.00**
□ **As above,** *Cuba.*
. . . . **210.00** **240.00**

☐ **Matanzas,** *oak, height 27½", dial 6", spring wound, c. 1898, 8 Day, alarm. (E1-155).*
. . . . 195.00   225.00

☐ **Mexico,** *walnut, height 27¼", dial 6", spring wound, c. 1898, 8 Day, alarm (E1-155).*
. . . . 245.00   275.00

☐ **Trinidad,** *walnut, height 27¼", dial 6", spring, c. 1898, 8 Day, alarm (E1-155).*
. . . . 195.00   225.00

MANTEL

☐ **Albion Oak,** *height 24", dial 6", spring wound, c. 1898, 8 Day, strike (E1-155).*
. . . . 115.00   140.00

☐ **Chicago Calendar,** *oak, barometer and thermometer, height 23", dial 6", spring wound, c. 1898, 8 Day, strike (E1-155).*
. . . . 175.00   200.00

☐ **Trinidad,** *dark wood or oak, height 27½", dial 6", spring wound, c. 1890, 8 Day, strike (E2-16).*
. . . . 230.00   260.00

☐ **Topaz Calendar,** *oak, barometer and thermometer, height 23", dial 6", spring wound, c. 1898, 8 Day, strike (E1-155).*
. . . . 175.00   200.00

MIRROR SIDES

□ **Reflector,** *ebony or mahogany, height 35", dial 6", spring wound, c. 1910, 8 Day, strike (E2-40).*
.... 550.00   625.00

□ **Triumph,** *dark wood or oak, silver cupid, plate glass mirrors, bronze ornaments, height 24½", dial 6", spring wound, c. 1900, 8 Day (E2-25).*
.... 285.00   325.00

□ **Triumph,** *walnut, silver cupids, plate glass mirrors, bronze ornaments, height 24½", dial 6", spring wound, c. 1890, 8 Day gong, strike (E2-22).*
.... 335.00   375.00

□ **As above,** *8 Day, strike, alarm.*
.... 355.00   395.00

□ **Windsor,** *dark wood or oak, silver cupids, plate glass mirrors, bronze ornaments, height 21½", dial 5", spring wound, c. 1900, 8 Day, strike (E2-25).*
.... 250.00   280.00

TEAR DROP

□ **King,** *dark wood or oak, height 24", dial 6", spring wound, c. 1900, 8 Day, strike (E2-25).*
.... 250.00   280.00

□ **King,** *walnut, height 24", dial 6", spring, c. 1890, 8 Day, strike, bell (E2-21).*
.... 240.00   260.00

□ **As above,** *8 Day, strike, alarm, bell.*
.... 260.00   280.00

□ **As above,** *8 Day, strike, gong.*
.... 240.00   260.00

□ **As above,** *8 Day, strike, alarm, gong.*
.... 260.00   280.00

□ **Parisian,** *dark wood or oak, height 23½", dial 6", spring wound, c. 1900, 8 Day, strike (E2-25).*
.... 260.00   280.00

**MANTEL
BLACK IRON**

☐ **Angelo,** *12½" x 14", dial 5",
spring, c. 1890, 8 Day, strike
(E2-26).*
. . . . **115.00   140.00**

☐ **Cardiff,** *black Japanned, gilt
engraved, 9½" x 11½", dial 5",
spring, c. 1898, 8 Day, strike
(E1-157).*
. . . . **60.00   75.00**

☐ **Parisian,** *walnut, height 24", dial
6", spring wound, c. 1890, 8 Day,
strike, bell (E2-21).*
. . . . **260.00   280.00**

☐ **As above,** *8 Day, strike, alarm,
bell.*
. . . . **280.00   300.00**

☐ **As above,** *8 Day, strike, gong.*
. . . . **260.00   280.00**

☐ **As above,** *8 Day, strike, alarm,
gong.*
. . . . **280.00   300.00**

☐ **Remus,** *dark wood or oak, height
23", dial 5", spring wound,
c. 1890, 8 Day, hour and ½ hour
strike (E2-16).*
. . . . **190.00   220.00**

☐ **Egypt,** *10¾" x 16", dial 4½",
spring, c. 1890, 8 Day, strike
(E2-26).*
. . . . **210.00   240.00**

☐ **Euclid, With Figure No.1042,** *bust included, 16" x 10", dial 5", spring, c. 1890, 8 Day, strike (E2-26).*

.... **165.00   190.00**

☐ **Nero,** *12¾" x 10¾", dial 4½", spring, c. 1890, 8 Day, strike (E2-26).*

.... **175.00   200.00**

☐ **Grenada,** *black Japanned with bronze ornaments, 8½" x 14¾", dial 5", spring, c. 1898, 8 Day, strike (E1-157).*

.... **60.00   75.00**

☐ **Nile,** *urn included, 18" x 13¼", dial 4½", spring, c. 1890, 8 Day, strike (E2-26).*

.... **150.00   175.00**

☐ **Parma, Figure No. 1069,** *11" x 22", dial 4½", spring, c. 1890, 8 Day, strike (E2-26).*

.... **245.00   275.00**

☐ **Pompeii,** *10¾" x 15", dial 4½",
spring, c. 1890, 8 Day, strike
(E2-26).*
.... 175.00   200.00

☐ **Rembrandt,** *20" x 11", dial 5",
spring, c. 1890, 8 Day, strike
(E2-26).*
.... 150.00   175.00

☐ **Saint Clair,** *11¼" x 10½", dial
4½", spring, c. 1890, 8 Day,
strike (E2-26).*
.... 180.00   210.00

☐ **Rosalind,** *12¼" x 15¼", dial 5",
spring, c. 1890, 8 Day, strike
(E2-26).*
.... 220.00   250.00

☐ **Timbrell,** *13" x 11", dial 4½",
spring, c. 1890, 8 Day, strike
(E2-26).*
.... 135.00   160.00

☐ **Unique,** *10½" x 9½", dial 5", spring, c. 1890, 8 Day, strike (E2-26).*
.... 105.00   125.00

☐ **Vendome,** *black Japanned, gilt ornaments, French rococo sash, cream porcelain dial, 11" x 12¾", dial 4⅛", spring, c. 1898 (E1-157).*
.... 60.00   75.00

BLACK WOOD

☐ **Boston Extra,** *enameled iron, bronze columns, French sash, beveled glass, porcelain dial, 11" x 15", dial 4", spring, c. 1917, 8 Day, strike (E1-178).*
.... 60.00   75.00

☐ **Savoy,** *black Japanned, oak, gilt trimmings, 9½" x 9", dial 5", spring, c. 1898, 8 Day, strike (E1-157).*
.... 65.00   85.00
☐ **As above,** *mahogany.*
.... 80.00   110.00

BRONZE

☐ **Emporia,** *height 18", base 11", spring, c. 1891, 8 Day, strike (E2-32).*
.... 440.00   500.00

☐ **Eureka,** *black enameled, silver finish, gilt dial, height 9", base 20", spring, c. 1891, 8 Day, strike (E2-32).*
.... 900.00   1000.00

☐ **Franconia,** *height 18", spring, c. 1891, 8 Day, strike (E2-32).*
.... 400.00   450.00

☐ **Lydia,** *height 19½", spring, c. 1891, 8 Day, strike (E2-32).*
.... 1150.00   1350.00

☐ **Senator,** *antique oak and brass, height 22", base 19½", spring, c. 1891, 8 Day, strike (E2-32).*
.... 1250.00   1500.00

MAGOHANY

☐ **Fairfax,** *mahogany case, fancy panels, 10⅞" x 15¼", spring, c. 1917, 8 Day, strike (E1-178).*
.... 55.00   70.00

☐ **Fairmont,** *mahogany, 10¾" x 15¾", spring, c. 1917, 8 Day, strike (E1-178).*
.... 55.00   70.00

☐ **Fenton,** *mahogany, bronze columns, 10¼" x 16", dial 4", spring, c. 1917, 8 Day, strike (E1-178).*
.... 55.00   70.00

☐ **Flanders,** *mahogany, bronze columns, 12¾" x 14", dial 4", spring, c. 1917, 8 Day, strike (E1-178).*
.... 55.00   70.00

☐ **Fowler,** *mahogany, bronze columns, 12⅝" x 16", dial 4", spring, c. 1917, 8 Day, strike (E1-178).*
.... 55.00   70.00

☐ **Fraser,** *mahogany, bronze columns, 12¼" x 13¼", dial 4", spring, c. 1917 (E1-178).*
.... 55.00   70.00

...E

☐ **Dorothy,** *black marble, 9½" x 13¾", porcelain dial 5", spring, c. 1898, 8 Day, strike (E1-157).* **115.00   140.00**

☐ **El Limon,** *black marble, 15½" x 14¼", porcelain dial 5", spring, c. 1898, 8 Day, strike (E1-157).* **105.00   130.00**

☐ **El Tule,** *black marble, 12" x 11¼", porcelain dial 5", spring, c. 1898, 8 Day, strike (E1-157).* **105.00   125.00**

☐ **Pinafore,** *black marble, 9½" x 14½", porcelain dial 5", spring, c. 1898, 8 Day, strike (E1-157).* **125.00   150.00**

METAL REGENCY

☐ **Amphion,** *rich gold, decorated porcelain panels, French rococo sash, beveled glass, porcelain dial 4¼", 15" x 10", spring, c. 1890, 8 Day, strike (E1-116).* **335.00   375.00**

☐ **Franconia,** *silver or Barbedienne, French rococo sash, beveled glass, porcelain visible escapement dial, 18" x 11", spring, c. 1890, 8 Day, strike (E1-115).* **285.00   325.00**

☐ **Lucania,** *gold bronze, French rococo sash, beveled glass, porcelain visible escapement dial, 13¾" x 7½", spring, c. 1890, 8 Day, strike (E1-115).* **310.00   350.00**

☐ **Orienta,** *rich gold, French rococo sash, beveled glass, porcelain visible escapement dial, 16¾" x 9¾", spring, c. 1890, 8 Day, strike (E1-116).*
.... 285.00   325.00

☐ **Peoria,** *silver or Barbedienne, French rococo sash, beveled glass, porcelain visible escapement dial, 19½" x 11½", spring, c. 1890, 8 Day, strike (E1-115).*
.... 360.00   400.00

☐ **Rococo,** *Syrian bronze, French rococo sash, beveled glass, porcelain visible escapement dial, 15½" x 11", dial 5½", spring, c. 1890, 8 Day, strike (E1-115).*
.... 335.00   375.00

☐ **Versailles,** *rich gold, decorated porcelain panel, French rococo sash, beveled glass, porcelain, 15" x 8", dial 4¼", spring, c. 1890, 8 Day, strike (E1-116).*
.... 310.00   350.00

ONYX

☐ **Winthrop,** *Brazilian green onyx case, bronze trimmings, rococo sash, cream porcelain dial 5", 11¼" x 11", spring, c. 1898, 8 Day, strike (E1-157).*
.... 115.00   140.00

PLUSH

☐ **Warren,** *Brazilian green onyx case, bronze trimmings, rococo sash, cream porcelain dial 5", 12" x 13", spring, c. 1898, 8 Day, strike (E1-157).*
.... 195.00   225.00

☐ **Florentine No.1,** *height 15½", dial 5½", spring, c. 1890, 8 Day (E2-31).*
.... 285.00   325.00

☐ **Florentine No.2,** *height 14", dial 5½", spring, c. 1890, 8 Day (E2-31).*
. . . . 190.00   220.00

☐ **Florentine No.3,** *with or without figure, height 13½", dial 5½", spring, c. 1890, 8 Day (E2-31).*
. . . . 190.00   220.00

☐ **Florentine No.4,** *silver or brass antique finish, height 15", dial 5½", spring, c. 1890, 8 Day (E2-31).*
. . . . 250.00   280.00

☐ **Florentine No.5,** *silver or brass antique finish, height 14", dial 4½", spring, c. 1890, 8 Day (E2-31).*
. . . . 190.00   220.00

☐ **Florentine No.6,** *height 16", dial 6¾", spring, c. 1890, 8 Day (E2-31).*
. . . . 210.00   240.00

NOVELTY

ANIMATED

☐ **Automatic Swing No.2,** *bronze and nickel finish, height 8", dial 4", spring, c. 1896, 1 Day (E2-14).*
. . . . 400.00   475.00

□ **Argyle,** *gold finish, height 8¾",
dial 2", spring, c. 1910, 8 Day
(E2-33).*
. . . . 90.00   110.00

ART NOUVEAU

□ **Alameda,** *gold finish, height
8¼", dial 2", spring, c. 1910,
8 Day (E2-33).*
. . . . 95.00   115.00

□ **Arverne,** *gold finish, height 9",
dial 2", spring, c. 1910, 8 Day
(E2-33).*
. . . . 95.00   115.00

□ **Cherry,** *gold finish, height 6½",
dial 2", spring, c. 1910, 1 Day
(E2-33).*
. . . . 50.00   65.00
□ **As above,** *8 Day.*
. . . . 90.00   110.00

□ **Chic,** *gold finish, height 8¾",
dial 2", spring, c. 1910, 1 Day
(E2-33).*
. . . . 50.00   65.00
□ **As above,** *8 Day.*
. . . . 90.00   110.00

□ **Cora,** *mahogany or oak with gilt
trimmings, height 7⅛", fancy dial
2", spring, c. 1898, 1 Day
(E1-161).*
. . . . 50.00   65.00

□ **Flora,** *gilt center, height 7⅜",
cream porcelain dial 2", spring,
c. 1898, 1 Day (E1-161).*
. . . . 65.00   85.00

□ **Harmony,** *gold finish, height 9",
dial 2", spring, c. 1910, 1 Day
(E2-33).*
. . . . **60.00   75.00**

□ **As above,** *8 Day.*
. . . . **105.00   125.00**

□ **Norwood,** *antique silver, height
5¾", fancy dial 2", spring,
c. 1898, 1 Day (E1-161).*
. . . . **30.00   40.00**

□ **Olga,** *gold finish, height 8¾",
dial 2", spring, c. 1910, 1 Day
(E2-33).*
. . . . **50.00   65.00**

□ **As above,** *8 Day.*
. . . . **90.00   110.00**

BISQUE

□ **Contemplation,** *bisque, height
5½", dial 2", spring, c. 1890,
1 Day (E2-28).*
. . . . **75.00   90.00**

□ **Friends,** *bisque, height 5½", dial
2", spring, c. 1890, 1 Day (E2-28).*
. . . . **80.00   100.00**

□ **Poodle,** *bisque, height 6", dial
2", spring, c. 1890, 1 Day (E2-28).*
. . . . **70.00   90.00**

□ **Restful,** *bisque, height 5½", dial
2", spring, c. 1890, 1 Day (E2-28).*
. . . . **70.00   90.00**

□ **Wildlife,** *bisque, height 7", dial
2", spring, c. 1890, 1 Day (E2-28).*
. . . . **70.00   90.00**

□ **Worker,** *bisque, height 7", dial
2", spring, c. 1890, 1 Day (E2-28).*
. . . . **100.00   120.00**

BRASS

☐ **Armour No.25,** *brass or steel finish, height 11", dial 2", spring, c. 1890, 1 Day (E2-30).*
. . . . **130.00**   **155.00**

☐ **Easel, No.1,** *height 11", dial 2", spring, c. 1890, 1 Day (E2-27).*
. . . . **80.00**   **100.00**
☐ **As above,** *No.2, painted or plain.*
. . . . **80.00**   **100.00**

☐ **As above,** *No.3.*
. . . . **80.00**   **100.00**

☐ **As above,** *No.5.*
. . . . **80.00**   **100.00**

☐ **Empire,** *antique brass or rich gold, height 9½", fancy dial 1½", spring, c. 1898, 1 Day (E1-158).*

.... **60.00**   **75.00**

☐ **Etruscan,** *brass or silver, height 14½", spring, c. 1890, 8 Day (E2-29).*

.... **360.00**   **400.00**

☐ **Renaissance,** *brass, silver or brass antique, c. 1890, 8 Day, strike (E2-29).*

.... **465.00**   **525.00**

CHINA

☐ **Pilgrim,** *height 7", dial 2", spring, c. 1890, 1 Day (E2-30).*

.... **40.00**   **55.00**

FANCY

☐ **Baby,** *rich burnished silver or gold, height 5¼", fancy dial 1½", spring, c. 1898, 1 Day (E1-161).*

.... **60.00**   **85.00**

☐ **Snap,** *bronze finish, height 11", dial 4", spring, c. 1883, 8 Day (E2-9).*

.... **65.00**   **80.00**

☐ **Twilight,** *rich burnished silver or gold, height 4¾", fancy dial 1¹⁄₁₆", spring, c. 1898, 1 Day (E1-161).*

.... **40.00**   **55.00**

GILT

☐ **Amigos,** *gold finish, jeweled, height 5¾", dial 2", spring, c. 1910, 1 Day (E2-33).*
.... **70.00 85.00**

☐ **Cantor,** *gold finish, height 9¼", dial 2", spring, c. 1910, 1 Day (E2-33).*
.... **70.00 90.00**

☐ **Ensign,** *rich burnished silver or gold, height 4¼", fancy dial 1½", spring, c. 1898, 1 Day (E1-161).*
.... **40.00 50.00**

☐ **Eveline,** *antique brass, rich gold, cream porcelain, gilt center, height 8¼", dial 2", spring, c. 1898, 1 Day (E1-161).*
.... **40.00 55.00**

☐ **Gladys,** *rich burnished silver or gold, height 5½", fancy dial 2", spring, c. 1898, 1 Day (E1-161).*
.... **70.00 85.00**

☐ **La Rose,** *rich burnished gold, height 6¼", fancy dial 1½", spring, c. 1898, 1 Day (E1-161).*
.... **45.00 60.00**

☐ **La Belle,** *gold finish, height 6¼", dial 2", spring, c. 1910, 1 Day (E2-33).*
.... **40.00 55.00**

☐ **Modern,** *gold finish, height 4¼", dial 2", spring, c. 1910, 1 Day (E2-33).*
.... **35.00 45.00**
☐ **As above,** *8 Day.*
.... **60.00 75.00**

☐ **Orchestra,** *rich burnished gold, height 4¼", fancy dial 2", spring, c. 1898, 1 Day (E1-161).*
.... **30.00 40.00**

☐ **Pepa,** *mirror, gold finish, height 8", dial 2", spring, c.1910, 8 Day (E2-33).*
.... **105.00 125.00**

☐ **Phyllis,** *silver and gold plate, gilt trimmings, cream porcelain dial, gilt centers, height 7", fancy dial 2", spring, c. 1898, 1 Day (E1-161).*
.... **45.00 60.00**

☐ **Play,** *gold finish, height 9¼",
dial 2", spring, c. 1910, 1 Day
(E2-33).*
.... 60.00   75.00

☐ **As above,** *8 Day.*
.... 105.00   125.00

☐ **Republic,** *rich burnished silver or
gold, height 8¼", fancy dial 2",
spring, c. 1898, 1 Day (E1-161).*
.... 55.00   70.00

☐ **Rita,** *gold finish, height 7", dial
2", spring, c. 1910, 8 Day (E2-33).*
.... 95.00   115.00

IRON

☐ **Barrow,** *height 4", dial 2, spring,
c. 1890, 1 Day (E2-30).*
.... 40.00   50.00

☐ **Beating Time,** *height 5", dial 2",
spring, c. 1890, 1 Day (E2-30).*
.... 55.00   70.00

☐ **Cadet,** *bronze, pendulum, height
4½", dial 2", spring, c. 1890,
1 Day (E2-30).*
.... 50.00   65.00

☐ **Carpenter,** *silver or gold plate,
height 7¼", dial 2", spring,
c. 1890, 1 Day (E2-31).*
.... 40.00   55.00

☐ **Chef,** *Japanese bronze or silver,
height 5½", fancy metal dial
1½", spring, c. 1898, 1 Day
(E1-158).*
.... 45.00   60.00

☐ **Cherub,** *silver or bronze finish,
height 4½", dial 2", spring,
c. 1890, 1 Day (E2-30).*
.... 45.00   60.00

☐ **Cupid Wreath,** *silver or bronze, height 5", dial 2", spring, c. 1890, 1 Day (E2-30).*
. . . . **60.00   75.00**

☐ **Dawn,** *old silver and gilt finish, c. 1890, 8 Day (E2-22).*
. . . . **60.00   75.00**

☐ **Duet,** *height 5½", dial 2", spring, c. 1890, 1 Day (E2-30).*
. . . . **45.00   60.00**

☐ **Engine,** *gilt and old silver finish, height 8", spring, c. 1891, 1 Day (E2-32).*
. . . . **60.00   75.00**

☐ **Eva,** *gold finish, beveled mirror, height 9¼", dial 2", spring, c.1910, 1 Day (E2-34).*
. . . . **60.00   85.00**
☐ **As above,** *8 Day.*
. . . . **105.00   125.00**

☐ **Fan,** *finished in silver and old silver, height 7¾", spring, c. 1891, 1 Day (E2-32).*
. . . . **60.00   85.00**

☐ **Fly,** *nickel, pendulum, height 4½", dial 2", spring, c. 1890, 1 Day (E2-30).*
. . . . **50.00   65.00**

☐ **Good Luck No.2,** *silver or gold plate, height 4½", dial 2", spring, c. 1890, 1 Day (E2-31).*
. . . . **45.00   60.00**

☐ **Good Luck No.3,** *silver or gold plate, height 4¾", dial 2", spring, c. 1890, 1 Day (E2-31).*
. . . . **40.00   50.00**

☐ **Hummingbird,** *silver or gold plate, height 7½", dial 2", spring, c. 1890, 1 Day (E2-31).*
. . . . **55.00   70.00**

☐ **Lock,** *height 6", dial 2", spring, c. 1891, 1 Day (E2-32).*
. . . . **60.00   75.00**

☐ **Navy,** *gilt finish, silver or old silver, height 12½", dial 2½", spring, c. 1891, 8 Day (E2-32).*
. . . . **80.00   100.00**

☐ **Navy,** *gold finish, height 12½", dial 2", spring, c. 1910, 1 Day (E2-34).*
. . . . **85.00   105.00**

□ **Novelty, No.44,** *height 7¾",* dial 2", spring, c. 1890, 1 Day (E2-30). **60.00** **75.00**

□ **Oriental Fan,** *silver or gold plate, height 6½",* dial 2", spring, c. 1890, 1 Day (E2-31). **55.00** **70.00**

□ **Pearl,** *bronze finish, dial 4",* spring, c. 1883, 1 Day (E2-9). **40.00** **50.00**

□ **Photo,** *gold finish, height 12½",* dial 2", spring, c. 1910, 8 Day (E2-34). **115.00** **140.00**

□ **Saw,** *height 4½",* dial 2", spring, c. 1890, 1 Day (E2-30). **40.00** **50.00**

□ **Ship,** *old silver finish, height 14½",* dial 3", spring, c. 1891, 1 Day (E2-32). **70.00** **90.00**

□ **Temple,** *old silver, height 9¾",* c. 1891, 8 Day (E2-32). **95.00** **115.00**

□ **Trotter,** *old silver, height 6",* dial 2½", spring, c. 1891, 8 Day (E2-32). **60.00** **75.00**

NIGHT LIGHT

□ **Aladdin Night Light,** *bronze and nickel finish, extra, dial 4",* spring, battery, c. 1883, 1 Day (E2-9). **120.00** **145.00**

PLUSH

□ **Brass Antique or Silver Antique,** *diameter 15", spring, c. 1890, 8 Day (E2-29).*
.... **130.00** **155.00**

□ **Pluribus,** *blue or red plush, bronze, silver and gilt finish, 18½" x 15", spring, c. 1890, 8 Day (E2-29).*
.... **170.00** **195.00**

□ **Richelieu,** *brass with plush, 16" x 18½", spring, c. 1890, 8 Day (E2-29).*
.... **170.00** **195.00**

□ **Round Plush Plaque,** *diameter 16", spring, c. 1890, 8 Day (E2-29).*
.... **150.00** **175.00**

□ **Square Plush Plaque,** *16" square, spring, c. 1890, 8 Day (E2-29).*
.... **155.00** **180.00**

WALL

□ **What-Not, No.1,** *wood, height 26", dial 8", spring, c. 1896, 8 Day (E2-14).*
.... **450.00** **525.00**

OFFICE INKS

☐ **Banker's Inkstand,** *bronze finish,
height 12", dial 4", spring,
c. 1883, 1 Day, calendar (E2-8).*
.... 285.00   325.00

☐ **Butterfly Ink,** *silver with nickel
finish, colored enameled bottles
and thermometer, height 10½",
dial 4", spring, c. 1890, 1 Day,
calendar (E2-27).*
.... 335.00   375.00

☐ **Bee Ink,** *solid brass, height 7¼",
dial 2½", spring, c. 1890, 8 Day
(E2-22).*
.... 60.00   80.00

☐ **Boudoir Ink,** *gold, height 6½",
dial 2", spring, c. 1910, 1 Day
(E2-34).*
.... 60.00   80.00

☐ **As above,** *8 Day.*
.... 100.00   120.00

☐ **Ladies' Ink,** *cut glass, blue or
ruby, height 8", dial 2", spring,
c. 1890, 1 Day (E2-27).*
.... 150.00   175.00

□ **Parlor Ink, No.1,** *solid brass, bee movement, height 9", dial 2", spring, c. 1890, 1 Day, perpetual calendar (E2-27).*
.... 230.00   260.00

□ **Marguerite,** *black enameled case, hand painted decorations, clock and mirror, height 13", dial 4", c. 1883, 1 Day, alarm (E2-8).*
.... 135.00   160.00

□ **Parlor Ink, No.3,** *brass, height 11", dial 4", spring, c. 1890, 1 Day, calendar (E2-27).*
.... 310.00   350.00

□ **Office Inkstand,** *bronze finish, height 13", dial 4", spring, c. 1883, 1 Day, calendar (E2-8).*
.... 270.00   300.00

□ **Studio Ink,** *gold, height 6", dial 2", spring, c. 1910, 1 Day (E2-34).*
.... 70.00   85.00
□ **As above,** *8 Day.*
.... 105.00   125.00

PORCELAIN CRYSTAL REGULATORS

☐ **Porcelain Regulator No.1,** *visible escapement, porcelain dial, white beveled plate glass front, back and sides, Bonn decorated top and bases, 17½" x 9", dial 4", spring, c. 1910, 8 Day, strike (E1-136).*
.... 1250.00   1550.00

☐ **Porcelain Regulator No.2,** *visible escapement, porcelain dial, white beveled plate glass front, back and sides, Bonn decorated top and bases, 17½" x 9¼", dial 4", spring, c. 1910, 8 Day, strike (E1-136).*
.... 1175.00   1425.00

☐ **Porcelain Regulator No.3,** *visible escapement, porcelain dial, white beveled plate glass front, back and sides, Bonn decorated*

top and base, 18¼" x 9¼", dial 4", spring, c. 1910, 8 Day, strike (E1-136).
.... 1250.00   1500.00

☐ **Porcelain Regulator No.4,** *visible escapement, porcelain dial, white beveled plate glass front, back and sides, Bonn decorated top and base, 17¾" x 9½", dial 4", spring, c. 1910, 8 Day, strike (E1-136).*
.... 1150.00   1400.00

☐ **Porcelain Regulator No.5,** *visible escapement, porcelain dial, white beveled plate glass front, back and sides, Bonn decorated top and base, 17½" x 8½", dial 4", spring, c. 1910, 8 Day, strike (E1-136).*
.... 1160.00   1410.00

☐ **Porcelain Regulator No.6,** *visible escapement, porcelain dial, white beveled plate glass front, back and sides, Bonn decorated top and base, 17½ " x 9", dial 4", spring, c. 1910, 8 Day, strike (E1-136).*
.... **1185.00   1435.00**

REGULATOR
ASTRONOMICAL

☐ **Regulator No.9,** *wood, 96" x 33", dial 16", c. 1910, 8 Day, weight (E2-42).*
.... **10000.00 12000.00**

☐ **Regulator No.8,** *wood, 105" x 36", dial 16", c. 1910, 8 Day, weight (E2-42).*
.... **8000.00   9000.00**

FIGURE EIGHT

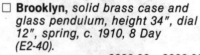

☐ **Brooklyn,** *solid brass case and glass pendulum, height 34", dial 12", spring, c. 1910, 8 Day (E2-40).*
.... 2800.00   3000.00
☐ **As above,** *8 Day, strike.*
.... 2900.00   3100.00

☐ **Hiogo,** *black enamel finish, height 28", dial 10", spring, c. 1890, 8 Day (E2-39).*
.... 325.00   350.00
☐ **As above,** *8 Day, strike.*
.... 350.00   375.00

☐ **Kobe,** *walnut, height 21½", dial 10", spring, c. 1890, 8 Day (E2-39).*
.... 325.00   350.00
☐ **As above,** *8 Day, strike.*
.... 350.00   375.00

☐ **Kobe,** *oak, height 21½", dial 10", spring, c. 1890, 8 Day (E2-39).*
.... 275.00   300.00
☐ **As above,** *8 Day, strike.*
.... 300.00   325.00

OCTAGON TOP, LONG DROP

☐ **Office Regulator,** *ash, duplex movement, retaining power, height 32", dial 12", spring, c. 1890, 8 Day (E2-39).*
.... 300.00   330.00
☐ **As above,** *8 Day, strike.*
.... 330.00   355.00
☐ **As above,** *8 Day, calendar.*
.... 355.00   380.00
☐ **As above,** *8 Day, strike, calendar.*
.... 380.00   405.00

☐ **Office Regulator,** *black walnut, duplex movement, retaining power, height 32", dial 12", spring, c. 1890, 8 Day (E2-39).*
.... 270.00   300.00
☐ **As above,** *8 Day, strike.*
.... 285.00   325.00
☐ **As above,** *8 Day, calendar.*
.... 310.00   350.00
☐ **As above,** *8 Day, strike, calendar.*
.... 335.00   375.00

☐ **Regulator "A",** *black walnut, height 32", dial 12", spring, c. 1890, 8 Day (E2-39).*
.... 325.00   350.00
☐ **As above,** *8 Day, strike.*
.... 350.00   375.00
☐ **As above,** *8 Day, calendar.*
.... 375.00   400.00
☐ **As above,** *8 Day, strike, calendar.*
.... 400.00   425.00

☐ **Regulator "A",** *ash, height 32", dial 12", spring, c. 1890, 8 Day (E2-39).*
.... 370.00   395.00
☐ **As above,** *8 Day, strike.*
.... 395.00   405.00
☐ **As above,** *8 Day, calendar.*
.... 405.00   435.00
☐ **As above,** *8 Day, strike, calendar.*
.... 435.00   470.00

☐ **Regulator,** *oak, height 32", dial 12", spring, c. 1890, 8 Day (E2-39).*
.... 335.00   375.00
☐ **As above,** *8 Day, strike.*
.... 360.00   400.00
☐ **As above,** *8 Day, calendar.*
.... 375.00   425.00
☐ **As above,** *8 Day, strike, calendar.*
.... 400.00   450.00

OCTAGON TOP, SHORT DROP

☐ **8″ Drop Octagon, R.C.,** oak, height 19½″, dial 12″, spring, c. 1890, 8 Day (E2-39).
.... 150.00   175.00
☐ **As above,** 8 Day, strike.
.... 175.00   200.00
☐ **As above,** 8 Day, calendar.
.... 195.00   225.00
☐ **As above,** 8 Day, strike, calendar.
.... 220.00   250.00

☐ **8″ Drop Octagon, R.C.,** rosewood veneer, height 19½″, dial 12″, spring, c. . 1890, 8 Day (E2-39).
.... 200.00   225.00
☐ **As above,** 8 Day, strike.
.... 225.00   250.00
☐ **As above,** 8 Day, calendar.
.... 245.00   275.00
☐ **As above,** 8 Day, strike, calendar.
.... 270.00   300.00

☐ **8″ Drop Octagon,** gilt rosewood veneer with gilt moulding, height 19½″, dial 12″, spring, c. 1890, 8 Day (E2-39).
.... 150.00   175.00
☐ **As above,** 8 Day, strike.
.... 175.00   200.00
☐ **As above,** 8 Day, calendar.
.... 195.00   225.00
☐ **As above,** 8 Day, strike, calendar.
.... 220.00   250.00

☐ **10″ Drop Octagon, R.C.,** oak, height 21½″, dial 12″, spring, c. 1890, 8 Day (E2-39).
.... 175.00   200.00
☐ **As above,** 8 Day, strike.
.... 195.00   225.00
☐ **As above,** 8 Day, calendar.
.... 220.00   250.00
☐ **As above,** 8 Day, strike, calendar.
.... 245.00   275.00

☐ **10″ Drop Octagon, R.C.,** rosewood veneer, height 21½″, dial 12″, spring, c. 1890, 8 Day (E2-39).
.... 225.00   250.00
☐ **As above,** 8 Day, strike.
.... 245.00   275.00

☐ **As above,** 8 Day, calendar.
.... 270.00   300.00
☐ **As above,** 8 Day, strike, calendar.
.... 295.00   325.00

☐ **10″ Drop Octagon,** gilt rosewood veneer with gilt moulding, height 21½″, dial 12″, spring, c. 1890, 8 Day (E2-39).
.... 175.00   200.00
☐ **As above,** 8 Day, strike.
.... 195.00   225.00
☐ **As above,** 8 Day, calendar.
.... 220.00   250.00
☐ **As above,** 8 Day, strike, calendar.
.... 245.00   275.00

☐ **12″ Drop Octagon, R.C.,** oak, height 24″, dial 12″, spring, c. 1890, 8 Day (E2-39).
.... 195.00   225.00
☐ **As above,** 8 Day, strike.
.... 220.00   250.00
☐ **As above,** 8 Day, calendar.
.... 245.00   275.00
☐ **As above,** 8 Day, strike, calendar.
.... 270.00   300.00

☐ **12" Drop Octagon, R.C.,** *rosewood veneer, height 24", dial 12", spring, c. 1890, 8 Day (E2-39).*
. . . . 245.00   275.00
☐ **As above,** *8 Day, strike.*
. . . . 270.00   300.00
☐ **As above,** *8 Day, calendar.*
. . . . 295.00   325.00
☐ **As above,** *8 Day, strike, calendar.*
. . . . 320.00   350.00

☐ **Office, No.2,** *walnut, height 26", dial 12", spring, c. 1900, 8 Day, strike (E2-24).*
. . . . 285.00   325.00

OPEN SWINGING

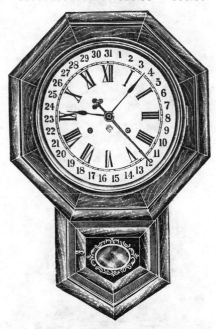

☐ **12" Drop Octagon,** *gilt rosewood veneer with gilt moulding, height 24", dial 12", spring, c. . 1890, 8 Day (E2-39).*
. . . . 195.00   225.00
☐ **As above,** *8 Day, strike.*
. . . . 220.00   250.00
☐ **As above,** *8 Day, calendar.*
. . . . 245.00   275.00
☐ **As above,** *8 Day, strike, calendar.*
. . . . 270.00   300.00

☐ **Antique Hanging,** *mahogany, oak, antique brass trimmings, gilt and silvered dial 9½", height 46½", c. 1910, 8 Day, weight, strike (E2-42).*
. . . . 4000.00   5000.00

☐ **Monarch,** *dark wood or oak, bronze ornaments, French sash, height 24½", dial 6", spring, c. 1900, 8 Day, gong (E2-25).*
. . . . 350.00   375.00
☐ **As above,** *8 Day, gong alarm.*
. . . . 360.00   385.00

☐ **Niobe,** *oak, antique brass trimmings, height 45", silvered dial 10", weight, c. 1910, 8 Day, strike (E2-40).*
. . . . 1000.00   1200.00

PARLOR SHELF
☐ **Broadway,** *dark wood or oak, height 24½", dial 6", spring, c. 1900, 8 Day, hour and ½ hour strike (E2-25).*
. . . . 310.00   350.00

☐ **Monarch,** *walnut, bronze ornaments, French sash, height 24½", dial 6", spring, c. 1890, 8 Day, gong strike (E2-22).*
. . . . 335.00   375.00
☐ **As above,** *8 Day, strike, alarm.*
. . . . 355.00   395.00

PARLOR WALL

☐ **Argentina,** *walnut, height 33",*
dial 6½", spring, c. 1910, 8 Day,
strike (E2-41).
.... 460.00   500.00
☐ **As above,** *mahogany.*
.... 435.00   475.00
☐ **As above,** *oak.*
.... 360.00   400.00

☐ **Bagdad,** *walnut, height 50½",*
dial 8", spring, c. 1896, 8 Day
(E1-153).
.... 725.00   800.00
☐ **As above,** *8 Day, strike, spring.*
.... 775.00   850.00
☐ **As above,** *8 Day, weight.*
.... 950.00   1050.00

☐ **Bagdad,** *ash, height 50½", dial*
8", spring, c. 1896, 8 Day
(E1-153).
.... 775.00   850.00

☐ **As above,** *8 Day, strike, spring.*
.... 825.00   900.00
☐ **As above,** *8 Day, weight.*
.... 1000.00   1150.00

☐ **Bagdad,** *mahogany, height*
50½", dial 8", spring, c. 1896, 8
Day (E1-153).
.... 700.00   775.00
☐ **As above,** *8 Day, strike, spring.*
.... 725.00   825.00
☐ **As above,** *8 Day, weight.*
.... 925.00   1025.00

☐ **Bagdad,** *oak, height 50½", dial*
8", spring, c. 1896, 8 Day
(E1-153).
.... 625.00   700.00
☐ **As above,** *8 Day, strike, spring.*
.... 675.00   750.00
☐ **As above,** *8 Day, weight.*
.... 850.00   950.00

☐ **Barcelona,** *walnut, 31½" x*
14¼", dial 8", spring, c. 1920,
8 Day (E1-185).
.... 370.00   400.00
☐ **As above,** *oak.*
.... 270.00   300.00
☐ **As above,** *mahogany.*
.... 370.00   400.00

☐ **Brazil,** *walnut, 32" x 15", dial 8",*
spring, c. 1920, 8 Day (E1-185).
.... 370.00   400.00
☐ **As above,** *mahogany.*
.... 345.00   375.00
☐ **As above,** *oak.*
.... 270.00   300.00

☐ **Capital,** *walnut, height 54", dial*
8", spring, c. 1896, 8 Day
(E1-153).
.... 675.00   750.00
☐ **As above,** *8 Day, strike*
.... 725.00   800.00
☐ **As above,** *8 Day, weight.*
.... 850.00   950.00

☐ **Capital,** *ash, height 54", dial 8",*
spring, c. 1896, 8 Day (E1-153).
.... 725.00   800.00
☐ **As above,** *8 Day, strike*
.... 775.00   850.00

☐ **As above,** *8 Day, weight.*
.... **900.00** **1000.00**

☐ **Capital,** *mahogany, height 54",*
dial 8", spring, c. 1896, 8 Day
(E1-153).
.... **640.00** **725.00**

☐ **As above,** *8 Day, strike*
.... **700.00** **775.00**

☐ **As above,** *8 Day, weight.*
.... **825.00** **925.00**

☐ **Capital,** *oak, height 54", dial 8",*
spring, c. 1896, 8 Day (E1-153).
.... **575.00** **650.00**

☐ **As above,** *8 Day, strike*
.... **625.00** **700.00**

☐ **As above,** *8 Day, weight.*
.... **750.00** **850.00**

☐ **Forrest,** *black walnut, height 41",*
dial 8", spring, c. 1910, 8 Day
(E2-40).
.... **490.00** **550.00**

☐ **As above,** *8 Day, strike.*
.... **540.00** **600.00**

☐ **Lisboa,** *walnut, 37" x 18¾", dial*
8", spring, c. 1920, 8 Day
(E1-185).
.... **370.00** **400.00**

☐ **As above,** *mahogany.*
.... **345.00** **375.00**

☐ **As above,** *oak.*
.... **270.00** **300.00**

☐ **Dispatch,** *wood, height 30", dial*
8", spring, c. 1910, 8 Day, strike
(E2-43).
.... **425.00** **475.00**

☐ **Major,** *wood, 30" x 14", dial 6",*
spring, c. 1910, 8 Day (E2-43).
.... **425.00** **475.00**

☐ **As above,** *8 Day, strike.*
.... **450.00** **500.00**

☐ **Para,** *black walnut, height 39",
dial 8", spring, c. 1910, 8 Day
(E2-40).*
. . . . 490.00   550.00
☐ **As above,** *8 Day, strike.*
. . . . 515.00   575.00
☐ **As above,** *8 Day, calendar.*
. . . . 540.00   600.00
☐ **As above,** *8 Day, strike, calendar.*
. . . . 550.00   625.00

☐ **Ponderosa,** *walnut, height 32",
dial 7", spring, c. 1910, 8 Day,
strike (E2-41).*
. . . . 475.00   525.00
☐ **As above,** *mahogany.*
. . . . 450.00   500.00
☐ **As above,** *oak.*
. . . . 375.00   425.00

☐ **Prompt,** *walnut, height 50", dial
8", spring, c. 1896, 8 Day
(E1-153).*
. . . . 725.00   800.00
☐ **As above,** *8 Day, strike, spring.*
. . . . 775.00   850.00
☐ **As above,** *8 Day, weight.*
. . . . 950.00   1050.00

☐ **Mississippi,** *wood, 27" x 12", dial
6", spring, c. 1910, 8 Day (E2-43).*
. . . . 360.00   400.00
☐ **As above,** *8 Day, strike.*
. . . . 375.00   425.00

☐ **Pampa,** *walnut, height 36", dial
8", spring, c. 1910, 8 Day, strike
(E2-41).*
. . . . 475.00   525.00
☐ **As above,** *mahogany.*
. . . . 450.00   500.00
☐ **As above,** *oak.*
. . . . 375.00   425.00

☐ **Prompt,** *ash, height 50", dial 8",
spring, c. 1896, 8 Day (E1-153).*
. . . . 775.00   850.00
☐ **As above,** *8 Day, strike, spring.*
. . . . 825.00   900.00
☐ **As above,** *8 Day, weight.*
. . . . 1000.00 1100.00

☐ **Prompt,** *mahogany, height 50",
dial 8", spring, c. 1896, 8 Day
(E1-153).*
. . . . 700.00   775.00
☐ **As above,** *8 Day, strike, spring.*
. . . . 750.00   825.00
☐ **As above,** *8 Day, weight.*
. . . . 925.00   1025.00

☐ **Prompt,** *oak, height 50", dial 8",
spring, c. 1896, 8 Day (E1-153).*
. . . . 625.00   700.00
☐ **As above,** *8 Day, strike, spring.*
. . . . 675.00   750.00
☐ **As above,** *8 Day, weight.*
. . . . 850.00   950.00

☐ **Queen Anne,** *oak, height 40½",
dial 8", spring, c. 1898, 8 Day
(E1-155).*
. . . . 540.00   600.00
☐ **As above,** *8 Day, strike, spring.*
. . . . 575.00   650.00

☐ **Queen Charlotte,** *oak, height 40",
dial 8", spring, c. 1898, 8 Day,
(E1-155).*
. . . . 575.00   650.00
☐ **As above,** *8 Day, strike, spring.*
. . . . 625.00   700.00

☐ **Queen Elizabeth,** *walnut, height
37", dial 8", spring, c. 1896,
8 Day (E1-153).*
. . . . 590.00   650.00
☐ **As above,** *8 Day, strike, spring.*
. . . . 640.00   700.00

☐ **Queen Elizabeth,** *mahogany,
height 37", dial 8", spring, c.
1896, 8 Day (E1-153).*
. . . . 565.00   625.00
☐ **As above,** *8 Day, strike, spring.*
. . . . 615.00   675.00

☐ **Queen Elizabeth,** *oak, height 37",
dial 8", spring, c. 1896, 8 Day
(E1-153).*
. . . . 490.00   550.00
☐ **As above,** *8 Day, strike, spring.*
. . . . 540.00   600.00

☐ **Queen Isabella,** *dark wood or
oak, height 38½", dial 8", spring,
c. 1910, 8 Day (E2-41).*
. . . . 400.00   450.00
☐ **As above,** *8 Day, strike.*
. . . . 425.00   475.00

☐ **Queen Jane,** *oak, height 41", dial
8", spring, c. 1898, 8 Day
(E1-155).*
. . . . 540.00   600.00
☐ **As above,** *8 Day, strike, spring.*
. . . . 575.00   650.00

☐ **Rio,** *oak, height 39", dial 8",*
spring, c. 1910, 8 Day (E2-40).
.... **490.00   550.00**
☐ **As above,** *8 Day, strike.*
.... **515.00   575.00**
☐ **As above,** *8 Day, calendar.*
.... **540.00   600.00**
☐ **As above,** *8 Day, strike, calendar.*
.... **550.00   625.00**

☐ **Rosario,** *walnut, 32" x 14½", dial*
8", spring, c. 1920, 8 Day
(E1-185).
.... **350.00   380.00**
☐ **As above,** *mahogany.*
.... **325.00   355.00**
☐ **As above,** *oak.*
.... **250.00   280.00**

☐ **San Luis,** *walnut, height 28", dial*
6½", spring, c. 1910, 8 Day,
strike (E2-41).
.... **410.00   450.00**

☐ **Queen Mab,** *dark wood or oak,*
height 36½", dial 8", spring,
c. 1910, 8 Day (E2-41).
.... **400.00   450.00**
☐ **As above,** *8 Day, strike.*
.... **425.00   475.00**

☐ **Queen Mary,** *walnut, height 42",*
dial 8", spring, c. 1896, 8 Day
(E1-153).
.... **590.00   650.00**
☐ **As above,** *8 Day, strike, spring.*
.... **675.00   750.00**

☐ **Queen Mary,** *oak, height 42", dial*
8", spring, c. 1896, 8 Day
(E1-153).
.... **490.00   550.00**
☐ **As above,** *8 Day, strike, spring.*
.... **575.00   650.00**

☐ **Uruguay,** *walnut, height 30", dial 7", spring, c. 1910, 8 Day, strike (E2-41).*
.... 410.00   450.00
☐ **As above,** *mahogany.*
.... 385.00   425.00
☐ **As above,** *oak.*
.... 310.00   350.00

☐ **Victoria,** *oak, 36" x 14½", dial 8", spring, c. 1920, 8 Day (E1-185).*
.... 310.00   350.00
☐ **As above,** *mahogany.*
.... 385.00   425.00

ROUND TOP, LONG DROP

☐ **English Drop,** *black walnut, height 32", dial 12", spring, c. 1910, 8 Day (E2-40).*
.... 310.00   350.00
☐ **As above,** *8 Day, strike.*
.... 335.00   375.00

☐ **As above,** *8 Day, calendar.*
.... 360.00   400.00
☐ **As above,** *8 Day, strike, calendar.*
.... 375.00   425.00

☐ **English Drop,** *ash, height 32", dial 12", spring, c. 1910, 8 Day (E2-40).*
.... 360.00   400.00
☐ **As above,** *8 Day, strike.*
.... 385.00   425.00
☐ **As above,** *8 Day, calendar.*
.... 410.00   450.00
☐ **As above,** *8 Day, strike, calendar.*
.... 425.00   475.00

☐ **Regulator,** *black walnut, height 32", dial 12", spring, c. 1890, 8 Day (E2-39).*
.... 310.00   350.00
☐ **As above,** *8 Day, strike.*
.... 335.00   375.00
☐ **As above,** *8 Day, calendar.*
.... 360.00   400.00
☐ **As above,** *8 Day, strike, calendar.*
.... 385.00   425.00

☐ **Regulator,** *oak, height 32", dial 12", spring, c. 1890, 8 Day (E2-39).*
.... 285.00   325.00
☐ **As above,** *8 Day, strike.*
.... 310.00   350.00
☐ **As above,** *8 Day, calendar.*
.... 335.00   375.00
☐ **As above,** *8 Day, strike, calendar.*
.... 360.00   400.00

☐ **Regulator,** *rosewood, height 32", dial 12", spring, c. 1890, 8 Day (E2-39).*
.... 335.00   375.00
☐ **As above,** *8 Day, strike.*
.... 360.00   400.00
☐ **As above,** *8 Day, calendar.*
.... 385.00   425.00
☐ **As above,** *8 Day, strike, calendar.*
.... 410.00   450.00

☐ **Regulator M.,** *walnut, 32" x 16¾", dial 12", spring, c. 1920, 8 Day (E1-185).*
.... 310.00   350.00

SECONDS BIT

☐ **Colonel,** *walnut, height 61", dial 18", c. 1910, 8 Day, weight (E2-43).*
. . . . **1650.00 1950.00**
☐ **As above,** *mahogany.*
. . . . **1600.00 1900.00**
☐ **As above,** *oak.*
. . . . **1450.00 1750.00**

☐ **General,** *walnut, height 68", dial 18", c. 1910, 8 Day, weight (E2-43).*
. . . . **2400.00 2700.00**
☐ **As above,** *mahogany.*
. . . . **2350.00 2650.00**

☐ **Mecca,** *black walnut, weight, height 58", porcelain dial 8", c. 1910, 8 Day (E2-40).*
. . . . **1000.00 1100.00**
☐ **As above,** *mahogany.*
. . . . **850.00 950.00**
☐ **Medina,** *black walnut, height 52", porcelain dial 8", weight, c. 1910, 8 Day (E2-40).*
. . . . **1000.00 1250.00**
☐ **As above,** *mahogany.*
. . . . **850.00 1100.00**

York

☐ **York,** *oak, height 46½", dial 8",*
spring, c. 1910, 8 Day, strike
(E2-43).
.... 950.00   1200.00
☐ **As above,** *8 Day, strike, spring.*
.... 1000.00   1250.00
☐ **As above,** *8 Day, weight.*
.... 1050.00   1300.00

☐ **York,** *mahogany, height 46½",*
dial 8", spring, c. 1910, 8 Day,
strike (E2-43).
.... 1100.00   1350.00
☐ **As above,** *8 Day, strike, spring.*
.... 1150.00   1400.00
☐ **As above,** *8 Day, weight.*
.... 1200.00   1450.00

STORE

☐ **Ledger No.1,** *dark wood or oak,*
height 25", dial 6", c. 1890, 8
Day, strike (E2-16).
.... 280.00   310.00
☐ **As above,** *8 Day.*
.... 230.00   260.00

SWEEP SECOND

☐ **Regulator, No.4,** *wood, height*
84", dial 12", c. 1910, 8 Day,
weight (E2-42).
.... 3500.00   4500.00
☐ **As above,** *8 Day, weight, strike.*
.... 4000.00   5000.00

☐ **Regulator No.11,** *wood, height 105", dial 14", c. 1910, 8 Day, weight, Mercury pendulum (E2-43).*
.... **7500.00 8500.00**
☐ **As above,** *8 Day, weight, Gridiron pendulum.*
.... **8000.00 9000.00**

☐ **Regulator No.14,** *wood, height 84", dial 12", c. 1910, 8 Day, weight (E2-42).*
.... **5500.00 6500.00**

STATUE
LARGE

☐ **Alpha,** *violet bronze, French rococo sash, beveled glass, porcelain dial, 24¼" x 11¾", dial 4¼", spring, c. 1890, 8 Day, strike (E1-113).*
.... **490.00 550.00**

☐ **Art and Commerce,** *Japanese bronze, French rococo sash, beveled glass, porcelain visible escapement dial, 20½" x 25½", spring, c. 1890, 8 Day, strike (E1-114).*
.... **750.00 850.00**

☐ **Attila,** *Japanese or Syrian bronze, French rococo sash, beveled glass, porcelain visible escapement dial, 21½" x 19½", spring, c. 1890, 8 Day, strike (E1-115).*
.... **490.00 550.00**

☐ **Combatants,** *Japanese bronze, French rococo sash, beveled glass, porcelain visible escapement dial, 21" x 19", spring, c. 1890, 8 Day, strike (E1-114).*
.... **625.00 750.00**

☐ **Cortez,** *Japanese or Syrian bronze, French rococo sash, beveled glass, porcelain visible escapement dial, 21¾" x 19½", spring, c. 1890, 8 Day, strike (E1-115).*
.... **450.00   500.00**

☐ **Fisher,** *bronze finish, French sash, beveled glass, porcelain dial, visible escapement, 22" x 15", dial 5½", spring, c. 1910, 8 Day, hour and ½ hour strike (E2-44).*
.... **465.00   525.00**

☐ **Fisher,** *Japanese, Barbedienne or Syrian bronze, French rococo sash, beveled glass, porcelain visible escapement dial, 22" x 15", dial 5½", spring, c. 1890, 8 Day, strike (E1-114).*
.... **540.00   600.00**

☐ **Fisher and Hunter,** *Japanese bronze, iron base, 21½" x 19", dial 5½", spring, c. 1898, 8 Day, strike (E1-155).*
.... **750.00   850.00**

☐ **Mars,** *Japanese or Syrian bronze, French rococo sash, beveled glass, porcelain visible escapement dial, 21½" x 19½", spring, c. 1890 (E1-115).*
.... **450.00   500.00**

□ **Muses,** *Japanese bronze, French rococo sash, beveled glass, porcelain visible escapement dial, 21½" x 19", spring, c. 1890, 8 Day, strike (E1-114).*
. . . . 750.00   850.00

□ **Music,** *Japanese bronze, black iron base, 21¾" x 19½", spring, c. 1898, 8 Day, strike (E1-155).*
. . . . 490.00   550.00

□ **Music and Poetry,** *Japanese bronze, French rococo sash, beveled glass, porcelain visible escapement dial, 20¾" x 20½", spring, c. 1890, 8 Day, strike (E1-114).*
. . . . 800.00   900.00

□ **Olympia,** *Syrian bronze, rich gold trimmings or rich gold, French rococo sash, beveled glass, porcelain dial 4¾", 24¾" x 15½", spring, c. 1890, 8 Day, strike (E1-113).*
. . . . 700.00   750.00

□ **Patricia,** *violet bronze, French rococo sash, beveled glass, porcelain 24½" x 9", dial 4¾", spring, c. 1890, 8 Day, strike (E1-113).*
. . . . 450.00   500.00

□ **Pizarro,** *Japanese or Syrian bronze, French rococo sash, beveled glass, porcelain visible escapement dial, 21¾" x 19½", spring, c. 1890, 8 Day, strike (E1-115).*
. . . . 450.00   500.00

□ **Pizarro and Cortez,** *Japanese bronze, French rococo sash, beveled glass, porcelain visible escapement dial, 20½" x 25¾", spring, c. 1890, 8 Day, strike (E1-114).*
. . . . 700.00   800.00

□ **Provocation,** *Japanese or Syrian bronze, French rococo sash, beveled glass, porcelain visible escapement dial, 21¾" x 21", spring, c. 1890, 8 Day, strike (E1-115).*
. . . . 450.00   500.00

☐ **Reflection,** *Syrian bronze, French rococo sash, beveled glass, porcelain visible escapement dial, 25" x 24½", dial 5½", spring, c. 1890, 8 Day, strike (E1-114).*

.... 1000.00   1100.00

☐ **Sappho,** *Barbedienne or Verde bronze, French rococo sash, cream porcelain dial 4¼", 25" x 9¼", spring, c. 1898, 8 Day, strike (E1-156).*

.... 500.00   550.00

☐ **Sibyl and Gloria,** *Barbedienne or Verde Clair bronze, French rococo sash, cream porcelain dial 4¾", 27½" x 10¾", spring, c. 1898, 8 Day, strike (E1-156).*

.... 600.00   650.00

☐ **Sibyl and Melody,** *Barbedienne or Verde bronze, French rococo sash, cream porcelain dial 4¼", 25¼" x 10¾", spring, c. 1898 (E1-156).*

.... 550.00   600.00

☐ **Spring,** *Syrian bronze, French rococo sash, beveled glass, porcelain visible escapement, 35" x 12¼", dial 5½", spring, c. 1890, 8 Day, strike (E1-113).*

.... 1000.00   1250.00

☐ **Superba and La Source,** *Art Nouveau, Syrian bronze, Brazilian onyx inlay, French rococo sash, beveled glass, porcelain dial, 28" x 15", dial 4", spring, c. 1890, 8 Day, strike (E1-113).*

.... 800.00   900.00

☐ **Tasso,** *Japanese or Syrian bronze, French rococo sash, beveled glass, porcelain visible escapement dial, 20½" x 25¾", spring, c. 1890, 8 Day, strike (E1-115).*
.... **400.00   450.00**

☐ **Teresa,** *violet bronze, French rococo sash, beveled glass, porcelain dial, 24" x 9", spring, c. 1890, 8 Day, strike (E1-113).*
.... **450.00   500.00**

☐ **Vocalists,** *Syrian bronze, French rococo sash, beveled glass, porcelain visible escapement dial 5½", 22" x 24", spring, c. 1890, 8 Day, strike (E1-114).*
.... **800.00   1000.00**

SMALL

☐ **No.1011,** *bronze finish, height 17", dial 4", spring, c. 1883, 1 Day (E2-9).*
.... **205.00   235.00**

☐ **Alcazar,** *gold, height 10¾", dial 2", spring, c. 1910, 1 Day (E2-34).*
.... **60.00   75.00**
☐ **As above,** *8 Day.*
.... **95.00   115.00**

☐ **Arion,** *bronze finish, French rococo sash, beveled glass, porcelain dial, visible escapement, 15" x 17½", dial 4½", spring, c. 1910, 8 Day, hour and ½ hour strike (E2-44).*
.... **250.00   280.00**

☐ **Armour,** *gold, height 8¼", dial 2", spring, c. 1910, 1 Day (E2-34).*
.... **65.00   80.00**
☐ **As above,** *8 Day.*
.... **100.00   120.00**

☐ **Artist,** *Japanese bronze, 11" x 14", dial 4¼", spring, c. 1898, 8 Day, strike (E1-155).*
.... **150.00   175.00**

☐ **Boar Hunter,** *Japanese bronze, French rococo sash, porcelain visible escapement dial, dial 5½", 15¾" x 26", spring, c. 1890, 8 Day, strike (E1-116).*
.... **575.00   650.00**

☐ **Cincinnatus,** *bronze finish, French rococo sash, beveled glass, porcelain dial, visible escapement, 16½" x 19", dial 4½", spring, c. 1910, 8 Day, hour and ½ hour strike (E2-44).*
.... **250.00   280.00**

☐ **Dagobert,** *bronze finish, French rococo sash, beveled glass, porcelain dial, visible escapement, 15¾" x 19", dial 5½", spring, c. 1910, 8 Day (E2-44).*
.... **335.00   375.00**

☐ **Denis Papin,** *Japanese or Syrian bronze, French rococo sash, beveled glass, porcelain dial, 16¼" x 19", spring, c. 1890, 8 Day, strike (E1-116).*
.... 285.00   325.00

☐ **Don Juan,** *Japanese or Syrian bronze, French rococo sash, beveled glass, porcelain visible escapement dial, 22" x 19½", dial 5½", spring, c. 1890, 8 Day, strike (E1-115).*
.... 490.00   550.00

☐ **Egyptian,** *Japanese bronze, black iron base, 17" x 15", dial 5½", spring, c. 1898, 8 Day, strike (E1-155).*
.... 335.00   375.00

☐ **Elf,** *gold, height 7¾", dial 2", spring, c. 1910, 1 Day (E2-34).*
.... 60.00   75.00

☐ **As above,** *8 Day.*
.... 95.00   115.00

☐ **Fantasy,** *bronze finish, French rococo sash, beveled glass, porcelain dial, visible escapement, 15" x 17½", dial 4½", spring, c. 1910, 8 Day, hour and ½ hour strike (E2-44).*
.... 250.00   280.00

☐ **Hector,** *Venetian bronze, French rococo sash, beveled glass, porcelain visible escapement dial, 18" x 9¼", dial 4½", spring, c. 1890, 8 Day, strike (E1-113).*
.... 270.00   300.00

☐ **Hermes,** *Japanese bronze, 11½" x 16", dial 5", spring, c. 1898, 8 Day, strike (E1-158).*
.... 310.00   350.00

☐ **Industry,** *Japanese bronze, French rococo sash, porcelain visible escapement dial, 16½" x 19½", spring, c. 1890, 8 Day, strike (E1-116).*
.... 310.00   350.00

☐ **Industry,** *Grecian or Venetian bronze, French rococo sash, beveled glass, porcelain dial, 19¼" x 10¾", dial 4¼", spring, c. 1890, 8 Day, strike (E1-115).*
.... 360.00   400.00

☐ **Knight,** *Japanese bronze, 11½" x 16", dial 5", spring, c. 1898, 8 Day, strike (E1-158).*
. . . . 335.00   375.00

☐ **Marcela,** *gold finish, height 14", dial 2", spring, c. 1910, 1 Day (E2-34).*
. . . . 60.00   85.00
☐ **As above,** *8 Day.*
. . . . 105.00   125.00

☐ **Mozart,** *gilt or Japanese bronze, Barbedienne or Syrian bronze, French rococo sash, beveled glass, porcelain visible escapement dial, 14½" x 18", dial 5½", spring, c. 1890, 8 Day, strike (E1-116).*
. . . . 310.00   350.00

☐ **Newton,** *Japanese or Syrian bronze, French rococo sash, beveled glass, porcelain visible escapement dial, 15" x 17½", dial 5½", spring, c. 1890, 8 Day, strike (E1-116).*
. . . . 310.00   350.00

☐ **Opera,** *Japanese or Syrian bronze, French rococo sash, beveled glass, porcelain visible escapement dial, 16¼" x 21", spring, c. 1890, 8 Day, strike (E1-116).*
. . . . 310.00   350.00

☐ **Philosopher,** *Japanese or Syrian bronze, French rococo sash, beveled glass, porcelain visible escapement dial, 15" x 17½", spring, c. 1890, 8 Day, strike (E1-116).*
. . . . 285.00   325.00

☐ **Racine,** *Verde bronze, French rococo sash, porcelain dial, 11" x 14", spring, c. 1917, 8 Day, strike (E1-180).*
. . . . 175.00   200.00

☐ **Reubens,** *Japanese bronze, French rococo sash, beveled glass, porcelain visible escapement dial, 16¼" x 21", spring, c. 1890, 8 Day, strike (E1-116).*
. . . . 360.00   400.00

☐ **Rex,** *bronze finish, French rococo sash, porcelain dial, visible escapement, 11½" x 16", dial 4", spring, c. 1910, 8 Day, hour and ½ hour strike (E2-44).*
. . . . 250.00   280.00

□ **Shakespeare,** *Japanese or Syrian bronze, French rococo sash, beveled glass, porcelain visible escapement dial, 15" x 17½", dial 5½", spring, c. 1890, 8 Day, strike (E1-116).*
. . . . 310.00   350.00

□ **Siren,** *Japanese or Syrian bronze, French rococo sash, beveled glass, porcelain visible escapement dial, 11½" x 16", dial 5", spring, c. 1890, 8 Day, strike (E1-116).*
. . . . 310.00   350.00

□ **Trilby,** *Japanese bronze, 11" x 14", dial 4¼", spring, c. 1898, 8 Day, strike (E1-156).*
. . . . 150.00   175.00

□ **Troubadour,** *Japanese bronze, French rococo sash, beveled glass, porcelain visible escapement dial, 16¼" x 21", spring, c. 1890, 8 Day, strike (E1-116).*
. . . . 310.00   350.00

□ **Vassar,** *Japanese bronze, 11" x 14", spring, c. 1898, 8 Day, strike (E1-155).*
. . . . 150.00   175.00

□ **Victory,** *bronze finish, French rococo sash, beveled glass, porcelain dial, visible escapement, 15" x 17½", dial 4½", spring, c. 1910, 8 Day, hour and ½ hour strike (E2-44).*
. . . . 250.00   280.00

SWING ARM

□ **Arcadia Ball Swing,** *bronze and nickel finish, height 31½", c. 1890, 8 Day (E1-113).*
. . . . 2400.00   2800.00

□ **Diana Swing,** *Japanese or French bronze, gilt and nickel finish, height 30", c. 1890, 8 Day (E1-113).*
. . . . 800.00   1000.00

□ **Double Figure Swing,** *Japanese or French bronze, gilt and nickel finish, height 27", c. 1890, 8 Day (E1-113).*
. . . . 2000.00   2250.00

□ **Juno Swing,** *Syrian bronze, clock and pendulum ball cobalt blue enameled, raised gold plated numerals and ornamentations, c. 1890, 8 Day (E1-113).*
. . . . 1200.00   1400.00

BOARDMAN-HUBBELL

Chauncey Boardman is best known for his uncased movements, and for continuing to produce the wooden tall clocks five years after most clock makers had virtually abandoned this style. Boardman did get into shelf clock production, though he never acquired a license or patent from Eli Terry, the original manufacturer of the design.

Boardman, and others (Hoadley, Leavenworth, and Ives) got around this sticky situation by producing clock movements of a unique style. Boardman's movement was of an overhead striking shelf clock. The clocks were similiar to Terry's, but not close enough to warrant legal action.

Boardman made movements for Chauncey Jerome at various times, went into partnership with J. Wells, and continued with his business in Bristol, and various other clockmaking ventures, until bankruptcy forced him out entirely.

Laporte Hubbell is associated primarily with the manufacture of marine clocks, and calendar clocks with a marine movement. Marine clocks are not necessarily found on seagoing vessels, but do have the advantage of running fairly accurately despite unstable positions. The marine clock movement evolved into the alarm clock.

Hubbel worked primarily with Hendrick, Clark and Barnes, and Levi Beach. He was associated with Chauncey Jerome in an unsuccessful business venture, and at one time formed a partnership with D.J. Mozart.

Foremost a mechanic, Hubbell, supplied countless marine movements to the trade for a great number of years.

CALENDAR

☐ **Shelf Model,** *8 Day lever, double spring, 16½" x 12½", dial 5½", calendar in aperture in bottom of door (M156-56).*
.... 2100.00 2500.00

☐ **Wall Model,** *8 Day lever, double spring, 25" x 18", dial 11½", month-date strip made of sized linen, calendar in aperture in bottom door (M158-57).*
.... 3700.00 4000.00

E. BURWELL-L.F. AND W.W. CARTER

A Bristol firm, Elias Burwell-Luther and William Carter prospered from an invention by Benjamin Bennett Lewis which featured a calendar clock.

Most of the wooden longcase clocks used a calendar device, and clockmakers considered it important that they remain relatively accurate. This meant they must account for irregularities such as leap year and 30 or 31 days in the month.

Although shelf clocks largely displaced the calendar mechanism, another famous clock company (Seth Thomas) revived them after purchasing an improved calendar patent from James and Eugene Mix. It was used for many years.

Lewis's mechanism was patented in 1862 and subsequently improved in the 80's. This calendar device was utlilized not only by Burwell and Carter, but by other prominent manufacturers as well: E. Ingraham Company and the E.N. Welch Manufacturing Company.

CALENDAR

☐ **Italian-Type Shelf,** *8 Day, spring, strike, calendar mechanism (M179A-64).*
.... 800.00 900.00

☐ **Lewis No. 2,** *8 Day, double weight retaining power, rolling pinions, year calendar mechanism, 31" x 15½", 12" time and 8" calendar dial (E1-22, M172-62).*
.... **1000.00 1200.00**

☐ **Lewis No. 3,** *8 Day, double weight retaining power, rolling pinions, year calendar mechanism, 43" x 18", 14" time and 10" calendar dial (M174-63).*
.... **1300.00 1400.00**

☐ **Lewis No. 6,** *8 Day, double spring, lever, jeweled balace, year calendar mechanism 28" x 12¾", 5½" time and 7½" calendar dial (E1-22, M178-64).*
.... **2600.00 2800.00**

☐ **Lewis No. 8,** *8 Day, double weight solid plates, rolling pinions, year calendar mechanism, 36" x 21", 8" time and 12" calendar dial (E1-22, M180-65).*
.... **1000.00 1150.00**

☐ **Round Drop Wall,** *8 Day, double weight retaining power, year calendar mechanism, 57" x 21", 15" time and 10" calendar dial (M176-63).*
.... **2200.00 2600.00**

☐ **Round Drop Wall,** *8 Day, double weight retaining power, year calendar mechanism, height 55", 18" time and 12" calendar dial (E1-22, M175-63).*
.... **1600.00 1800.00**

☐ **Round Drop Wall,** *8 Day, time spring, strike, year calendar mechanism 26" x 13½", 9" time and 5½" calendar dial (M171-62).*
.... **950.00 1100.00**

☐ **Round Drop Wall,** *8 Day, spring, year calendar mechanism, 27½" x 15", 11" time and 5½" calendar dial (M173-62).*
.... **1250.00 1500.00**

☐ **Shelf,** *manufactured by B.B. Lewis for L.F. and W.W. Carter, Bristol, CT, 8 Day, spring, strike, year calendar mechanism, 21" x 13½", dials 6" (M183-65).*
.... **800.00 1100.00**

☐ **Shelf,** *8 Day, spring, strike, year calendar mechanism, 22" x 13½", dials 6" (M182-65).*
.... **875.00 1075.00**

CLINTON AND MOOD

CALENDAR

☐ **1873 Patent Calendar Mechanism,** *8 Day, double spring, pendulum, glass sided wood top and bottom case (M161-58).*
.... 4000.00   4500.00

DAVIS CLOCK COMPANY

CALENDARS

☐ **Column Flat Top,** *shelf, Columbus, MI, 8 Day, strike, simple calendar, 25" x 15¼", dial, 7" (M448-139).*
.... 400.00   450.00

☐ **Shelf Clock,** *Texarkana, AR, 8 Day, strike, simple calendar, 27" x 15½", dial, 7" (M450-139).*
.... 500.00   575.00

☐ **Shelf Clock,** *Texarkana, AR, 8 Day, strike, simple calendar, 27½" x 15½", dial, 7" (M451-139).*
.... 475.00   575.00

EMPIRE CALENDAR CLOCK COMPANY

CALENDAR

☐ **Victorian Kitchen,** *8 Day, strike, simple calendar, 20½" x 12", dial, 6" (M470-145).*
.... 500.00   600.00

☐ **Victorian Kitchen,** *8 Day, strike, simple calendar, 22" x 12½", dial, 6" (M471-145).*
.... 700.00   800.00

C.W. FEISHTINGER

CALENDAR

☐ **Victorian Kitchen,** *8 Day, strike, 22" x 13½", dials, 5" (M477-146).*
.... 700.00   800.00

☐ **Victorian Kitchen,** *8 Day, strike, 22" x 13½", dials, 5" (M479-147).*
.... 725.00   825.00

☐ **Victorian Kitchen,** *8 Day, strike, 22" x 13½", dials, 5" (M480-147).*
.... 700.00   800.00

☐ **Victorian Kitchen,** *8 Day, strike, 22" x 13½", dials, 5" (M481-147).*
.... 700.00   800.00

FRANKLIN-MORSE

CALENDAR

☐ **Franklin-Morse Calendar,** *8 Day, strike, 22½" x 16", (M489-150).*
.... 500.00   600.00

D.J. GALE

Also associated exclusively with the calendar clock, D.J. Gale, developed an intricate operational mechanism, that was patented in the last quarter of the 19th century. The rights were purchased by a Bristol company that was fairly prominent: Welch, Spring and Company.

A Wisconsin native, Gale's invention is much sought after by modern clock enthusiasts.

CALENDAR

☐ **Arditi, E.N.,** *Welch Manufacturing Company, 8 Day, strike, 27½" x 17½", dials, 8" (E1-163, M505-155).*
. . . . **1250.00   1500.00**

☐ **Astronomical,** *Welch, Spring and Company, 8 Day, lever, dial, 24", 1877 patent calendar mechanism (E1-22, M498-153).*
. . . . **4000.00   4500.00**

☐ **Damrosch,** *E.N. Welch Manufacturing Company, 8 Day, strike, height 41", dials, 8" (E1-163, M508-155).*
. . . . **2100.00   2400.00**

☐ **Gale Drop,** *Welch, Spring and Company, 8 Day, strike, height 30", dial 12" (E1-32, M501-154).*
. . . . **3000.00   3500.00**

GILBERT

A product of the age of manufacturing, William Lewis Gilbert was once the employer of Silas Terry in Winsted. Terry moved to Waterbury before the entire factory burned. Gilbert, alas, did not.

Gilbert began his clockmaking career in the first quarter of the 19th century at a small clock shop which he owned in conjunction with a relative by marriage, named George Marsh. Gilbert also was in partnership with a John Birge in Bristol, and later with Chanucey and Noble Jerome.

After the Winsted factory burned, large brick buildings housed the facilities of the manufacturer. Eventually a corporation, Gilbert continued clock manufacturing until after World War II, when a decline that had been spiraling downward for years, caused it to be absorbed by a computing machines company.

Gilbert is best known for manufacturing inexpensive brass and alarm clocks.

ALARM
DRUM

☐ **Artistic,** *nickel, long alarm, gilt perforated dial, height 6¾" dial 4½", c. 1896, 1 Day, alarm (E2-45).*
. . . . **40.00   50.00**

☐ **Basket Alarm,** *basket work sides of brass, fancy brass matting and nickel trimmings, height 6¼", dial 4", c. 1896, 1 Day, alarm (E2-45).*
. . . . **45.00   60.00**

☐ **Blossom Alarm,** *floral decorations on sides, assorted colors, nickel trimmings, height 6¼" dial 4", 1 Day (E2-45).*
. . . . **40.00   50.00**

☐ **Drum,** *nickel, intermitting alarm, height 6¾", gilt perforated dial 4½", c. 1896, 1 Day, alarm (E2-45).*
. . . . **45.00   60.00**

☐ **Ossa,** *height 6", dial 4½", c. 1896, 1 Day, (E2-45).*
. . . . **15.00   25.00**
☐ **As above,** *1 Day, alarm.*
. . . . **20.00   30.00**
☐ **As above,** *1 Day, calendar.*
. . . . **60.00   80.00**
☐ **As above,** *1 Day, alarm, calendar.*
. . . . **70.00   85.00**

☐ **Pet,** *nickel, long alarm, height 6¾", dial 4½", c. 1896, 1 Day, alarm (E2-45).*
. . . . **30.00   45.00**

☐ **Reveille,** *intermitting alarm, nickel, height 6¾", dial 4⅛", c. 1896, 1 Day, alarm (E2-45).*
. . . . **40.00   50.00**
☐ **Rob Roy Alarm,** *marbleized, assorted colors, height 6¼", dial 4", c. 1896, 1 Day, alarm (E2-45).*
. . . . **30.00   40.00**
☐ **Spy,** *nickel, dial 4", c. 1896, 1 Day, (E2-45).*
. . . . **20.00   30.00**
☐ **Wake-Up,** *nickel, dial 4", c. 1896, 1 Day, alarm (E2-45).*
. . . . **25.00   35.00**

FANCY

☐ **Cannon,** *long alarm, marbleized wood case, gilt ornaments, gilt perforated dial, height 12", width 5", c. 1896, 1 Day, alarm (E2-46).*
. . . . **100.00   120.00**

☐ **Lighter Time,** *red enamel clock case, oak battery box, height 6¼", width 5", c. 1896, 1 Day, (E2-45).*
. . . . **75.00   90.00**

☐ **Dewey Long Alarm,** *nickel or gilt finish, ivory porcelain dial, height 8¾", base 9", dial 4", c. 1896 (E2-46).*
. . . . **105.00   125.00**

☐ **Liberty Alarm,** *antique oak, brass pillars, height 9", dial 3", c. 1896, 1 Day, alarm (E2-46).*
. . . . **70.00   85.00**

☐ **Salute Long Alarm,** *gilt clock and ornaments, marbleized base, height 9¼", dial 4", base 9", c. 1896, 1 Day, alarm (E2-46).*
. . . . **80.00   95.00**

☐ **Singal Long Alarm,** *bronze or gilt, height 9¼", width 8¼", dial 4", c. 1896, 1 Day, alarm (E2-46).*
. . . . **65.00   80.00**

□ **Champion No.1,** *oak, height 17",
dial 5½", c. 1899, 8 Day, strike
(E2-60).*
.... 150.00   175.00

□ **Champion No. 2,** *oak, height 17",
dial 5½", c. 1899, 8 Day, strike,
(E2-60).*
.... 150.00   175.00

□ **Champion No. 3,** *oak, height 17",
dial 5½", c. 1899, 8 Day, strike,
(E2-60).*
.... 150.00   175.00

□ **Sunlight Alarm,** *nickel, oak
battery box, height 8¼", width
5", c. 1896, 1 Day, alarm (E2-45).*
.... 90.00   110.00

CABINET

□ **Excelsior No. 1,** *oak, height 16½",
dial 5½", c. 1899, 8 Day, strike,
(E2-60).*
.... 160.00   180.00

□ **Excelsior No. 2,** *oak, height
16½", dial 5½", c. 1899, 8 Day,
strike, (E2-60).*
.... 160.00   180.00

□ **Excelsior No. 3,** *oak, height
16½", dial 5½", c. 1899, 8 Day,
strike, (E2-60).*
.... 160.00   180.00

□ **Excelsior No. 4,** *oak, height
16½", dial 5½", c. 1899, 8 Day,
strike, (E2-60).*
.... 160.00   180.00

CALENDAR

☐ **Alpine,** *gallery type, height 24",*
dial 12", 8 Day, strike, simple
calendar (E2-63).
.... **225.00   250.00**

☐ **Benworth,** *27" x 15", dial 8", 8*
Day, strike, simple calendar
(E1-152, E2-61).
.... **700.00   800.00**

☐ **Columbia (Oak Wall),** *height*
37½", dial 8", 8 Day, strike,
simple calendar (E2-58).
.... **550.00   625.00**

☐ **Concord (Kitchen),** *thermometer*
and barometer, height 23½", dial
6", 8 Day, strike, simple calendar
(E2-57).
.... **175.00   200.00**

☐ **Concord,** *23½" x 14½", 8 Day,*
strike, simple calendar (M442-137).
.... **160.00   185.00**

☐ **Consort Octagon Top,** *height 31",*
dial 12", 8 Day, strike, simple
calendar (E2-63).
.... **325.00   375.00**

☐ **Eureka,** *29" x 15½", 8 Day, strike,*
simple calendar, spring
(M443-137).
.... **350.00   400.00**

☐ **Excelsior,** *27½" x 15½", 8 Day, strike, simple calendar, spring (M444-138).*
.... 350.00   400.00

☐ **Janeiro-Figure 8,** *height 22", dial 10", 8 Day, strike, simple calendar (E2-63).*
.... 325.00   375.00

☐ **Longbranch,** *28" x 16", dial 8", 8 Day, strike, simple calendar, spring (E2-61, M447-138).*
.... 400.00   450.00

☐ **Mountauk Octagon Top,** *short drop, height 26", dial 12", 8 Day, strike, simple calendar (E2-63).*
.... 325.00   375.00

☐ **National,** *thermometer and barometer, 27½" x 16", dial 8", 8 Day, strike, simple calendar, spring (M446-138).*
.... 450.00   500.00

☐ **Octagon Top,** *short drop, height 22½", dial 12", 8 Day, strike, simple calendar (M439-136).*
.... 300.00   350.00

☐ **Octagon Top,** *short drop gilt, height 20½", dial 8", 8 Day, strike, simple calendar (E2-63).*
.... 225.00   250.00

☐ **Octagon Top,** *short drop gilt, height 23½", dial 10", 8 Day, strike, simple calendar (E2-63).*
.... 250.00   275.00

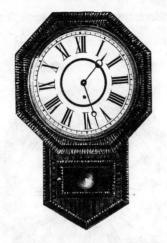

☐ **Octagon Top,** *short drop gilt, height 25½", dial 12", 8 Day, strike, simple calendar (E2-63).*
. . . . **250.00   300.00**

☐ **Regulator A-Long Drop,** *height 31", dial 12", 8 Day, strike, simple calendar (E2-63).*
. . . . **325.00   375.00**

☐ **Regulator B Octagon Top,** *height 29", dial 12", 8 Day, strike, simple calendar (E2-63).*
. . . . **325.00   375.00**

☐ **Riverside Octagon Top,** *short drop, height 23", dial 10", 8 Day, strike, simple calendar (E2-63).*
. . . . **325.00   375.00**

☐ **Ossa (Round Alarm),** *height 6", dial 4½", 1 Day, alarm, simple calendar (E2-45).*
. . . . **65.00   85.00**

☐ **Standard Admiral Octagon Top,** *short drop, height 24″, dial 12″, 8 Day, strike, simple calendar (E2-63, M437-136).*
.... **300.00   325.00**

☐ **Saratoga Wall Regulator,** *height 39″, dial 8″, 8 Day, strike, simple calendar (E2-64).*
.... **450.00   500.00**

☐ **Star Octagon Top,** *long drop, height 32½″, dial 12″ 8 Day, strike, simple calendar (E2-62).*
.... **450.00   500.00**

☐ **Victorian Shelf No. 28,** *19½″ x 12″, 8 day, strike, simple calendar (M440-137).*
.... **150.00   175.00**

CARRIAGE

☐ **All Right,** *oxidized copper or brass, height 10", dial 2¾", c. 1896, 1 Day, alarm (E2-46).*
. . . . **100.00** **120.00**

☐ **Graduate Alarm,** *nickel-plated frame and sides, gilt front, height 9", dial 3", c. 1896, 1 Day, alarm (E2-46).*
. . . . **85.00** **105.00**

☐ **Hello Alarm,** *nickel-plated frame, leatherette, glass sides, height 9", dial 2¾", c. 1896, 1 Day, alarm (E2-46).*
. . . . **90.00** **110.00**

☐ **Hello Long Alarm,** *nickel-plated frame, glass sides, height 9", dial 2¾", c. 1896, 1 Day, alarm (E2-46).*
. . . . **90.00** **110.00**

☐ **Interval,** *intermitting alarm, nickel-plated frame, glass sides, height 9", dial 2¾", c. 1896, 1 Day, alarm (E2-46).*
. . . . **95.00** **115.00**

☐ **'76 Alarm, Rolling Bell,** *nickel-plated frame and sides, height 9", dial 3", c. 1896, 1 Day, alarm (E2-46).*
. . . . **90.00** **110.00**

☐ **Turnout,** *nickle-plated frame and sides, height 9", dial 3", c. 1896, 1 Day,alarm (E2-46).*
.... 80.00   100.00

CONNECTICUT SHELF
BEE HIVE

☐ **Round Gothic,** *walnut, height 19", c. 1875, 1 Day, strike (E1-18).*
.... 90.00   110.00
☐ **As above,** *8 day, strike*
.... 110.00   135.00

COLUMN

☐ **Column Spring,** *dark wood, rose, shell and gilt columns, spring, 15" x 10⅝", c. 1875, 1 Day, strike (E2-52).*
.... 105.00   130.00
☐ **As above,** *8 day, strike*

.... 140.00   165.00

☐ **Column Spring,** *rosewood, shell or gilt columns, height 15", c. 1875, 1 Day, strike, (E1-61).*
.... 175.00   200.00
☐ **As above,** *8 day, strike*
.... 195.00   225.00

☐ **Column Weight,** *dark wood, weight, rose, shell and gilt columns, 25" x 15⅛", c. 1875, 1 Day, strike (E2-52).*
.... 150.00   170.00

☐ **Extra Rolling Pinion,** *rosewood, rose shell or gilt column, height 30½", c. 1875, 8 Day, weight, stirke (E1-19).*
.... 285.00   325.00

☐ **Gilt And Shell Column,** *rosewood, mahogany and zebra, height weight clocks, 25", spring clocks, 18", c. 1875, 1 Day, strike, mahogany (E1-19).*
.... 125.00   150.00
☐ **As above,** *8 Day, strike, mahogany*
.... 150.00   175.00
☐ **As above,** *1 Day, strike, rosewood*
.... 150.00   175.00
☐ **As above,** *8 Day, strike, rosewood*
.... 150.00   175.00
☐ **As above,** *1 Day, strike, zebra*
.... 160.00   185.00

☐ **As above,** *8 Day, strike, zebra*
.... **185.00   210.00**

☐ **London Mantel,** *rosewood, rose and gilt pillars, height 17½", c. 1875, 8 Day, simple spring (E1-19).*
.... **175.00   200.00**

☐ **Paragon,** *dark wood, rose or gilt ornaments, spring, 15" x 10⅝", c. 1875, 1 Day, strike (E2-52).*
.... **105.00   125.00**

☐ **As above,** *8 Day, strike*
.... **140.00   165.00**

☐ **Paragon Spring,** *rosewood or gilt ornamented, height 15", c. 1875, 1 day, strike (E1-61).*
.... **140.00   165.00**

☐ **As above,** *8 Day, strike*
.... **165.00   190.00**

COTTAGE

☐ **Cottage,** *walnut, height 11" to 13", c. 1875, 1 Day, simple spring (E1-18).*
.... **65.00   80.00**

☐ **No. 2 Cottage Time,** *dark wood, 12" x 8", c. 1875, 1 Day (E2-52).*
.... **70.00   90.00**

☐ **Coupon,** *dark wood, spring, 13¼" x 10⅝", c. 1875, 1 Day, strike (E2-53).*
.... **70.00   90.00**

☐ **As above,** *8 Day, strike*
.... **105.00   125.00**

☐ **Coupon,** *walnut veneer, 14" x 11" spring, c. 1875, 1 Day (E2-53).*
.... **70.00   90.00**

☐ **As above,** *8 Day*
.... **105.00   125.00**

☐ **As above,** *8 Day, strike*
.... **110.00   135.00**

☐ **Favorite,** *dark wood, spring, height 13½", weight 11⅛", c. 1875, 1 Day, strike (E2-51).*
.... **65.00   80.00**

☐ **As above,** *8 Day, strike*
.... **90.00   110.00**

☐ **Rose Cottage Time,** *rose sash, dark wood, 9⅞" x 7¾", c. 1875, 1 Day (E2-52).*
.... **70.00   85.00**

☐ **Rose Gilt,** *rosewood, height 9½", c. 1875, 1 Day, spring (E1-18).*
.... **70.00   85.00**

☐ **Rose Gilt Time,** *gilt sash, dark wood, 9⅞" x 7¾", c. 1875, 1 Day.*
.... **70.00**   **85.00**

☐ **Rose Mantel,** *rosewood, height 12", c. 1875, 1 Day, simple spring (E1-18).*
.... **80.00**   **100.00**

☐ **As above,** *8 Day, simple spring*
.... **105.00**   **125.00**

☐ **Victoria,** *walnut, height 14½", c. 1875, 8 Day, simple spring (E1-18).*
.... **150.00**   **175.00**

☐ **Waverly,** *dark wood, spring, 13¼" x 10⅝", c. 1875, 1 Day, strike (E2-52).*
.... **80.00**   **100.00**

☐ **As above,** *8 Day, strike*
.... **110.00**   **135.00**

OCTAGON TOP

☐ **Comet,** *walnut veneer, 14" x 11", spring, c. 1875, 1 Day (E2-53).*
.... **65.00**   **80.00**

☐ **As above,** *1 Day, strike*
.... **70.00**   **90.00**

☐ **As above,** *8 Day*
.... **80.00**   **100.00**

☐ **As above,** *8 Day, strike*
.... **90.00**   **110.00**

☐ **Comet,** *dark wood, spring, height 14¾", weight 10⅝", c. 1875, 1 Day, strike (E1-53).*
.... **60.00**   **75.00**

☐ **As above,** *8 Day, strike*
.... **75.00**   **90.00**

☐ **Comet Time,** *walnut veneer, height 11", width 9", spring, c. 1875, 1 Day, (E2-53).*
.... **80.00**   **100.00**

☐ **Octagon Top,** *walnut, height 10", c. 1875, 1 Day, spring (E1-19).*
.... **70.00**   **85.00**

☐ **Octagon Top,** *walnut, height 13½", c. 1875, 1 Day, simple spring (E1-19).*
.... **70.00**   **85.00**

☐ **As above,** *8 Day, simple spring*
.... **85.00**   **105.00**

O.G.

☐ **O.O.G. Spring,** *dark wood, spring, 18⅜" x 11¾", c. 1875, 1 Day, strike (E2-51).*
.... **80.00**   **100.00**

☐ **As above,** *8 Day, strike*
.... **125.00   150.00**

☐ **O.G. Weight,** *dark wood, 25⅞" x 15⅜", c. 1875, 1 Day, strike (E2-51).*
.... **100.00   120.00**

☐ **As above,** *8 Day, strike*
.... **135.00   160.00**

ROUND TOP

☐ **Carved Walnut,** *walnut, height 19", c. 1875, 8 Day, simple spring (E1-19).*
.... **95.00   115.00**

☐ **Keystone,** *polished rosewood, height 17¾", c. 1875, 1 Day, simple spring (E1-58).*
.... **150.00   175.00**

☐ **As above,** *8 Day, simple spring*
.... **175.00   200.00**

☐ **Key-Stone,** *dark wood, spring, 17¾" x 12⅝", c. 1875, 1 Day, strike, (E2-51).*
.... **150.00   175.00**

☐ **As above,** *8 Day, strike*
.... **175.00   200.00**

☐ **Round Top,** *dark wood, spring, 13⅜" x 10⅜", c. 1875, 1 Day, strike (E2-51).*
.... **70.00   90.00**

☐ **As above,** *8 Day, strike*
.... **110.00   135.00**

☐ **Round Top Time,** *dark wood, 11" x 8⅛", c. 1875, 1 Day, strike (E2-51).*
.... **80.00   100.00**

☐ **As above,** *8 Day, strike*
.... **105.00   125.00**

☐ **Star Round Top,** *dark wood, spring, 16¾" x 11⅝", c. 1875, 1 Day, strike (E2-53).*
.... **90.00   110.00**

☐ **As above,** *8 Day, strike*
.... **120.00   145.00**

☐ **Star Round Top Extra,** *dark wood, spring, 16¾" x 11¾", c. 1875, 1 Day, strike (E2-53).*
.... **90.00   110.00**

☐ **As above,** *8 Day, strike*
.... **120.00   145.00**

☐ **Venetian,** *rosewood, rose and gilt, height 15", c. 1875, 1 Day, simple spring (E1-19).*
.... **95.00   115.00**

☐ **As above,** *height 18", 8 Day, simple spring*
.... 115.00   140.00

☐ **Walnut Arch Top,** *walnut, height 13½", c. 1875, 8 Day, simple spring (E1-18).*
.... 125.00   150.00

☐ **Walnut Crown,** *spring, 21" x 11", c. 1875, 8 Day, strike (E2-53).*
.... 150.00   175.00

☐ **Walnut Round Gothic,** *walnut, height 13", c. 1875, 1 Day, simple spring (E1-18).*
.... 65.00   85.00

☐ **Walnut Round Top,** *walnut, height 10", c. 1875, 1 Day, simple spring (E1-19).*
.... 75.00   90.00

SPLIT TOP

☐ **Gilbert Gem,** *dark wood, spring, 17¼" x 10¾", c. 1875, 1 Day, strike (E2-52).*
.... 105.00   125.00

☐ **As above,** *8 Day, strike*
.... 125.00   150.00

☐ **Rocket,** *dark wood, spring, 15½" x 11⅛", c. 1875, 1 Day, strike (E2-52).*
.... 75.00   95.00

☐ **As above,** *8 Day, strike*
.... 95.00   105.00

☐ **Rose Doric,** *rosewood, height 16", c. 1875, 1 Day, simple spring (E1-19).*
.... 105.00   125.00

☐ **Walnut Gothic,** *walnut, height 14½", c. 1875, 8 Day, simple spring (E1-19).*
.... 70.00   85.00

☐ **Walnut Gothic Pillar,** *walnut, height 15", c. 1875, 8 Day, simple spring (E1-19).*
.... 105.00   125.00

STEEPLE

☐ **Sharp Gothic,** *walnut, height 20", c. 1875, 1 Day, simple spring (E1-19).*
.... 95.00   115.00

CRYSTAL REGULATORS

☐ **Tarsus,** *onyx base, rich ormolu gold finish, fancy visible pendulum, ivory porcelain dial, visible escapement, 16¾" x 11", c. 1910 (E1-125).*
.... **575.00   650.00**

☐ **Terese,** *rich ormolu gold finish, mercurial pendulum, ivory porcelain dial, visible escapement, white beveled plate glass front, back and sides, 17" x 8¾", c. 1910 (E1-125).*
.... **540.00   600.00**

☐ **Sharp Gothic,** *dark wood, spring, 19½" x 11¼", c. 1875, 1 Day, strike (E2-51).*
.... **95.00   115.00**
☐ **As above,** *8 Day, strike*
.... **125.00   150.00**

☐ **Small Gothic,** *walnut, height 14½", c. 1875, 1 Day, simple spring (E1-18).*
.... **100.00   120.00**

☐ **Small Sharp Gothic,** *dark wood, 14¾" x 8⅞", c. 1875, 1 Day (E2-51).*
.... **80.00   100.00**
☐ **As above,** *1 Day, strike*
.... **100.00   120.00**

☐ **Winstead Gothic Extra,** *dark wood, 17¼" x 10½", c. 1875, 1 Day, strike (E2-51).*
.... **80.00   100.00**
☐ **As above,** *8 Day, strike*
.... **110.00   135.00**

☐ **Trinity,** *rich ormolu gold finish, fancy visible pendulum, four fancy columns, ivory porcelain dial, visible escapement, 16½" x 10½", c. 1910 (E1-125).*
.... **625.00   700.00**

☐ **Tunis,** *rich ormolu gold finish, mercurial pendulum, ivory porcelain dial, visible escapement, white beveled plate glass front, back and sides, 10½" x 8¾", c. 1910 (E1-125).*
.... 425.00   475.00

☐ **Tuscan,** *Brazilian green onyx columns, onyx cap and base, mercurial pendulum, rich ormolu gold finish, porcelain dial, visible escapement, 19" x 11½", c. 1910, (E1-125).*
.... 675.00   750.00

☐ **Valerie,** *polished brass finish, mercurial pendulum, ivory porcelain dial, visible escapement, white beveled plate glass front, back and sides, 9¼" x 6⅜", c. 1910 (E1-125).*
.... 205.00   235.00

☐ **Venice,** *rich ormolu gold finish, mercurial pendulum, ivory porcelain dial, visible escapement, white beveled plate glass front, back and sides, 16" x 7¾", c. 1910 (E1-125).*
.... 490.00   550.00

☐ **Verdi,** *rich ormolu gold finish, mercurial pendulum, ivory porcelain dial, visible escapement, white beveled plate glass front, back and sides, 15" x 8¾", c. 1910 (E1-125).*
.... 800.00   900.00

☐ **Vista,** *polished brass finish, mercurial pendulum, porcelain dial, visible escapement, white beveled plate glass front, back and sides, 10¾" x 6⅜", c. 1910 (E1-125).*
.... 245.00   275.00

GALLERY

☐ **Brass Lever,** *brass, dial, 5", c. 1875, 1 Day (E1-18).*
.... 105.00   125.00

☐ **Bronze Lever,** *bronze, dial, 4", c. 1875, 1 Day (E1-18).*
.... 60.00   75.00

☐ **Corridor,** *varnished oak finish, 24" x 15½", c. 1920, 8 Day (E1-184).*
.... 105.00   125.00

☐ **Octagon Lever,** *oak, 4" dial, c. 1875, 1 Day (E2-54).*
.... 45.00   60.00
☐ **As above,** *6" dial, 1 Day.*
.... 65.00   80.00
☐ **As above,** *6" dial, 1 Day, alarm.*
.... 75.00   90.00
☐ **As above,** *6" dial, 1 Day, strike.*
.... 80.00   100.00
☐ **As above,** *8" dial, 1 Day.*
.... 105.00   125.00
☐ **As above,** *8" dial, 1 Day, alarm.*
.... 110.00   135.00
☐ **As above,** *8" dial, 1 Day, strike.*
.... 125.00   150.00

☐ **Plain Gilt Gallery,** *pendulum, spring, 12", c. 1875, 8 Day, strike (E1-18).*
.... 335.00   375.00
☐ **As above,** *10", 8 Day, strike.*
.... 285.00   325.00
☐ **As above,** *8", 8 Day, strike.*
.... 245.00   275.00

KITCHEN

☐ **Austin No. 45,** *oak, height 22½",*
dial 6", c. 1900, 8 Day, strike,
spring wound, (E2-56).
. . . . 135.00   160.00

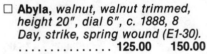

☐ **Abyla,** *walnut, walnut trimmed,*
height 20", dial 6", c. 1888, 8
Day, strike, spring wound (E1-30).
. . . . **125.00   150.00**
☐ **As above,** *ash.*
. . . . **175.00   200.00**

☐ **Albany No. 44,** *oak, height 22½",*
dial 6", c. 1900, 8 Day, strike,
spring wound (E2-56).
. . . . **135.00   160.00**

☐ **Alpine,** *walnut, height 19½", dial*
6", c. 1888, 1 Day, strike, spring
wound (E1-30).
. . . . **120.00   145.00**
☐ **As above,** *ash.*
. . . . **170.00   195.00**

☐ **Britannic No. 47,** *oak, height 25",
dial 6", c. 1900, 8 Day, strike,
spring wound (E2-56).*
. . . . **155.00   180.00**

☐ **Cairo,** *oak, height 23", dial 6", c.
1905, 8 Day, strike, spring wound
(E2-55).*
. . . . **150.00   175.00**

☐ **Calla,** *walnut, height 20", dial 6",
c. 1888, 8 Day, strike, spring
wound (E1-30).*
. . . . **115.00   140.00**

☐ **Calpe,** *ash, walnut trimmed,
height 20", dial 6", spring
wound, c. 1888 (E1-30).*
. . . . **120.00   145.00**

☐ **Calypso,** *walnut, height 20½",
dial 6", c. 1888, 8 Day, strike,
spring wound (E1-30).*
. . . . **115.00   140.00**

☐ **Clay,** *oak, height 24", dial 6", c.
1900, 8 Day, strike, spring wound
(E2-55).*
. . . . **150.00   175.00**

☐ **Concord,** *oak, height 23½", dial
6", c. 1903, 8 Day, strike, spring
wound (E2-57).*
. . . . **150.00   175.00**

☐ **Concord Calendar,** *oak, height
23½", dial 6", c. 1903, 8 Day,
strike, spring wound (E2-57).*
. . . . **175.00   200.00**

☐ **Crius,** *walnut, height 19½", dial
6", c. 1888, 1 Day, strike, spring
wound (E1-30).*
. . . . **110.00   135.00**

☐ **As above,** *ash.*
. . . . **160.00   185.00**

☐ **Dio,** *walnut, height 20", dial 6",
c. 1888, 8 Day, strike, spring
wound (E1-30).*
. . . . **115.00   140.00**

☐ **Eagle,** *oak, height 22", dial 6", c. 1896, 8 Day, strike, spring wound (E2-59).*
.... 145.00   170.00
☐ **As above,** *walnut*
.... 170.00   195.00

☐ **Dove,** *oak, height 22", dial 6", c. 1896, 8 Day, strike, spring wound (E2-59).*
.... 145.00   170.00
☐ **As above,** *walnut*
.... 170.00   195.00

☐ **Eclipse,** *oak, height 25", dial 6", c. 1903, 8 Day, strike, spring wound (E2-57).*
.... 160.00   185.00

☐ **Edina,** *walnut, height 18¾", dial 5", c. 1888, 1 Day, strike, spring wound (E1-30).*
.... 105.00   125.00

☐ **Egypt,** *oak, height 23" dial 6", c. 1905, 8 Day, strike, spring wound (E2-55).*
.... 150.00   175.00

☐ **Erie,** *oak, height 22½", dial 6", c. 1896, 8 Day, strike, spring wound (E2-59).*
.... 140.00   165.00
☐ **As above,** *walnut*
.... 165.00   190.00

☐ **Eros,** *walnut, height 19½", dial 6", c. 1888, 8 Day, strike, spring wound (E1-30).*
.... 115.00   140.00

☐ **Ersa,** *walnut, height 19½", dial 6", c. 1888, 8 Day, strike, spring wound (E1-30).*
.... 115.00   130.00

☐ **As above,** *ash*
.... 165.00   180.00

☐ **Flora,** *walnut with ash trimmings, height 17", dial 5", c. 1888, 1 Day, strike, spring wound ((E1-30).*
.... 110.00   135.00

☐ **Geranium,** *oak, height 24", dial 6", c. 1903, 8 Day, strike, spring wound (E2-57).*
.... 150.00   175.00

☐ **Fruit,** *oak, height 24½", dial 6", c. 1903, 8 Day, strike, spring wound (E2-57).*
.... 160.00   185.00

☐ **As above,** *walnut*
.... 185.00   210.00

☐ **Hawk,** *oak, height 22", dial 6", c.1896, 8 Day, strike, spring wound (E2-59).*
.... 150.00   170.00

☐ **As above,** *walnut*
.... **175.00** **195.00**

☐ **Hestia,** *walnut, height 20½", dial 6", c. 1888, 1 Day, strike, spring wound (E1-30).*
.... **110.00** **135.00**

☐ **Iowa No. 23,** *height 24", dial 6", c. 1900, 8 Day, strike, spring wound (E2-56).*
.... **155.00** **180.00**

☐ **Huron,** *oak, height 22½", dial 6", c. 1896, 8 Day, strike, spring wound (E2-59).*
.... **145.00** **170.00**

☐ **As above,** *walnut*
.... **170.00** **195.00**

☐ **Indiana No. 25,** *oak, height 24", dial 6", c. 1900, 8 Day, strike, spring wound (E2-56).*
.... **155.00** **180.00**

□ **Laurel, Thermometer And Barometer,** *oak, height 24", dial 6", c. 1903, 8 Day, strike, spring wound (E2-57).*
.... **160.00** **185.0**

□ **Lesbia,** *walnut, height 16½", dial 5", c. 1888, 1 Day, strike, spring wound (E1-30).*
.... **105.00** **125.00**

□ **Lincoln,** *oak, height 23", dial 6", c. 1900, 8 Day, strike, spring wound (E2-55).*
.... **150.00** **175.00**

□ **Mahuta,** *walnut, height 18½", dial 6", c. 1888, 1 Day, strike, spring wound (E1-30).*
.... **110.00** **135.00**

□ **Michigan,** *oak, height 22½", dial 6", c. 1896, 8 Day, strike, spring wound (E2-59).*
.... **140.00** **165.00**
□ **As above,** *walnut*
.... **165.00** **190.00**
□ **Missouri No. 26,** *oak, height 24", dial 6", c. 1900, 8 Day, strike, spring wound (E2-56).*
.... **155.00** **180.00**

□ **Mogul,** *oak, height 23, dial 6", c. 1900, 8 Day, strike, spring wound (E2-55).*
.... **150.00** **175.00**

☐ **Ontario,** *oak, height 22½", dial 6", c. 1896, 8 Day, strike, spring wound (E2-59).*
.... 145.00   170.00

☐ **As above,** *walnut*
.... 170.00   195.00

☐ **Oregon No. 24,** *oak, height 24", dial 6", c. 1900, 8 Day, strike, spring wound (E2-56).*
.... 155.00   180.00

☐ **Owl,** *oak, height 22", dial 6", c. 1896, 8 Day, strike, spring wound (E2-59).*
.... 145.00   170.00

☐ **As above,** *walnut*
.... 170.00   195.00

☐ **Pasha,** *oak, height 23", dial 6", c. 1905, 8 Day, strike, spring wound (E2-55).*
.... 150.00   175.00

☐ **Perfect,** *oak, height 23½", dial 6", c. 1903, 8 Day, strike, spring wound (E2-57).*
.... 145.00   170.00

☐ **Perfect, Thermometer And Barometer,** *oak, height 23½", dial 6", c. 1903, 8 Day, strike, spring wound (E2-57).*
.... 155.00   180.00

☐ **Peto,** *walnut, height 20", dial 6", c. 1888, 8 Day, strike, spring wound (E1-30).*
.... 115.00   140.00

☐ **Petrel No. 28,** *oak, height 24", dial 6", c. 1900, 8 Day, strike, spring wound (E2-56).*
.... 155.00   180.00

☐ **Pharaoh,** *oak, height 23", dial 6", c. 1905, 8 Day, strike, spring wound (E2-55).*
.... 150.00   175.00

☐ **Polk,** *oak, height 23", dial 6", c. 1900, 8 Day, strike, spring wound (E2-55).*
.... 150.00   175.00

☐ **Pyramid**, *oak, height 23", dial 6", c. 1905, 8 Day, strike, spring wound (E2-55).*
.... **150.00   175.00**

☐ **Prince**, *walnut, height 20½", dial 6", c. 1888, 8 Day, strike, spring wound (E1-30).*
.... **115.00   140.00**

☐ **Superior**, *oak, height 22½", dial 6", c. 1896, 8 Day, strike, spring wound (E2-59).*
.... **145.00   170.00**
☐ **As above**, *walnut*
.... **170.00   195.00**

☐ **Swan**, *oak, height 22", dial 6", c. 1896, 8 Day, strike, spring wound (E2-59).*
.... **145.00   170.00**
☐ **As above**, *walnut*
.... **170.00   195.00**

☐ **Trenton No. 43,** *oak, height 22½", dial 6", c. 1900, 8 Day, strike, spring wound (E2-56).*
.... **135.00 160.00**

☐ **Walnut Enterprise,** *21¾" x 12", c. 1875, 8 Day, strike, spring wound (E2-51).*
.... **145.00 170.00**

☐ **Washington,** *oak, height 23", dial 6", c. 1900, 8 Day, strike, spring wound (E2-55).*
.... **150.00 175.00**

☐ **Teutonic No. 46,** *oak, height 25", dial 6", c. 1900, 8 Day, strike, spring wound (E2-56).*
.... **155.00 180.00**

☐ **Winnipeg,** *oak, height 22½", dial 6", c. 1896, 8 Day, strike, spring wound (E2-59).*
.... **145.00 170.00**
☐ **As above,** *walnut*
.... **170.00 195.00**

KITCHEN
HANGING

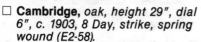

☐ **Cambridge,** *oak, height 29", dial 6", c. 1903, 8 Day, strike, spring wound (E2-58).*
.... 250.00   280.00
☐ **As above,** *walnut*
.... 300.00   330.00

☐ **Drexel,** *oak, height 24", dial 6", c. 1903, 8 Day, strike, spring wound (E2-58).*
.... 210.00   240.00

☐ **Dundee,** *oak, height 24", dial 6", c. 1903, 8 Day, strike, spring wound (E2-58).*
.... 210.00   240.00

☐ **Durham,** *oak, height 24", dial 6", c. 1903, 8 Day, strike, spring wound (E2-58).*
.... 210.00   240.00

☐ **Girard,** *oak or walnut, height 29", dial 6", c. 1903, 8 Day, strike, spring wound (E2-58).*
.... 250.00   280.00

☐ **Oxford,** *oak, height 28", dial 6",
c. 1903, 8 Day, strike, spring
wound (E2-58).*
.... 230.00   260.00
☐ **As above,** *walnut*
.... 280.00   310.00

SERIES

☐ **Bird Set (6),** *oak, height 22", dial
6", c. 1896, spring wound (E2-59).*
.... 145.00   170.00
☐ **As above,** *walnut*
.... 135.00   160.00

☐ **Capitol Set (3),** *oak only, height
22½", dial 6", c. 1900, 8 Day,
strike, spring wound (E2-56).*
.... 135.00   160.00

☐ **Citizen Set (6),** *oak, c. 1900, 8
Day, strike, spring wound (E2-55).*
.... 150.00   175.00

☐ **Egyptian Set (6),** *oak, c. 1905, 8
Day, strike, spring wound (E2-55).*
.... 150.00   175.00

TEAR DROP

☐ **Walnut Shell,** *dark wood, 21" x
13", c. 1875, 8 Day, strike, spring
wound (E2-51).*
.... 150.00   175.00

MANTEL

ONYX

☐ **Onyx No. 1,** *green onyx, gilt
metal trimmings, 17½", x 9½",
porcelain dial 4½", c. 1910, 8
Day, strike (E2-47).*
.... 200.00   240.00

☐ **Onyx No. 2,** *green onyx, gilt metal trimmings, 15" x 8", porcelain dial 4½", c. 1910, 8 Day, strike (E2-47).*
.... **210.00   240.00**

☐ **Onyx No. 3,** *green onyx, gilt metal trimmings, 16¼" x 8", porcelain dial 4½", c. 1910, 8 Day, strike (E2-47).*
.... **190.00   220.00**

ROUND TOP
☐ **Medal,** *walnut, pendulum, 9" x 8", c. 1875, 8 Day (E2-53).*
.... **115.00   140.00**

☐ **Rose Grecian,** *rosewood, height 13½", c. 1875, 1 Day, simple spring (E1-18).*
.... **175.00   200.00**

NOVELTY
GILTS
☐ **Amarna,** *metal gold ormolu, plain sash or Venetian green and gold, 11" x 5¼", dial 2", c. 1910, 1 Day (E2-47).*
.... **80.00   100.00**

☐ **Amon,** *metal gold ormolu, plain sash or Venetian green or gold, 14¾" x 5¾", dial 2", c. 1910, 1 Day (E2-47).*
.... **100.00   120.00**

☐ **Apsu,** *ormolu gold, Venetian bronze and barbedienne, French sash, 11" x 9", dial 2¾", c. 1910, 1 Day (E2-50).*
. . . . 50.00   65.00

☐ **Arch Altar,** *metal gold ormolu, plain sash, 8¼" x 5", dial 2", c. 1910, 1 Day (E2-48).*
. . . . 85.00   105.00

☐ **Balli,** *metal gold ormolu, plain sash, 9" x 6", dial 2", c. 1910, 1 Day (E2-49).*
. . . . 45.00   60.00

☐ **Castle,** *ormolu gold, Venetian bronze and barbedienne, French sash, 13¾" x 7", ivory dial 4", c. 1910, 8 Day, strike (E2-50).*
. . . . 100.00   120.00

☐ **Chariot No. 1,** *metal gold ormolu, plain sash, 6¼" x 9", dial 2", c. 1910, 1 Day (E2-48).*
. . . . 50.00   65.00

☐ **Chariot No. 2,** *metal gold ormolu, plain sash, 8" x 8", dial 2", c. 1910, 1 Day (E2-48).*
. . . . 65.00   80.00

☐ **Cheri,** *gilt, plain or jeweled sash, 7" x 3½", dial 2", c. 1910, 1 Day (E2-49).*
. . . . 40.00   55.00

☐ **Clarence,** *ormolu gold, Venetian bronze and barbedienne, French sash, 12" x 7", ivory dial 4", c. 1910, 8 Day, strike (E2-50).*
. . . . 105.00   130.00

☐ **Clyde,** *ormolu gold, Venetian bronze and barbedienne, French sash, 13½" x 9½", ivory dial 4", c. 1910, 8 Day, strike (E2-50).*
. . . . 105.00   125.00

☐ **Comforter,** *metal gold ormolu, plain gold or jeweled sash, 10½" x 5¼", dial 2", c. 1910, 1 Day (E2-47).*
. . . . 55.00   70.00

☐ **Content,** *metal gold ormolu, plain or jeweled sash, 10¼" x 5¼", dial 2", c. 1910, 1 Day (E2-47).*
. . . . 55.00   70.00

☐ **Cortige,** *gilt, plain or jeweled sash, 6½" x 4", dial 2", c. 1910, 1 Day (E2-49).*
. . . . 50.00   65.00

☐ **Darius,** *metal gold ormolu, plain or jeweled sash, 9¾" x 5¼", dial 2", c. 1910, 1 Day (E2-47).*
.... 60.00   75.00

☐ **Duo,** *metal gold ormolu, plain sash, 10¾" x 5¾", dial 2", c. 1910, 1 Day (E2-47).*
.... 65.00   80.00

☐ **Fairy,** *ormolu gold, Venetian bronze and barbedienne, French sash, 15½" x 7½", ivory dial 4", c. 1910, 8 Day, strike (E2-50).*
.... 105.00   130.00

☐ **Father Time,** *metal gold ormolu, 10¼" x 9¾", dial 2¾", c. 1910, 1 Day (E2-49).*
.... 65.00   80.00

☐ **Fedora,** *ormolu gold, Venetian bronze and barbedienne, French sash, 15" x 6", ivory dial 4", c. 1910, 8 Day, strike (E2-50).*
.... 95.00   115.00

☐ **Fidelity,** *ormolu gold, Venetian bronze and barbedienne, French sash, onyx base, 14½" x 7", ivory dial 4", c. 1910, 8 Day, strike (E2-50).*
.... 105.00   130.00

☐ **Florence,** *metal gold ormolu, plain sash or Venetian green, 12¾" x 6¾", dial 2", c. 1910, 1 Day (E2-48).*
.... 95.00   115.00

☐ **Floss,** *ormolu gold, Venetian bronze and barbedienne, French sash, 14" x 7½", ivory dial 4", c. 1910, 8 Day, strike (E2-50).*
.... 125.00   140.00

☐ **Freedom,** *metal gold ormolu, plain sash or Venetian green, 10" x 3¾", dial 2", c. 1910, 1 Day (E2-47).*
.... 85.00   105.00

☐ **Good Luck,** *metal gold ormolu, enameled, 3¾" x 3¾", dial 2", c. 1910, 1 Day (E2-48).*
.... 30.00   40.00

☐ **Gold Pillar,** *metal gold ormolu, plain sash, 9½" x 4½", dial 2", c. 1910, 1 Day (E2-48).*
.... 85.00   105.00

☐ **Hester,** *ormolu gold, Venetian bronze and barbedienne, French sash, 13¾" x 7½", ivory dial 4", c. 1910, 8 Day, strike (E2-50).*
.... 105.00   130.00

☐ **Huny,** *metal gold ormulu, plain or jeweled sash, 8" x 6½", dial 2", c. 1910, 1 Day (E2-48).*
.... 50.00   65.00

☐ **Innocence,** *metal gold ormolu, plain sash, 11" x 5", dial 2", c. 1910, 1 Day (E2-48).*
. . . . **55.00**   **70.00**

☐ **Joy,** *metal gold ormolu, plain or jeweled sash, 10" x 5", dial 2", c. 1910, 1 Day (E2-47).*
. . . . **55.00**   **70.00**

☐ **Pami,** *metal gold ormolu, plain or jeweled sash, 9¼" x 3¾", dial 2", c. 1910, 1 Day (E2-47).*
. . . . **55.00**   **70.00**

☐ **Lacanada,** *metal gold ormolu, plain or jeweled sash, 10" x 6", dial 2", c. 1910, 1 Day (E2-49).*
. . . . **90.00**   **110.00**

☐ **Lasanada,** *metal gold ormolu, plain or jeweled sash, 10" x 6", dial 2", c. 1910, 1 Day (E2-49).*
. . . . **55.00**   **70.00**

☐ **Localla,** *gilt finish, plain or jeweled sash, 8½" x 4½", dial 2", c. 1910, 1 Day (E2-49).*
. . . . **55.00**   **70.00**

☐ **Menes,** *metal gold ormolu, plain or jeweled sash, 10" x 6½", dial 2", c. 1910, 1 Day (E2-48).*
. . . . **60.00**   **75.00**

☐ **Nefer,** *metal gold ormolu, plain or jeweled sash, 10¾" x 4", dial 2", c. 1910, 1 Day (E2-48).*
. . . . **65.00**   **80.00**

☐ **Playful,** *metal gold ormolu, plain sash, 9¾" x 5¼", dial 2", c. 1910, 1 Day (E2-48).*
. . . . **55.00**   **70.00**

☐ **Ramese,** *metal gold ormolu, plain sash, 8½" x 4½", dial 2", c. 1910, 1 Day (E2-47).*
. . . . **45.00**   **60.00**

☐ **Ramone,** *metal gold ormolu, plain sash, 9¾" x 4½", dial 2", c. 1910, 1 Day (E2-47).*
. . . . **55.00**   **70.00**

☐ **Reason,** *metal gold ormolu, plain sash, 11" x 4¾", dial 2", c. 1910, 1 Day (E2-48).*
. . . . **60.00**   **75.00**

☐ **Restful,** *metal gold ormolu, plain sash, 10" x 5", dial 2", c. 1910, 1 Day (E2-48).*
. . . . **60.00**   **75.00**

☐ **Rococo No. 1,** *gilt finish, enameled circle around dial in blue and pink, 9" x 7", dial 2¾", c. 1910, 1 Day (E2-49).*
.... 40.00   50.00

☐ **Rococo No. 2,** *gilt finish, enameled circle around dial in blue and pink, 9" x 7½", dial 2¾", c. 1910, 1 Day (E2-49).*
.... 40.00   55.00

☐ **Rococo No. 3,** *gilt finish, enameled circle around dial in blue and pink, 7¾" x 7", dial 2¾", c. 1910, 1 Day (E2-49).*
.... 40.00   50.00

☐ **Rose No. 1,** *gold ormolu with metal leaves (dark green) and roses, natural color, 9" x 7", dial 2", c. 1910, 1 Day (E2-49).*
.... 70.00   85.00

☐ **Rose No. 2,** *gold ormolu with metal leaves (dark green) and roses, natural color, 9½" x 6", dial 2", c. 1910, 1 Day (E2-49).*
.... 65.00   80.00

☐ **Rose No. 3,** *gold ormolu with metal leaves (dark green) and roses, natural color, 8" x 5½", dial 2", c. 1910, 1 Day (E2-49).*
.... 60.00   75.00

☐ **Rose No. 4,** *gold ormolu with metal leaves (dark green) and roses, natural color, 10½" x 5½", dial 2", c. 1910, 1 Day (E2-49).*
.... 70.00   85.00

☐ **Rose No. 5,** *gold ormolu with metal leaves (dark green) and roses, natural color, 11" x 6", dial 2", c. 1910, 1 Day (E2-49).*
.... 70.00   85.00

☐ **Rose No. 6,** *gold ormolu with metal leaves (dark green) and roses, natural color, 9" x 5½", dial 2", c. 1910, 1 Day (E2-49).*
.... 65.00   80.00

☐ **Tahar,** *metal gold ormolu, plain or jeweled sash, onyx base, 9½" x 4", dial 2", c. 1910, 1 Day (E2-47).*
.... 50.00   65.00

☐ **Teti,** *metal gold ormolu, plain or jeweled sash, 11½" x 5¼", dial 2", c. 1910, 1 Day (E2-48).*
.... 65.00   80.00

☐ **Trumpeter,** *metal gold ormolu, plain sash, 9" x 7", dial 2", c. 1910, 1 Day (E2-47).*
.... 70.00   85.00

☐ **Trumpeter,** *metal gold ormolu, plain sash or Venetian green, 12½" x 7", dial 2", c. 1910, 1 Day (E2-48).*
.... 105.00   130.00

☐ **Yawn,** *metal gold ormolu, plain sash, 11¼" x 4½", dial 2", c. 1910, 1 Day (E2-48).*
.... 60.00   75.00

WALL

□ **Masonic Lever,** *walnut, height 14½", dial 4", c. 1875, 1 Day (E2-54).*
. . . . 65.00   80.00

□ **Walnut Parachute,** *height 15¼", c. 1875, 8 Day (E2-53).*
. . . . 85.00   105.00

OFFICE INK

□ **Parlor Ink,** *metal gold ormolu, jeweled sash, 6½" x 10", dial 2", c. 1910, 1 Day (E2-48).*
. . . . 75.00   90.00

REGULATOR

OCTAGON TOP, LONG DROP

□ **Consort,** *varnished oak finish, 32" x 18", c. 1920, 8 Day (E1-184).*
. . . . 270.00   300.00

□ **Regulator B.,** *oak, height 29", dial 12", c. 1896, 8 Day (E1-149).*
. . . . 325.00   375.00

☐ **Regulator No. 2,** *oak, height 33½", c. 1875, 8 Day, weight (E2-54).*
. . . . 675.00   750.00

OCTAGON TOP, SHORT DROP

☐ **Admiral,** *varnished oak finish, 27½" x 18", 8 Day, c. 1920 (E1-184).*
. . . . 175.00   200.00

☐ **Armiral,** *oak, height 26¾", dial 12", c. 1896, 8 Day, (E1-149).*
. . . . 195.00   225.00
☐ **As above,** *8 Day, strike.*
. . . . 220.00   250.00
☐ **As above,** *8 Day, calendar.*
. . . . 245.00   275.00
☐ **As above,** *8 Day, strike, calendar.*
. . . . 270.00   300.00

☐ **Hampton,** *light or dark finish, height 23", dial 10", c. 1896, 8 Day (E1-149).*
. . . . 175.00   200.00
☐ **As above,** *8 Day, strike.*
. . . . 195.00   225.00

☐ **Regulator,** *walnut, spring, 22½" x 15½", c. 1875, 8 Day (E2-54).*
. . . . 245.00   275.00
☐ **As above,** *8 Day, strike.*
. . . . 270.00   300.00
☐ **As above,** *8 Day, strike, calendar.*
. . . . 285.00   325.00

PARLOR WALL

☐ **Asbury,** *oak, height 37", dial 8", c. 1896, 8 Day, (E1-149).*
. . . . 540.00   600.00
☐ **As above,** *8 Day, gong, cathedral.*
. . . . 575.00   650.00
☐ **As above,** *walnut, 8 Day.*
. . . . 640.00   700.00
☐ **As above,** *walnut, 8 Day, gong cathedral.*
. . . . 675.00   750.00

☐ **Berkshire,** *oak, height 38", dial 8", c. 1896, 8 Day, calendar (E1-149).*
.... 1050.00   1350.00
☐ **As above,** *walnut, 8 Day, calendar.*
.... 1150.00   1450.00

☐ **Bonita,** *mahogany flat finish, 33" x 13", c. 1920, 8 Day (E1-183).*
.... 230.00   260.00

☐ **Brighton,** *oak, height 38", dial 8", c. 1896, 8 Day (E1-149).*
.... 540.00   600.00
☐ **As above,** *8 Day, gong, cathedral.*
.... 575.00   650.00
☐ **As above,** *walnut, 8 Day.*
.... 640.00   700.00
☐ **As above,** *8 Day, gong, cathedral.*
.... 675.00   750.00

☐ **Columbia,** *oak, height 37½", dial 8", c. 1903, 8 Day (E2-58).*
.... 425.00   475.00
☐ **As above,** *8 Day, strike.*
.... 465.00   525.00
☐ **As above,** *8 Day, calendar.*
.... 515.00   575.00
☐ **As above,** *8 Day, strike, calendar.*
.... 550.00   625.00

☐ **Defender,** *oak, dial 12", c. 1896, 8 Day (E1-153).*
.... 725.00   800.00
☐ **As above,** *8 Day, cathedral.*
.... 750.00   850.00

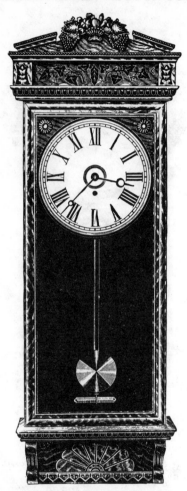

☐ **Leeds,** *mahogany flat finish, 31½" x 14½", c. 1920, 8 Day (E1-183).*
.... **190.00   220.00**

☐ **Observatory,** *varnished oak finish, 36" x 15½", c. 1920, 8 Day (E1-184).*
.... **245.00   275.00**

☐ **Oldham,** *fumed oak finish, 31½" x 14¾", c. 1920, 8 Day (E1-183).*
.... **200.00   240.00**

☐ **Defender,** *oak, 49½" x 20", dial 12", c. 1903, 8 Day (E2-58).*
.... **725.00   800.00**
☐ **As above,** *8 Day, gong, cathedral.*
.... **750.00   850.00**

☐ **Habana,** *mahogany flat finish, 37" x 13½", c. 1920, 8 Day (E1-184).*
.... **190.00   220.00**

☐ **Hanging Weight,** *walnut, height 47", c. 1875, 1 Day, strike, weight (E2-54).*
.... **675.00   750.00**

☐ **Regulator No. 4,** *walnut, glass sides, dead beat escapement, height 51", dial 8", c. 1888, 8 Day, weight (E1-24).*
. . . . **900.00   1100.00**

☐ **Regulator No. 9,** *hanging, walnut, dead beat escapement, sweep center second, 6'6" x 1'10½", dial (porcelain) 12", c. 1896 (E1-153).*
. . . . **2100.00   2400.00**
☐ **As above,** *oak.*
. . . . **2000.00   2300.00**
☐ **As above,** *cherry.*
. . . . **2150.00   2450.00**
☐ **As above,** *ash.*
. . . . **2150.00   2450.00**

ROUND TOP, LONG DROP

☐ **Regulator No. 1,** *dark wood, dead beat escapement, height 33½", c. 1875, 8 Day (E2-54).*
. . . . **700.00   800.00**

SECONDS BIT

☐ **Regulator No. 10,** *walnut, glass sides, dead beat escapement, height 53", dial 10", c. 1888, 8 Day, weight (E1-24).*
. . . . **1000.00   1200.00**

☐ **Regulator No. 11,** *walnut, glass sides, height 50", dial 8", c. 1888, 8 Day, weight (E1-24).*
.... **1000.00   1200.00**
☐ **As above,** *8 Day, weight, strike.*
.... **1100.00   1350.00**
☐ **As above,** *ash, 8 Day, weight, strike.*
.... **1300.00   1500.00**
☐ **As above,** *ash, 8 Day, weight.*
.... **1250.00   1450.00**

☐ **Regulator No. 14,** *oak only, dead beat escapement, retaining power, 50" x 20", dial 12", 8 Day, weight (E2-64).*
.... **1000.00   1100.00**

REGULATOR SWEEP SECOND

(Note: Any of these sweep second regulators may have American, French, or Swiss pinwheel escapements and the prices are based on a pinwheel movement. Deduct at least $500.00 if not.)
☐ **Regulator No. 9,** *walnut, glass sides, dead beat escapement, sweep second, height 78", porcelain dial 12", c. 1888, 8 Day, weight (E1-24).*
.... **2200.00   2500.00**
☐ **As above,** *mahogany.*
.... **2000.00   2300.00**
☐ **As above,** *ash.*
.... **2250.00   2550.00**

☐ **Regulator No. 9,** *walnut, dead beat escapement, height 6'6", dial 12", c. 1903 (E2-65).*
.... **2450.00   2950.00**
☐ **As above,** *oak.*
.... **2250.00   2750.00**
☐ **As above,** *ash.*
.... **2500.00   3000.00**
☐ **As above,** *cherry.*
.... **2500.00   3000.00**

☐ **Regulator No. 12,** *standing, walnut, Swiss movement, dead beat escapement, retaining power, 8'6" x 2'6", dial 12", c. 1903 (E2-65).*
.... **4050.00   4450.00**

☐ **As above,** *oak.*
.... **3850.00   4250.00**
☐ **Regulator No. 12,** *hanging, walnut, 7' x 2'6", c. 1903 (E2-65).*
.... **3950.00   4200.00**
☐ **As above,** *oak.*
.... **3750.00   4000.00**

☐ **Regulator No. 18,** *oak, retaining power, dead beat escapement, 7'7" x 2'1", dial 12", c. 1903 (E2-65).*
.... **2600.00   3000.00**

☐ **As above,** *cherry.*
.... 2850.00   3250.00
☐ **As above,** *walnut.*
.... 2800.00   3200.00

STATUE
LARGE

☐ **Regulator No. 20,** *fine quartered oak, dead beat escapement, retaining power, 6'11" x 20½", dial 12", c. 1903 (E2-65).*
.... 2750.00   3250.00

☐ **Angel,** *extra gold finish, ivory porcelain dial, French sash, beveled glass, 24" x 9", dial 4½", c. 1910, 8 Day, strike (E2-69).*
.... 270.00   300.00

□ **Archer,** *barbedienne finish, gold trimmings, ivory porcelain dial, French sash, beveled glass, 32" x 12", dial 4", c. 1910, 8 Day, strike (E2-68).*
.... 490.00   550.00

□ **Cinderella,** *imperial green, gold trimmings, ivory porcelain dial, French sash, beveled glass, 23" x 12", dial 4", c. 1910, 8 Day, strike (E2-68).*
.... 335.00   375.00

□ **Dandy,** *gold and imperial green finish, ivory porcelain dial, French sash, fancy gilt center, beveled glass, 22½" x 9½", dial 4½", c. 1910, 8 Day, strike, (E2-67).*
.... 175.00   200.00

□ **Mildred,** *gold finish, ivory porcelain dial, French sash, fancy gilt center, beveled glass, 30" x 9", dial 4½", c. 1910, 8 Day, strike (E2-67).*
.... 210.00   240.00

□ **Philip,** *gold finish, ivory porcelain dial, French sash, fancy gilt center, beveled glass, 21¾" x 9", dial 4½", c. 1910, 8 Day, strike (E2-67).*
.... 155.00   180.00

□ **Princess,** *gold finish, ivory porcelain dial, French sash, fancy gilt center, beveled glass, 27" x 10¾", dial 4½", c. 1910, 8 Day, strike (E2-67).*
.... 230.00   260.00

□ **Sandy,** *gold and barbedienne finish, ivory porcelain dial, French sash, fancy gilt center, beveled glass, 23¾" x 9", dial 4½", c. 1910, 8 Day, strike (E2-67).*
.... 170.00   195.00

□ **Torch-Bearer,** *barbedienne finish, gold trimmings, ivory porcelain dial, French sash, beveled glass, 29" x 12", c. 1910, 8 Day, strike (E2-68).*
.... 425.00   475.00

PART ONYX

□ **Cherub,** *gold finish, onyx pedestal, ivory porcelain dial, visible escapement, rococo sash, beveled glass, 22½" x 12¾", dial 4", c. 1910, 8 Day, strike (E2-66).*
.... 465.00   525.00

□ **Tease,** *rich gold finish, onyx inlay, ivory porcelain dial, French sash, beveled glass, 22" x 15½", c. 1910, 8 Day, strike (E2-69).*
.... 625.00   750.00

□ **Tiamut,** *marble inlay, ivory porcelain dial, French sash, beveled glass, 25½" x 17½", dial 4½", c. 1910, 8 Day, strike (E2-69).*
.... 490.00   550.00

PORCELAIN PANEL

□ **Claribel,** *gold finish, china inlay, ivory porcelain dial, French sash, beveled glass, 13" x 7", 4" dial, c. 1910, 8 Day, strike (E2-68).*
.... 270.00   300.00

□ **Estelle,** *rich ormolu gold finish, china inlay, ivory porcelain dial, French sash, beveled glass, 14" x 8½", dial 4", c. 1910, 8 Day, strike (E2-68).*
.... 335.00   375.00

☐ **Gabriel,** *rich ormolu gold finish, china egg and inlay, ivory porcelain dial, French sash, beveled glass, 14" x 7½", dial 4", c. 1910, 8 Day, strike (E2-68).*
. . . . 310.00   350.00

☐ **Forever,** *French gold finish, porcelain inlay, ivory porcelain dial, French sash, beveled glass, 16" x 13¾", dial 4½", c. 1910, 8 Day, strike (E2-69).*
. . . . 335.00   375.00

☐ **Kingston,** *gold finish, porcelain inlay, ivory porcelain dial, French sash, beveled glass, 14½" x 8½", dial 4", c. 1910, 8 Day, strike (E2-68).*
. . . . 310.00   350.00

☐ **Marlboro,** *gold finish, decorated porcelain inlay, onyx top, ivory porcelain dial, visible escapement, rococo sash, beveled glass, 10¾" x 17", dial 4", c. 1910, 8 Day, strike (E2-66).*
. . . . 310.00   350.00

☐ **Marquess,** *gold finish, decorated porcelain inlay, ivory porcelain dial, visible escapement, rococo sash, beveled glass, 14½" x 19", dial 4", c. 1910, 8 Day, strike (E2-66).*
. . . . 490.00   550.00

☐ **Belmar,** *gold or Venetian green finish, ivory porcelain dial, French sash, fancy gilt center, beveled glass, 12" x 14½", dial 4½", c. 1910, 8 Day, strike (E2-69).*
. . . . 170.00   195.00

☐ **Maybell,** *rich ormolu gold finish, decorated china inlay, ivory porcelain dial, French sash, beveled glass, dial 4", c. 1910, 8 Day, strike (E2-68).*
. . . . 335.00   375.00

☐ **Muriel,** *rich ormolu gold finish, decorated china egg and inlay, ivory porcelain dial, French sash, beveled glass, 14" x 10", dial 4", c. 1910, 8 Day, strike (E2-68).*
. . . . 335.00   375.00

☐ **Violinist,** *decorated porcelain inlay, onyx pedestal, French sash, ivory porcelain dial, visible escapement, rococo sash, beveled glass, 23" x 13", dial 4", c. 1910, 8 Day, strike (E2-66).*
. . . . 465.00   525.00

SMALL

☐ **Airondack,** *gold and bronze finish, marbleized base, ivory porcelain dial, French sash, fancy gilt center, beveled glass, 12" x 14½", dial 4½", c. 1910 (E2-67).*
. . . . 190.00   220.00

☐ **Bramble,** *ormolu gold finish, ivory porcelain dial, visible escapement, rococo sash, beveled glass, 13½" x 12", dial 4", c. 1910, 8 Day, strike (E2-66).*
. . . . 210.00   240.00

☐ **Charger,** *gold or Venetian green finish, ivory porcelain dial, French sash, fancy gilt center, beveled glass, 12" x 14½", dial 4½", c. 1910, 8 Day, strike (E2-69).*
. . . . 170.00   195.00

☐ **Edward,** *gold finish, ivory porcelain dial, French sash, fancy gilt center, beveled glass, 13½" x 14", dial 4½", c. 1910, 8 Day, strike (E2-67).*
. . . . 190.00   220.00

☐ **Elenor,** *gilt or Venetian green finish, ivory porcelain dial, French sash, beveled glass, 12" x 8½", dial 4½", c. 1910, 8 Day, strike (E2-69).*
. . . . 160.00   185.00

☐ **Frolic,** *ormolu gold, ivory porcelain dial, visible escapement, rococo sash, beveled glass, 16" x 13", dial 4", c. 1910, 8 Day, strike (E2-66).*
. . . . 250.00   280.00

☐ **Grace,** *ormolu gold, ivory porcelain dial, visible escapement, rococo sash, beveled glass, 15½" x 11½", dial 4", c. 1910, 8 Day, strike (E2-66).*
. . . . 190.00   220.00

☐ **Grecian,** *gold or Venetian green finish, ivory porcelain dial, French sash, fancy gilt center, beveled glass, 12" x 14½", dial 4½", c. 1910, 8 Day, strike (E2-67).*
. . . . 170.00   195.00

☐ **Hercules,** *gold finish, ivory porcelain dial, visible escapement, rococo sash, beveled glass, 16½" x 14½", dial 4", c. 1910, 8 Day, strike (E2-66).*
. . . . 250.00   280.00

☐ **Holland,** *barbedienne or gilt finish, ivory porcelain dial, visible escapement, rococo sash, beveled glass, 12" x 14½", dial 4", c. 1910, 8 Day, strike (E2-66).*
. . . . 230.00   260.00

☐ **Mignon,** *gold or bronze finish, marbleized base, ivory porcelain dial, French sash, beveled glass, 12" x 14½", dial 4½", c. 1910, 8 Day, strike (E2-69).*
. . . . 165.00   190.00

☐ **Republic,** *rich ormolu gold finish, onyx base and back, fancy visible pendulum, ivory porcelain dial, French sash, beveled glass, 15" x 9½", dial 4", c. 1910, 8 Day, strike (E2-68).*
. . . . 550.00   625.00

☐ **Salvator,** *gold or Venetian green finish, ivory porcelain dial, French sash, beveled glass, 12" x 14½", c. 1910, 8 Day, strike, (E2-69).*
. . . . 170.00   195.00

☐ **Serenade,** *gold or Venetian green finish, ivory porcelain dial, French sash, fancy gilt center, beveled glass, 12" x 14½", dial 4½", c. 1910, 8 Day, strike (E2-67).*
. . . . 170.00   195.00

☐ **Sportsman,** *gold or bronze finish, ivory porcelain dial, French sash, beveled glass, 13½ x 14", dial 4½", c. 1910, 8 Day, strike (E2-69).*
. . . . 170.00   195.00

GILBERT DIAL

CALENDAR

☐ **Victorian Kitchen,** *spring, 20" x 11½", dial 5", 8 Day, strike (M432-135).*
. . . . 225.00   275.00

☐ **Victorian Kitchen,** *dial 5", 8 Day, strike (M433-135).*
. . . . 250.00   295.00

GILBERT-MARANVILLE

CALENDAR

☐ **Round Drop Wall**, *spring, 33" x 18½", dial 14", 8 Day (E2-62, M424-133).*
.... 900.00 1000.00

☐ **Round Drop Wall**, *spring, 34½" x 18½", dial 14", 8 Day, simple calendar (M427-133).*
.... 500.00 600.00

GILBERT-MC CABE

CALENDAR

☐ **Bershire**, *spring, 39" x 14", dial 8", 8 Day (E2-62, E1-149, M461-142).*
.... 1800.00 2100.00

☐ **Elberon**, *spring, 30½ x 15", dial 8", 8 Day, strike, perpetual calendar (E2-61).*
.... 1400.00 1750.00

☐ **Lenox**, *spring, 35½" x 15", dial 8", 8 Day (E1-149, M462-142).*
.... 1800.00 2050.00

☐ **Maine**, *spring, 49" x 18", dial 12", 8 Day, strike, (E2-62, M466-143).*
.... 2200.00 2150.00

☐ **Oriental**, *spring, 30" x 15½", dial 8", 8 Day, strike, perpetual calendar (E1-152, E2-61).*
.... 1500.00 1850.00

☐ **Sharon**, *spring, 38" x 14½", dial 8", 8 Day (E1-149, M463-142).*
.... 1850.00 2100.00

☐ **Sharon**, *spring, 38" x 14½", dial 8", 8 Day (E1-149, M464-142).*
.... 1850.00 2100.00

E. HOWARD CLOCK COMPANY

David Porter Davis is NOT associated with the first immigrant clockmaker, William Davis of Boston, although the surname does lend a good auspice to his career, and his association with Edward Howard.

D.P. Davis, a former apprentice of the prestigious Willard brothers, was in partnership with Howard for a time in a company known as Howard and Davis. Howard was trained in Boston and apprenticed (as was Davis) under Aaron Willard. A Luther Stephenson entered into the two men's company partnership for a time, but he lasted only five seasons. Interestingly enough Howard and Davis produced items for other fields besides horology, and even received awards for the fine manufacturing insured in all their wares.

Howard and Davis were the recipients of two of the first 28 day watches manufactured by Aaron Dennison. They had financed the ingenious inventor, and these particular watches are engraved with their names.

Davis eventually left the partnership because of severe financial problems within the firm. Howard perserved through the difficulties, and ended up retiring with a fortune.

Howard is also associated with the manufacture of tower clocks, in which the Seth Thomas Company was his primary rival.

Howard clocks are considered by some collectors to be the most desirable of all. This is the main reason the prices are at such a high level. Seldom do you see any Howards on the market except for some of the small regulators. I'm sure some of the bigger clocks occasionally change hands but not often in public because old time collectors and dealers know where they are and when they are sold it usually is done privately.

Howard Regulators No. 1, 2, 3, 4 and 5 were being copied even in the 1860's, or maybe a better explanation is that a number of companies were making similar clocks with Howard being the surviving maker. Out of the No. 1 to No. 10 Regulator series, two or three models have been reproduced at one time or another, and currently the No. 1 is being made and offered for sale as an original. The Howard Company is presently making limited editions of some of its old model, small regulators.

With all the above in mind, before a prospective buyer will lay down the high dollar that is now being asked, "he will frequently ask for the original dust." Howard clocks should never be refinished unless it is an absolute must. Refinishing almost always reduces the value.

The clocks on this page came out of an 1858 company catalog, this being the successor to Howard and Davis Clock Company in 1857. The company continued to make some of these clocks for many years. I have no way of knowing how many of each model was made. I know that there are not enough for every collector to have one. I have indicated which of the small regulators that collectors consider scarce or rare. Only the most serious collectors will pay much for some models, especially the marble, marble dial and watchmen's clock.

All of the Howard section of this book was selected from original factory catalogs and the general catalogs of some of their dealers. A few models appear in all catalogs and some only one time, which would tend to indicate some models were not successful and were made only for a short time. It would take a book on the Howard Company alone to discuss it thoroughly.

I offer the values and these short comments in an effort to help you as much as I can in the limited space available. On the clocks not priced, I just can't get a handle on what they may be worth. Most of these sales will be what the seller can get the buyer to pay, but more often (and this is where you come in), the seller will not have the knowledge or the guts to ask you the true value and you will be able to get a fine clock for very little money.

I can remember a day less than ten years ago, being called down to a local hospital that had closed to look at an old clock. They were selling the odds and ends that were left and he asked me $750.00 for the clock. I looked all over for a name and all I could find was a name I recognized as a high-class jewelry firm in New York City. Not having the knowledge to know what the clock was, I turned it down. A short time later, while looking through a Howard catalog, I realized the clock was a No. 46 Regulator. As you can guess, I have thought about that mistake many times.

I think many of the larger Howard clocks were pretty much custom made as to case wood, size, and movement. Movements are very important. For instance, if any clock I have priced has a "No. 1 Dennison's Gravity Escapement" add $150.00 to the value of the clock.

In short, with Howard clocks being so scarce, plenty of buyers with money around, and money not being worth what it used to be, it's just about impossible to put a value on one. I think the beauty of the clock, the desire of the buyer and his ability to pay (coupled with the seller's knowledge or lack of same), will determine the actual value for that point in time.

Good luck in your search for a Howard clock for your home, office or collection.

ASTRONOMICAL

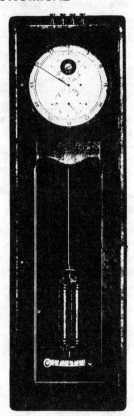

☐ **No. 74,** *four jar mercury pendulum, made in three grades, 60" x 19", rare.*
.... **15000.00 20000.00**
Note: The No. 74 Astronomical clock was manufactured in three grades for the principal observatories in the United States. According to a Howard catalog issued around 1915, at least 75 of these clocks were made.

ASTRONOMICAL DIAL
STANDING, SQUARE TOP, DECORATED

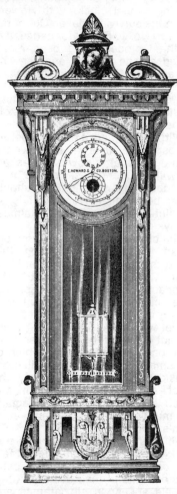

☐ **No. 43 Regulator,** *walnut, Graham dead beat escapement, height 8'8", dial 14" (E1-91).*
.... **12500.00 15000.00**

☐ **No. 48 Regulator,** *walnut,*
Graham dead beat escapement,
height 9'6", dial 14" (E1-91).
. . . . **12000.00 15000.00**

WALL, SQUARE TOP, DECORATED

☐ **No. 49 Regulator,** *walnut,*
Graham dead beat escapement,
height 7'6", dial 14" (E1-92).
. . . . **14500.00 16000.00**

☐ **No. 45 Regulator,** *walnut,*
Graham dead beat escapement,
height 8'2", dial 14" (E1-91).
. . . . **15000.00 17500.00**

☐ **No. 46 Regulator,** *walnut,*
Graham dead beat escapement,
height 10'6", dial 18" (E1-91).
. . . . **12000.00 15000.00**

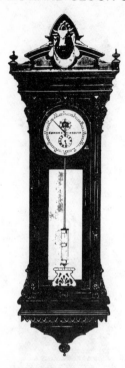

☐ **No. 67 Regulator,** *walnut,*
Graham dead beat escapement,
height 10'3", dial 16" (E1-94).
. . . . **14000.00 16000.00**
☐ **As above,** *height 9'3".*
. . . . **13000.00 14000.00**
☐ **As above,** *height 8'9", dial 14".*
. . . . **12000.00 13000.00**
☐ **As above,** *height 7'9", dial 14".*
. . . . **11000.00 12000.00**

ASTRONOMICAL REGULATOR DIAL

STANDING, ROUND TOP
☐ **No. 22 Regulator,** *walnut,*
Graham dead beat escapement,
height 8'9", dial 16" (E1-91).
. . . . **12000.00 18000.00**

☐ **No. 23 Regulator,** *walnut,*
Graham dead beat escapement,
height 7'3", dial 16" (E1-91).
. . . . **12000.00 15000.00**

☐ **No. 1 Regulator,** *stained rosewood or cherry, dead beat escapement, height 4'2", dial 12" (E1-90).*
.... **6000.00   7000.00**

☐ **No. 24 Regulator,** *walnut, Graham dead beat escapement, height 8', dial 14" (E1-91).*
.... **15000.00   18000.00**

☐ **No. 25 Regulator,** *walnut, Graham dead beat escapement, height 6'9", dial 14" (E1-91).*
.... **12500.00   15000.00**

☐ **No. 47 Regulator,** *walnut, Graham dead beat escapement, height 9'6", dial 14" (E1-94).*
.... **18000.00   22000.00**

☐ **No. 2 Regulator,** *stained rosewood, recoil escapement, height 3'8", dial 9" (E1-90).*
. . . . 5000.00   6000.00

☐ **No. 3 Regulator,** *stained rosewood, recoil escapement, height 3'2", dial 9" (E1-90).*
. . . . 4000.00   4500.00

☐ **No. 4 Regulator,** *imitation rosewood, recoil escapement, height 2'8", dial 8" (E1-90).*
. . . . 2000.00   2500.00

☐ **No. 5 Regulator,** *imitation rosewood, recoil escapement, height 2'5", dial 7" (E1-90).*
. . . . 2250.00   2600.00

☐ **No. 5 Regulator,** *imitation rosewood, recoil escapement, height 2'5", square, dial 7" (E1-90).*
. . . . 1900.00   2200.00

BANJOS, FIGURE EIGHT

☐ **No. 6 Regulator,** *walnut, Graham dead beat escapement, height 4'10", dial 14" (E1-93).*
. . . . 12500.00 15000.00

☐ **No. 66-2,** *height 23" square,
dial 16".*
. . . . **155.00   180.00**

☐ **No. 66-3,** *height 28" square,
dial 20".*
. . . . **175.00   200.00**

GRANDFATHER c. 1880-1890's

☐ **No. 7 Regulator,** *walnut, oak or
cherry, recoil escapement, height
4'2", dial 12" (E1-93).*
. . . . **9500.00 11000.00**

☐ **No. 8 Regulator,** *walnut, oak or
cherry, recoil escapement, height
3'8", dial 11" (E1-93).*
. . . . **6500.00   7500.00**

ELECTRIC GALLERY

☐ **No. 66-1 Square, ,** *walnut case,
height 17" square, dial 12"
(E1-93).*
. . . . **125.00   150.00**

☐ **No. 77,** *dark mahogany, beveled
French plate, wire gong, hour
strike, Graham dead beat
escapement, height 8'10".*
. . . . **4750.00   5000.00**

☐ **No. 79,** *mahogany, Westminster chimes on wire gongs, Cambridge chimes on saucer gongs, Graham dead beat escapement, height 10'2".*
.... 19500.00 20000.00

☐ **No. 82-13,** *mahogany, beveled French plate, Graham dead beat escapement, cathedral gong, hour and half hour strike, height 8'3".*
.... 6800.00 7200.00

☐ **No. 82-15,** *mahogany or oak, Westminster chimes on saucer gongs, Graham dead beat escapement, height 9'3".*
.... 15750.00 16500.00

☐ **No. 80,** *mahogany, rich carvings, beveled French plate, cathedral gong, hour strike, Westminster chimes on wire gongs, Cambridge chimes on saucer gongs, Graham dead beat escapement, height 8'11".*
.... 14700.00 15200.00

☐ **No. 83,** *mahogany, brass ornaments, saucer gong, hour strike, Graham dead beat escapement, height 7'9½".*
. . . . 3125.00   3400.00

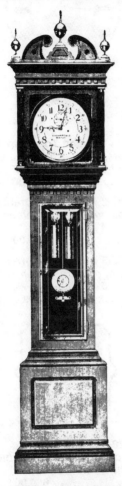

☐ **No. 84,** *dark mahogany, beveled French plate, wire gong, hour strike, Graham dead beat escapement, height 8'4".*
. . . . 4820.00   5000.00

☐ **No. 87,** *mahogany or oak, beveled French plate, cathedral gong, hour and half hour strike, Graham dead beat escapement, height 8'7".*
. . . . 7325.00   7500.00

☐ **No. 88,** *mahogany or oak, beveled French plate, cathedral gong, hour and half hour strike, Graham dead beat escapement, height 8'10".*
. . . . 6025.00   6300.00

HANGING REGULATOR

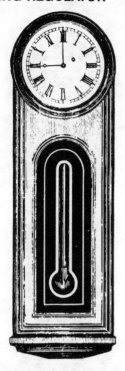

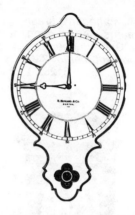

☐ **No. 15-1 Round Top Drop,** *Italian marble, recoil escapement, height 4' 9", dial 36" (E1-93).*
.... **1800.00 2000.00**

☐ **No. 15-2 Round Top Drop,** *Italian marble, recoil escapement, height 4', dial 30".*
.... **2000.00 2200.00**

☐ **No. 15-3 Round Top Drop,** *Italian marble, recoil escapement, height 3' 6", dial 24"*
.... **1600.00 1800.00**

☐ **No. 14 Regulator,** *walnut, recoil escapement, no seconds bit, height 3' 6", dial 10" (E1-92).*
.... **2600.00 3000.00**

MARBLE DIAL

WALL, VARIOUS STYLES, NO SECONDS BIT

☐ **No. 16 Round Top Drop,** *recoil escapement, Italian marble, height 4' 3", dial 30" (E1-93).*
.... **1500.00 2000.00**

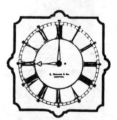

☐ **No. 20-1 Square,** *recoil escapement, Italian marble, height 2', dial 24" (E1-94).*
.... **650.00 700.00**

☐ **No. 20-2,** *As above, height 1' 10", dial 22".*
.... **650.00 700.00**

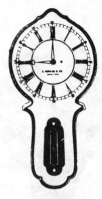

□ **No. 27 Round Top Drop,** *Italian marble, height 2' 11", dial 18" (E1-94).*
.... 2000.00   2200.00
□ **As above,** *height 2' 4", dial 14"*
.... 1800.00   2000.00

□ **No. 21 Round,** *Italian marble, height 2', dial 24" (E1-94).*
.... 500.00   600.00
□ **As above,** *height 2' 6", dial 30"*
.... 500.00   600.00
□ **As above,** *height 3', dial 36"*
.... 500.00   600.00

□ **No. 29 Round,** *walnut case, recoil escapement, 3' 2" x 5' 3", dial 24" (E1-94).*
.... 1250.00   1500.00

□ **No. 30 Round,** *pine case, recoil escapement, height 2', dial 24" (E1-94).*
.... 1250.00   1500.00

□ **No. 33 Round,** *walnut case, recoil escapement, 4' 2" x 5'9", dial 24" (E1-92).*
.... 4250.00   4800.00

□ **No. 35 Round,** *walnut case, recoil escapement, 4' x 3'4", dial 24" (E1-92).*
.... 4250.00   4500.00

☐ **No. 52 Round,** *walnut case, recoil escapement, height 3' 11", dial 20" (E1-94).*
.... **3800.00   4200.00**
☐ **As above,** *height 3', dial 16"*
.... **3750.00   3850.00**

☐ **No. 65 Round,** *walnut case, height 5' 3", dial 24" (E1-94).*
.... **4000.00   4500.00**
☐ **As above,** *height 4' 5", dial 20"*
.... **3500.00   4000.00**

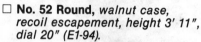

☐ **No.63 Round,** *walnut case, recoil escapement, 5'2" x 3½", dial 24", (E1-93).*
.... **4000.00   4500.00**

☐ **NO. 73 French Glass,** *walnut case, height 3', dial 30" (E1-93).*
.... **2500.00   3000.00**
☐ **As above,** *height 2' 6", dial 24"*
.... **2000.00   2500.00**

REGULATOR
ROUND TOP LONG DROP

☐ **No. 11,** *cherry or stained rosewood, height 31", dial 11" (E1-93).*
.... **3750.00   4000.00**

WALL SQUARE TOP, WALL DECORATED, NO SECONDS BIT

☐ **No. 39,** *walnut, recoil escapement, height 5', dial 12" (E1-92).*
.... **5000.00   6000.00**

☐ **No. 40,** *walnut, recoil escapement, height 4' 6", dial 11" (E1-92).*
.... **4500.00   5000.00**

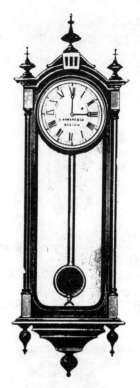

☐ **No. 41,** *walnut, recoil escapement, height 4', dial 9"* *(E1-92).*
. . . . **3500.00 4000.00**

☐ **No. 42,** *walnut, recoil escapement, height 3' 8", dial 8"* *(E1-92).*
. . . . **3000.00 3500.00**

WALL, VARIOUS STYLES, NO SECONDS BIT

☐ **No. 58,** *walnut, recoil escapement, height 5' 4", dial 12" (E1-93).*
. . . . **4500.00 5000.00**

☐ **As above,** *height 4' 3", dial 10"*
. . . . **4000.00 4500.00**

☐ **As above,** *height 3' 5", dial 8"*
. . . . **2500.00 2800.00**

☐ **No. 59,** *walnut, recoil escapement, height 5' 10", dial 12" (E1-93).*
. . . . **8000.00 9000.00**

☐ **As above,** *height 4' 8", dial 10"*
. . . . **6000.00 6500.00**

☐ **As above,** *height 3' 10", dial 8"*
. . . . **5000.00 5500.00**

☐ **As above,** *height 3', dial 6"*
. . . . **4000.00 4500.00**

No. 70

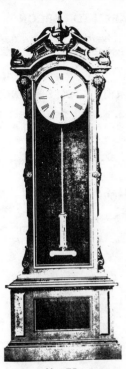

No. 75

☐ **No. 70,** *walnut, oak or cherry, recoil escapement, height 4' 8", dial 24" (E1-93).*
.... 6000.00   6500.00
☐ **As above,** *height 4", dial 20"*
.... 4000.00   4500.00
☐ **As above,** *height 3" 5", dial 16"*
.... 2000.00   2500.00

WATCHMAKERS REGULATORS

STANDING, ARCH TOP, SECONDS BIT

☐ **No. 61,** *walnut, Graham dead beat escapement, height 7' 10", dial 14" (E1-94).*
.... 7000.00   8000.00

☐ **No. 75,** *walnut, mahogany or oak, recoil escapement, height 5', dial 14" (E1-93).*
.... 6000.00   6500.00
☐ **As above,** *height 2' 10", dial 12"*
.... 3500.00   4000.00

No. 61

WALL, ARCH TOP, SECONDS BIT

☐ **No. 71,** *walnut, Graham dead beat escapement, height 5' 10", dial 12" (E1-94).*
. . . . **8000.00 10000.00**

WALL, ROUND TOP, SECONDS BIT

☐ **No. 13,** *walnut, beats seconds, dead beat escapement, height 4' 8", dial 12" (E1-92).*
. . . . **3000.00 3500.00**

WALL DECORATED, ROUND TOP, SECONDS BIT

☐ **No. 36,** *walnut, Graham dead beat escapement, height 6', dial 14" (E1-94).*
. . . . **9000.00 9500.00**

No. 13

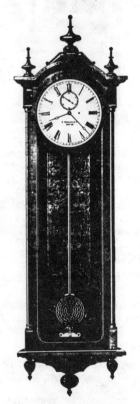

No. 71

No. 36

WALL DECORATED, SQUARE TOP, SECONDS BIT

☐ **No. 38,** *walnut, Graham dead beat escapement, height 6', dial 14" (E1-92).*
.... 7500.00   8000.00

☐ **No. 57,** *walnut, Graham dead beat escapement, height 6' 2", dial 14" (E1-93).*
.... 8000.00   8500.00

☐ **No. 86,** *walnut, Graham dead beat escapement, height 6' 4", dial 14" (E1-94).*
.... 6000.00   6500.00

WALL, VARIOUS STYLES, SECONDS BIT

☐ **No. 72,** *walnut, Graham dead beat escapement, height 5' 5", dial 14" (E1-94).*
.... 4000.00   4500.00

☐ **As above,** *height 5' 4", dial 12"*
.... 3750.00   4250.00

WATCHMENS CLOCK, WALL

☐ **No. 85,** *mahogany, Graham dead
beat escapement, height 5', dial
14" (E1-94).*
.... 6500.00   7000.00

☐ **No. 89,** *walnut, Graham dead
beat escapement, height 5' 5",
dial 12" (E1-94).*
.... 2500.00   3000.00

☐ **No. 26 Regulator,** *walnut, height
4', dial 9" (E1-92).*
.... 800.00   1000.00

E. INGRAHAM COMPANY

Elias Ingraham a former cabinet maker, originally worked for a merchant named George Mitchell in Bristol. Mitchell set him to the task of case making, where he did exceptionally well, inventing a carved model of mahogany, occasionally embellished with bronze.

After two years Ingraham began working for C. and L.C. Ives, where he invented a case called the triple-decker. He also designed the steeple case.

After going through several transitions, including a cabinet making shop used exclusively for the making of clock cases, the E. Ingraham Company was formed, which eventually became simply The Ingraham Company. New plants were opened in Canada, Kentucky, and North Carolina. In the latter location electric and battery clocks were made.

ALARM

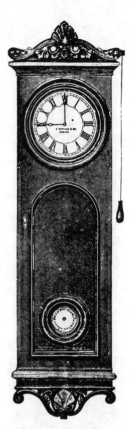

☐ **No. 37 Regulator,** *walnut, height 5' 6", dial 11" (E1-92).*
. . . . **1850.00   2200.00**

☐ **Ace,** *solid brass, nickeled, height 6", c. 1917, 8 Day, alarm (E1-173).*
. . . . **35.00   45.00**

BANJO
SPRING

☐ **Autocrat Intermittent,** *nickel and brass, height 7¼", c. 1917, 1 Day, alarm (E1-173).*
.... 20.00   30.00

☐ **Cinch Intermittent,** *solid brass, nickeled, height 6", c. 1917, 1 Day, alarm (E1-173).*
.... 15.00   25.00

☐ **Ideal Intermittent,** *nickel, height 6", c. 1917, 1 Day, alarm (E1-173).*
.... 15.00   25.00

☐ **Indian,** *nickel, height 6", c. 1917, 1 Day, alarm (E1-173).*
.... 20.00   30.00

☐ **Premier Intermittent,** *solid brass, nickeled, height 7½", c. 1917, 8 Day, alarm (E1-173).*
.... 35.00   45.00

☐ **Sentry,** *nickel, height 6", c. 1917, 1 Day, alarm (E1-173).*
.... 20.00   30.00

☐ **Nile,** *mahogany finish, 39" x 10", iveroid or silver dial 8", c. 1900, 8 Day, (E2-77).*
.... 250.00   300.00
☐ **As above,** *8 Day, strike*
.... 300.00   350.00

□ **Norway,** *red or green finished, circular finish silver plated dial, height 26", c. 1932, 8 Day, marine (E1-108).*
.... **75.00   90.00**

□ **Nyanza,** *mahogany, convex glass, 39" x 10", dial 8", c. 1917, 8 Day, strike (E1-172).*
.... **310.00   350.00**

SPRING LEVER

□ **Neptune,** *mahogany finish, green, rose or blue in crackle finish, circular silver plated dial, height 26", c. 1932, 8 Day, marine (E1-108).*
.... **80.00   100.00**

□ **Nurse,** *mahogany or green finish, circular finish silver plated dial, height 26", c. 1932, 8 Day, marine (E1-108).*
.... **80.00   100.00**

SPRING PENDULUM

☐ **Treasure,** *mahogany finish, height 39", dial 8", c. 1932, 8 Day (E1-108).*
.... 310.00   350.00

CABINET

☐ **Acme,** *oak, height 17", dial 5", c. 1898, 8 Day, strike (E1-160).*
.... 115.00   140.00

☐ **Bazar,** *oak, height 18½", dial 5", c. 1898, 8 Day, strike (E1-160).*
.... 130.00   150.00

☐ **Bismarck,** *oak, fancy gilt, 15" x 10½", dial 6", 8 Day, strike (E1-144).*
.... 80.00   100.00

☐ **Cabinet No. 1,** *oak, height 15½", dial 5", c. 1894, 8 Day, strike (E1-139).*
.... 80.00   100.00

☐ **Cabinet No. 2,** *oak, height 15½", dial 5", c. 1894, 8 Day, strike (E1-139).*
.... 80.00   100.00

☐ **Cabinet No. 3,** *oak, height 15½", dial 5", c. 1894, 8 Day, strike (E1-139).*
.... 80.00   100.00

☐ **Cabinet No. 4,** *oak, height 15½", dial 5", c. 1894, 8 Day, strike (E1-139).*
.... 80.00   100.00

☐ **Cabinet No. 5,** *oak, height 15½ ", dial 5", c. 1894, 8 Day, strike (E1-144).*
.... **80.00   100.00**

☐ **Cabinet No. 6,** *oak, height 15½ ", dial 5", c. 1894, 8 Day, strike (E1-144).*
.... **80.00   100.00**

☐ **Cabinet No. 7,** *oak, height 15½ ", dial 5", c. 1894, 8 Day, strike (E1-141).*
.... **80.00   100.00**

☐ **Cabinet No. 8,** *oak, height 15½ ", dial 5", c. 1894, 8 Day, strike (E1-141).*
.... **80.00   100.00**

☐ **Cabinet No. 9,** *oak, height 15½ ", dial 5", c. 1894, 8 Day, strike (E1-141).*
.... **80.00   100.00**

☐ **Cabinet No. 10,** *oak, height 15½ ", dial 5", c. 1894, 8 Day, strike (E1-141).*
.... **80.00   100.00**

☐ **Cabinet No. 11,** *oak, height 15½ ", dial 5", c. 1894, 8 Day, strike (E1-141).*
.... **80.00   100.00**

☐ **Cabinet No. 12,** *oak, height 15½ ", dial 5", c. 1894, 8 Day, strike (E1-141).*
.... **80.00   100.00**

☐ **Gladstone,** *oak, fancy gilt, 15" x 10½ ", dial 6", 8 Day, strike (E1-144).*
.... **80.00   100.00**

☐ **Tablet,** *walnut, cathedral bell, patent regulator, height 15", dial 5", c. 1894, 8 Day, strike (E1-143).*
.... **80.00   100.00**

☐ **Target,** *walnut, cathedral bell, patent regulator, height 16", dial 5", c. 1894, 8 Day, strike (E1-143).*
.... **80.00   100.00**

☐ **Thistle,** *light wood, black ornaments, cathedral bell, patent regulator, height 16½ ", dial 5", c. 1894, 8 Day, strike (E1-143).*
.... **80.00   100.00**

☐ **Thorn,** *oak, cathedral bell, patent regulator, height 12", dial 5", c. 1894, 8 Day, strike (E1-143).*
.... **80.00   100.00**

☐ **Verona,** *oak, marbleized column, height 15¾ ", dial 5", 8 Day, strike (E1-160).*
.... **125.00   150.00**

CALENDAR

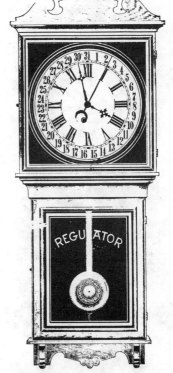

☐ **Aliance Square Top,** *38½ " x 16", dial 12", 8 Day, strike, simple calendar, spring wound (E2-76, M224-77).*
.... **450.00   500.00**

☐ **Artic,** *office wall regulator, 37",
dial 8", 8 Day, strike, simple
calendar, spring wound (E1-154).*
.... 600.00   650.00

☐ **Aurora,** *Victorian kitchen,
thermometer and barometer,
height 25", dial 6", 8 Day, strike,
simple calendar, spring wound
(E2-74).*
.... 200.00   225.00

☐ **Boston 12" Octagon Top,** *long
drop, oak, height 32", 8 Day,
strike, simple calendar (E2-78).*
.... 325.00   375.00

Aurora

Artic

Boston 12"

☐ **8″ Bristol Octagon Top,** *short drop, oak, height 19″, 8 Day, strike, simple calendar (E2-78).* 225.00   250.00

☐ **10″ Bristol Octagon Top,** *short drop, oak, height 21″, 8 Day, strike, simple calendar (E2-78).* 250.00   275.00

☐ **12″ Bristol Octagon Top,** *short drop, oak, height 25″, 8 Day, strike, simple calendar (E2-78).* 250.00   300.00

☐ **Chicago,** *Victorian kitchen, thermometer and barometer, height 23″, dial 6″, 8 Day, strike, simple calendar, spring wound (E2-75).* 200.00   225.00

☐ **Commercial Octagon Top,** *long drop, oak, height 32″, dial 12″, 8 Day, strike, simple calendar (E2-78).* 325.00   375.00

☐ **Dew Drop Octagon,** *24″ x 16″, dial 11″, 8 Day, strike, simple calendar, spring wound (E1-156, M225-77).* 300.00   350.00

☐ **Figure 8 (Wall),** *B.B. Lewis V calendar mechanism, 22″ x 13½″, 9″ time and 5½″ calendar dial, 8 Day, strike, double dial (M217-75).* 1600.00   1800.00

☐ **Gila,** *barometer left of door, thermometer right of door, 23″, dial 6″, 8 Day, strike, simple calendar, spring wound (M221-76).* 225.00   250.00

☐ **Hartford 12″ Octagon Top,** *long drop, oak, height 32″, 8 Day, strike, simple calendar (E2-75).*
.... 350.00   400.00

☐ **Landau,** *wall regulator, oak, 38¼″, dial 10″, 8 Day, strike, simple calendar (E2-78).*
.... 300.00   350.00

☐ **Lyric Octagon Top,** *short drop, height 27″, dial 12″, 8 Day, strike, simple calendar (E2-75).*
.... 250.00   300.00

Landau

Hartford 12″

Lyric

☐ **Mosaic Figure 8,** *B.B. Lewis V calendar mechanism, 29 " x 16", 11" time and 10" calendar dial, 8 Day, double dial, spring wound (M218-75).*
. . . . 850.00   1050.00

☐ **Minerva,** *Victorian kitchen, thermometer and barometer, height 25", dial 6", 8 Day, strike, simple calendar (E2-74).*
. . . . 200.00   225.00

☐ **8" Octagon,** *short drop, 19", 8 Day, strike, simple calendar, spring wound (E1-156).*
. . . . 300.00   350.00

☐ **10" Octagon,** *short drop, 21", 8 Day, strike, simple calendar, spring wound (E1-156).*
. . . . 350.00   375.00

☐ **Misay Octagon,** *short drop, 24", dial 12", 8 Day, strike, simple calendar, spring wound (E1-156).*
. . . . 300.00   350.00

☐ **12" Octagon,** *short drop, 24", 8 Day, strike, simple calendar, spring wound (E1-156).*
. . . . 350.00   400.00

☐ **Ormond,** *round top long drop regulator, 35½", dial 12", 8 Day, simple calendar, spring wound (E1-175).*
.... 350.00   400.00

☐ **Parlor Shelf,** *B.B. Lewis V calendar mechanism, 22" x 12", 5" time and 7" calendar dial, 8 Day, double dial (E1-141, M216-75).*
.... 1400.00   1600.00

☐ **Round Drop,** *wall, 24" x 16", dial 11", 8 Day, strike, simple calendar, spring wound (M222-77).*
.... 300.00   350.00

☐ **8" Octagon Top,** *short drop, oak, height 19", 8 Day, strike, simple calendar (E2-75).*
.... 225.00   250.00

☐ **10" Octagon Top,** *short drop, oak, height 21", 8 Day, strike, simple calendar (E2-75).*
.... 250.00   275.00

☐ **12" Octagon Top,** *short drop, oak, height 24", 8 Day, strike, simple calendar (E2-75).*
.... 250.00   300.00

☐ **8" Octagon,** *short drop, oak, height 19", 8 Day, strike, simple calendar (E2-78).*
.... 225.00   250.00

☐ **10" Octagon,** *short drop, oak, height 21", 8 Day, strike, simple calendar (E2-78).*
.... 250.00   275.00

☐ **12" Octagon,** *short drop, oak, height 25", 8 Day, strike, simple calendar (E2-78).*
.... 250.00   300.00

☐ **Topaz,** *Victorian kitchen, thermometer and barometer, height 23", dial 6", 8 Day, strike, simple calendar, spring wound (E2-75).*
.... 200.00   225.00

☐ **Trenton,** *wall box regulator, oak, or mahogany, height 38", dial 12", 8 Day, strike, simple calendar (E2-78).*
.... 300.00   350.00

☐ **Urania,** *Victorian kitchen, thermometer and barometer, height 25", dial 6", 8 Day, strike, simple calendar, spring wound (E2-74).*
.... 200.00   225.00

☐ **Western Union,** *box wall regulator, oak, height 36", dial 12", 8 Day, strike, simple calendar (E2-78).*
.... 300.00   350.00

Urania

Trenton

Western Union

CONNECTICUT SHELF
COTTAGE

☐ **Cottage Extra,** *polished, veneered, height 12¾", dial 6", c. 1894, 1 Day, strike (E1-140).*
. . . . **70.00**   **85.00**
☐ **As above,** *8 Day, strike*
. . . . **80.00**   **100.00**

OCTAGON TOP
☐ **Britannic,** *wood, height 16", c. 1880, 1 Day, strike (E2-72).*
. . . . **115.00**   **140.00**

☐ **Crystal,** *wood, height 15½", c. 1880, 1 Day, strike (E2-70).*
. . . . **75.00**   **90.00**
☐ **As above,** *8 Day, strike*
. . . . **95.00**   **115.00**

☐ **Era,** *wood, height 15¼", c. 1880, 1 Day, strike (E2-70).*
. . . . **80.00**   **100.00**
☐ **As above,** *8 Day, strike*
. . . . **105.00**   **125.00**

☐ **Octagon Doric,** *wood, height 16", c. 1880, 1 Day, strike (E2-70).*
. . . . **80.00**   **100.00**
☐ **As above,** *8 Day, strike*
. . . . **105.00**   **125.00**

☐ **Octagon Doric,** *extra, wood, height 16", c. 1880, 1 Day, strike (E2-72).*
. . . . **80.00**   **100.00**
☐ **As above,** *8 Day, strike*
. . . . **105.00**   **125.00**

☐ **Octagon Doric,** *gilt column, wood, height 16", c. 1880, 1 Day, strike (E2-70).*
. . . . **80.00**   **100.00**

☐ **Octagon Doric,** *mosaic, wood, height 16", c. 1880, 1 Day, strike (E2-70).*

.... 80.00   100.00

☐ **As above,** *8 Day, strike*

.... 105.00   125.00

O.G.

☐ **O.G. Weight,** *polished, veneered, height 26", dial 8", c. 1894, 1 Day, strike (E1-140).*

.... 130.00   155.00

☐ **As above,** *8 Day, strike*

.... 175.00   200.00

ROUND TOP

☐ **Baltic,** *wood, height 16", c. 1880, 1 Day, strike (E2-72).*

.... 115.00   140.00

☐ **As above,** *8 Day, strike*

.... 140.00   165.00

☐ **Empire,** *wood, height 18", c. 1880, 8 Day, strike (E2-72).*

.... 175.00   200.00

☐ **Idaho,** *wood, gilt columns, height 18", c. 1880, 8 Day, strike (E2-72).*

.... 140.00   165.00

☐ **Venetian No. 2,** *wood, gilt columns, height 18", c. 1880, 8 Day, strike (E2-71).*

.... 150.00   175.00

☐ **Venetian No. 2,** *extra, wood, gilt columns, height 18", c. 1880, 8 Day, strike (E2-71).*

.... 155.00   180.00

☐ **Venetian No. 2,** *mosaic, wood, height 18", c. 1880, 1 Day, strike (E2-71).*

.... 130.00   155.00

☐ **As above,** *8 Day, strike*

.... 155.00   180.00

☐ **Venetian No. 3,** *wood, height 16",*
c. 1880, 1 Day, strike (E2-70).
. . . . **115.00**   **140.00**
☐ **As above,** *8 Day, strike.*
. . . . **140.00**   **165.00**

☐ **Venetian No. 3,** *extra, wood,*
height 16", c. 1880, 1 Day, strike
(E2-71).
. . . . **130.00**   **150.00**

☐ **Venetian No. 3,** *mosaic, wood,*
height 16", c. 1880, 1 Day, strike
(E2-71).
. . . . **130.00**   **150.00**
☐ **As above,** *8 Day, strike*
. . . . **150.00**   **175.00**

SPLIT TOP

☐ **Doric,** *wood, height 16", c. 1880,*
1 Day, strike (E2-70).
. . . . **75.00**   **90.00**
☐ **As above,** *8 Day, strike*
. . . . **105.00**   **125.00**

☐ **Doric,** *extra, wood, height 16", c.*
1880, 1 Day, strike (E2-72).
. . . . **80.00**   **100.00**
☐ **As above,** *8 Day, strike*
. . . . **105.00**   **125.00**

☐ **Doric,** *gilt column, wood, height*
16", c. 1880, 1 Day, strike (E2-70).
. . . . **80.00**   **100.00**
☐ **As above,** *8 Day, strike*
. . . . **105.00**   **125.00**

☐ **Arctic,** *wood, height 16", c. 1880,*
1 Day, strike (E2-71).
. . . . **75.00**   **90.00**
☐ **As above,** *8 Day, strike*
. . . . **95.00**   **115.00**

☐ **Doric,** *extra, gilt columns, wood,*
height 16", c. 1880, 1 Day, strike
(E2-70).
. . . . **90.00**   **110.00**
☐ **As above,** *8 Day, strike*
. . . . **110.00**   **135.00**

☐ **Doric,** *mosaic, wood, height 16",*
c. 1880, 1 Day, strike (E2-70).
.... 80.00   100.00
☐ **As above,** *8 Day, strike*
.... 105.00   125.00

☐ **Pony,** *extra, wood, height 14", c.*
1880, 1 Day, strike (E2-72).
.... 75.00   90.00
☐ **As above,** *8 Day, strike*
.... 95.00   115.00

☐ **Ricarda,** *wood, height 16", c.*
1880, 1 Day, strike (E2-71).
.... 75.00   90.00
☐ **As above,** *8 Day, strike*
.... 95.00   115.00

GALLERY

☐ **Gallery,** *corrugated walnut,*
chestnut and gilt, 10" c. 1880, 8
Day and 8 Day, gilt (E2-72).
.... 195.00   225.00
☐ **As above,** *12"*
.... 220.00   250.00
☐ **As above,** *14"*
.... 245.00   275.00
☐ **As above,** *18"*
.... 270.00   300.00
☐ **As above,** *20"*
.... 270.00   300.00
☐ **As above,** *24"*
.... 270.00   300.00

☐ **Gallery,** *walnut, chestnut and*
gilt, 10" c. 1880, 8 Day and 8 Day,
gilt (E2-73).
.... 175.00   200.00
☐ **As above,** *12"*
.... 195.00   225.00
☐ **As above,** *14"*
.... 220.00   250.00
☐ **As above,** *18"*
.... 245.00   275.00
☐ **As above,** *20"*
.... 270.00   300.00

☐ **Maxim,** *solid oak, dial 10", c.*
1900, 8 Day (E2-78).
.... 175.00   200.00

☐ **Milford,** *oak, dial 12", c. 1900, 8*
Day (E2-78).
.... 175.00   200.00
☐ **As above,** *8 Day, strike*
.... 185.00   210.00
☐ **As above,** *walnut, 8 Day*
.... 225.00   250.00
☐ **As above,** *walnut, 8 Day, strike*
.... 235.00   260.00

KITCHEN

☐ **Albion,** *oak, height 24", dial 6", c. 1894, 8 Day, strike, spring wound (E1-142).*
. . . . 115.00   140.00

☐ **Antler,** *oak, walnut trimmings, height 24", dial 6", c. 1894, 8 Day, strike, spring wound (E1-142).*
. . . . 125.00   150.00

☐ **Astra,** *oak, height 22", dial 6", c. 1898, 8 Day, strike, spring wound (E1-160).*
. . . . 140.00   165.00

☐ **Aurora Calendar,** *oak, barometer and thermometer, height 25", dial 6", c. 1905, 8 Day, strike, calendar, spring wound (E2-74).*
. . . . 190.00   220.00

☐ **Aztec,** *oak, height 24", dial 6", c. 1894, 8 Day, strike, spring wound (E1-142).*
. . . . 125.00   150.00

☐ **Bazar,** *oak, cathedral gong, height 18½", dial 5", c. 1894, 8 Day, strike, spring wound (E1-144).*
. . . . 160.00   185.00

☐ **Brazos,** *oak, height 23", dial 6", c. 1905, 8 Day, strike, spring wound (E2-76).*
. . . . 145.00   170.00

☐ **Bullion,** *walnut, gilt trimmings, height 24", dial 6", c. 1894, 8 Day, strike, spring wound (E1-140).*
. . . . 140.00   165.00

☐ **Capitol,** *oak, height 22", dial 6", c. 1905, 8 Day, strike, spring wound (E2-75).*
. . . . 210.00   240.00

☐ **Carmen,** *light wood, black trimmings, cathedral bell, height 18", dial 5", c. 1894, 8 Day, strike, spring wound (E1-144).*
. . . . 195.00   225.00

☐ **Cayuga,** *oak, height 22", dial 6", c. 1905, 8 Day, strike, spring wound (E2-74).*
. . . . 150.00   175.00

☐ **Chicago Combination,** *oak, thermometer and barometer, height 23", dial 6", c. 1905, 8 Day, strike, calendar, spring wound (E2-75).*
. . . . 190.00   220.00

☐ **Contest,** *walnut, height 16", dial 6", c. 1894, 1 Day, strike, spring wound (E1-141).*
. . . . 70.00   85.00

☐ **Dahlia,** *oak, height 22", dial 6", c. 1894, 8 Day, strike, spring wound (E1-142).*
. . . . 110.00   135.00

☐ **Delaware,** *oak, height 23", dial 6", c. 1905, 8 Day, strike, spring wound (E2-76).*
. . . . 145.00   170.00

☐ **Diana,** *oak, thermometer and barometer, height 25", dial 6", c. 1905, 8 Day, strike, spring wound (E2-74).*
.... 155.00 185.00

☐ **Divan,** *walnut, cathedral bell, height 16½", dial 5", c. 1894, 8 Day, strike, spring wound (E1-144).*
.... 195.00 225.00

☐ **Ducat,** *oak, height 24", dial 6", c. 1894, 8 Day, strike, spring wound (E1-140).*
.... 135.00 160.00

☐ **Easton,** *walnut, height 19", dial 6", c. 1894, 1 Day, strike, spring wound (E1-141).*
.... 100.00 120.00

☐ **Gila,** *oak, height 23", dial 6", c. 1905, 8 Day, strike, spring wound (E2-76).*
.... 145.00 170.00

☐ **Globe,** *oak, height 23", dial 6", c. 1894, 1 Day, spring wound (E1-140).*
.... 95.00 115.00

☐ **As above,** *8 Day, spring wound.*
.... 115.00 140.00

☐ **Globe, Calendar,** *oak, height 23", dial 6", c. 1894, 8 Day, strike, calendar, spring wound (E1-142).*
.... 125.00 150.00

☐ **Globe, Extra,** *oak, thermometer and barometer, height 23", dial 6", c. 1894, 8 Day, strike, spring wound (E1-142).*
.... 150.00 175.00

☐ **As above,** *walnut.*
.... 175.00 200.00

☐ **Ingot,** *walnut, height 24", dial 6", c. 1894, 8 Day, strike, spring wound (E1-140).*
.... 140.00 165.00

☐ **Itasca,** *oak, height 22", dial 6", c. 1905, 8 Day, strike, spring wound (E2-74).*
.... 150.00 175.00

☐ **Jasper,** *oak, dial 6", c. 1898, 8 Day, strike, spring wound (E1-160).*
.... 135.00 160.00

☐ **Juno,** *oak, height 22", dial 6", c. 1898, 8 Day, strike, spring wound (E1-160).*
.... 140.00 165.00

☐ **Lilac,** *walnut, height 23", dial 6", c. 1894, 8 Day, strike, spring wound (E1-142).*
.... 115.00 140.00

☐ **Lily,** *oak, height 22", dial 6", c. 1894, 8 Day, strike, spring wound (E1-141).*
.... 110.00 135.00

☐ **Lion,** *oak, height 22", dial 6", c. 1905, 8 Day, strike, spring wound (E2-75).*
.... 170.00 195.00

☐ **Maine,** *oak, height 23", dial 6", c. 1905, 8 Day, strike, spring wound (E2-75).*
.... 210.00 240.00

☐ **Mars,** *oak, walnut trimmings, height 22", dial 6", c. 1898, 8 Day, strike, spring wound (E1-160).*
.... 140.00 165.00

☐ **McKinley,** *oak, height 23", dial 6", c. 1905, 8 Day, strike, spring wound (E2-75).*
.... 210.00 240.00

☐ **Minerva Calendar,** *oak, barometer and thermometer, height 25", dial 6", c. 1905, 8 Day, strike, calendar, spring wound (E2-74).*
.... 190.00 220.00

☐ **Mt. Vernon,** *oak, height 22", dial 6", c. 1905, 8 Day, strike, spring wound (E2-75).*
.... 210.00 240.00

☐ **Niagara,** *oak, height 23", dial 6", c. 1905, 8 Day, strike, spring wound (E2-76).*
.... 145.00 170.00

☐ **No. 2,** *oak, height 22", dial 6", c. 1905, 8 Day, strike, spring wound (E2-74).*
.... **145.00   170.00**

☐ **No. 4,** *oak, height 22", dial 6", c. 1905, 8 Day, strike, spring wound (E2-74).*
.... **140.00   165.00**

☐ **No. 6,** *oak, walnut trimmings, height 22", dial 6", c. 1905, 8 Day, strike, spring wound (E2-74).*
.... **140.00   165.00**

☐ **Oneida,** *oak, height 22", dial 6", c. 1905, 8 Day, strike, spring wound (E2-74).*
.... **150.00   175.00**

☐ **Onyx,** *oak, walnut trimmings, dial 6", c. 1898, 8 Day, strike, spring wound (E1-160).*
.... **135.00   160.00**

☐ **Opal,** *oak, height 22", dial 6", c. 1905, 8 Day, strike, spring wound (E2-75).*
.... **150.00   175.00**

☐ **Orion,** *walnut, height 22", dial 6", c. 1898, 8 Day, strike, spring wound (E1-160).*
.... **140.00   165.00**

☐ **Peace,** *oak, height 22", dial 6", c. 1905, 8 Day, strike, spring wound (E2-75).*
.... **170.00   195.00**

☐ **Post,** *oak, height 23", dial 6", c. 1894, 1 Day, spring wound (E1-140).*
.... **95.00   115.00**
☐ **As above,** *8 Day, spring wound.*
.... **115.00   140.00**

☐ **Press,** *walnut, height 23", dial 6", c. 1894, 1 Day, spring wound (E1-140).*
.... **95.00   115.00**
☐ **As above,** *8 Day, spring wound.*
.... **115.00   140.00**

☐ **Press, Calendar,** *walnut, height 23", dial 6", c. 1894, 8 Day, strike, spring wound (E1-142).*
.... **115.00   140.00**
☐ **As above,** *gong, 8 Day, strike, calendar, spring wound.*
.... **150.00   175.00**

☐ **Press, Extra, Calendar,** *oak, thermometer and barometer, height 23", dial 6", c. 1894, 8 Day, strike, spring wound (E1-142).*
.... **150.00   175.00**
☐ **As above,** *walnut, spring wound.*
.... **165.00   205.00**

☐ **Puck,** *oak, height 24", dial 6", c. 1894, 8 Day, strike, spring wound (E1-140).*
.... **125.00   150.00**

☐ **Rondo,** *walnut, height 18½", dial 5", c. 1898, 8 Day, strike, spring wound (E1-160).*
.... **140.00   165.00**

☐ **Rose,** *walnut, height 22", dial 6", c. 1894, 8 Day, strike, spring wound (E1-141).*
.... **110.00   135.00**

☐ **Ruby,** *walnut, dial 6", c. 1898, 8 Day, strike, spring wound (E1-160).*
.... 135.00   160.00

☐ **Sapphire,** *oak, dial 6", c. 1898, 8 Day, strike, spring wound (E1-160).*
.... 135.00   160.00

☐ **Saturn,** *oak, height 22", dial 6", c. 1898, 8 Day, strike, spring wound (E1-160).*
.... 140.00   165.00

☐ **Semi-Cabinet,** *oak, height 19", dial 6", c. 1905, 8 Day, strike, spring wound (E2-76).*
.... 75.00   90.00

☐ **As above,** *8 Day, strike, alarm, spring wound.*
.... 85.00   100.00

☐ **As above,** *mahogany, 8 Day, strike, spring wound.*
.... 100.00   115.00

☐ **As above,** *8 Day, strike, alarm, spring wound.*
.... 110.00   125.00

☐ **Shekel,** *oak, height 24", dial 6", c. 1894, 8 Day, strike, spring wound (E1-142).*
.... 125.00   150.00

☐ **Sun,** *walnut, height 23", dial 6", c. 1894, 1 Day, spring wound (E1-140).*
.... 95.00   115.00

☐ **As above,** *8 Day, spring wound.*
.... 115.00   140.00

☐ **Suwanee,** *oak, height 23", dial 6", c. 1905, 8 Day, strike, spring wound (E2-76).*
.... 145.00   170.00

☐ **Thalia,** *oak, thermometer and barometer, height 25", dial 6", c. 1905, 8 Day, strike, spring wound (E2-74).*
.... 160.00   185.00

☐ **Times,** *walnut, height 23", dial 6", c. 1894, 1 Day (E1-140).*
.... 90.00   110.00

☐ **Topaz,** *oak, dial 6", c. 1898, 8 Day, strike (E1-160).*
.... 135.00   160.00

☐ **Topaz Combination,** *oak, thermometer and barometer, height 23", dial 6", c. 1905, 8 Day, strike, calendar (E2-75).*
.... 190.00   220.00

☐ **Tulip,** *walnut, height 23", dial 6", c. 1894, 8 Day, strike (E1-142).*
.... 115.00   140.00

☐ **Urania Calendar,** *oak, thermometer and barometer, height 25", dial 6", c. 1905, 8 Day, strike, calendar (E2-74).*
.... 190.00   220.00

☐ **Venus,** *oak, height 22", dial 6", c. 1898, 8 Day, strike (E1-160).*
.... **140.00   165.00**

☐ **Vesta,** *oak, thermometer and barometer, height 25", dial 6", c. 1905, 8 Day, strike (E2-74).*
.... **160.00   185.00**

☐ **Violet,** *oak, height 22", dial 6", c. 1894, 8 Day, strike (E1-142).*
.... **110.00   135.00**

☐ **Wabash,** *oak, height 23", dial 6", c. 1905, 8 Day, strike (E2-76).*
.... **145.00   170.00**

☐ **Warwick,** *walnut, cathedral bell, height 18", dial 5", c. 1894, 8 Day, strike (E1-144).*
.... **175.00   200.00**

☐ **World,** *oak, height 23", dial 6", c. 1894, 1 Day (E1-140).*
.... **90.00   110.00**
☐ **As above,** *8 Day.*
.... **115.00   140.00**

SERIES

☐ **Jewel,** *oak, dial 6", c. 1898 (E1-160).*
.... **135.00   160.00**
☐ **As above,** *walnut.*
.... **160.00   185.00**

☐ **Planet (6),** *oak, height 22", dial 6", c. 1898, 8 Day, strike (E1-160).*
.... **140.00   165.00**
☐ **As above,** *walnut.*
.... **165.00   190.00**

MANTEL
BLACK WOOD

☐ **Adrian,** *enameled wood case, green marbleized mouldings and columns, gilt trimmings, cathedral gong, height 11", base 17½", iveroid dial 5½", c. 1900, 8 Day, strike (E2-77).*
.... **90.00   110.00**

☐ **Desoto,** *enameled wood case, mahogany finished panels, inlaid silver and gilt, imitation onyx columns, gilt trimmings, cathedral gong, height 10½", base 20", iveroid dial 5½", c. 1900, 8 Day, strike (E2-77).*
.... **100.00   120.00**

☐ **Majestic,** *enameled wood case, green marbleized mouldings, imitation onyx columns, gilt trimmings, cathedral gong, height 12½", base 17", iveroid dial 5½", c. 1900, 8 Day, strike (E2-77).*
.... **90.00   110.00**

☐ **Palace,** *enameled wood case, cathedral glass window effect, green metal columns, gilt trimmings, cathedral gong, height 11", base 20½", iveroid dial 5½", c. 1900, 8 Day, strike (E2-77).*
.... **100.00   120.00**

☐ **Sigma,** *enameled wood case, cathedral glass window effect, green metal columns, gilt trimmings, cathedral gong, height 10¼", base 16¾", iveroid dial 5½", c. 1900, 8 Day, strike (E2-77).*
.... **75.00   90.00**

☐ **Stanford,** *enameled wood case, green metal columns, green mouldings, gilt trimmings, cathedral gong, height 12", base 17", iveroid dial 5½", c. 1900, 8 Day, strike (E2-77).*
.... 80.00   100.00

☐ **Stratford,** *enameled wood case, imitation onyx columns, green marbleized mouldings and panel, gilt trimmings, cathedral gong, height 11", base 17", iveroid dial 5½", c. 1900, 8 Day, strike (E2-77).*
.... 85.00   105.00

MAHOGANY CASE

☐ **Belmont,** *mahogany finish, 12" x 9", iveroid dial 5", c. 1917, 8 Day, strike (E1-173).*
.... 40.00   50.00

☐ **Berlin,** *mahogany finish, 12¼" x 9", iveroid dial 5", c. 1917, 8 Day, strike (E1-173).*
.... 40.00   50.00

☐ **Burgundy,** *mahogany finish, 10½" x 11", iveroid dial 5", c. 1917, 8 Day, strike (E1-173).*
.... 45.00   60.00

☐ **Elegant,** *mahogany, scratched brass sash, convex glass, 11" x 15", dial 8", c. 1917 (E1-172).*
.... 40.00   50.00

☐ **Empire,** *mahogany, scratched brass sash, convex glass, 12" x 14", dial 8", c. 1917 (E1-172).*
.... 60.00   75.00

☐ **Hampton,** *mahogany, 11" x 14", dial 5", c. 1917 (E1-172).*
.... 40.00   50.00

☐ **Hanover,** *mahogany, 10" x 14", dial 5", c. 1917 (E1-172).*
.... 40.00   50.00

☐ **Howard,** *mahogany, 10" x 16", dial 5", c. 1917 (E1-172).*
.... 40.00   50.00

☐ **Lander,** *mahogany finish, 11" x 19", iveroid dial 5", c. 1917, 8 Day, strike (E1-173).*
.... 65.00   70.00

☐ **Saturn,** *mahogany, porcelain dial, 7" x 6", c. 1917, 8 Day, alarm (E1-172).*
.... 30.00   40.00

☐ **Seville,** *mahogany, porcelain dial, 7" x 6", c. 1917, 8 Day, alarm (E1-172).*
.... 30.00   40.00

☐ **Sibyl,** *mahogany, porcelain dial, 8" x 6", c. 1917, 8 Day, alarm (E1-172).*
.... 30.00   40.00

ROUND TOP

☐ **Dakota,** *wood, height 15¾", c. 1905, 8 Day, strike (E2-73).*
.... 210.00   240.00

□ **Grecian,** *wood, height 15", c. 1880, 1 Day, strike (E2-73).*
.... **175.00   200.00**

□ **As above,** *8 Day, strike.*
.... **195.00   225.00**

□ **Grecian,** *mosaic, wood, height 15", c. 1880, 1 Day, strike (E2-73).*
.... **175.00   200.00**

□ **Huron,** *wood, height 15¾", c. 1905, 8 Day, strike (E2-73).*
.... **210.00   240.00**

TAMBOUR

□ **Grinnell,** *mahogany finish, inaloid decoration, 10" x 19", iveroid dial 5", c. 1917, 8 Day, strike (E1-173).*
.... **40.00   50.00**

□ **Hammond,** *mahogany, 11" x 19", dial 5", c. 1917 (E1-172).*
.... **35.00   45.00**

□ **Nomad,** *mahogany finish, 10" x 19¼", iveroid dial 5", c. 1917, 8 Day, strike (E1-173).*
.... **40.00   50.00**

□ **Sage,** *mahogany, porcelain dial, 6" x 8", c. 1917, 8 Day, alarm (E1-172).*
.... **30.00   40.00**

□ **Sancho,** *mahogany, porcelain dial, 6" x 11", c. 1917, 8 Day, alarm (E1-172).*
.... **35.00   45.00**

□ **Sorrento,** *mahogany, paper dial, lever, 8" x 15", dial 5", c. 1917, 8 Day (E1-172).*
.... **35.00   45.00**

MIRROR SIDE

☐ **Occidental,** *walnut, height 24",
dial 6", c. 1894, 8 Day, strike
(E1-140).*
.... **285.00 325.00**
☐ **As above,** *oak.*
.... **250.00 280.00**

REGULATOR
FIGURE "8"

☐ **12" Ionic,** *wood, height 22", c.
1905, 8 Day (E2-73).*
.... **285.00 325.00**
☐ **As above,** *8 Day, strike.*
.... **310.00 350.00**
☐ **As above,** *8 Day, calendar.*
.... **335.00 375.00**
☐ **As above,** *8 Day, strike, calendar.*
.... **360.00 400.00**

☐ **12" Ionic,** *mosaic, wood, height
22", c. 1880, 8 Day (E2-73).*
.... **285.00 325.00**
☐ **As above,** *8 Day, strike.*
.... **310.00 350.00**
☐ **As above,** *8 Day, calendar.*
.... **335.00 375.00**

☐ **Reflector,** *rosewood, height
29½", dial 12", c. 1898, 8 Day
(E1-156).*
.... **310.00 350.00**

OCTAGON TOP, LONG DROP

☐ **Boston,** *solid oak, height 32",*
dial 12", c. 1900, 8 Day (E2-78).
.... 270.00   300.00
☐ **As above,** *8 Day, strike*
.... 285.00   325.00
☐ **As above,** *8 Day, calendar*
.... 310.00   350.00
☐ **As above,** *8 Day, strike, calendar*
.... 335.00   375.00

☐ **Commercial,** *solid oak, height*
32", dial 12", c. 1900, 8 Day
(E2-78).
.... 270.00   300.00
☐ **As above,** *8 Day, strike*
.... 285.00   325.00
☐ **As above,** *8 Day, calendar*
.... 310.00   350.00
☐ **As above,** *8 Day, strike, calendar*
.... 335.00   375.00

☐ **Hartford,** *oak, height 32", dial*
12", c. 1905, 8 Day (E2-76).
.... 285.00   325.00
☐ **As above,** *8 Day, strike*
.... 310.00   350.00
☐ **As above,** *8 Day, calendar*
.... 335.00   375.00
☐ **As above,** *8 Day, strike, calendar*
.... 360.00   400.00

☐ **Reflector No. 2,** *wood, height*
32", c. 1905, 8 Day (E2-73).
.... 310.00   350.00
☐ **As above,** *8 Day, strike*
.... 335.00   375.00

OCTAGON TOP, SHORT DROP

☐ **Bristol,** *solid oak, height 19", dial 8", c. 1900, 8 Day (E2-78).*
. . . . 150.00   175.00
☐ **As above,** *8 Day, strike*
. . . . 175.00   200.00
☐ **As above,** *8 Day, calendar*
. . . . 195.00   225.00
☐ **As above,** *8 Day, strike, calendar*
. . . . 220.00   250.00

☐ **Bristol,** *solid oak, height 21", dial 10", c. 1900, 8 Day (E2-78).*
. . . . 175.00   200.00
☐ **As above,** *8 Day, strike*
. . . . 195.00   225.00
☐ **As above,** *8 Day, calendar*
. . . . 220.00   250.00
☐ **As above,** *8 Day, strike, calendar*
. . . . 245.00   275.00

☐ **Bristol,** *solid oak, height 25", dial 12", c. 1900, 8 Day (E2-78).*
. . . . 195.00   225.00
☐ **As above,** *8 Day, strike*
. . . . 220.00   250.00
☐ **As above,** *8 Day, calendar*
. . . . 245.00   275.00

☐ **Drop Octagon,** *oak, height 19", dial 12", c. 1905, 8 Day (E2-75).*
. . . . 195.00   225.00
☐ **As above,** *8 Day, strike*
. . . . 220.00   250.00
☐ **As above,** *8 Day, calendar*
. . . . 245.00   275.00
☐ **As above,** *8 Day, strike, calendar*
. . . . 270.00   300.00

☐ **Drop Octagon,** *oak, height 19", dial 10", c. 1905, 8 Day (E2-75).*
. . . . 175.00   200.00
☐ **As above,** *8 Day, strike*
. . . . 195.00   225.00
☐ **As above,** *8 Day, calendar*
. . . . 220.00   250.00
☐ **As above,** *8 Day, strike, calendar*
. . . . 245.00   275.00

☐ **Drop Octagon,** *oak, height 19", dial 8", c. 1905, 8 Day (E2-75).*
. . . . 150.00   175.00
☐ **As above,** *8 Day, strike*
. . . . 175.00   200.00
☐ **As above,** *8 Day, calendar*
. . . . 195.00   225.00
☐ **As above,** *8 Day, strike, calendar*
. . . . 220.00   250.00

☐ **Drop Octagon,** *solid oak, height 19", dial 8", c. 1900, 8 Day (E2-78).*
.... 150.00   175.00
☐ **As above,** *8 Day, strike*
.... 175.00   200.00
☐ **As above,** *8 Day, calendar*
.... 195.00   225.00
☐ **As above,** *8 Day, strike, calendar*
.... 220.00   250.00

☐ **Drop Octagon,** *solid oak, height 21", dial 10", c. 1900, 8 Day (E2-78).*
.... 175.00   200.00
☐ **As above,** *8 Day, strike*
.... 195.00   225.00
☐ **As above,** *8 Day, calendar*
.... 220.00   250.00
☐ **As above,** *8 Day, strike, calendar*
.... 245.00   275.00

☐ **Drop Octagon,** *solid oak, height 25", dial 12", c. 1900, 8 Day (E2-78).*
.... 195.00   225.00
☐ **As above,** *8 Day, strike*
.... 220.00   250.00
☐ **As above,** *8 Day, calendar*
.... 245.00   275.00
☐ **As above,** *8 Day, strike, calendar*
.... 270.00   300.00

☐ **Drop Octagon,** *oak, rosewood or walnut, c. 1898 (E1-156) Rosewood, height 19", dial 8", 8 Day.*
.... 225.00   250.00
☐ *Rosewood, height 19", dial 8", 8 Day, strike*
.... 245.00   275.00
☐ *Rosewood, height 21", dial 10", 8 Day.*
.... 270.00   300.00
☐ *Rosewood, height 21", dial 10", 8 Day, strike*
.... 295.00   325.00
☐ *Walnut, height 19", dial 8", 8 Day.*
.... 225.00   250.00

☐ *Walnut, height 19", dial 8", 8 Day, strike*
.... 245.00   275.00
☐ *Walnut, height 21", dial 10", 8 Day.*
.... 270.00   300.00
☐ *Walnut, height 21", dial 10", 8 Day, strike*
.... 295.00   325.00
☐ *Oak, height 19", dial 8", 8 Day.*
.... 175.00   200.00
☐ *Oak, height 19", dial 8", 8 Day, strike*
.... 195.00   225.00
☐ *Oak, height 21", dial 10", 8 Day.*
.... 220.00   250.00
☐ *Oak, height 21", dial 10", 8 Day, strike*
.... 245.00   275.00

☐ **Drop Octagon,** *oak, height 24", dial 12", c. 1898, 8 Day (E1-156).*
.... 195.00   225.00
☐ **As above,** *8 Day, strike.*
.... 220.00   250.00
☐ **As above,** *8 Day, calendar.*
.... 245.00   275.00
☐ **As above,** *8 Day, strike, calendar.*
.... 270.00   300.00

☐ **Lyric,** *oak, height 27", dial 10", c. 1905, 8 Day (E2-75).*
.... 175.00   200.00
☐ **As above,** *8 Day, strike.*
.... 195.00   225.00
☐ **As above,** *8 Day, calendar.*
.... 220.00   250.00
☐ **As above,** *8 Day, strike, calendar.*
.... 245.00   275.00

☐ **Lyric,** *oak, height 27", dial 12", c. 1905, 8 Day (E2-75).*
.... 195.00   225.00
☐ **As above,** *8 Day, strike.*
.... 220.00   250.00
☐ **As above,** *8 Day, calendar.*
.... 245.00   275.00
☐ **As above,** *8 Day, strike, calendar.*
.... 270.00   300.00

□ **As above,** *8 Day, strike.*
.... **270.00   300.00**
□ **As above,** *8 Day, calendar.*
.... **285.00   325.00**
□ **As above,** *8 Day, strike, calendar.*
.... **310.00   350.00**

PARLOR WALL

□ **Lyric,** *oak, height 27", dial 8", c. 1905, 8 Day (E2-75).*
.... **150.00   175.00**
□ **As above,** *8 Day, strike.*
.... **175.00   200.00**
□ **As above,** *8 Day, calendar.*
.... **195.00   225.00**
□ **As above,** *8 Day, strike, calendar.*
.... **220.00   250.00**

□ **Misay,** *rosewood, height 21", dial 12", c. 1898, 8 Day (E1-156).*
.... **245.00   275.00**

□ **Arctic,** *oak, height 37", dial 8", c. 1898, 8 Day (E1-154).*
.... **450.00   500.00**
□ **As above,** *8 Day, strike.*
.... **490.00   550.00**
□ **As above,** *8 Day, calendar.*
.... **540.00   600.00**
□ **As above,** *8 Day, strike, calendar.*
.... **575.00   650.00**

☐ **Bartholdi,** *oak, height 44", dial 8", c. 1898, 8 Day (E1-154).*
.... 450.00   500.00
☐ **As above,** 8 *Day, strike.*
.... 490.00   550.00
☐ **As above,** *walnut, 8 Day.*
.... 550.00   600.00

☐ **Indus,** *oak, height 29", dial 6", c. 1898, 8 Day (E1-154).*
.... 335.00   375.00
☐ **As above,** 8 *Day, strike.*
.... 360.00   400.00
☐ **As above,** 8 *Day, calendar.*
.... 375.00   425.00

☐ **Landau,** *solid oak, height 38¼", dial 10", c. 1900, 8 Day (E2-78).*
.... 245.00   275.00
☐ **As above,** 8 *Day, strike.*
.... 270.00   300.00
☐ **As above,** 8 *Day, calendar.*
.... 285.00   325.00
☐ **As above,** 8 *Day, strike, calendar.*
.... 310.00   350.00

☐ **Pacific,** *oak, height 37", dial 8", c. 1898, 8 Day (E1-154).*
.... 540.00   600.00
☐ **As above,** 8 *Day, strike.*
.... 575.00   650.00
☐ **As above,** 8 *Day, calendar.*
.... 625.00   700.00
☐ **As above,** 8 *Day, strike, calendar.*
.... 675.00   750.00

ROUND TOP, SHORT DROP

☐ **Dew Drop,** *oak, height 23½", dial 12", c. 1898, 8 Day (E1-156).*
.... 175.00   200.00
☐ **As above,** 8 *Day, strike.*
.... 195.00   225.00
☐ **As above,** 8 *Day, calendar.*
.... 220.00   250.00
☐ **As above,** 8 *Day, strike, calendar.*
.... 245.00   275.00
☐ **As above,** *rosewood, 8 Day.*
.... 225.00   250.00
☐ **As above,** 8 *Day, strike.*
.... 245.00   275.00
☐ **As above,** 8 *Day, calendar.*
.... 270.00   300.00
☐ **As above,** 8 *Day, strike, calendar.*
.... 295.00   325.00
☐ **As above,** *walnut, 8 Day.*
.... 225.00   250.00
☐ **As above,** 8 *Day, strike.*
.... 245.00   275.00
☐ **As above,** 8 *Day, calendar.*
.... 270.00   300.00
☐ **As above,** 8 *Day, strike, calendar.*
.... 295.00   325.00

REGULATOR
SQUARE TOP

STORE

☐ **Aliance,** *oak, 38½" x 16", dial 12", c. 1905, 8 Day (E2-76).*
.... 360.00   400.00
☐ **As above,** *8 Day, strike.*
.... 375.00   425.00
☐ **As above,** *8 Day, calendar.*
.... 400.00   450.00
☐ **As above,** *8 Day, strike, calendar.*
.... 425.00   475.00

☐ **Trenton,** *golden oak, height 38", dial 12", c. 1900, 8 Day (E2-78).*
.... 245.00   275.00
☐ **As above,** *8 Day, strike.*
.... 270.00   300.00
☐ **As above,** *8 Day, calendar.*
.... 285.00   325.00
☐ **As above,** *8 Day, strike, calendar.*
.... 310.00   350.00
☐ **As above,** *mahogany, 8 Day.*
.... 265.00   295.00
☐ **As above,** *8 Day, strike.*
.... 295.00   325.00
☐ **As above,** *8 Day, calendar.*
.... 310.00   350.00
☐ **As above,** *8 Day, strike, calendar.*
.... 335.00   375.00

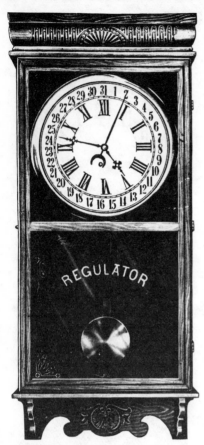

ITHACA CALENDAR CLOCK COMPANY

Solely a calendar clock manufacturing company, Ithaca began due to the business ingenuity of Henry Horton. He invented the calendar mechanism that was used by the company he originated.

The most unique aspect of Ithaca, was not in the movements themselves, but in their area of production output. The cases and calendar mechanisms were produced in Ithaca, New York rather than Connecticut.

CALENDAR

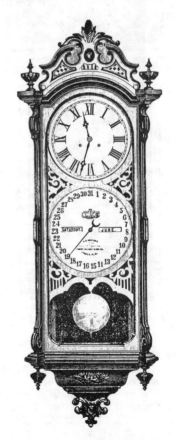

☐ **Western Union,** *solid oak, height 36", dial 12", c. 1900, 8 Day, (E2-78).*
. . . . 245.00   275.00
☐ **As above,** *8 Day, strike.*
. . . . 270.00   300.00
☐ **As above,** *8 Day, calendar.*
. . . . 285.00   325.00
☐ **As above,** *8 Day, strike, calendar.*
. . . . 310.00   350.00

☐ **Bank No. 0,** *double weight, 61" x 20", dials 12", 8 Day (E1-82, M78-31).*
.... **4300.00   4800.00**

☐ **Bank Regulator No. 1,** *sweep second, 72" x 19½", dials 12", 8 Day (E1-82, M79-32).*
.... **7000.00   8000.00**

☐ **Belgrade Hanging No. 5½,** *spring, 37½" x 14", dials 7", 8 Day, strike (E1-26, M99-38).*
.... **2500.00   2800.00**

☐ **Bank No. 2,** *weight, 61" x 20", dials 12", 8 Day (E1-82, M81-31).*
.... **2900.00   3250.00**

Brisbane No. 2½

☐ **Brisbane No. 2½**, *spring, 40" x
16", both dials 10½", 8 Day,
strike (E1-26, M84-33).*
.... 2250.00   2500.00

☐ **Chronometer,** *spring,
"Chronometer" in gold on glass,
height 33", dials 7", 8 Day, strike
(M135-50).*
.... 1250.00   1650.00

☐ **Combination Time And Date Dial
Shelf Clock,** *spring, open
escapement, black enameled
wood, 16½" x 12½", 8 Day,
strike (M143-52).*
.... 2500.00   2800.00

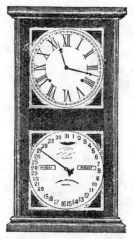

☐ **Farmers (Old.) No. 10,** *alarm,
double spring, 21" x 12", dials 7",
8 Day, strike (E1-80, M119-45).*
.... 600.00   650.00

☐ **Emerald Shelf No. 5,** *spring, 33"
x 15", 6½" time and 8" calendar
dial, 8 Day, strike (E1-82, M97-37).*
.... 1750.00   1950.00

☐ **Farmers With Pillars No. 10,**
*alarm, spring, 21½" x 12", dials
7", 8 Day, strike (M120-45).*
.... 890.00   950.00

☐ **Granger No. 14,** *spring, 26" x 12", dials 7", 8 Day, strike (E1-26, M130-48).*

.... **1000.00   1250.00**

☐ **Favorite Shelf No. 4½,** *spring, "Favorite" on door glass in gold, 32" x 13½", dials 7", 8 Day, strike (E1-83, M95-37).*

.... **1600.00   2000.00**

☐ **Hanging Cottage (Old.) No. 7,** *spring, 25" x 12", 5" time and 7" calendar dial, 8 Day, strike (E1-80, M113-43).*

.... **925.00   1025.00**

☐ **Hanging Cottage (New.) No. 7,** *alarm, spring, 29" x 13½", 5" time and 7" calendar dial, 8 Day, strike (E1-83, M116-44).*

.... **950.00   1050.00**

☐ **Hanging Index No. 16,** *spring, 30½" x 15", dials 7", 8 Day, strike (M132-49).*

.... **900.00   1000.00**

□ **Hanging Library (Old.) No. 6,** *double spring, 28" x 12", 6" time and 8" calendar dial, 8 Day (E1-81, M105-40).*
.... **950.00   1050.00**

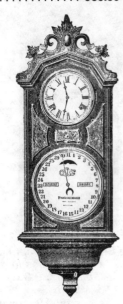

□ **Hanging Kildare No. 12,** *spring, calendar, 33" x 13", dials 8", 8 Day, strike (E1-83, M125-47).*
.... **3000.00   3400.00**

□ **Hanging Library (New.) No. 6,** *spring, 32" x 12", 5" time and 7" calendar dial, 8 Day, strike (E1-83, M110-42).*
.... **1000.00   1200.00**

☐ **Iron Case,** *double spring, 21" x 9", 5" time and 7" calendar dial, 30 Day (M68-26).*
.... 3200.00   3500.00

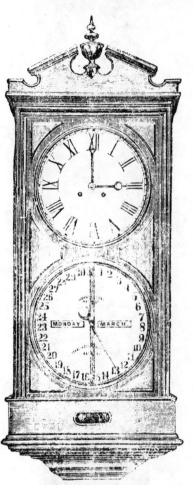

☐ **Hanging Office No. 4,** *double spring, 28" x 15½", 12" time and 9" calendar dial, 30 Day (E1-26, M91-36).*
.... 900.00   1000.00

☐ **Hanging Regulator No. 0,** *double weight, height 52", both dials 12", 8 Day (M71-29).*
.... 3500.00   4000.00

☐ **Hanging Steeple,** *spring, 32½" x 12", 7" time and 8" calendar dial, 8 Day, strike (M136-50).*
.... 1750.00   1950.00

☐ **Index Advertising,** *spring(?), 36" x 14", dials 7", 8 Day, strike (M134-49).*
.... 1000.00   1050.00

☐ **Index,** *spring, "Index" in gold on glass, 33½" x 15", dials 7", 8 Day, time, strike (M138-51).*
.... 1500.00   1775.00

☐ **Iron Case,** *double spring, 21" x 9", 5" time and 7" calendar dial, 8 Day, strike (M64-26).*
.... 3100.00   3400.00

☐ **Iron Case,** *figure 8 double dial wall calendar, spring, height 19", 5" time and 8" calendar dial, 8 Day (M63-26).*
.... 3500.00   3700.00

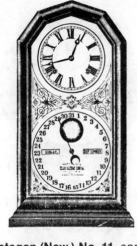

☐ **Mantel Index No. 17,** *spring, 28½ " x 15½ ", dials 7", 8 Day, strike (E1-83, M133-49).*
.... **900.00 1000.00**

☐ **Octagon (New.) No. 11,** *spring, 21" x 11", 7" time and 8" calendar dial, 8 Day, strike (E1-26, M124-46).*
.... **750.00 850.00**

☐ **Melrose No. 15,** *spring, crystal bob, cherry case, ebony finish, 22" x 12", 6" time and 8" calendar dial (black and gold), 8 Day, strike (E1-83, M131-48).*
.... **6000.00 7000.00**

☐ **Parlor No. 3½,** *1st model, spring, black dials, silvered hands, 20" x 10", 5" time and 8" calendar dial, 8 Day, spring (E1-82, M86-34).*
.... **2800.00 3400.00**

Winter and Summer, *Ansonia, large Syrian bronze, double statue, 22" x 24", dial 5½", 8 day, strike spring, pendulum* **$1500.00-1700.00**

Fashion Calendar No.4, *Southern Calendar Clock Co., St. Louis, Missouri, double dial shelf calendar, 8 day, strike spring, 32" x 16", dials 7½", short pendulum.........* **$1600.00-2000.00**

Fashion Calendar No.2, *Southern Calendar Clock Co., double dial shelf calendar, short pendulum, 21" x 15", dials 7½", 8 day, strike spring....* **$1250.00-1450.00**

Ithaca Parlor, double dial, shelf calendar, black dials, silvered hands, cut glass pendulum, 5" time and 8" calendar dial, 20" x 10", 8 day, strike spring............. **$2800.00-3400.00**

Ithaca Favorite, double dial shelf calendar, "Favorite" on door glass in gold, 32" x 13½", 7" dials, 8 day, strike spring............. **$1600.00-2000.00**

Fisher Swing. *Ansonia. French bronze finish, height 30",
dial 4½", 8 day.* **$1000.00-1300.00**

Arcadia Swing. *Ansonia. Syrian bronze finish, clock and
pendulum ball cobalt blue, enameled, raised gold plated
numerals, dials and raised ornaments, 31" x 4½", 8 day.* . .
. . . . **$2400.00-2800.00**

Apex, Crystal Regulator, Ansonia, visible escapement, white beveled plate glass, 4" porcelain dial, c. 1920 completely restored. 18½" x 10½", 8 day, spring, hour and half hour gong strike. **$2350.00-2500.00**

Regent, Ansonia, Syrian bronze gilt finish, cathedral gong, half hour strike, height 20½", dial 5", 8 day. **$1050.00-1250.00**

Orrin Hart, *Transitional Clock 1830 to 1832, wood groaner movement, high winding arbors, reeded door, original glass, 1 day, strike weight. . . .* **$700.00-900.00**

Belgium with Horse and Rider, *Ansonia, black enameled, iron case, French sash, beveled glass, cathedral gong, white porcelain dial, open escapement, 11¼" x 17¾".* **$350.00-400.00**

Elisha Manross, steeple on steeple, rosewood case, original tablet, c. 1840 to 1850, 8 day fusee. **$1750.00-1950.00**

Birge and Fuller, steeple on steeple, cut glass tablets, veneered mahogany front, c. 1840 to 1850, 8 day wagon spring, strike pendulum. **$2650.00-2950.00**

Howard No.27, *Italian marble front, length 2' -11", 8 day weight pendulum*
. . . . **$1650.00-1850.00**

☐ **Regulator Shelf No. 0,** *double weight, height 52", both dials 12", 8 Day (M71A-29).*
. . . . **2000.00   2500.00**

☐ **Regulator Shelf No. 1,** *double weight, 43" x 19", dials 12", 8 Day (M75-30).*
. . . . **2400.00   2700.00**

☐ **Regulator Shelf No. 2,** *double weight, 42" x 19", both dials 12", 8 Day (M76A-31).*
. . . . **1750.00   1900.00**

☐ **Regulator Hanging No. 3,** *double weight, 45" x 19", both dials 12", 8 Day (M77-31).*
. . . . **1550.00   1700.00**

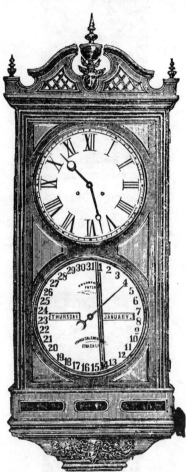

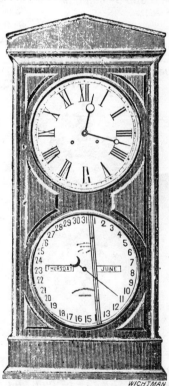

WICHTMAN

☐ **Regulator Hanging No. 1,** *double weight 49" x 19", both dials 12", 8 Day (M72-29).*
. . . . **3000.00   3500.00**

☐ **Regulator Shelf No. 1,** *double weight, 43" x 19", dials 12", 8 Day (M73-29).*
. . . . **2900.00   3200.00**

☐ **Regulator Shelf No. 3,** *double weight, 39" x 19", both dials 12", 8 Day (E1-81, M77A-31).*
. . . . **1100.00   1300.00**

☐ **Reno,** *"Reno" in gold on glass, 8 Day, time, strike (M139-51).*
. . . . **1100.00   1300.00**

☐ **Round Top Shelf (Old.) No. 5,** *double spring, height 20", 5" time and 7" calendar dial, 8 Day (M101-39).*
.... 600.00   675.00

☐ **Round Top Shelf (New.) No. 5,** *double spring, 22½" x 11", 6" time and 7" calendar dial, 8 Day (M102-39).*
.... 750.00   850.00

☐ **Round Top Shelf No. 102A,** *double spring, 22½" x 11", 7" time and 8" calendar dial, 8 Day (E1-81).*
.... 600.00   700.00

☐ **Shelf Cottage No. 7,** *spring, 25" x 12", 5" time and 7" calendar dials, 8 Day, time, strike (E1-57).*
.... 700.00   775.00

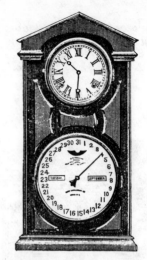

☐ **Shelf Cottage (New.) No. 9,** *spring, 24" x 12", 5" time and 7" calendar dial, 8 Day, strike (E1-83, M117-44).*
.... 950.00   1050.00

☐ **Shelf Cottage (Old.) No. 9,** *spring, 22" x 12", 5" time and 7" calendar dial, 8 Day, strike (E1-80, M114-43).*
.... 650.00   700.00

☐ **Shelf Library,** *alarm, spring, 31½" x 11½", 6" time and 8" calendar dial, 8 Day, time, strike (M140-51).*
.... 900.00   1050.00

☐ **Shelf Steeple,** *spring, 25½" x 12", 6½" time and 7½" calendar dial, 8 Day, time, strike (M137-50).*
. . . . **1600.00   1850.00**

☐ **Skeleton,** *spring, nickel plated bell, silver cast iron dial and frame, (walnut with ebony trim), 24" x 12", 4½" time and 6½" calendar dial, 8 Day, time, strike (M145-53).*
. . . . **7000.00   8000.00**

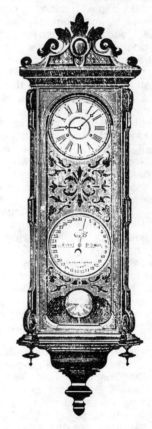

☐ **Shelf Library (Old.) No. 8,** *spring, 25½" x 12", 5" time and 7" calendar dial, 8 Day (M106-40).*
. . . . **700.00   800.00**

☐ **Shelf Library (New.) No. 8,** *alarm, spring, 26" x 12", 5" time and 7" calendar dial, 8 Day, strike (E1-83, M112-42).*
. . . . **950.00   1050.00**

☐ **Vienna No. 3,** *double spring, 52" x 16", dials 8", 30 Day (E1-82, M85-33).*
. . . . **3250.00   3500.00**

JEROME AND COMPANY

So much has been written about Chauncey Jerome, perhaps it is safe to say he exemplified the image of the clock manufacturers of the time. An imposing looking man, his face was etched with stern lines above the stiff high collars he wore in the fashion of the times. He was bright, creative, ingenious, he formed and dissolved partnerships, had his finger in every clock making "pie," resorted to desperate measures, and eventually failed to provide a sound financial foundation to his clockmaking business.

He began his career in transit; purchasing clock movements and cases in Bristol, and assembling them in Virginia. He and his brother, Noble with whom he was in partnership, eventually moved to Bristol where they succeeded in selling vast quantities of shelf clocks. History was made when Noble obtained the patent for the cheap brass clock movement. Most clocks were still made with wooden movements up until that time — a difficult time consuming task. Noble and Chauncey were responsible for revolutionizing the entire clockmaking industry.

The Jerome brothers were able to sell the brass clocks at extremely low prices. Chauncey is also credited with opening up the market for American clock exports. By this time they were the largest of the clock manufacturing firms.

Chauncey Jerome committed his fatal mistake by entering a partnership with Theodore Terry and the notorious P.T. Barnum. It is rumored that Barnum was not strictly aboveboard in his disposal of company funds. At any rate the trios' combined investment was gone in short order, leaving the Jerome empire bankrupt and Chauncey destitute. It is said he ended his days in a white apron at the watchmakers bench.

Many thousands of clocks were produced by the various Jerome Companies but not too many survive. The values vary considerably according to the type and the period. The period is indicated by the label.

The early clocks by Jeromes and Darrow, C. and N. Jerome, and Jeromes, Gilbert, Grant and Company are rare collector items, and the values are subject to negotiations with the individuals concerned. The early labels used from 1841-44 of Chauncey Jerome and Jeromes and Company have a higher value than the later labels of Jerome Company and Jerome and Company of New Haven.

The name of The Jerome Manufacturing Company was used from 1851-55. After 1855 the New Haven Clock Company often used the label, Chauncey Jerome, which is not as prized by collectors as the earlier labels. The New Haven Clock Company also used the label, Jerome and Company, which is the least desired of all.

A rare variation and highly desirable was used by Chauncy Jerome 1844-45 — "Chauncey Jerome, Clockmaker". These labels were all printed by Benham, 650 Orange St., N.H.

Other labels show sales subsidiaries of Jerome, the southern companies being particularly desirable.

The last label used by C. Jerome in the 1860's is "Chauncey Jerome, Austin", which is rare.

In summary, if it has no label, the value will be decreased considerably, and the label must be considered to establish the period and the value. Every company making clocks during this period made similar clocks. Thus creating various values according to the fame of the maker.

CALENDAR

☐ **Alarm,** *nickel, dial 3¾", 1 Day, alarm, simple calendar (M404-126).*
. . . . **100.00   130.00**

☐ **Crown,** *spring, calendar mechanism, 34½" x 19½", 8½" depth, dials 7", 8 Day, strike (M395-124).*
.... **1250.00   1600.00**

☐ **Wall Clock,** *spring, calendar mechanism, 40" x 15", dials 8", 8 Day (M401-125).*
.... **1750.00   1900.00**

CONNECTICUT SHELF
BEE HIVE

☐ **Tudor Style,** *with and without alarms, mahogany, black walnut, rosewood, height 19", 8 Day (E1-7).*
.... **160.00   180.00**
☐ **As above,** *8 Day, alarm.*
.... **165.00   185.00**
☐ **As above,** *1 Day.*
.... **140.00   160.00**
☐ **As above,** *1 Day, alarm.*
.... **145.00   165.00**

☐ **Dneister,** *spring, B.B. Lewis V calendar mechanism, 36¾" x 15", dials 7½", 8 Day (E1-103, M402-126).*
.... **1000.00   1100.00**

☐ **Register,** *spring, calendar mechanism, 33¾" x 12", dials 7½", 8 Day, strike (E1-104, M399-125).*
.... **1150.00   1300.00**

☐ **Tudor,** *striking, also alarms, mahogany, walnut, zebra and rosewood, height 19", 8 Day (E1-7).*
.... **160.00   180.00**
☐ **As above,** *8 Day, strike.*
.... **165.00   185.00**
☐ **As above,** *8 Day, alarm.*
.... **170.00   190.00**

☐ **Rokeby Wall,** *weight, B.B. Lewis V calendar mechanism, 64" x 19½", 8 Day (E1-104, M403-126).*
.... **1500.00   1750.00**

☐ **As above,** *1 Day.*
.... **145.00   165.00**
☐ **As above,** *1 Day, alarm.*
.... **150.00   170.00**

☐ **Shelf Clock,** *calendar mechanism, 21½" x 12¾", 5" time and 3½" calendar dial, 8 Day, strike (M390-123).*
.... **1200.00   1400.00**

☐ **Tudor Style,** *30 hour lever, striking, height 14", 1 Day (E1-7).*
.... 140.00   160.00

☐ **Tudor Style,** *height 14", 8 Day (E1-7).*
.... 160.00   180.00

COTTAGE

☐ **Cottage,** *mahogany and black walnut, height 12", 30 hour*
.... 120.00   130.00
☐ **As above,** *striking.*
.... 130.00   150.00

☐ **David Crocket,** *mahogany and walnut, time piece, height 12", 30 hour*
.... 120.00   130.00

☐ **French Style,** *marble, height 13", 8 Day*
.... 130.00   150.00

☐ **French Style,** *rosewood, height 13", 8 day*
.... 110.00   130.00

☐ **N.E. Company,** *mahogany, walnut, zebra, time piece, height 11", 30 hour*
.... 110.00   125.00
☐ **As above,** *with alarms, (E1-8).*
.... 115.00   130.00

☐ **Prince Albert,** *mahogany, rosewood, height 15", 8 Day (E1-8)*
.... 155.00   175.00
☐ **As above,** *1 Day.*
.... 135.00   155.00

☐ **Prince Albert,** *mahogany, height 15", 30 hour, striking (E1-8).*
.... 130.00   150.00
☐ **As above,** *rosewood.*
.... 140.00   160.00
☐ **As above,** *zebra.*
.... 150.00   170.00

☐ **Prince Albert,** *rosewood, height 15", 8 day, striking (E1-8).*
.... 140.00   160.00

☐ **S.B.T.,** *time piece, height 10½", 30 hour*
.... 170.00   190.00

☐ **Union,** *mahogany, rosewood, height 13", 8 Day, striking*
.... **120.00   140.00**
☐ **As above,** *with alarms, 1 Day (E1-8).*
.... **110.00   130.00**

☐ **Union,** *mahogany, rosewood, height 13", 30 hour, striking*
.... **110.00   130.00**
☐ **As above,** *with alarms (E1-8).*
.... **115.00   135.00**

☐ **Union,** *mahogany, black walnut, rosewood, height 13", 8 day*
.... **120.00   140.00**
☐ **As above,** *30 hour (E1-8).*
.... **110.00   130.00**

☐ **Union,** *rosewood with gilt moldings, height 13", 8 Day, striking (E1-8)*
.... **120.00   140.00**

☐ **Union,** *rosewood with elaborate gilt moldings, height 13", 8 Day (E1-8).*
.... **130.00   150.00**

☐ **Victoria,** *rosewood, height 15", 30 hour, striking (E1-7).*
.... **130.00   150.00**

EMPIRE AND COLUMN

☐ **Column,** *mahogany, rosewood, gilt and rose pillars, 30 hour*
.... **175.00   225.00**

☐ **Column Spring Clock,** *mahogany, rosewood, gilt and rose pillars, height 20", 8 Day*
.... **220.00   240.00**
☐ **As above,** *30 hour*
.... **155.00   175.00**

☐ **Cornice Top,** *mahogany, extra column, rolling pinion, height 33", 8 Day, with weights (E1-8).*
.... **385.00   435.00**

☐ **Cornice Top,** *gilt and rose columns, height 24", 8 Day, striking (E1-8).*
.... 230.00   250.00

☐ **Extra Column,** *scenic picture on case under dial, height 25", with alarms (E1-6)*
.... 185.00   235.00

☐ **Gilt Top And Column,** *mahogany, rolling pinion, 8 Day, with weights*
.... 525.00   575.00

MANTEL LEVER

☐ **Bronze Lever,** *silent, height 9", 1 Day*
.... 110.00   130.00
☐ **As above,** *8 Day*
.... 125.00   145.00

☐ **Bronze Lever Time Piece,** *1 Day*
.... 180.00   200.00
☐ **As above,** *8 Day*
.... 220.00   240.00

☐ **Bronze Lever Time Piece,** *1 Day*
.... 180.00   200.00
☐ **As above,** *8 Day*
.... 200.00   240.00

☐ **Mantel Lever,** *rosewood, carved base, striking, height 12", 1 Day*
.... 110.00   130.00
☐ **As above,** *1 Day, strike*
.... 115.00   135.00
☐ **As above,** *8 Day*
.... 125.00   155.00
☐ **As above,** *8 Day, strike*
.... 140.00   160.00

☐ **Mantel Lever,** *rosewood and mahogany, silent, height 10", 1 Day*
.... 110.00   130.00
☐ **As above,** *1 Day, strike*
.... 115.00   135.00
☐ **As above,** *8 Day*
.... 125.00   155.00
☐ **As above,** *8 Day, strike*
.... 140.00   160.00

☐ **Mantel Lever Time Piece,** *rosewood, 1 Day*
.... 110.00   130.00
☐ **As above,** *1 Day, alarm*
.... 115.00   135.00
☐ **As above,** *8 Day*
.... 125.00   155.00
☐ **As above,** *8 Day, alarm*
.... 130.00   150.00
☐ **As above,** *8 Day, strike, alarm*
.... 140.00   160.00

O.G. AND O.O.G.

☐ **Barnum,** *mahogany, walnut, rosewood, zebra, height 15", 30 hour, 1 Day*
.... 130.00   150.00
☐ **As above,** *1 Day, strike*
.... 140.00   160.00

☐ **O.G. AND O.O.G.,** *8 Day*
.... 230.00   250.00
☐ **As above,** *8 Day, strike*
.... 240.00   260.00

- O.G. AND O.O.G. *mahogany and zebra, 30 hour, 1 Day*
  .... 145.00   165.00
- As above, *1 Day, strike*
  .... 155.00   175.00

- O.O.G., *height 18", 1 Day*
  .... 130.00   150.00
- As above, *1 Day, strike*
  .... 140.00   160.00
- As above, *1 Day, alarm*
  .... 150.00   170.00

- O.O.G., *height 15", 30 hour, 1 Day*
  .... 145.00   165.00

- O.O.G., *with weights, height 39", 1 Day*
  .... 120.00   140.00
- As above, *1 Day, strike*
  .... 130.00   150.00
- As above, *1 Day, alarm*
  .... 140.00   160.00
- As above, *8 Day*
  .... 210.00   230.00
- As above, *8 Day, strike*
  .... 230.00   240.00
- As above, *8 Day, strike, alarm*
  .... 230.00   250.00

- Reversed O.G., *mahogany, walnut, rosewood, zebra, 30 hour, 1 Day*
  .... 160.00   180.00
- As above, *1 Day, strike*
  .... 170.00   190.00

- Rough And Ready No. 1, *rosewood, height 16", 30 hour, 1 Day*
  .... 160.00   180.00
- As above, *1 Day, alarm*
  .... 170.00   190.00
- As above, *1 Day, strike*
  .... 180.00   190.00
- As above, *1 Day, strike, alarm*
  .... 190.00   200.00

PAPIER MÂCHÉ
- French Style, *height 13", 8 Day.*
  .... 165.00   185.00
- As above, *30 hour*
  .... 145.00   160.00

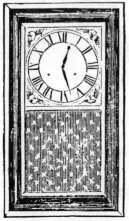

Gothic Style

☐ **Gothic Style,** *lever, height 14", 30 hour, 1 Day*
.... 140.00   160.00
☐ **As above,** *8 Day*
.... 160.00   180.00
☐ **As above,** *8 Day, strike*
.... 180.00   200.00

☐ **Kossuth,** *height 16", 30 hour, 1 Day*
.... 140.00   160.00
☐ **Kossuth,** *height 16", 8 Day*
.... 160.00   180.00
☐ **As above,** *8 Day, strike*
.... 180.00   200.00

☐ **Kossuth Style,** *lever, height 11", 1 Day*
.... 140.00   160.00
☐ **As above,** *8 Day*
.... 160.00   180.00
☐ **As above,** *8 Day, strike*
.... 180.00   200.00

☐ **Mantel Lever,** *height 11", 1 Day*
.... 135.00   155.00
☐ **As above,** *1 Day, strike*
.... 155.00   175.00
☐ **As above,** *8 Day*
.... 165.00   185.00
☐ **As above,** *8 Day, strike*
.... 175.00   195.00

☐ **As above,** *8 Day, strike*
.... 350.00   400.00

☐ **Paris Style,** *height 16", 8 Day*
.... 160.00   180.00
☐ **As above,** *8 Day, strike*
.... 180.00   200.00

☐ **Paris Style,** *striking lever, height 16", 30 hour, 1 Day*
.... 140.00   160.00
☐ **As above,** *1 Day, strike*
.... 160.00   180.00

☐ **Paris Style,** *lever, silent, height 10", 1 Day*
.... 135.00   155.00
☐ **As above,** *1 Day, strike*
.... 145.00   165.00

☐ **Navy,** *time piece, dial 9", 1 Day.*
.... 300.00   325.00
☐ **As above,** *8 Day*
.... 325.00   375.00

☐ **As above,** *8 Day, strike*
.... **165.00** **185.00**

☐ **Putnum Style,** *lever, height 10",*
1 Day
.... **135.00** **155.00**

☐ **As above,** *1 Day, strike*
.... **145.00** **165.00**

☐ **As above,** *8 Day*
.... **155.00** **175.00**

☐ **As above,** *8 Day, strike*
.... **165.00** **185.00**

☐ **Union Style,** *1 Day*
.... **135.00** **155.00**

☐ **As above,** *1 Day, strike*
.... **145.00** **165.00**

☐ **As above,** *8 Day*
.... **155.00** **175.00**

☐ **As above,** *8 Day, strike*
.... **165.00** **185.00**

☐ **Union Style,** *lever, 1 Day*
.... **140.00** **160.00**

☐ **As above,** *1 Day, strike*
.... **150.00** **170.00**

☐ **As above,** *8 Day*
.... **160.00** **180.00**

☐ **As above,** *8 Day, strike*
.... **170.00** **190.00**

PEARL INLAID

☐ **Jenny Lind,** *height 15", 30 hour, 1*
Day
.... **160.00** **180.00**

☐ **As above,** *8 Day*
.... **170.00** **190.00**

☐ **As above,** *8 Day, strike*
.... **180.00** **200.00**

☐ **Kossuth,** *height 19", 8 Day*
.... **180.00** **200.00**

☐ **As above,** *8 Day, strike*
.... **200.00** **220.00**

☐ **LaFayette,** *height 13", 8 Day*
.... **140.00** **160.00**

☐ **As above,** *8 Day, strike*
.... **160.00** **180.00**

☐ **Mantel,** *lever, with alarms, height*
11", 30 hour, 1 Day
.... **125.00** **145.00**

☐ **Mantel Lever Time Piece,**
striking, height 11", 1 Day
.... **130.00** **150.00**

☐ **Tom Thumb Jr.,** *lever, metal case,*
height 8", 30 hour, 1 Day
.... **165.00** **185.00**

☐ **Union,** *striking, height 13", 1 Day*
.... **125.00** **145.00**

☐ **As above,** *8 Day*
.... **150.00** **170.00**

☐ **As above,** *8 Day, strike*
.... **160.00** **180.00**

☐ **Washington,** *height 10", 1 Day*
.... **140.00** **160.00**

☐ **As above,** *8 Day*
.... **160.00** **180.00**

☐ **As above,** *8 Day, strike*
.... **180.00** **200.00**

☐ **Washington,** *lever, time piece,*
height 10½", 1 Day
.... **160.00** **185.00**

☐ **Eight Day Pearl Inlaid,** *iron*
frame, 1 Day
.... **140.00** **160.00**

☐ **As above,** *8 Day*
.... **160.00** **180.00**

☐ **As above,** *8 Day, strike*
.... **180.00** **200.00**

STEEPLE

☐ **Gothic,** *mahogany, rosewood, black walnut, height 19", 8 Day.*
.... 180.00   200.00
☐ **As above,** *with alarms.*
.... 190.00   210.00
☐ **As above,** *30 hour.*
.... 145.00   165.00
☐ **As above,** *30 hour, with alarms.*
.... 155.00   175.00

☐ **Gothic,** *mahogany, rosewood, walnut, zebra, height 20", 8 Day, striking.*
.... 190.00   210.00
☐ **As above,** *with alarms.*
.... 200.00   220.00
☐ **As above,** *30 hour.*
.... 155.00   175.00
☐ **As above,** *30 hour, with alarms.*
.... 165.00   185.00

GALLERY

☐ **Gallery,** *gilt frames, mahogany, diameter 14", 8 Day.*
.... 230.00   250.00
☐ **As above,** *diameter 16", 1 Day.*
.... 200.00   220.00

☐ **Gallery,** *diameter 22", 8 Day.*
.... 325.00   345.00
☐ **As above,** *diameter 20".*
.... 300.00   325.00
☐ **As above,** *diameter 18".*
.... 270.00   290.00
☐ **As above,** *diameter 16".*
.... 230.00   250.00
☐ **As above,** *diameter 14".*
.... 210.00   230.00

☐ **Gilt Gallery,** *dial 15", 8 Day.*
.... 240.00   260.00

OCTAGON TOP, SHORT DROP

☐ **Gilt Gallery,** *dial 10", 8 Day, lever.*
 . . . . 180.00   200.00

☐ **Octagon,** *mahogany, rosewood,
 dial 10", 8 Day (E1-8).*
 . . . . 220.00   230.00
☐ **As above,** *striking.*
 . . . . 230.00   250.00
☐ **As above,** *dial 12".*
 . . . . 245.00   265.00
☐ **As above,** *dial 12", striking.*
 . . . . 255.00   275.00

☐ **Gilt Gallery,** *dial 12", 8 Day.*
 . . . . 180.00   200.00

☐ **Gilt Gallery,** *dial 8", 8 Day, lever.*
 . . . . 160.00   180.00
☐ **As above,** *30 hour, lever.*
 . . . . 140.00   160.00

Octagon, 10″ Timepiece

☐ **Octagon,** *mahogany, rosewood, time piece 10", dial 12", 8 Day, striking (E1-8).*
.... 250.00   270.00

☐ **Octagon,** *mahogany, rosewood, dial 12", 8 Day.*
.... 245.00   265.00
☐ **As above,** *striking.*
.... 255.00   275.00

☐ **Octagon,** *mahogany, rosewood, time piece 12", dial 12", 8 Day.*
.... 240.00   260.00
☐ **As above,** *8 Day, striking.*
.... 250.00   270.00

OCTAGON LEVER

☐ **Detached Lever Time Pieces,** *mahogany, rosewood, walnut,*

zebra, dial 6", 30 hour.
.... 110.00   130.00
☐ **As above,** *dial 8", 8 Day.*
.... 130.00   150.00
☐ **As above,** *8 Day, strike.*
.... 140.00   160.00
☐ **As above,** *dial 10", 8 Day.*
.... 140.00   160.00
☐ **As above,** *8 Day, strike.*
.... 150.00   170.00
☐ **As above,** *dial 9", 8 Day.*
.... 140.00   160.00
☐ **As above,** *8 Day, strike.*
.... 145.00   165.00

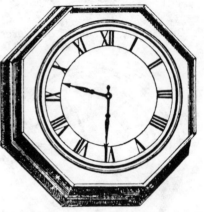

☐ **Octagon 8 Day Bank Clock,** *white and gilt dial 18", 8 Day.*
.... 230.00   250.00
☐ **As above,** *8 Day, strike*
.... 250.00   270.00

☐ **Octagon Lever,** *dial 6", 8 Day.*
.... 130.00   150.00
☐ **As above,** *8 Day, strike*
.... 140.00   160.00

☐ **Octagon Lever,** *mahogany, rosewood, dial 8", 8 Day.*
.... 135.00   155.00
☐ **As above,** *8 Day, strike*
.... 145.00   165.00

☐ **Octagon Lever,** *papier mâché, dial 10", 8 Day.*
.... 170.00   180.00
☐ **As above,** *8 Day, strike*
.... 190.00   210.00

☐ **Octagon Lever,** *mahogany, rosewood, dial 10", 8 Day.*
.... 140.00   160.00

☐ **As above,** *8 Day, strike*
.... 150.00   170.00

☐ **Octagon Papier Mâché Lever,** *dial 8", 8 day.*
.... 135.00   155.00

☐ **As above,** *8 Day, strike*
.... 155.00   175.00

☐ **Octagon Mâché papier Lever Time Piece,** *dial 6", 1 Day.*
.... 120.00   140.00

☐ **As above,** *1 Day, strike*
.... 140.00   160.00

☐ **Papier Mâché,** *dial 10", 8 Day.*
.... 130.00   150.00

☐ **As above,** *8 Day, strike*
.... 140.00   160.00

KEYLESS AUTO CLOCK COMPANY

AUTOMOBILE CLOCKS c. 1916

☐ **Abro,** *an offset clock with Best keywinding movement, thief proof, black and nickel finish, dial 2¼", 8 Day.*
.... 30.00   50.00

☐ **Belmont,** *keywind, a cowl clock that sets close to the dash, black and nickel finish, dial 2¾", 8 Day.*
.... 30.00   45.00

☐ **Denver Cowl,** *keywind, a cowl clock that sits close to the dash, all nickel, or black and nickel case, dial 2¼", 8 Day.*
.... 30.00   45.00

☐ **No. K2N,** *keywind, cowl, all nickel case, dial 2½", 1 Day.*
.... 30.00   45.00

☐ **No. K1BN,** *keywind, offset model, black and nickel case, dial 2½", 1 Day.*
.... 25.00   40.00

Knockabout Klock, *guaranteed for one year, can be adjusted to fit any angle dash, by simple ball joint which can be adjusted and tightened to any angle making it possible to see the face of the clock, regardless of how far it is from the lamp.*

☐ **No. KAB,** *Black, Japanese finish.*
.... 25.00   40.00

Model L, *rim wind-rim set, straight base.*

☐ **No. KLN,** *all nickel case, height 2¼", dial 2¼".*
.... 40.00   55.00

☐ **No. KLBN,** *black and nickel case.*
.... 40.00   55.00

Model M And M Jr., *rim wind-rim set, offset model, thief proof, a very reliable timepiece.*

☐ **No. KMN,** *all nickel, dial 2¾", 8 Day.*

.... 40.00   65.00

☐ **No. KMBN,** *black and nickel, dial 2¾", 8 Day.*

.... 40.00   65.00

☐ **No. KMJRN,** *all nickel, dial 2¼", 8 Day.*

.... 40.00   65.00

☐ **No. KMJRBN,** *black and nickel, dial 2¼", 8 Day.*

.... 40.00   65.00

New Ormond, *keywind, an offset clock with the highest grade movement, thief proof locking plate.*

☐ **No. NOBN,** *black and nickel case, dial 3", 8 Day.*

.... 35.00   50.00

NOJAR, *stem wind, for any dash, any make of car, rubber retained clock for dash, drill holes for screws are attached permanently to metal base, embody in rubber, tighten ends, and the clock is ready for use, 1 Day.*

☐ **No. FD2,** *clock retained in red rubber holder, weight per clock ¾ pounds.*

.... 25.00   40.00

NOJAR, *stem wind, for steering wheel on Ford or Dodge cars, rubber retained, no trouble to attach, simply remove nut from top of steering wheel and attach to the clock, may be adjusted at any angle as the rubber holder is movable on the metal base, a good timekeeper, 1 Day.*

☐ **No. FN1,** *clock retained in red rubber holder, weight per clock ½ pound.*

.... 25.00   40.00

☐ **Rim Wind-Rim Set No. K4RD,** *for Ford cars, thief proof, black and nickel case, dial 2¼", 8 Day.*

.... 40.00   55.00

☐ **Rim Wind-Rim Set No. 7N,** *a very reliable timepiece, all nickel dial 2¾", 8 Day.*

.... 60.00   70.00

☐ **No. 7BN,** *black and nickel, dial 2¾", 8 Day.*

.... 60.00   70.00

☐ **No. 12N,** *all nickel, dial 2¼", 8 Day.*

.... 60.00   70.00

☐ **No. 12BN,** *black and nickel, dial 2¼", 8 Day.*

.... 60.00   70.00

☐ **Rim Wind-Rim Set *No. K9N,** *all nickel, dial 2¾", 8 Day.*

.... 60.00   75.00

☐ ***No. K9BN,** *black and nickel, dial 2¾", 8 Day.*

.... 60.00   75.00

☐ ***No. K12BAN,** *all nickel, dial 2¼", 8 Day.*

.... 60.00   75.00

☐ ***No. 12BBN,** *black and nickel, dial 2¼", 8 Day.*

.... 60.00   70.00

*Note: Model 9 for Cadillac, Hudson, White, Buick, Overland, Cole, Studebaker, Lewis, Austin. Model 12B for Chandler, Paige, Hudson, Hupmobile, Overland, Buick, Dodge, Mercer, Pathfinder.

Shasta, *keywind, an offset clock of the most approved type, no locking plate, dial 2¼".*

☐ **No. KSN,** *all nickel case, 8 Day.*

.... 30.00   45.00

☐ **No. KSBN,** *black and nickel case, 8 Day.*
.... 30.00   45.00

☐ **Stem Wind,** *Devere, heavy, solid brass case, polished, with offset holding a complete watch, stem wind and set, 3½ " x 2⅞ ", white dial 1⅛ ", 1 Day.*
.... 35.00   55.00

☐ **Stem Wind,** *Duane, light, solid brass case, polished, with offset holding a complete watch, stem wind and set 3½ " x 2⅞ ", white dial 1½ ", 1 Day.*
.... 35.00   55.00

☐ **No. FIAT,** *stem wind, for steering wheel on Ford or Dodge cars, sets on top of steering column, no bolts or screws needed,*

simply raise the nut on steering column, slide in clock and screw in tight, 1 Day.
.... 20.00   40.00

☐ **No. PANAMA,** *stem wind, black and nickel case, with this clock it is not necessary to cut cowl board, 1 Day.*
.... 20.00   40.00

☐ **Uncle Dudley-BN,** *stem wind, black and nickel case, an attractive clock with beveled crystal and non-glaring silver reflector, 1 Day.*
.... 30.00   45.00

F. KROEBER

CALENDAR

☐ **Desk Inkwell,** *patent date May 28, 1878, 1 Day, alarm, simple calendar (M487-149).*
.... 200.00   250.00

☐ **Galena,** *23½ " x 14½ ", 8 Day, strike (M484-148).*
.... 350.00   450.00

☐ **Round Alarm,** *patent date May 28, 1878, 1 Day, alarm, simple calendar (M488-149).*
.... 200.00   225.00

MACOMB CALENDAR COMPANY

CALENDAR

☐ **Shelf Model,** *spring, 30" x 15½ ", time dial 6", moon phase dial 6½ ", 8 Day, strike (M323-105).*
.... 2500.00   3000.00

☐ **Shelf Model,** *spring, 30" x 15½ ", time dial 6", moon phase dial 6½ ", 8 Day, strike (M325-105).*
.... 2800.00   3200.00

☐ **Wall Model,** *spring, 30" x 14½",
time dial 6", moon phase dial
6½", 8 Day, strike, (M324-105).*
.... 2500.00   3000.00

G. MARANVILLE

CALENDAR

☐ **Octagon Drop Wall,** *spring, 24" x
17", dial 11½", 8 Day, strike
(M417-130).*
.... 700.00   800.00

☐ **Octagon Drop Wall,** *spring, 23½"
x 16¼", dial 11", 8 Day, strike
(M420-131).*
.... 750.00   850.00

☐ **Round Drop Wall,** *weight, 34" x
16", dial 11", 8 Day (M421-132).*
.... 1500.00   1700.00

MONARCH CALENDAR
CLOCK COMPANY

CALENDAR

☐ **Shelf Clock,** *spring, made by
New Haven Clock Co., 32" x
17½", dials 7", 8 Day, strike
(M383-121).*
.... 1000.00   1200.00

MOZART, BEACH
AND HUBBELL

CALENDAR

☐ **Wall Clock,** *25" x 13", time with
seconds bit 7", day of week dial
2¾", month and date dial 5¼",
1 year (M150-54).*
.... 5000.00   6000.00

MUELLER AND SON

CHARACTER

☐ **Guardian,** *cast iron front, height
15½", 8 Day, strike (E1-15).*
.... 175.00   200.00

☐ **Old Man,** *cast iron front, visible
pendulum, height 13", 1 Day,
strike (E1-10).*
.... 140.00   165.00

☐ **Scotchman,** *cast iron front, visible pendulum, height 18", 8 Day, strike (E1-10).*
.... **195.00   225.00**

☐ **Etruscan,** *solid cast iron, height 18", 8 Day, strike (E1-14).*
.... **175.00   200.00**

☐ **Shepherd Children,** *cast iron front, visible pendulum, height 17½", 8 Day, strike (E1-10).*
.... **160.00   185.00**

ETRUSCAN

☐ **Doric,** *iron, height 14½", 1 Day, strike.*
.... **115.00   120.00**

Etruscan

☐ **Etruscan,** *solid cast iron, height 18½", 8 Day, strike (E1-11).*
. . . . 165.00   190.00

☐ **Grisi,** *iron, height 18", 8 Day, strike.*
. . . . 179.00   190.00

☐ **Temple,** *solid cast iron, visible pendulum, height 18¾", 1 Day, strike (E1-13).*
. . . . 125.00   150.00
☐ **As above,** *8 Day, strike.*
. . . . 175.00   200.00

☐ **Lattice,** *iron, height 18½", strike.*
. . . . 150.00   200.00
☐ **Pompeii,** *solid cast iron, height 18½", 8 Day, strike (E1-10).*
. . . . 165.00   190.00

☐ **Washington,** *iron, height 20", 8 Day, strike.*
.... 150.00   215.00
☐ **As above,** *height 17", 1 Day, strike.*
.... 135.00   150.00

FLORA AND FAUNA

☐ **Arbor,** *cast iron fronts, visible pendulum, height 17½", 1 Day, strike (E1-13).*
.... 125.00   150.00
☐ **As above,** *height 20", 8 Day, strike.*
.... 175.00   200.00

☐ **Bouquet,** *cast iron front, visible pendulum, height 16", 1 Day, strike (E1-15).*
.... 125.00   150.00
☐ **As above,** *height 19", 8 Day, strike.*
.... 175.00   200.00

☐ **Cupid,** *iron front, visible pendulum, three cherubs, floral pattern, height 18½", 8 Day, strike (E1-15).*
.... 145.00   170.00

☐ **As above,** *height 16", 8 Day, strike.*
.... 135.00   160.00
☐ **As above,** *height 16", 1 Day, strike.*
.... 110.00   135.00

☐ **Doric,** *cast iron front, visible pendulum, height 14½", 1 Day, strike (E1-14).*
.... 95.00   115.00

☐ **Dragon,** *cast iron front, visible pendulum, height 15½", 1 Day, strike (E1-15).*
.... 110.00   135.00

☐ **Eagle,** *cast iron front, visible pendulum, height 15", 1 Day, strike (E1-15).*
.... 220.00   250.00

☐ **Eagle,** *cast iron front, visible pendulum, height 18½", 8 Day, strike (E1-11).*
.... 220.00   250.00

☐ **Fox And Hare,** *cast iron front, visible pendulum, height 19¾", 8 Day, strike (E1-11).*
.... 195.00   225.00

☐ **Grisi,** *cast iron front, visible pendulum, height 16½", 1 Day, strike (E1-15).*
.... 150.00   175.00
☐ **As above,** *height 18", 8 Day, strike.*
.... 175.00   200.00

☐ **Juno,** *cast iron front, visible pendulum, height 16½", 1 Day, strike (E1-14).*
.... 150.00   175.00
☐ **As above,** *height 19½", 8 Day, strike.*
.... 195.00   225.00

☐ **Lattice,** *cast iron front, visible pendulum, height 18½", 1 Day, strike (E1-12).*
.... 125.00   150.00
☐ **As above,** *8 Day, strike.*
.... 175.00   200.00

Lion Head, *cast iron front, visible pendulum, height 15", 1 Day, strike (E1-11).*
. . . . **125.00   150.00**

Renaissance, *cast iron front, visible pendulum, height 16", 1 Day, strike (E1-10).*
. . . . **160.00   185.00**

Ruin, *cast iron front, floral pattern, height 12½", 8 Day, strike (E1-10).*
. . . . **140.00   165.00**

Washington, *cast iron front, visible pendulum, height 17", 1 Day, strike (E1-12).*
. . . . **125.00   150.00**
As above, *height 20", 8 Day, strike.*
. . . . **185.00   215.00**

FLORAL PAINTED

Franklin, *cast iron front, extra pearl, height 16", 1 Day, strike (E1-15).*
. . . . **80.00   100.00**

Rococo, *cast iron front, height 14½", 8 Day, strike (E1-10).*
. . . . **135.00   160.00**

☐ **Urn,** *cast iron front, height 13", 1 Day, strike (E1-10).*
. . . . **110.00** **135.00**

☐ **Wide Awake,** *large, cast iron front, height 16¼", 1 Day, strike (E1-11).*
. . . . **100.00** **120.00**

☐ **Wide Awake,** *small, cast iron front, height 11", 1 Day, strike (E1-15).*
. . . . **95.00** **105.00**

GOTHIC

☐ **Evangelist,** *gothic cast iron front, height 17", 1 Day, strike.*
. . . . **150.00** **175.00**

☐ **Evangelist,** *gothic cast iron front, height 20", 8 Day, strike (E1-11).*
. . . . **195.00** **225.00**

☐ **Gilt Gothic,** *cast iron front, height 16½", 1 Day, strike.*
. . . . **125.00** **150.00**

☐ **Gilt Gothic,** *cast iron front, height 19½", 8 Day, strike (E1-9).*
. . . . **175.00** **200.00**

☐ **Gothic,** *cast iron front, height 16¼", 1 Day, strike.*
. . . . **125.00** **150.00**

☐ **Gothic,** *cast iron front, height 18½", 8 Day, strike (E1-11).*
. . . . **175.00** **200.00**

☐ **Peter And Paul,** *gothic cast iron front, height 20", 8 Day, strike (E1-12).*
. . . . **195.00   225.00**

☐ **Oak Leaf,** *cast iron front, height 20", 8 Day, strike (E1-12).*
. . . . **150.00   175.00**

☐ **Opera,** *gothic cast iron front, height 18", 8 Day, strike (E1-12).*
. . . . **175.00   200.00**

☐ **Vine Gothic,** *cast iron front, height 16½", 1 Day, strike (E1-9).*
. . . . **105.00   125.00**

IRON AND BRONZE

□ **Birds,** *bronze, height 21", 8 Day, strike.*
.... 180.00   225.00

□ **Dragon,** *bronze, height 15½", 1 Day, strike.*
.... 120.00   135.00

□ **Fox And Hare,** *bronze, height 19¾", 8 Day, strike.*
.... 210.00   225.00

□ **Eagle,** *bronze, height 18½", 8 Day, strike.*
.... 205.00   250.00

□ **Eagle,** *iron, height 15", 1 Day, strike.*
.... 205.00   250.00

□ **Juno,** *bronze, height 19½", 8 Day, strike.*
.... 210.00   225.00

□ **As above,** *height 16½", 1 Day, strike.*
.... 160.00   175.00

☐ **Lion Head,** *bronze, height 15", 1 Day, strike.*
.... 135.00   150.00

NOVELTY (ANIMATED) ONE DAY WINKER

☐ **Topsey,** *iron, winker, height 16", 1 Day (E1-9).*
.... 800.00   900.00

PARLOR

☐ **Continental,** *iron, winker, height 16", 1 Day (E1-9).*
.... 800.00   900.00

☐ **Organ Grinder,** *iron, winker, height 17½", 1 Day (E1-9).*
.... 850.00   950.00

☐ **Sambo,** *iron, winker, height 16", 1 Day (E1-9).*
.... 800.00   900.00

☐ **Borne,** *iron parlor, height 10", 8 Day, strike (E1-12).*
.... 110.00   135.00

☐ **Fluted Column,** *iron parlor, height 16", 8 Day, strike (E1-14).*
.... 125.00   150.00

☐ **Parlor,** *iron, black, marbleized and ornamental, height 12" to 14", 1 Day, strike (E1-12).*
.... 80.00   100.00

☐ **As above,** *8 Day, strike.*
.... **105.00   125.00**

☐ **Parlor,** *iron, plain or ornamented, height 10", 8 Day, strike (E1-15).*
.... **80.00   100.00**

☐ **Parlor,** *iron, plain or ornamented, height 10½", 8 Day, strike (E1-12).*
.... **70.00   95.00**

☐ **Parlor,** *iron, plain, or ornamented, height 10½", 8 Day, strike (E1-15).*
.... **80.00   100.00**

☐ **Parlor,** *iron, plain or ornamented, height 10½", 8 Day, strike (E1-15).*
.... **85.00   105.00**

☐ **Webster,** *iron parlor, visible pendulum, height 15", 8 Day, strike (E1-13).*
.... **105.00   125.00**

STATUE

☐ **Amor,** *bronze front, height 20", 8 Day, strike (E1-11).*
.... **195.00   225.00**

☐ **Armorer,** *bronze front, height 18", 8 Day, strike (E1-15).*
.... **145.00   170.00**

☐ **Boy And Dog,** *bronze front, lever, height 11", 1 Day, strike (E1-10).*
.... 60.00   75.00

☐ **Chase And Figure,** *bronze front, height 21", 8 Day, strike (E1-13).*
.... 175.00   200.00

☐ **Drummer,** *bronze front, height 18½", 8 Day, strike (E1-15).*
.... 150.00   175.00

☐ **Dolphin,** *bronze front, height 20", 8 Day, strike (E1-13).*
.... 195.00   225.00

☐ **Drama,** *bronze front, height 16", 1 Day, strike (E1-12).*
.... 125.00   150.00

☐ **As above,** *8 Day, strike.*
.... 175.00   200.00

☐ **Evangeline,** *bronze front, height 19", 8 Day, strike (E1-9).*
.... 155.00   180.00

☐ **Fisher Boy And Dog,** *bronze front, height 18", 8 Day, strike (E1-14).*
.... 140.00   165.00

☐ **French,** *bronze front, height 20",*
8 Day, strike (E1-9).
. . . . 155.00   180.00

☐ **Highlander,** *bronze front, height*
19½", 8 Day, strike (E1-14).
. . . . 175.00   200.00

☐ **Horse,** *bronze front, height 21", 8*
Day, strike (E1-14).
. . . . 155.00   180.00

☐ **Horse,** *(small) bronze front,*
height 14", 8 Day, strike (E1-9).
. . . . 110.00   135.00

☐ **Gleaner,** *bronze front, height*
18½", 8 Day, strike (E1-14).
. . . . 175.00   200.00

☐ **Globe,** *bronze front, height*
19½", 8 Day, strike (E1-11).
. . . . 195.00   225.00

☐ **Lady Lever,** *bronze front, height 13", 1 Day (E1-15).*
. . . . 110.00   135.0

☐ **Mermaid,** *bronze front, height 14¾", 1 Day (E1-14).*
. . . . 105.00   130.00

☐ **Louis XV,** *bronze front, height 18", 8 Day, strike (E1-13).*
. . . . 175.00   200.00

☐ **Lovers,** *bronze front, height 17", 8 Day, strike (E1-12).*
. . . . 175.00   200.00

☐ **Mountaineer,** *bronze front, height 20", 8 Day, strike (E1-14).*
. . . . 175.00   200.00

☐ **Mustang,** *bronze front, height 15", 8 Day, strike (E1-12).*
. . . . 175.00   200.00

☐ **Neptune,** *bronze front, height 19", 8 Day, strike (E1-13).*
. . . . 175.00   200.00

☐ **Reaper,** *bronze front, height 18½ ", 8 Day, strike (E1-11).*
.... **150.00   175.00**

☐ **Patchen,** *bronze front, height 19", 8 Day, strike (E1-13).*
.... **175.00   200.00**

☐ **Savoyard,** *bronze front, height 18½ ", 8 Day, strike (E1-10).*
.... **140.00   165.00**

☐ **Pleasant Girl,** *bronze front, height 19", 8 Day, strike (E1-9).*
.... **155.00   180.00**

☐ **Setter,** *bronze front, height 17", 8 Day, strike (E1-10).*
.... **125.00   150.00**

□ **Trophy,** *bronze front, height 18½", 8 Day, strike (E1-10).*
.... **195.00   225.00**

□ **Vintner,** *bronze front, height 19", 8 Day, strike (E1-15).*
.... **150.00   175.00**

□ **Wine Drinker,** *bronze front, height 20", 8 Day, strike (E1-14).*
.... **175.00   200.00**

NATIONAL CALENDAR CLOCK COMPANY

CALENDAR

□ **Column Shelf,** *spring, dials 7", 8 Day, strike, simple calendar (M381-120).*
.... **575.00   725.00**

□ **Fashion Styled Shelf,** *spring, dials 7", 8 Day, strike, simple calendar (M375-119).*
.... **1300.00   1475.00**

□ **O.G.,** *spring, cathedral gong, 26" x 15½", dials 7", 8 Day, strike, simple calendar (M380-120).*
.... **525.00   675.00**

NEW HAVEN CLOCK COMPANY

Hiram Camp was the president of the New Haven Clock Company during the time it was reputed to be one of the largest American clock manufacturing dealers. They produced a very wide range of clocks, scorning solely American models and traditional designs.

The New Haven Company managed to purchase the bankrupt Jerome Clock Company after the ill-fated Terry, Barnum, and Jerome partnership dissolved. Before this time New Haven had only produced movements; now they had the facilities necessary to manufacture whole clocks. From the existing records of the Company's sales performance, it seems they had some difficulty in turning a profit. Colleagues suggested that this was due to the tremendous variety New Haven offered rather than any lack of quality or endurance as far as the reputation of the company was concerned.

Like so many other clock companies of the times, New Haven put out a cheap pocket watch of the non-jeweled variety, as a means of staying afloat in troubled financial waters.

Early in the 20th century they added wristwatches to their inventory.

The New Haven Clock Company lasted until well into the mid 1960's, when the entire plant was sold at a public auction.

ALARMS

☐ **Bullfight,** *nickel, dial 4", c. 1900, 1 Day, alarm (E2-127).*
.... **175.00   200.00**

☐ **Mandolin,** *nickel, dial 4", c. 1900, 1 Day, alarm (E2-127).*
.... **150.00   175.00**

☐ **Pet,** *nickel, dial 4", c. 1900, 1 Day (E2-127).*
.... **195.00   225.00**

☐ **Puff,** *nickel, dial 4", c. 1900, 1 Day (E2-127).*
.... **175.00   200.00**

☐ **Shaver,** *nickel, dial 4", c. 1900, 1 Day, alarm (E2-127).*
.... **175.00   200.00**

FANCY

☐ **Herald,** *wood case, nickel or brass front, height 6½", dial 4", c. 1900, 1 Day, alarm (E2-111).*
.... **45.00   65.00**

☐ **Little Duke,** *height 6¼", c. 1890, 1 Day (E2-88).*
.... **80.00   90.00**
☐ **As above,** *1 Day, alarm.*
.... **90.00   110.00**

ROUND

☐ **Acorn,** *dial 2½", c. 1890, 1 Day (E2-88).*
.... **35.00   45.00**

☐ **As above,** *1 Day, alarm.*
.... **40.00   50.00**

☐ **Elfin,** *nickel, plain or fancy dial 6", c. 1890, 1 Day, alarm (E2-88).*
.... **30.00   40.00**
☐ **As above,** *1 Day, strike.*
.... **25.00   35.00**

☐ **Beacon,** *dial 4", c. 1890, 1 Day, alarm (E2-88).*
.... **35.00   45.00**

☐ **Flash,** *luminous dial 4", c. 1890 1 Day (E2-88).*
.... **25.00   35.00**
☐ **As above,** *1 Day, alarm.*
.... **25.00   35.00**

☐ **Champion,** *seamless case 4½", dial 4", c. 1890, 1 Day, alarm (E2-88).*
.... **25.00   35.00**

☐ **Kelpie,** *height 7", dial 4½", c. 1890, 1 Day, strike (E2-88).*
.... 30.00   40.00

☐ **Sprite,** *nickel, dial 4½", c. 1890, 1 Day, alarm (E2-88).*
.... 35.00   45.00

☐ **As above,** *1 Day, alarm, calendar.*
.... 60.00   85.00

☐ **The Fly,** *nickel, dial 4", c. 1890, 1 Day (E2-88).*
.... 20.00   30.00

☐ **As above,** *1 Day, alarm.*
.... 25.00   35.00

☐ **Globe Calendar,** *height 6", dial 4", c. 1890, 1 Day, calendar (E2-88).*
.... 70.00   90.00

☐ **Start,** *nickel, dial 4", c. 1890, 1 Day, alarm (E2-88).*
.... 25.00   35.00

Sting

☐ **Sting,** *dial 2", c. 1890, 1 Day (E2-88).*
.... 35.00   45.00

☐ **Sting Alarm,** *nickel, or gilt, dial 2", c. 1890, 1 Day, alarm (E2-88).*
.... 40.00   50.00

☐ **Sting Repeating Strike,** *nickel, dial 2", 1 Day.*
.... 195.00   220.00

☐ **Tattoo Alarm Luminous,** *international alarm movement, seamless case 4½", black dial 4", c. 1890, 1 Day, alarm (E2-88).*
.... 25.00   35.00

☐ **Tattoo,** *intermittent alarm, dial 4½", c. 1890, 1 Day, alarm (E2-88).*
.... 35.00   45.0

☐ **The Beacon,** *nickel or enamel, 6½" x 4¼", dial 4", c. 1890, 1 Day (E2-88).*
.... 25.00   35.0

☐ **As above,** *1 Day, calendar.*
.... 65.00   80.0

☐ **As above,** *1 Day, alarm.*
.... 60.00   75.0

☐ **As above,** *1 Day, alarm, calendar.*
.... 70.00   85.00

☐ **Tocsin,** *nickel, dial 4½", c. 1900, 1 Day, alarm (E1-44).*
.... 20.00   30.00

AUTOMOBILE CLOCKS

☐ **Cowl-NH,** *most accurate keywinding cowl clock made, black and nickel case, dial 2¼", 8 Day.*
.... 30.00   50.00

☐ **Frisco 1,** *stem wind, matching screw, winding stem concealed, dial 2½", 1 Day.*
.... 25.00   30.00

☐ **Frisco Cowl 2,** *stem wind, concealed winding stem, dial 2½", 1 Day.*
.... 25.00   30.00

BANJO

☐ **Willis No. 2,** *mahogany, porcelain or silver dial, 17¾" x 5", c. 1917, 8 Day (E1-173).*
.... 115.00   140.00

CABINET

☐ **Albatross,** *richly modeled, cast brass frame, panels of Chelsea tiles, cathedral gong, height 12", breadth 9", dial 4½", c. 1900, 8 Day, strike (E2-91).*
. . . . **195.00   220.00**

☐ **Amphion,** *oak, cathedral gong, height 18½", dial 5", c. 1900, 8 Day, strike (E2-91).*
. . . . **140.00   165.00**

☐ **Angela,** *oak, richly ornamented with cast brass trimmings, in antique finish, cathedral gong, height 21¾", dial 4½", c. 1900, 8 Day, strike (E2-93).*
. . . . **270.00   300.00**

Amphion

Albatross

Angela

Anita, *mahogany, richly ornamented with cast brass trimmings, in antique finish, height 16", dial 4", c. 1900, 15 Day, strike (E2-93).*
. . . . **195.00   220.00**

□ **Arab,** *antique oak, ivorized dial, height 18½", dial 4", c. 1900, 15 Day, strike (E2-93).*
. . . . **220.00   250.00**

□ **Argyle Time,** *wood, height 13", c. 1894, 1 Day (E2-125).*
. . . . **125.00   150.00**

□ **Argyle,** *wood, height 17", c. 1894, 1 Day, strike (E2-125).*
. . . . **125.00   150.00**
□ **As above,** *8 Day, strike.*
. . . . **175.00   200.00**

☐ **Aurania,** *antique oak, heavily gilt ornaments, cathedral gong, height 19¼", dial 5", c. 1900, 8 Day, strike (E2-92).*
. . . . **160.00   185.00**

☐ **As above,** *walnut.*
. . . . **185.00   210.00**

☐ **Arrow,** *walnut, brass trimmings, height 16¼", dial 5", c. 1900, 8 Day, strike (E2-92).*
. . . . **140.00   165.00**

☐ **Bahama,** *wood, height 12", silver dial 8½", c. 1894, 8 Day, strike (E2-125).*
. . . . **80.00   100.00**

☐ **Banshee,** *cherry, brass ornaments, height 13½", dial 5", c. 1900, 1 Day, strike, alarm (E2-92).*
. . . . **165.00   190.00**

☐ **Bermuda,** *oak, height 12", dial 4", c. 1894, 8 Day, strike (E2-124).*
. . . . 85.00   105.00

☐ **Cabinet No. 2,** *mahogany, height 17½", dial 5", c. 1900, 8 Day, strike (E2-92).*
. . . . 165.00   190.00

☐ **Caliban,** *oak, cathedral gong, 14¾" x 11", white, gilt or ivorine dial 6", c. 1910, 8 Day, strike (E2-90).*
. . . . 130.00   155.00

☐ **Cato,** *polished oak, 15" x 12", c. 1900 (E2-128).*
. . . . 120.00   145.00

☐ **Cato,** *oak, cathedral gong, 15" x 11½", fancy gilt or ivorine dial 5", c. 1910, 8 Day, strike (E2-90).*
. . . . 160.00   185.00

☐ **Clifton,** *oak, cathedral gong,*
11½" x 13¼", white, gilt or
ivorine dial 6", c. 1910, 8 Day,
strike (E2-90).
. . . . **130.00   155.00**

☐ **Funston,** *oak cabinet, barometer,*
thermometer and spirit level,
cathedral gong, 15½" x 11¾",
white, gilt or ivorine dial 6", c.
1910, 8 Day, strike (E2-90).
. . . . **165.00   190.00**

☐ **Etruria,** *antique oak, heavily gilt*
ornaments, cathedral gong,
height 18", base 21", dial 5", c.
1900, 8 Day, strike (E2-92).
. . . . **195.00   220.00**
☐ **As above,** *walnut, 8 Day, strike.*
. . . . **220.00   245.00**

☐ **Gallia,** *antique oak, heavily gilt*
ornaments, cathedral gong,
height 19", dial 5", c. 1900, 8
Day, strike (E2-92).
. . . . **160.00   185.00**
☐ **As above,** *walnut, 8 Day, strike.*
. . . . **185.00   210.00**

□ **Granada,** *wood, height 12", silver dial 8½", c. 1894, 8 Day, strike (E2-125).*
.... **80.00   100.00**

□ **Hidalgo,** *mahogany, solid wood, dead finish, height 17¾", dial 5", c. 1900, 8 Day, strike (E2-91).*
.... **150.00   175.00**

□ **Harlequin,** *bronze or silver trimmings, visible escapement, French sash, height 16", porcelain dial 4½", c. 1900, 8 Day, strike (E2-91).*
.... **190.00   220.00**

☐ **Martinique,** *oak, height 12", dial 4", c. 1894, 8 Day, strike (E2-124).*
. . . . **85.00   105.00**

☐ **Melita,** *oak, cathedral gong, 15¼" x 11¾", fancy gilt or ivorine dial 5", c. 1910, 8 Day, strike (E2-90).*
. . . . **160.00   185.00**

☐ **Medea,** *oak, cathedral gong, 15¼" x 11¾", fancy gilt or ivorine dial 5", c. 1910, 8 Day, strike (E2-90).*
. . . . **160.00   185.00**

☐ **Mendon,** *oak, cathedral gong, 15¼" x 11¾", fancy gilt or ivorine dial 5", c. 1910, 8 Day, strike (E2-90).*
. . . . **160.00   185.00**

☐ **Nero,** *polished oak, 16" x 12", c. 1900, 8 Day, strike (E-92).*
. . . . **125.00   150.00**

☐ **Nero,** *oak, cathedral gong, 16" x 12", fancy gilt or ivorine dial 5", c. 1910, 8 Day, strike (E2-90).*
. . . . 160.00   185.00

☐ **Penobscot,** *mahogany, solid wood, dead finish, height 16¼", dial 5", c. 1900, 8 Day, strike (E2-92).*
. . . . 165.00   190.00

☐ **Olga,** *oak, height 13¼", dial 5", c. 1900, 8 Day, strike (E2-92).*
. . . . 135.00   160.00
☐ **As above,** *mahogany.*
. . . . 160.00   185.00

□ **Russia,** *antique oak, heavily gilt ornaments, cathedral gong, height 18½", dial 5", c. 1900, 8 Day, strike (E2-92).*
.... **150.00   175.00**
□ **As above,** *walnut, 8 Day, strike.*
.... **175.00   200.00**

□ **Scipio,** *oak, cathedral gong, 16" x 11¾", fancy gilt or ivorine dial 5", c. 1910, 8 Day, strike (E2-90).*
.... **160.00   185.00**

□ **Trinidad,** *oak, height 12", dial 4", c. 1894, 8 Day, strike (E2-124).*
.... **80.00   100.00**

□ **Servia,** *antique oak, heavily gilt ornaments, cathedral gong, height 19", dial 5", c. 1900, 8 Day, strike (E2-92).*
.... **150.00   175.00**
□ **As above,** *walnut, 8 Day, strike.*
.... **175.00   200.00**

□ **Umbria,** *oak, heavily gilt ornaments, cathedral gong, 18" x 22½", dial 5", c. 1900, 8 Day, strike (E2-92).*
.... **195.00   220.00**

☐ **Vreda,** *polished antique oak, cathedral gong, height 20½", dial 8", c. 1900, 8 Day, strike (E2-91).*
.... **140.00   165.00**

WESTMINSTER CHIMES

☐ **The "Abbey" Chime Clock,** *oak, cast Rococo sash, 17¼" x 12⅝", pearl dial 6", c. 1900 (E1-41).*
.... **180.00   210.00**

☐ **Eight-Bell Chime No. 1,** *mahogany, French satin gilt trimmings, height 18", metal dial 7", c. 1890, 8 Day, strike (E2-89).*
.... **565.00   625.00**

No. 3

No. 4

No. 5

☐ **Four-Bell Westminster Chime No.
3,** *wood, 18½" x 12", c. 1890, 8
Day, strike (E2-89).*
. . . . 230.00   260.00

☐ **Four-Bell Westminster Chime No.
5,** *light oak, oxidized silver or
bronze trimmings, 22¼" x 12¼",
metal dial 6", c. 1890, 8 Day,
strike (E2-89).*
. . . . 230.00   260.00

☐ **As above,** *mahogany, French
satin gold trimmings, 8 Day,
strike.*
. . . . 255.00   285.00

☐ **Westminster Chime No. 4,**
*mahogany, richly ornamented
metal dial, 20" x 11", dial 5½", c.
1900, 8 Day, strike (E1-41).*
. . . . 220.00   250.00

CALENDAR

☐ **Barbara,** *47" x 18½ ", dial 10", 30 Day, simple calendar, double dial (E2-125).*
.... **900.00   975.00**

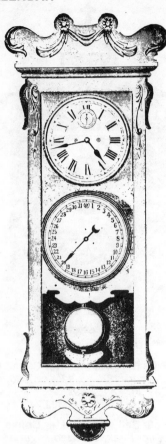

☐ **Austrian,** *49" x 19", dial 10", 30 Day, simple calendar, double dial (E2-125).*
.... **900.00   950.00**

☐ **Austrian,** *wall regulator, 49" x 19", dial 10", 8 Day, strike, simple calendar (E2-125).*
.... **500.00   575.00**

☐ **Bank Regulator,** *long drop, spring, 33" x 18", dial 12", 8 Day, simple calendar (M411-128).*
.... **350.00   400.00**

☐ **Barbara,** *wall regulator, 47" x 18½ ", dial 10", 8 Day, strike, simple calendar (E2-125).*
.... **500.00   600.00**

☐ **Columbia Regulator,** *spring 48½" x 14½", dial 8", 8 Day, simple calendar (E1-164).*
.... 750.00   850.00

label, *height 31", dials 8", 8 Day (E1-103).*
.... 1000.00   1100.00

☐ **Conroy Victorian Shelf,** *spring, thermometer and barometer, 25" x 15½", dial 6", 8 Day, strike, simple calendar (E1-167).*
.... 200.00   215.0^

☐ **12" Drop Octagon,** *height 24", dial 12", 8 Day, strike, simple calendar (E2-122).*
.... 300.00   350.00

☐ **8" Drop Octagon,** *short, brass bands, height 19" (E2-122).*
.... 225.00   275.00

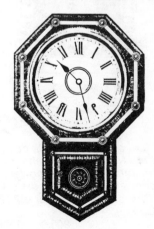

☐ **Dneister,** *double dial wall or shelf, spring, also with Jerome*

☐ **10″ Drop Octagon,** *short, brass bands, height 21″ (E2-122).*
.... **350.00   400.00**

☐ **12″ Drop Octagon,** *short, brass bands, height 23″ (E2-122).*
.... **275.00   325.00**

☐ **Emperor,** *Square Top Short Drop, oak, height 25½″, dial 12″, 8 Day, strike, simple calendar (E2-122).*
.... **250.00   300.00**

☐ **Elfrida,** *double dial wall, double spring, New Haven calendar mechanism, retaining power, seconds bit, 58″ x 21″, dials 10″, 30 Day, simple calendar (E2-123, M410-128).*
.... **900.00   1100.00**

☐ **Emperor,** *Square Top Short Drop, brass bands, height 25½″, dial*

12", 8 Day, strike, simple calendar (E2-122).
.... 275.00   325.00

☐ **10" Gilt Octagon Top,** *height 21", dial 10", 8 Day, strike, simple calendar (E2-122).*
.... 275.00   350.00

☐ **12" Gilt Octagon Top,** *height 24", dial 12", 8 Day, strike, simple calendar (E2-122).*
.... 300.00   325.00

☐ **Globe,** *round nickel, dial 4", 1 Day, alarm, simple calendar (E2-88).*
.... 70.00   90.00

☐ **Erie Standard Time,** *octagon top long drop, wall, spring, 33½" x 18½", dial 12", 8 Day, simple calendar (E1-183).*
.... 350.00   400.00

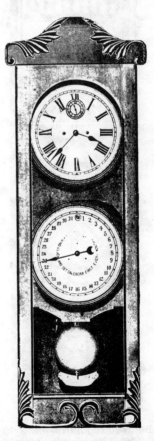

☐ **Gloriana,** *42" x 15½", 30 Day, simple calendar, double dial (E2-125).*
.... 800.00   900.00

☐ **Gloriana,** *wall regulator, 42" x 15½", dial 10", 8 Day, strike, simple calendar (E2-125).*
.... **525.00   575.00**

☐ **Hebe,** *49" x 15½", dial 10", 30 Day, simple calendar, double dial (E2-125).*
.... **900.00   950.00**

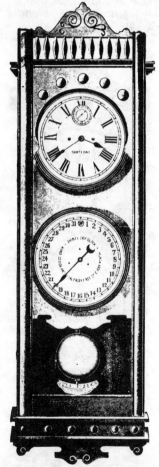

☐ **Heron Figure 8,** *double dial wall, spring, some have labels, height 31", time dial 12", calendar dial 8", 8 Day (E1-103).*
.... **1100.00   1200.00**

☐ **Indicator D. R.,** *figure 8 wall regulator, spring, height 30½", dial 12", 8 Day, simple calendar (E1-46).*
.... **450.00   500.00**

☐ **Intrepid,** *49" x 17", dial 10", 30 Day, simple calendar, double dial (E2-125).*
.... **900.00   1000.00**

☐ **Intrepid,** *wall regulator, 49" x 17", dial 10", 8 Day, strike, simple calendar (E2-125).*
.... **500.00   600.00**

☐ **Hebe,** *wall regulator, 49" x 15½", dial 10", 8 Day, strike, simple calendar (E2-125).*
.... **500.00   575.00**

☐ **Maywood Wall Regulator,** *spring,*
43½" x 17", dial 8", 8 Day,
simple calendar (E1-164).
. . . . 650.00   750.00

☐ **Ionic Figure 8,** *double dial wall,*
spring, height 29½", time dial
12", calendar dial 10", 8 Day
(E1-101).
. . . . 1000.00   1100.00

☐ **12" Mosaic Octagon Top Short**
Drop, *height 24", 8 Day, strike,*
simple calendar (E2-122).
. . . . 250.00   300.00

☐ **Octagon Lever Wall,** *spring,*
Mother-of-Pearl inlaid on wood
dial 9¼", diameter 13", 1 Day,
strike, simple calendar
(M405-127).
. . . . 250.00   275.00

☐ **Octagon R.C. Lever,** *width 12",*
dial 8", 1 Day, simple calendar
(E2-95).
. . . . 175.00   200.00

☐ **Octagon R.C. Lever,** *width 14",*
dial 10", 8 Day, simple calendar
(E2-95).
. . . . 225.00   275.00

☐ **Louis Inkstand,** *brass, height*
11½", dial 4", 1 Day, simple
calendar (E2-112).
. . . . 300.00   350.00

☐ **10" Octagon Top Short Drop,** *gilt*
buttons, height 21", dial 10", 8
Day, strike, simple calendar
(E2-122).
. . . . 300.00   350.00

☐ **Maintenon Inkstand,** *brass, 12" x*
11", dial 4", 1 Day, simple
calendar (E2-112).
. . . . 325.00   375.00

☐ **Octagon Top Short Drop,** *height 24", dial 11", 8 Day, strike, simple calendar (M414-129).*
.... **275.00   300.00**

☐ **Octagon Top Short Drop,** *spring, height 24", dial 12", 8 Day, strike, simple calendar (M413-129).*
.... **300.00   350.00**

☐ **Octagon Top Short Drop,** *spring, height 27", dial 12", 8 Day, strike, simple calendar (M412-129).*
.... **325.00   375.00**

☐ **Plush Manual,** *height 7", dial 2", 1 Day, simple calendar (E2-103).*
.... **125.00   175.00**

☐ **8" R.C. Drop Octagon,** *short, height 19" (E2-122).*
.... **225.00   250.00**

☐ **10" R.C. Drop Octagon,** *short, height 21" (E2-122).*
.... **250.00   275.00**

☐ **Referee Standard Time Wall,** *spring, square cornered rectangle with trim, 35½" x 16", dial 12", 8 Day, simple calendar (E1-183).*
.... **350.00   400.00**

☐ **Register,** *double dial wall, spring, also with Jerome label, height 31", dials 8", 8 Day (E1-104).*
.... **1200.00   1300.00**

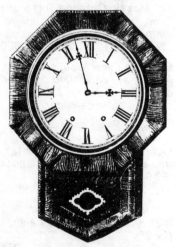

☐ **12" R.C. Drop Octagon,** *short, height 24" (E2-122).*
.... **275.00   300.00**

□ **Regulator D.R.,** *figure 8 type, height 31", dial 12", 8 Day, strike, simple calendar (E2-93).*
. . . . 350.00   400.00

□ **Regulator Round Top Long Drop,** *height 32", dial 12", 8 Day, strike, simple calendar (E2-94).*
. . . . 325.00   375.00

□ **Rokeby,** *double dial wall, spring, also with Jerome label, height 63", dials 12", 8 Day (E1-104).*
. . . . 1450.00   1650.00

□ **Round Lever,** *wall, spring, dial 8", 8 Day, simple calendar (E1-45).*
. . . . 175.00   200.00

□ **Regulator Round Top Long Drop,** *spring, 32¼" x 17¾", dial 12", 8 Day, simple calendar (E1-183).*
. . . . 325.00   375.00

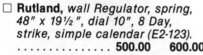

☐ **Sampson Victorian Shelf,** *spring, with thermometer and barometer, 25" x 14½", dial 6", 8 Day, strike, simple calendar (M407-127).*
.... **200.00   215.00**

☐ **Sampson Victorian Shelf,** *spring, with thermometer and barometer, 25" x 15½", dial 6", 8 Day, strike, simple calendar (E1-167).*
.... **200.00   215.00**

☐ **Rutland,** *wall Regulator, spring, 48" x 19½", dial 10", 8 Day, strike, simple calendar (E2-123).*
.... **500.00   600.00**

☐ **Rutland,** *wall Regulator, spring, 48" x 19½", dial 10, 30 Day, double dial (E2-123).*
.... **800.00   900.00**

☐ **Sampson Victorian Shelf,** *spring, with thermometer and barometer, 23½" x 15", dial 6", 8 Day, strike, simple calendar (E2-88).*
.... **200.00   215.00**

☐ **8" Saxon,** *figure 8, height 20" (E2-122).*
.... **300.00   350.00**

☐ **10" Saxon,** *figure 8, height 22" (E2-122).*
.... **325.00   375.00**

☐ **12" Saxon,** *figure 8, height 24"*
(E2-122).

.... 350.00   400.00

☐ **8" Saxon Mosaic,** *figure 8, height*
20", 8 Day, strike, simple
calendar (E2-122).

.... 325.00   350.00

☐ **10" Saxon Mosaic,** *figure 8,*
height 22", 8 Day, strike, simple
calendar (E2-122).

.... 325.00   375.00

☐ **12" Saxon Mosaic,** *figure 8,*
height 24", 8 Day, strike, simple
calendar (E2-122).

.... 350.00   400.00

☐ **Scribe Inkstand,** *plated, 12" x*
14", dial 3", 1 Day, simple
calendar (E2-112).

.... 300.00   350.00

☐ **Start,** *round nickel, dial 4", 1*
Day, alarm, simple calendar
(E2-88).

.... 60.00   80.00

☐ **Sprite,** *round nickel, dial 4½", 1*
Day, alarm, simple calendar
(E2-88).

.... 65.00   85.00

☐ **The Beacon,** *round nickel, dial*
4¼", 1 Day, alarm, simple
calendar (E2-88).

.... 60.00   85.00

□ **Trojan Wall Regulator,** *spring, 44" x 13½", dial 8", 8 Day, simple calendar (E1-164).*
.... 650.00   700.00

□ **Vamoose Wall Regulator,** *spring, 45" x 15½", dial 10", 8 Day, simple calendar (E1-164).*
.... 400.00   450.00

□ **Wall,** *double dial, double spring, New Haven calendar mechanism, retaining power, seconds bit, 54" x 19", dials 10", 30 Day, simple calendar (M409-128).*
.... 850.00   950.00

□ **Wood Lever Octagon,** *veneered, width 12", dial 8", 1 Day, simple calendar (E2-118).*
.... 150.00   175.00

□ **Wood Lever Octagon,** *veneered, width 14", dial 10", 1 Day, simple calendar (E2-118).*
.... 175.00   200.00

CARRIAGE

☐ **Adela,** *solid cast brass, hand finished, height 8¾", dial 2½", c. 1900, 8 Day (E2-111).*
.... **175.00   200.00**

☐ **Alert,** *nickel, height 6½", c. 1890, 1 Day, alarm (E2-88).*
.... **145.00   170.00**

☐ **Alert,** *nickel, height 7", dial 3", c. 1900, 1 Day, alarm (E1-44).*
.... **150.00   175.00**

☐ **Badger,** *nickel, single spring movement, with spring in barrel, height 7¼", c. 1900, 1 Day, alarm (E2-126).*
.... **175.00   200.00**

☐ **Cavalier,** *height 6", c. 1890, 1 Day, alarm (E2-88).*
.... **105.00   125.00**

☐ **Lantern Night Clock,** *brass hall lantern, studded with jewels, containing translucent dial clock, finished in antique brass and antique silver, opal dial 5", c. 1900, 1 Day (E2-111).*
.... **125.00   150.00**

☐ **Messenger,** *nickel with gilt mat, height 7¼", dial 2¾", c. 1900, 1 Day, alarm (E2-126).*
.... **105.00   125.00**
☐ **As above,** *1 Day, strike.*
.... **110.00   135.00**

☐ **Peacock,** *extra gold plated, height 6½", dial 2½", c. 1900, 8 Day (E2-111).*
.... **140.00   165.00**

☐ **Pilgrim,** *nickel, two-spring movement, c. 1900, 1 Day, alarm (E2-126).*
.... **105.00   125.00**
☐ **As above,** *1 Day, strike.*
.... **110.00   135.00**
☐ **As above,** *1 Day, strike, alarm.*
.... **120.00   145.00**

☐ **Pilgrim,** *height 6", c. 1890, 1 Day, alarm (E2-88).*
.... **105.00   125.00**

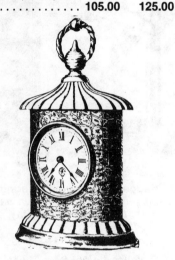

☐ **Puck,** *gilt, height 9", dial 3", c. 1900, 1 Day, strike (E2-126).*
.... **110.00   135.00**
☐ **As above,** *1 Day, strike, alarm.*
.... **120.00   145.00**
☐ **As above,** *1 Day, alarm.*
.... **130.00   155.00**

☐ **Toulon,** *French gilt case, 5" x 2⅝", porcelain dial, c. 1900, 1 Day (E1-44).*
.... **195.00   225.00**

☐ **Truro,** *5" x 2¾", c. 1900, 8 Day (E2-112).*
.... **125.00   150.00**

CHINA
LARGE

☐ **Gerald,** *decorated porcelain, visible escapement, 13" x 14¾", dial 5", c. 1900, 8 Day, strike (E1-42).*
.... **310.00   350.00**

☐ **Hamilton,** *decorated porcelain, visible escapement, 12⅛" x 8½", dial 5", c. 1900, 8 Day, strike (E1-42).*
.... **145.00   170.00**

☐ **Haverford,** *decorated porcelain, visible escapement, 13¼" x 13⅞", dial 5", c. 1900, 8 Day, strike (E1-43).*
.... **290.00   330.00**

☐ **Herbert,** *decorated porcelain, 12" x 9¼", dial 5", c. 1900, 8 Day, strike (E1-42).*
.... **145.00   170.00**

☐ **Holly,** *decorated porcelain, visible escapement, 14⅝" x 13¼", porcelain dial 5", c. 1900, 8 Day, strike (E1-43).*
.... **320.00   360.00**

☐ **Horicon,** *decorated porcelain, visible escapement, 13⅞" x 12⅜", c. 1900, 8 Day, strike (E1-42).*
.... **300.00   340.00**

☐ **Hyperion,** *decorated porcelain, 11¾" x 8⅝", porcelain dial 5", c. 1900, 8 Day, strike (E1-43).*
.... **145.00   170.00**

☐ **Malabar,** *decorated porcelain, 10⅝" x 12¼", porcelain dial 5", c. 1900, 8 Day, strike (E1-43).*
.... **145.00   170.00**

☐ **Nivian,** *porcelain, 11¾" x 10¾", dial 5", c. 1900, 8 Day, strike (E2-121).*
.... **190.00   220.00**

☐ **Rockland,** *decorated porcelain, 10¾" x 11⅝", porcelain dial 5", c. 1900, 8 Day, strike (E1-43).*
.... **155.00   180.00**

☐ **Rosendale,** *decorated porcelain, 10¼″ x 12″, porcelain dial 5″, c. 1900, 8 Day, strike (E1-43).*
.... 155.00   180.00

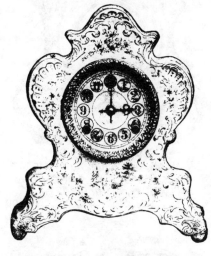

☐ **Tancred,** *porcelain, 12″ x 10½″, dial 5″, c. 1900, 8 Day, strike (E2-121).*
.... 190.00   220.00

SMALL

☐ **Achilles,** *decorated porcelain, 10¼″ x 10″, dial 4″, c. 1900, 8 Day, strike (E1-42).*
.... 140.00   165.00

☐ **Audubon,** *decorated porcelain, 10½″ x 7⅝″, dial 4″, c. 1900, 8 Day, strike (E1-42).*
.... 115.00   140.00

☐ **Bayard,** *decorated porcelain, 8″ x 3⅜″, dial 2″, c. 1900, 1 Day (E1-37).*
.... 45.00   60.00

☐ **Clinton,** *decorated porcelain, 12″ x 6¾″, dial 4″, c. 1900, 8 Day, strike (E1-43).*
.... 120.00   145.00

☐ **Creighton,** *decorated porcelain, 5½″ x 6⅞″, dial 2″, c. 1900, 1 Day (E1-42).*
.... 40.00   55.00

☐ **Fleetwood,** *decorated porcelain, 5½″ x 3¼″, dial 2″, c. 1900, 1 Day (E1-43).*
.... 30.00   40.00

☐ **Lionel,** *decorated porcelain, 5″ x 4¼″, dial 2″, c. 1900, 1 Day (E1-42).*
.... 30.00   40.00

☐ **Mabel,** *decorated porcelain, 11″ x 11¼″, dial 5″, c. 1900, 8 Day, strike (E1-42).*
.... 155.00   180.00

☐ **Morton,** *decorated porcelain, 5⅛″ x 4½″, dial 2″, c. 1900, 1 Day (E1-43).*
.... 30.00   40.00

☐ **Parry,** *decorated porcelain, 5⅞″ x 7″, dial 2″, c. 1900, 1 Day (E1-43).*
.... 40.00   55.00

☐ **Richmond,** *decorated porcelain, 6½″ x 3½″, dial 2″, c. 1900, 1 Day (E1-37).*
.... 40.00   50.00

☐ **Rupert,** *decorated porcelain, 4¾″ x 6⅜″, dial 2″, c. 1900, 1 Day (E1-43).*
.... 40.00   55.00

☐ **Waldorf,** *porcelain, fancy etched silver, 8¼" x 7½", dial 3", c. 1900, 1 Day, alarm (E2-121).*
.... **90.00   110.00**

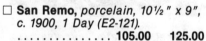

☐ **San Remo,** *porcelain, 10½" x 9", c. 1900, 1 Day (E2-121).*
.... **105.00   125.00**

☐ **St. Cloud,** *porcelain, height 7½", dial 2", c. 1900, 1 Day (E2-121).*
.... **80.00   100.00**

☐ **St. Louis,** *porcelain, height 7", dial 2", c. 1900, 1 Day (E2-121).*
.... **80.00   100.00**

☐ **Turenne,** *porcelain, 9¾" x 7¾", dial 3", c. 1900, 8 Day, strike (E2-121).*
.... **150.00   175.00**

☐ **Wakefield,** *decorated porcelain, 4⅝" x 5⅛", dial 2", c. 1900, 1 Day (E1-42).*
.... **30.00   40.00**

☐ **Windsor,** *porcelain, fancy etched silver, 8¼" x 7½", dial 3", c. 1900, 1 Day, alarm (E2-121).*
.... **110.00   135.00**

CONNECTICUT SHELF
ARCH TOP

☐ **Arch Top,** *wood, c. 1900, 8 Day, strike (E2-94).*
.... 160.00   185.00
☐ **As above,** *8 Day, strike, alarm*
.... 175.00   200.00

BEE HIVE

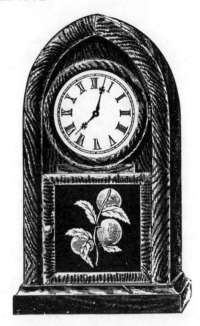

☐ **Gothic,** *wood, height 19¼", c. 1900, 1 Day, strike (E2-94).*
.... 90.00   110.00
☐ **As above,** *8 Day, strike*
.... 110.00   135.00

☐ **Round Gothic,** *wood, height 19", c. 1900, 1 Day, simple spring (E1-45).*
.... 90.00   110.00
☐ **As above,** *8 Day, simple spring*
.... 110.00   135.00

COTTAGE

☐ **Auburn,** *wood, height 14", c. 1900, 1 Day, strike (E2-94).*
.... 75.00   90.00

☐ **Cottage,** *wood, height 12", c. 1900, 1 Day, strike (E1-45).*
.... 55.00   70.00
☐ **As above,** *1 Day, simple spring*
.... 75.00   95.00

☐ **Cottage Extra,** *wood, height 12", c. 1900, 1 Day (E2-94).*
.... 65.00   80.00
☐ **As above,** *height 13", 1 Day, strike*
.... 75.00   95.00
☐ **As above,** *height 13", 8 Day, strike*
.... 100.00   120.00

☐ **Cottage Extra,** *zebra, height 14", dial 6", c. 1900, 1 Day, strike (E2-94).*
.... 110.00   125.00
☐ **As above,** *zebra, 8 Day, strike*
.... 120.00   140.00
☐ **As above,** *mahogany, 1 Day, strike*
.... 75.00   90.00
☐ **As above,** *mahogany, 8 Day, strike*
.... 85.00   105.00

☐ **Cottage No. 2,** *wood, height 12", c. 1900, 1 Day, (E2-94).*
.... 55.00   70.00
☐ **As above,** *1 Day, strike*
.... 70.00   85.00

☐ **Cottage No. 2**, *zebra, height 12",
dial 6", c. 1900 1 Day (E2-94).*
. . . . **100.00   115.00**
☐ **As above**, *zebra, 1 Day, strike*
. . . . **115.00   130.00**
☐ **As above**, *mahogany, 1 Day.*
. . . . **65.00   80.00**
☐ **As above**, *mahogany, 1 Day,
strike*
. . . . **80.00   95.00**

☐ **Gem Cottage**, *wood, height 9", c.
1900, 1 Day (E2-94).*
. . . . **55.00   70.00**
☐ **As above**, *1 Day, alarm*
. . . . **70.00   85.00**

☐ **Prize**, *wood, height 14", c. 1900, 1
Day, simple spring (E1-46).*
. . . . **65.00   80.00**
☐ **As above**, *8 Day, simple spring*
. . . . **85.00   105.00**

☐ **Rattler**, *wood, height 10¾", c.
1900, 1 Day (E2-95).*
. . . . **70.00   85.00**

☐ **Rose Gilt**, *wood, height 9½", c.
1900, 1 Day, strike.*
. . . . **50.00   65.00**

OCTAGON TOP
☐ **Alps**, *wood, height 17", c. 1900, 1
Day, strike (E2-94).*
. . . . **80.00   100.00**
☐ **As above**, *8 Day, strike*
. . . . **105.00   125.00**

☐ **Dreadnaught**, *mahogany, height
14", dial 5", c. 1900, 1 Day, strike
(E2-94).*
. . . . **80.00   100.00**
☐ **As above**, *rosewood, 1 Day,
strike*
. . . . **105.00   125.00**
☐ **As above**, *zebra, 1 Day, strike*
. . . . **115.00   135.00**

☐ **Duchess**, *mahogany, height 18",
dial 6", c. 1900, 8 Day, strike
(E2-94).*
. . . . **105.00   125.00**
☐ **As above**, *zebra, 8 Day, strike*
. . . . **140.00   160.00**

☐ **Gem**, *wood, height 15", c. 1900, 1
Day, simple spring (E1-46).*
. . . . **65.00   80.00**
☐ **As above**, *8 Day, simple spring*
. . . . **85.00   105.00**

☐ **Octagon Prize**, *wood, height
14½", c. 1900, 1 Day (E2-94).*
. . . . **70.00   85.00**
☐ **As above**, *1 Day, alarm*
. . . . **75.00   90.00**

☐ **Octagon Prize**, *V.P. wood, height
18", c. 1900, 1 Day, simple spring
(E1-46).*
. . . . **75.00   90.00**
☐ **As above**, *8 Day, simple spring*
. . . . **95.00   115.00**

☐ **As above,** *rosewood, 8 Day, strike*
.... 105.00   125.00
☐ **As above,** *zebra, 1 Day, strike*
.... 115.00   135.00
☐ **As above,** *zebra, 8 Day, strike*
.... 140.00   155.00

☐ **Octagon Rocket,** *imitation zebra, height 13", dial 4", c. 1900, 1 Day (E2-94).*
.... 75.00   90.00

☐ **Octagon Prize,** *wood, height 17¼", c. 1900, 1 Day, strike (E2-94).*
.... 75.00   90.00
☐ **As above,** *8 Day, strike*
.... 95.00   115.00

☐ **Small Octagon Prize Extra,** *rosewood, height 16", dial 5", c. 1900, 1 Day, strike (E2-94).*
.... 75.00   90.00
☐ **As above,** *8 Day, strike*
.... 95.00   115.00

O.G. AND O.O.G.

☐ **O.G. (Weight No. 1 or No. 2),** *mahogany, height 26", dial 8", c. 1900, 1 Day, strike, weight (E2-93).*
.... 140.00   165.00
☐ **As above,** *zebra, 1 Day, strike, weight*
.... 150.00   175.00

☐ **Octagon Prize,** *V.P., rosewood, height 17¾", dial 6", c. 1900, 1 Day, strike (E2-94).*
.... 80.00   100.00

☐ **O.O.G.,** *mahogany, height 30", c. 1900, 1 Day, strike, weight (E2-93).*
.... **175.00** **200.00**

☐ **As above,** *mahogany, 8 Day, strike, weight*
.... **140.00** **165.00**

☐ **As above,** *zebra, 1 Day, strike, weight*
.... **185.00** **210.00**

☐ **As above,** *zebra, 8 Day, strike, weight*
.... **150.00** **175.00**

☐ **O.O.G.,** *wood, height 26", c. 1900, 1 Day, strike, weight (E1-46).*
.... **105.00** **125.00**

ROUND TOP

☐ **Guide,** *wood, height 17¼", c. 1900, 1 Day, strike (E2-94).*
.... **80.00** **100.00**

☐ **As above,** *8 Day, strike*
.... **105.00** **125.00**

☐ **Guide, Full Gilt,** *finished with full gilt columns and mouldings, height 17¼", dial 6", c. 1900, 1 Day, strike (E2-94).*
.... **75.00** **90.00**

☐ **As above,** *8 Day, strike*
.... **95.00** **115.00**

☐ **Guide,** *V.P., wood, height 17", c. 1900, 1 Day, simple spring (E1-4).*
.... **90.00** **110.00**

☐ **As above,** *8 Day, simple spring*
.... **110.00** **135.00**

☐ **Round Gothic Extra,** *wood, height 17¼", c. 1900, 1 Day, strike (E2-94).*
.... **95.00** **115.00**

☐ **As above,** *8 Day, strike*
.... **115.00** **140.00**

☐ **Round Gothic,** *V.P., rosewood, height 17¼", dial 6", c. 1900, 1 Day, strike (E2-94).*
.... **95.00** **115.00**

☐ **As above,** *rosewood, 8 Day, strike*
.... **115.00** **140.00**

☐ **As above,** *zebra, 1 Day, strike*
.... **105.00** **125.00**

☐ **As above,** *zebra, 8 Day, strike*
.... **125.00** **150.00**

SPLIT TOP

☐ **Gem Cottage,** *wood, height 14",*
c. 1900, 1 Day, strike (E2-95).
. . . . 105.00   125.00
☐ **As above,** *8 Day, strike*
. . . . 125.00   150.00

☐ **Andes,** *wood, height 17", c. 1900,*
1 Day, strike (E2-95).
. . . . 75.00   90.00
☐ **As above,** *8 Day, strike*
. . . . 95.00   115.00

☐ **Gothic Gem,** *wood, height 17¾",*
c. 1900, 1 Day, strike (E2-95).
. . . . 80.00   100.00
☐ **As above,** *8 Day, strike*
. . . . 105.00   125.00

☐ **Coupon Preferred,** *wood, height*
15½", c. 1900, 1 Day, strike
(E2-95).
. . . . 70.00   85.00
☐ **As above,** *8 Day, strike*
. . . . 90.00   110.00

☐ **Eclipse,** *rosewood, height 17",*
dial 6", c. 1900, 1 Day, strike
(E2-95).
. . . . 90.00   110.00
☐ **As above,** *8 Day, strike*
. . . . 110.00   135.00

☐ **Gothic Gem D.R.,** *wood, height*
18", c. 1900, 1 Day, strike (E2-95).
. . . . 80.00   100.00

☐ **Rocket,** *chestnut or imitation zebra, height 10¾", dial 4", c. 1900, 1 Day (E2-95).*
.... 60.00   75.00

☐ **Móttled Tuscan,** *wood, height 16", dial 5", c. 1900, 1 Day, strike (E2-95).*
.... 80.00   100.00
☐ **As above,** *8 Day, strike*
.... 105.00   125.00

☐ **Small Tuscan Extra,** *rosewood, height 16", c. 1900, 1 Day, strike (E2-95).*
.... 65.00   80.00
☐ **As above,** *8 Day, strike*
.... 95.00   115.00
☐ **Solo,** *wood, height 9¼", c. 1900, 1 Day (E2-95).*
.... 60.00   75.00
☐ **As above,** *1 Day, alarm*
.... 80.00   100.00
☐ **Tuscan,** *V.P., wood, height 17¾", c. 1900, 1 Day, strike (E2-95).*
.... 75.00   90.00
☐ **As above,** *8 Day, strike*
.... 95.00   115.00
☐ **Tuscan,** *wood, height 17¾", c. 1900, 1 Day, strike (E2-95).*
.... 75.00   90.00
☐ **As above,** *8 Day, strike*
.... 95.00   115.00
☐ **As above,** *height 14½", 1 Day.*
.... 70.00   85.00

☐ **Pyramid,** *wood, height 17", c. 1900, 1 Day, strike (E2-95).*
.... 75.00   90.00
☐ **As above,** *8 Day, strike*
.... 95.00   115.00
☐ **Reliable,** *wood, height 9¼", c. 1900, 1 Day (E2-95).*
.... 60.00   75.00

STEEPLE

☐ **Derby,** *T.P., wood, height 17″, dial 5″, c. 1900, 1 Day (E2-96).*
.... **105.00   125.00**

☐ **Derby,** *wood, height 18½″, dial 5½″, c. 1900, 1 Day, strike (E2-96).*
.... **105.00   125.00**

☐ **Dolphin,** *zebra, veneered, height 17¾″, dial 5″, c. 1900, 1 Day (E2-96).*
.... **105.00   125.00**
☐ **As above,** *1 Day, strike*
.... **115.00   140.00**
☐ **As above,** *8 Day, strike*
.... **125.00   150.00**

☐ **Diadem,** *zebra, veneered, height 18″, dial 5″, c. 1900, 1 Day (E2-96).*
.... **105.00   125.00**
☐ **As above,** *1 Day, strike*
.... **115.00   140.00**

☐ **Large Gothic,** *V.P., wood, height 21″, c. 1900, 1 Day, simple spring (E1-46).*
.... **90.00   110.00**
☐ **As above,** *8 Day, simple spring*
.... **110.00   135.00**

□ **Sharp Gothic,** *rosewood, height 20½", dial 6", c. 1900, 1 Day, strike (E2-96).*
.... 105.00   125.00
□ **As above,** *rosewood, 8 Day, strike*
.... 160.00   185.00
□ **As above,** *mahogany, 1 Day, strike*
.... 105.00   125.00
□ **As above,** *mahogany, 8 Day, strike*
.... 160.00   185.00
□ **As above,** *zebra, 1 Day, strike*
.... 115.00   135.00
□ **As above,** *zebra, 8 Day, strike*
.... 170.00   195.00

□ **Sharp Gothic,** *V.P., mahogany, height 21", dial 6", c. 1900, 1 Day, strike (E2-96).*
.... 105.00   125.00
□ **As above,** *mahogany, 8 Day, strike*
.... 160.00   185.00
□ **As above,** *rosewood, 1 Day, strike*
.... 105.00   125.00
□ **As above,** *rosewood, 8 Day, strike*
.... 160.00   185.00
□ **As above,** *zebra, 1 Day, strike*
.... 115.00   135.00

□ **Small Gothic,** *V.P., rosewood, height 16", c. 1900, 1 Day (E2-96).*
.... 105.00   125.00
□ **As above,** *rosewood, 1 Day, strike*
.... 110.00   135.00
□ **As above,** *zebra, 1 Day.*
.... 115.00   135.00
□ **As above,** *zebra, 1 Day, strike*
.... 120.00   145.00

□ **Small Gothic,** *rosewood, height 15½", dial 5", c. 1900, 1 Day (E2-96).*
.... 105.00   125.00
□ **As above,** *rosewood, 8 Day.*
.... 125.00   150.00
□ **As above,** *zebra, 1 Day.*
.... 115.00   135.00
□ **As above,** *zebra, 8 Day.*
.... 135.00   160.00

CRYSTAL REGULATOR

□ **Thieta,** *mahogany, 13" x 9", dial 7", c. 1917, 8 Day, strike (E1-173).*
.... 265.00   305.00

☐ **As above,** *8", 1 Day, strike* 135.00   160.00
☐ **As above,** *6", 8 Day.* 125.00   150.00
☐ **As above,** *8", 8 Day.* 140.00   165.00
☐ **As above,** *8", 8 Day, strike* 150.00   175.00

☐ **Thoreau,** *ormolu gold plate or antique Verde case, with beveled French plate glass sides, back and front, 15" x 8½", porcelain dial 4", c. 1900, 8 Day, strike (E2-119).*
. . . . 425.00   475.00

☐ **Tuxford,** *mahogany, 10½" x 6", dial 4", c. 1917, 8 Day, strike (E1-173).*
. . . . 245.00   275.00

GALLERY

☐ **Canton,** *nickel or brass, lever, c. 1900, 6", 1 Day (E2-118).*
. . . . 105.00   125.00
☐ **As above,** *6", 1 Day, alarm* 110.00   135.00
☐ **As above,** *6", 1 Day, strike* 115.00   140.00
☐ **As above,** *8", 1 Day.* 125.00   150.00

☐ **Eagle,** *carved oak, height 40", dial 17", c. 1900, 8 Day (E1-101).*
. . . . 360.00   400.00
☐ **As above,** *cherry* 410.00   450.00

☐ **R.C. Calendar Lever,** *wood, dial 10", c. 1900, 1 Day, strike (E2-95).*
. . . . 175.00   200.00
☐ **As above,** *dial 8", 8 Day.* 245.00   275.00

☐ **Wood Lever,** *polished veneered, c. 1900, 4", 1 Day (E2-118).*
. . . . 90.00   110.00
☐ **As above,** *6", 1 Day.* 100.00   120.00
☐ **As above,** *6", 1 Day, alarm* 105.00   130.00
☐ **As above,** *6", 1 Day, strike* 115.00   140.00

☐ **As above,** *8", 1 Day.*
.... 115.00   140.00
☐ **As above,** *8", 1 Day, alarm*
.... 125.00   150.00
☐ **As above,** *8", 1 Day, strike*
.... 135.00   160.00
☐ **As above,** *10", 1 Day.*
.... 135.00   160.00
☐ **As above,** *10", 1 Day, strike*
.... 145.00   170.00
☐ **As above,** *6", 8 Day.*
.... 125.00   150.00
☐ **As above,** *8", 8 Day.*
.... 135.00   160.00
☐ **As above,** *8", 8 Day, strike*
.... 145.00   170.00
☐ **As above,** *10", 8 Day.*
.... 135.00   160.00
☐ **As above,** *10", 8 Day, strike*
.... 145.00   170.00
☐ **As above,** *12", 8 Day.*
.... 145.00   170.00
☐ **As above,** *12", 8 Day, strike*
.... 155.00   180.00

☐ **Round Calendar Lever,** *wood, 8",
c. 1900, 8 Day (E1-45).*
.... 105.00   125.00

MARBLE

☐ **Wood Lever,** *calendar, polished
veneered, c. 1900, 8", 1 Day,
calendar (E2-118).*
.... 150.00   175.00
☐ **As above,** *10", 1 Day, calendar*
.... 175.00   200.00

☐ **No. 1,** *marble, 20" diameter, dial
17", c. 1910, 15 Day (E2-128).*
.... 245.00   275.00

☐ **No. 2,** *marble, diameter 27½",
dial 23", c. 1910, 15 Day (E2-128).*
.... 245.00   275.00

☐ **No. 3,** *marble, Graham dead-beat
escapement 27½" x 23", dial
17", c. 1910, 15 Day (E2-128).*
.... 270.00   300.00

☐ **No. 4,** *marble, Graham dead-beat escapement, 36″ x 30″, dial 23″, c. 1910, 15 Day (E2-128).*
.... **270.00   300.00**

☐ **No. 5,** *marble, Graham dead-beat escapement, 24″ x 24″, dial 17″, c. 1910, 15 Day (E2-128).*
.... **270.00   300.00**

☐ **No. 6,** *marble, Graham dead-beat escapement, 32″ x 32″, dial 23″, c. 1910, 15 Day (E2-128).*
.... **270.00   300.00**

☐ **No. 7,** *marble, Graham dead-beat escapement, 29½″ x 16″, dial 13″, c. 1910, 15 Day (E2-128).*
.... **360.00   400.00**
☐ **As above,** *15 Day, strike*
.... **375.00   425.00**

GRANDFATHER

☐ **Chippendale,** *oak, weights, pendulum, dial and movement polished and lacquered, solid brass dial with black numerals on a raised silver circle, 8′ x 22½″, dial 12″, c. 1900, 8 Day, strike (E1-35).*
.... **1800.00   2200.00**
☐ **As above,** *mahogany*
.... **1875.00   2275.00**

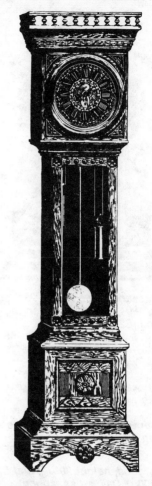

☐ **Hall Clock, No. 1,** *oak, hand carved, cabinet finished, height 84″, dial 12″, c. 1900, 8 Day, strike (E1-104).*
.... **2000.00   2500.00**
☐ **As above,** *mahogany*
.... **2075.00   2575.00**

KITCHEN

☐ **Alderman,** *oak, interchangeable tops, "Hustler Series", dial 6″, c. 1896, 8 Day, strike, spring wound (E2-106).*
.... **145.00   170.00**

□ **Ambassador,** *oak, height 23", dial 16, c. 1894, 1 Day, strike, spring wound (E2-103).*
.... **120.00   145.00**
□ **As above,** *oak, 8 Day, strike, spring wound*
.... **145.00   170.00**
□ **As above,** *walnut, 1 Day, strike, spring wound*
.... **145.00   170.00**
□ **As above,** *walnut, 8 Day, strike, spring wound*
.... **170.00   195.00**

□ **Aral,** *wood, height 20¼", dial 5", c. 1900, 1 Day, strike, spring wound (E2-98).*
.... **145.00   170.00**

□ **Avon,** *wood, height 21", dial 5", c. 1900, 8 Day, strike, spring wound (E2-98).*
.... **145.00   170.00**

□ **Ayr,** *wood, height 20¼", dial 5", c. 1900, 8 Day, strike, spring wound (E2-98).*
.... **145.00   170.00**

□ **Bobolink,** *wood, height 17½", dial 6", c. 1900, 1 Day, strike, spring wound (E2-98).*
.... **140.00   165.00**

□ **Bonita,** *wood, height 17¾", dial 6", c. 1900, 1 Day, strike, spring wound (E2-98).*
.... **135.00   160.00**

□ **Boreas,** *wood, height 21½", dial 6", c. 1900, 1 Day, strike, spring wound (E2-98).*
.... **145.00   170.00**

☐ **Calumet,** *height 20¾", dial 6", 1 Day, strike, spring wound.*
. . . . **165.00**   **185.00**

☐ **Calumet,** *height 20¾", dial 6", 1 Day, strike, spring wound (E2-98).*
. . . . **140.00**   **165.00**

☐ **Carmen,** *wood, height 21½", dial 6", c. 1900, 8 Day, strike, spring wound (E2-98).*
. . . . **140.00**   **165.00**

☐ **Captain,** *oak, "Great Military Series", 22" x 14", dial 6", spring wound (E2-103).*
. . . . **140.00**   **165.00**
☐ **As above,** *walnut, spring wound*
. . . . **165.00**   **185.00**

Cecile

☐ **Cecile,** *wood, height 22", dial 6", 8 Day, strike, spring wound (E2-98).*
.... 145.00   170.00

☐ **Charmer,** *wood, height 22½", dial 5", c. 1900, 8 Day, strike, spring wound (E2-98).*
.... 140.00   165.00

☐ **Celeste,** *wood, height 21", dial 5", c. 1900, 8 Day, strike, spring wound (E2-98).*
.... 140.00   165.00

☐ **Christine,** *wood, height 20¾", dial 5", c. 1900, 1 Day, strike, spring wound (E2-98).*
.... 135.00   160.00

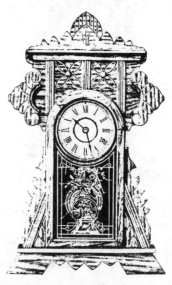

□ **Clarita,** *wood, height 22", dial 5", c. 1900, 8 Day, strike, spring wound (E2-97).*
. . . . **145.00   170.00**

□ **Cinderella,** *wood, height 25", dial 6", c. 1900, 8 Day, strike, spring wound (E2-97).*
. . . . **150.00   175.00**

□ **Clochette,** *wood, height 18", dial 6", c. 1900, 1 Day, strike, spring wound (E2-97).*
. . . . **135.00   160.00**

□ **Clyde,** *wood, height 23", dial 5½", c. 1900, 8 Day, strike, spring wound (E2-97).*
. . . . **150.00   175.00**

□ **Colonel,** *oak, "Great Military Series" 22" x 14", dial 6", c. 1894, 8 Day, strike, spring wound (E2-103).*
. . . . **140.00   165.00**
□ **As above,** *walnut, spring wound*
. . . . **165.00   190.00**

□ **Conroy,** *oak, "Norwich Series", 25" x 15½", dial 6", c. 1900, 8 Day, strike, spring wound (E2-104).*
. . . . **160.00   185.00**
□ **As above,** *walnut, spring wound*
. . . . **185.00   210.00**

□ **Coquette,** *wood, height 22", dial 6", c. 1900, 8 Day, strike, spring wound (E2-97).*
. . . . **150.00   175.00**

□ **Councilman,** *oak, interchangeable tops, "Hustler Series", dial 6", c. 1896, 8 Day, strike, spring wound (E2-106).*
□ **As above,** *oak, spring wound*
. . . . **145.00   170.00**
□ **As above,** *walnut, spring wound*
. . . . **170.00   195.00**

□ **Cygnet,** *wood, height 23½", dial 6", c. 1900, 8 Day, strike, spring wound (E2-97).*
. . . . **155.00   180.00**

□ **Danube,** *wood, height 24", dial 6", c. 1900, 8 Day, strike, spring wound (E2-97).*
. . . . **155.00   180.00**

☐ **Dee,** *oak, "D Series", 24⅜" x 15⅝", dial 6", c. 1900, 8 Day, strike, spring wound (E2-104).*
.... **150.00   175.00**
☐ **As above,** *walnut, spring wound*
.... **175.00   195.00**

☐ **Don,** *oak, "D Series", 24⅜" x 15⅝", dial 6", c. 1900, 8 Day, strike, spring wound (E2-104).*
.... **150.00   175.00**
☐ **As above,** *walnut, spring wound*
.... **175.00   200.00**

☐ **Dee,** *wood, height 21", dial 5", c. 1900, 8 Day, strike, spring wound (E2-97),*
.... **150.00   175.00**

☐ **Don,** *wood, height 18", dial 5½", c. 1900, 1 Day, strike, spring wound (E2-97).*
.... **130.00   155.00**

☐ **Doon,** *oak, "D Series", 24⅜" x 15⅝", dial 6", c. 1900, 8 Day, strike, spring wound (E2-104).*
.... 150.00   175.00
☐ **As above,** *walnut, spring wound*
.... 175.00   200.00

☐ **Dora,** *wood, height 20", dial 5", c. 1900, 8 Day, strike, spring wound (E2-97).*
.... 145.00   170.00

☐ **Douro,** *wood, height 21½", dial 5", c. 1900, 8 Day, strike, spring wound (E2-97).*
.... 140.00   165.00

☐ **Drave,** *wood, height 20", dial 5", c. 1900, 8 Day, strike, spring wound (E2-97).*
.... 145.00   170.00

☐ **Duna,** *wood, height 22", dial 6", c. 1900, 8 Day, strike, spring wound (E2-97).*
.... 140.00   165.00

☐ **Electra,** *walnut or mahogany veneered, brass ornaments, height 19½", dial 5", c. 1890, 8 Day, strike, spring wound (E2-89).*
.... 150.00   175.00

☐ **Elma,** *wood, height 21", dial 6", c. 1900, 8 Day, strike, spring wound (E2-100).*
.... 150.00   175.00

☐ **Estelle,** *walnut or mahogany veneered, brass ornaments, height 19½", dial 5", c. 1890, 8 Day, strike, spring wound (E2-89).*
.... 150.00   175.00

☐ **Felix,** *oak, height 22", rococo dial 6", c. 1917, 8 Day, strike, spring wound(E1-174).*
.... 115.00   140.00

☐ **Festus,** *oak, height 22", rococo dial 6", c. 1917, 8 Day, strike, spring wound(E1-174).*
.... 115.00   140.00

☐ **Forum,** *oak, height 22", rococo dial 6", c. 1917, 8 Day, strike, spring wound(E1-174).*
.... 115.00   140.00

☐ **General,** *oak, "Great Military Series", 22" x 14", dial 6", c. 1894, 8 Day, strike, spring wound (E2-103).*
.... 140.00   165.00
☐ **As above,** *walnut, spring wound*
.... 165.00   190.00

☐ **Governor,** *oak, height 23", dial 16", c. 1894, spring wound (E2-103).*
.... **145.00   170.00**
☐ **As above,** *walnut, spring wound*
.... **170.00   195.00**

☐ **Grayling,** *wood, height 19½", dial 5", c. 1900, 8 Day, strike, spring wound(E2-100).*
.... **135.00   160.00**

☐ **Humber,** *wood, height 21", dial 6", c. 1900, 8 Day, strike, spring wound (E2-100).*
.... **165.00   190.00**

☐ **Imitation Walnut Or Chestnut,** *height 19", dial 5", c. 1900, 1 Day, strike, spring wound (E2-100).*
.... **105.00   125.00**
☐ **As above,** *height 21", 8 Day, strike, spring wound*
.... **150.00   175.00**
☐ **Irex,** *wood, height 23½", dial 6", c. 1900, 8 Day, strike, spring wound (E2-100).*
.... **150.00   175.00**

☐ **Janitor,** *oak, interchangeable tops, "Hustler Series", dial 6", c. 1896, 8 Day, strike, spring wound (E2-106).*
.... **145.00   170.00**
☐ **As above,** *walnut, spring wound*
.... **170.00   195.00**

☐ **Lieutenant,** *oak, "Great Military Series", 22" x 14", dial 6", c. 1894, 8 Day, strike, spring wound (E2-103).*
.... 140.00   165.00
☐ **As above,** *walnut, spring wound*
.... 165.00   190.00

☐ **Mail,** *wood, height 16", dial 5", c. 1900, 1 Day, strike , spring wound (E2-100).*
.... 105.00   130.00

☐ **Liris,** *wood, height 22½", dial 5", c. 1900, 1 Day, strike, spring wound (E2-100).*
.... 105.00   130.00

☐ **Lobbyist,** *oak, height 23", dial 16", c. 1894, 1 Day, strike, spring wound (E2-103).*
.... 120.00   145.00
☐ **As above,** *oak, 8 Day, strike, spring wound*
.... 145.00   170.00
☐ **As above,** *walnut, 1 Day, strike, spring wound*
.... 145.00   170.00
☐ **As above,** *walnut, 8 Day, strike, spring wound*
.... 170.00   195.00

☐ **Major,** *oak, "Great Military Series", 22" x 14", dial 6", c. 1894, 8 Day, strike, spring wound (E2-103).*
.... 140.00   165.00
☐ **As above,** *walnut, spring wound*
.... 165.00   190.00

☐ **Marshall,** *oak, interchangeable tops, "Hustler Series", dial 6", c. 1896, 8 Day, strike, spring wound (E2-106).*
.... **145.00   170.00**
☐ **As above,** *walnut, spring wound*
.... **170.00   195.00**

☐ **Morgath,** *oak, "Norwich Series", 25" x 15½", dial 6", c. 1900, 8 Day, strike, spring wound (E2-104).*
.... **160.00   185.00**
☐ **As above,** *walnut, spring wound*
.... **185.00   210.00**

☐ **Mayflower,** *wood, height 20½", dial 6", c. 1900, 8 Day, strike, spring wound (E2-100).*
.... **150.00   175.00**

☐ **Mayor,** *oak, interchangeable tops, "Hustler Series", dial 6", c. 1896, 8 Day, strike, spring wound (E2-106).*
.... **145.00   170.00**
☐ **As above,** *walnut, spring wound*
.... **170.00   195.00**

☐ **Mersey,** *wood, height 21", dial 5", c. 1900, 1 Day, strike, spring wound (E2-100).*
.... **105.00   130.00**

☐ **Moselle,** *wood, height 26", dial 6", c. 1900, 8 Day, strike, spring wound (E2-99).*
.... **190.00 220.00**

☐ **Nectar,** *wood, height 24", dial 6", c. 1900, 8 Day, strike, spring wound (E2-99).*
.... **160.00 185.00**

☐ **Nereid,** *wood, height 23½", dial 6", c. 1900, 8 Day, strike, spring wound (E2-99).*
.... **145.00 170.00**

☐ **Neva,** *wood, height 19", dial 5½", c. 1900, 8 Day, strike, spring wound (E2-99).*
.... **145.00 170.00**

☐ **Orphic,** *wood veneer, 17½" x 10½", c. 1900, 1 Day, spring wound (E2-96).*
.... **115.00 140.00**

☐ **As above,** *1 Day, strike, spring wound.*
.... **135.00 160.00**

☐ **Orphir,** *wood veneer, 18" x 10½", c. 1900, 1 Day, spring wound (E2-96).*
.... **115.00 140.00**

☐ **As above,** *1 Day, strike, spring wound.*
.... **135.00 160.00**

☐ **Oruba,** *wood veneer, 19½" x 10½", c. 1900, 1 Day, spring wound (E2-96).*
.... **115.00 140.00**

☐ **As above,** *1 Day, strike, spring wound.*
.... **135.00 160.00**

☐ **Oder,** *wood, height 20½", dial 6", c. 1900, 8 Day, strike, spring wound (E2-99).*
.... **145.00 170.00**

☐ **Orient,** *wood veneer, 18¾" x 10½", c. 1900, 1 Day, spring wound (E2-96).*
.... **115.00 140.00**

☐ **As above,** *1 Day, strike, spring wound.*
.... **135.00 160.00**

☐ **Osage,** *wood, height 21", dial 6", c. 1900, 8 Day, strike, spring wound (E2-99).*
.... **175.00 200.00**

☐ **Ouse,** *wood, height 19", dial 5",
c. 1900, 1 Day, strike, spring
wound (E2-99).*
.... 135.00   160.00

☐ **President,** *walnut, height 23",
dial 16", c. 1894, 1 Day, strike,
spring wound (E2-103).*
.... 145.00   170.00
☐ **As above,** *8 Day, strike, spring
wound.*
.... 170.00   195.00
☐ **As above,** *oak, 1 Day, strike,
spring wound.*
.... 120.00   145.00
☐ **As above,** *8 Day, strike, spring
wound.*
.... 145.00   170.00

☐ **Rambler,** *wood, height 19½", dial
5", c. 1900, 8 Day, strike, spring
wound (E2-99).*
.... 150.00   175.00

☐ **Rarus, T.P.,** *wood, height 15½",
dial 5", c. 1900, 1 Day, spring
wound (E2-99).*
.... 105.00   130.00

☐ **Rarus,** *wood, height 17½", dial 5½", c. 1900, 1 Day, strike, spring wound (E2-99).*
.... **105.00**   **130.00**

☐ **Recorder,** *oak, interchangeable tops, "Hustler Series," dial 6", c. 1896, 8 Day, strike, spring wound (E2-106).*
.... **145.00**   **170.00**

☐ **Saline,** *wood, height 21½", dial 6", c. 1900, 1 Day, strike, spring wound (E2-101).*
.... **105.00**   **130.00**

☐ **Rhine,** *wood, height 21", dial 6", c. 1900, 8 Day, strike, spring wound (E2-99).*
.... **135.00**   **160.00**

☐ **Sampson,** *wood, thermometer, barometer, and spirit level, 23¾" x 15", dial 6", c. 1910, 8 Day, simple calendar, spring wound (E-90).*
.... **160.00**   **185.00**

Sampson

Sampson, oak, "Norwich Series,"
25" x 15½", dial 6", c. 1900, 8
Day, strike, spring wound
(E2-104).
.... 160.00   185.00

As above, walnut, 8 Day, strike,
spring wound.
.... 185.00   210.00

Sanches, solid oak, flemish
finish, "Sancho Series," 22½" x
13", dial 6", c. 1900, 8 Day, strike,
spring wound (E2-104).
.... 135.00   160.00

Secretary, walnut, height 23",
dial 16", c. 1894, 1 Day, strike,
spring wound (E2-103).
.... 145.00   170.00

As above, 8 Day, strike, spring
wound.
.... 170.00   195.00

As above, oak, 1 Day, strike,
spring wound.
.... 120.00   145.00

As above, oak, 8 Day, strike,
spring wound.
.... 145.00   170.00

Segura, solid oak, flemish finish,
"Sancho Series," 22½" x 13",
dial 6", c. 1900, 8 Day, strike,
spring wound (E2-104).
.... 135.00   160.00

Seine, wood, height 23", dial 6",
c. 1900, 1 Day, strike, spring
wound (E2-101).
.... 105.00   130.00

Seminole, wood, height 22¾",
dial 6", c. 1900, 8 Day, strike,
spring wound (E2-101).
.... 160.00   185.00

Senator, walnut, height 23", dial
16", c. 1894, 1 Day, strike, spring
wound (E2-103).
.... 145.00   170.00

As above, 8 Day, strike, spring
wound.
.... 170.00   195.00

As above, oak, 1 Day, strike,
spring wound.
.... 120.00   145.00

As above, oak, 8 Day, strike,
spring wound.
.... 145.00   170.00

☐ **Sergeant,** *walnut, 22" x 14", dial 6", "Great Military Series," c. 1894, 8 Day, strike, spring wound (E2-103).*
.... 165.00   190.00
☐ **As above,** *oak, 8 Day, strike, spring wound.*
.... 140.00   165.00

☐ **Shamrock,** *wood, height 23½", dial 6", c. 1900, 8 Day, strike, spring wound (E2-101).*
.... 155.00   180.00

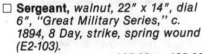

☐ **Severn,** *wood, height 19", dial 5½", c. 1900, 1 Day, strike, spring wound (E2-101).*
.... 105.00   125.00

☐ **Shannon,** *wood, height 18", dial 5½", c. 1900, 1 Day, strike, spring wound (E2-101).*
.... 105.00   125.00

☐ **Sorry,** *solid oak, flemish finish,*
"Sancho Series," 22½" x 13",
dial 6", c. 1900, 8 Day, strike,
spring wound (E2-104).
.... 135.00   160.00

☐ **Thames,** *wood, height 23", dial*
6", c. 1900, 8 Day, strike, spring
wound (E2-101).
.... 160.00   185.00

☐ **Tagus,** *wood, height 19", dial*
5½", c. 1900, 1 Day, strike,
spring wound (E2-101).
.... 105.00   125.00

☐ **Tamar,** *wood, height 21¼", dial*
6", c. 1900, 8 Day, strike, spring
wound (E2-101).
.... 145.00   170.00

☐ **Theiss,** *wood, height 19½", dial*
5", c. 1900, 1 Day, strike, spring
wound (E2-101).
.... 105.00   130.00

□ **Tiber,** *wood, height 19", dial 5½", c. 1900, 1 Day, strike, spring wound (E2-101).*
. . . . 105.00   130.00

□ **Titania,** *wood, height 24", dial 6", c. 1900, 8 Day, strike, spring wound (E2-101).*
. . . . 160.00   185.00

□ **Tomahawk,** *wood, height 23", dial 6", c. 1900, 8 Day, strike, spring wound (E2-102).*
. . . . 150.00   175.00

□ **Vampire,** *wood, height 21½", dial 6", c. 1900, 8 Day, strike, spring wound (E2-102).*
. . . . 145.00   170.00

□ **Vindex,** *wood, height 21½", dial 6", c. 1900, 8 Day, strike, spring wound (E2-102).*
. . . . 150.00   175.00

□ **Volga,** *wood, height 21½", dial 6", c. 1900, 8 Day, strike, spring wound (E2-102).*
. . . . 140.00   165.00

□ **Walnut,** *wood, height 20½", dial 5", c. 1900, 8 Day, strike, spring wound (E2-102).*
. . . . 145.00   170.00

□ **As above,** *height 21½", 8 Day, strike, spring wound.*
. . . . 150.00   175.00

☐ **Weser,** *wood, height 20½ ", dial 6", c. 1900, 8 Day, strike, spring wound (E2-102).*
.... **140.00   165.00**

☐ **Yarana,** *wood, height 21¼ ", dial 6", c. 1900, 8 Day, strike, spring wound (E2-102).*
.... **145.00   170.00**

☐ **Zingara,** *wood, height 21", dial 6", c. 1900, 8 Day, strike, spring wound (E2-102).*
.... **150.00   175.00**

SERIES

☐ **Assortment 7-18,** *oak, height 22½ ", dial 6", c. 1900, 8 Day, strike, spring wound (E1-38).*
.... *each* **100.00   120.00**

☐ **As above,** *walnut, 8 Day, strike, spring wound.*
.... *each* **125.00   150.00**

☐ **Brazilian Line,** *oak or with metal trimmings, packed assorted six in a case, no individual names, 22¼ " x 15", dial 6", c. 1900, 8 Day, strike, spring wound (E2-105).*
.... *each* **155.00   180.00**

☐ **Camden Series,** *oak, assorted patterns, three patterns, no individual names, 22" x 14", dial 6", c. 1900, 8 Day, strike, spring wound (E2-107).*
.... *each* **145.00** **170.00**

☐ **Camden Series Hanging,** *oak, three clocks shown, no names, 25" x 14", dial 6", c. 1900, 8 Day, strike, spring wound (E2-107).*
.... *each* **210.00   240.00**

☐ **As above,** *walnut.*
.... *each* **235.00   275.00**

☐ **Colonial Series,** *cherry, wire bell, assortment of six clocks, three cherry and three oak, height 18", dial 6", c. 1910, 8 Day, strike, spring wound (E2-128).*
.... *each* **155.00   180.00**

☐ **As above,** *oak.*
.... *each* **130.00   155.00**

☐ **"D" Series,** *walnut, Dee, Don, Doon, 24⅜" x 15⅜", dial 6", c. 1900, 8 Day, strike, spring wound (E2-104).*
.... *each* **150.00   175.00**

Dandy No. 1

Dandy No. 3

Dandy No. 2

☐ **Dandy Series,** *wood, six different patterns, Dandy No. 1, Dandy No. 2, Dandy No. 3, Dandy No. 4, Dandy No. 5 and Dandy No. 6, height 22", dial 6", c. 1896, 8 Day, strike, spring wound (E2-106).*
.... *each* **145.00   170.00**

☐ **Great Military Series,** *oak, Sergeant, Colonel, Lieutenant, Captain, General, Major, 22" x 14", dial 6", c. 1894, 8 Day, strike, spring wound (E2-103).*
.... *each* **120.00   145.00**
☐ **As above,** *walnut.*
.... *each* **140.00   165.00**

☐ **Hustler Series,** *oak, interchangeable tops, Recorder, Alderman, Councilman, Marshall, Janitor, Mayor, dial 6", c. 1896, 8 Day, strike, spring wound (E2-106).*
.... *each* **125.00   150.00**
☐ **As above,** *walnut.*
.... *each* **145.00   170.00**

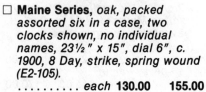

☐ **Merchants Series,** *oak, comes two each pattern in case, two clocks shown, no names, 22" x 15", dial 6", c. 1917, 8 Day, strike, spring wound (E1-174).*
. . . . *each* **140.00   165.00**

☐ **Maine Series,** *oak, packed assorted six in a case, two clocks shown, no individual names, 23½" x 15", dial 6", c. 1900, 8 Day, strike, spring wound (E2-105).*
. . . . *each* **130.00   155.00**

☐ **Mersey Series,** *oak, assorted patterns, three patterns, no individual names, 23" x 14", dial 6", c. 1900, 8 Day, strike, spring wound (E2-107).*
.... *each* **150.00   175.00**
☐ **As above,** *walnut.*
.... *each* **175.00   200.00**

☐ **Norwich Series,** *oak, Sampson,*
Conroy, Morgath, Mantel, 25" x
15½", dial 6", c. 1900, 8 Day,
strike, spring wound (E2-104).
.... *each* **160.00   185.00**
☐ **As above,** *walnut.*
.... *each* **185.00   210.00**

☐ **Patrol Series,** *oak, packed*
assorted six in a case, three
clocks shown, no individual
names, 22¾" x 14¼", dial 6", c.
1900, 8 Day, strike, spring wound
(E2-105).
.... *each* **150.00   175.00**
☐ **As above,** *walnut.*
.... *each* **175.00   200.00**

☐ **Picket Series,** *oak, three*
patterns, no individual names,
22" x 13½", dial 6", c. 1900, 8
Day, strike, spring wound
(E2-107).
.... *each* **145.00   170.00**
☐ **As above,** *walnut.*
.... *each* **170.00   195.00**

☐ **Sancho Series,** *solid oak, flemish*
finish, Segura, Sanches, Sorry,
22½" x 13", dial 6", c. 1900, 8
Day, strike, spring wound
(E2-104).
.... *each* **135.00   160.00**

☐ **Government Series,** *oak, Lobbyist, Governor, Senator, Ambassador, Secretary, President, c. 1894, 8 Day, strike, spring wound (E2-103).*
.... *each* **125.00**   **150.00**

☐ **As above,** *walnut.*
.... *each* **145.00**   **170.00**

TEAR DROP

WALL

☐ **Hudson,** *cherry or walnut, height 26½", dial 5", c. 1900, 8 Day, strike, spring wound (E2-102).*
.... **230.00**   **260.00**

☐ **Elbe,** *wood, height 24", dial 6", c. 1900, 8 Day, strike, spring wound (E2-100).*
.... **250.00**   **280.00**

☐ **Parisan,** *wood, height 24", dial 6", c. 1900, 8 Day, strike, spring wound (E2-99).*
.... **250.00**   **280.00**

☐ **Salem,** *oak, 26½" x 12¾", dial 6", c. 1900, 8 Day, strike, spring wound (E2-105).*
.... **230.00**   **260.00**

Matanzas

☐ **Matanzas,** *oak, 27½″ x 14¾″, dial 6″, c. 1921, 8 Day, strike, spring wound (E1-183).*
.... **245.00**   **275.00**

☐ **Arno,** *enameled iron, Empire sash with porcelain or pearl dial, visible escapement, c. 1900, 8 Day, strike (E1-40).*
.... **120.00**   **145.00**

☐ **Standish,** *oak, 26¼″ x 13″, dial 6″, c. 1900, 8 Day, strike, spring wound (E2-105).*
.... **210.00**   **240.00**

☐ **Stanton,** *oak, 28″ x 14¼″, dial 6″, c. 1900, 8 Day, strike, spring wound (E2-105).*
.... **210.00**   **240.00**

MANTEL

BLACK

☐ **Ailene,** *solid case brass frame, richly ornamented silver panels, hand modeled, height 9″, dial 3¼″, c. 1900, 8 Day, strike (E1-101).*
.... **625.00**   **700.00**

☐ **Charlemont,** *enameled iron, French gilt trimmings, black or green marble finish, cast French sash, 11⅝″ x 8⅝″, porcelain dial 3″, c. 1900, 8 Day, strike (E1-37).*
.... **105.00**   **130.00**

☐ **Fortuna,** *enameled iron, Empire sash with porcelain or pearl dial, visible escapement, c. 1900, 8 Day, strike (E1-39).*
. . . . 100.00   120.00

☐ **Charlton,** *enameled iron, French gilt trimmings, black or green marble finish, cast French sash, 14⅝" x 9", porcelain dial 4", c. 1900, 8 Day, strike (E1-37).*
. . . . 125.00   150.00

☐ **Chateau,** *enameled iron, black or green marble, bronze or gilt trimmings, 9½" x 11½", dial 4", c. 1900, 8 Day, strike (E1-39).*
. . . . 100.00   120.00

☐ **Chistlehurst,** *enameled iron, black or green marble, bronze or gilt trimmings, 10¾" x 10", dial 4", c. 1900, 8 Day, strike (E1-39).*
. . . . 100.00   120.00

☐ **Clarendon,** *black enameled wood, 10¼" x 13", white, gilt or pearl dial 6", c. 1900, 8 Day, strike (E1-40).*
. . . . 55.00   70.00

☐ **Florence,** *enameled iron, Empire sash with porcelain or pearl dial, visible escapement, c. 1900, 8 Day, strike (E1-39).*
. . . . 75.00   90.00

☐ **Galatea,** *enameled iron, Empire sash with porcelain or pearl dial, visible escapement, c. 1900, 8 Day, strike (E1-39).*
. . . . 105.00   130.00

☐ **Harcourt,** *enameled iron, Empire sash with porcelain or pearl dial, visible escapement, c. 1900, 8 Day, strike (E1-39).*
. . . . 105.00   130.00

☐ **Leland,** *black enameled iron with gilt ornamentation, Empire sash with porcelain dial, 12⅛" x 9¾", dial 6", c. 1900, 8 Day, strike, (E1-39).*
.... **100.00   120.00**

☐ **Mona,** *enameled iron, Empire sash, with porcelain or pearl dial, visible escapement, c. 1900, 8 Day, strike (E1-39).*
.... **80.00   100.00**

☐ **Montrose,** *enameled iron, Empire sash with porcelain or pearl dial, visible escapement, c. 1900, 8 Day, strike (E1-40).*
.... **105.00   125.00**

☐ **New Monaco,** *enameled iron, Empire sash with porcelain or pearl dial, visible escapement, c. 1900, 8 Day, strike (E1-39).*
.... **100.00   120.00**

☐ **Olinda,** *black enameled iron, bronze or gilt trimmings, Empire sash, visible escapement, plain white or mother-of-pearl dial, 12¼" x 11½", dial 6", c. 1900, 8 Day, strike (E1-39).*
.... **95.00   115.00**

☐ **Pocahontas,** *enameled iron, Empire sash, porcelain or pearl dial, visible escapement, c. 1900, 8 Day, strike (E1-39).*
.... **115.00   140.00**

☐ **Rosalind,** *enameled iron, Empire sash with porcelain or pearl dial, visible escapement, c. 1900, 8 Day, strike (E1-40).*
.... **105.00   125.00**

☐ **Thetis,** *enameled iron, Empire sash with porcelain or pearl dial, visible escapement, c. 1900, 8 Day, strike (E1-39).*
.... **90.00   110.00**

☐ **Triad,** *dark blue or dark green porcelain bowl with best gold finish trimmings, cathedral gong, ivorized porcelain dial, fancy gilt center or decorated porcelain dial, Empire sash and heavy beveled glass, 21½" x 9", dial 4", c. 1900, 8 Day, strike (E2-110).*
.... **190.00   220.00**

WOOD

☐ **Alexander,** *black enameled wood, white, gilt or pearl dial, 11¾″ x 16″, dial 6″, c. 1900, 8 Day, strike (E1-40).*
. . . . **75.00** **90.00**

☐ **Bancroft,** *black enameled wood, white, gilt or pearl dial, bronze or gilt trimmings, 11″ x 16″, dial 6″, c. 1900, 8 Day, strike (E1-40).*
. . . . **80.00** **95.00**

☐ **Brandon,** *black enameled wood, white, gilt or pearl dial, bronze or gilt trimmings, 11″ x 16″, dial 6″, c. 1900, 8 Day, strike (E1-40).*
. . . . **75.00** **90.00**

☐ **Burlington,** *black enameled wood, white, gilt or pearl dial, bronze or gilt trimmings, 11″ x 16″, dial 6″, c. 1900, 8 Day, strike (E1-40).*
. . . . **75.00** **90.00**

☐ **Numa,** *black enameled wood, white, gilt or pearl dial, 11″ x 16″, dial 6″, c. 1900, 8 Day, strike (E1-40).*
. . . . **75.00** **90.00**

☐ **Pembroke,** *black enameled wood, white, gilt or pearl dial, 10⅞″ x 16″, dial 6″, c. 1900, 8 Day, strike (E1-40).*
. . . . **70.00** **85.00**

Seneca

☐ **Seneca,** *black enameled wood, white, gilt or pearl dial, 11" x 16", dial 6", c. 1900, 8 Day, strike (E1-40).*
. . . . 80.00   95.00

☐ **Winifred,** *black enameled wood, white, gilt or pearl dial, 10½" x 14⅜", dial 6", c. 1900, 8 Day, strike (E1-40).*
. . . . 65.00   80.00

BRASS FINISH

☐ **Antique Brass No. 2,** *visible escapement, height 13½", dial 4", c. 1900, 8 Day, strike (E2-126).*
. . . . 220.00   250.00

☐ **Czar,** *brass finish, cathedral gong, visible escapement, height 13½", base 15", dial 5½", c. 1900, 8 Day, strike (E2-93).*
. . . . 220.00   250.00

☐ **Iroquois,** *brass finish, visible escapement, French sash, porcelain dial, height 18¼", dial 5½", c. 1900, 8 Day, strike (E2-93).*
. . . . 230.00   260.00

MAHOGANY CASE

☐ **Auris,** *mahogany, bowed glass, 10⅛" x 8⅞", dial 6", 8 Day, strike (E1-172).*
. . . . 30.00   40.00

☐ **Ausprey,** *mahogany, bowed glass, 8⅞" x 15¾", dial 6", c. 1911, 8 Day, strike (E1-172).*
.... 30.00   40.00

☐ **Auston,** *mahogany, 10¼" x 8¼", dial 6", c. 1911, 8 Day, strike (E1-172).*
.... 20.00   35.00

☐ **Austro,** *mahogany, bowed glass, 9¾" x 8¼", dial 6", 8 Day, strike (E1-172).*
.... 20.00   35.00

☐ **Author,** *mahogany, 9" x 14¾", dial 6", c. 1911, 8 Day, strike (E1-172).*
.... 35.00   45.00

☐ **Garcia,** *mahogany, 6¼" x 13", dial 4½", c. 1911, 1 Day, alarm (E1-172).*
.... 20.00   30.00

☐ **Green,** *mahogany, 6¾" x 7¼", dial 4½", c. 1911, 1 Day, alarm (E1-172).*
.... 15.00   25.00

☐ **Oval No. 52,** *mahogany, 6¼" x 7½", dial 3½", c. 1917, 8 Day (E1-173).*
.... 15.00   25.00

☐ **Oval No. 53,** *mahogany, 6¼" x 12", dial 3½", c. 1917, 8 Day (E1-173).*
.... 20.00   30.00

☐ **Wager,** *mahogany, 6" x 5⅞", dial 3½", c. 1917, 8 Day, strike (E1-173).*
.... 20.00   30.00

ONYX

☐ **Malcolm,** *Brazilian onyx, ivorized porcelain dial, gilt center, Empire sash, heavy beveled glass, cathedral gong, 11¼" x 15¾", dial 4", c. 1900, 8 Day, strike (E2-110).*
.... 140.00   165.00

☐ **Mandan,** *Brazilian onyx, ivorized porcelain dial, gilt center, Empire sash, heavy beveled glass, cathedral gong, 18½" x 9¾", dial 4", c. 1900, 8 Day, strike (E2-110).*
.... 190.00   220.00

☐ **Marston,** *Brazilian onyx, ivorized porcelain dial, gilt center, Empire sash, heavy beveled glass, cathedral gong, 16½" x 9½", dial 4", c. 1900, 8 Day, strike (E2-110).*
.... 190.00   220.00

☐ **Mercy,** *Brazilian onyx, ivorized porcelain dial, gilt center, Empire sash, heavy beveled glass, cathedral gong, 10" x 12", dial 4", c. 1900, 8 Day, strike (E2-110).*
.... 135.00   160.00

☐ **Monroe,** *Brazilian onyx, ivorized porcelain dial, gilt center, Empire sash, heavy beveled glass, cathedral gong, 10¼" x 10¼", dial 4", c. 1900, 8 Day, strike (E2-110).*
.... 125.00   150.00

☐ **Myrtle,** *Brazilian onyx, ivorized porcelain dial, gilt center, Empire sash, heavy beveled glass, cathedral gong, 11" x 11¾", dial 4", c. 1900, 8 Day, strike (E2-110).*
.... 135.00   160.00

TAMBOUR

☐ **Garfield,** *mahogany, 6½" x 13", dial 4½", c. 1911, 1 Day, alarm (E1-172).*
.... 20.00   30.00

☐ **Jacobean No. 55,** *mahogany, porcelain or silver dial, 6½" x 13½", dial 3½", c. 1917, 8 Day (E1-173).*
...+............. 20.00   30.00

☐ **Quayle,** *mahogany, porcelain or silver dial, 6½" x 12¼", dial 3½", c. 1917, 8 Day (E1-173).*
.... 15.00   25.00

☐ **Tambour No. 1,** *mahogany, porcelain or silver dial, 10¼" x 21½", dial 6", c. 1917, 8 Day, strike (E1-173).*
.... 60.00   75.00

☐ **Tambour No. 2,** *mahogany, porcelain or silver dial, 11½" x 24", dial 7", c. 1917, 8 Day, strike (E1-173).*
.... 75.00   95.00

☐ **Tambour No. 6,** *mahogany, porcelain or silver dial, 11½" x 24½", dial 7", c. 1917, 8 Day, strike (E1-173).*
.... 65.00   80.00

☐ **Tambour No. 13,** *mahogany, 10" x 22", dial 6", c. 1911, 8 Day, strike (E1-172).*
.... 40.00   50.00

☐ **Tambour No. 15,** *mahogany, 12¼" x 29½", dial 7½", c. 1917, 8 Day, strike (E1-173).*
.... 80.00   100.00

☐ **Tambour No. 16,** *mahogany, bowed glass, 9" x 18", dial 6", c. 1911, 8 Day, strike (E1-172).*
.... 25.00   35.00

☐ **Tambour No. 17,** *mahogany, bowed glass, 9⅞" x 15⅞", dial 6", c. 1911, 8 Day, strike (E1-172).*
.... 30.00   40.00

MIRROR SIDES

☐ **Apollo,** *wood, height 20", dial 5½", c. 1890, 8 Day, strike (E2-89).*
.... 260.00   280.00
☐ **As above,** *8 Day, alarm.*
.... 275.00   300.00

☐ **Countess,** *black walnut, 12 mirrors and solid metal head, height 26", dial 6", c. 1890, 8 Day, strike (E2-89).*
.... 285.00   325.00

☐ **Oakdale,** *oak, silver ornaments, 24" x 15¼", dial 6", c. 1910, 8 Day, strike (E2-90).*
.... 285.00   325.00
☐ **As above,** *walnut, gilt ornaments.*
.... 315.00   355.00

☐ **Occidental,** *oak, silver ornaments, height 24", dial 6", c. 1910, 8 Day, strike (E2-90).*
.... 285.00   325.00
☐ **As above,** *walnut, gilt ornaments.*
.... 315.00   355.00

MISSION

☐ **San Jose,** *oak, cast numerals, polished brass hands and pendulum ball, 24½" x 13", dial 12", c. 1920, 8 Day, strike (E1-183).*
.... 65.00   80.00

CABINET

☐ **Alva,** *solid oak, Flemish finish, wood dial with white figures painted on a dark blue background, pendulum movement, brass hands, 13" x 6½", dial 4", 1 Day (E2-108).*
.... 70.00   85.00

☐ **Arco,** *solid oak, Flemish finish, wood dial with white figures painted on a dark blue background, lever movement, 13" x 4½", dial 2", 1 Day (E2-108).*
.... 80.00   95.00

☐ **Los Alamos,** *solid oak, Flemish finish, wood dial with brass hands and numerals, 14½" x 11¾", dial 6", c. 1910, 8 Day, strike (E2-109).*
.... 100.00   120.00

☐ **Los Barrios,** *solid oak, Flemish finish, wood dial with brass hands and numerals, 13½" x 11½", dial 6", c. 1910, 8 Day, strike (E2-109).*
.... 100.00   120.00

☐ **Los Santos,** *solid oak, Flemish finish, wood dial with brass hands and numerals, 13¼" x 12¼", dial 6", c. 1910, 8 Day, strike (E2-109).*
.... 100.00   120.00

☐ **Moro,** *solid oak, Flemish finish, wood dial with white figures painted on a dark blue background, pendulum movement, brass hands, 13" x 6½", dial 4", 1 Day.*
.... 70.00   85.00

☐ **Pasco,** *solid oak, Flemish finish, wood dial with white figures painted on a dark blue background, lever movement, brass hands, 13" x 5½", dial 3", 1 Day.*
.... 70.00   85.00

☐ **San Carlos,** *weathered oak, wooden dial with white figures on a background of dark brown, fancy brass hands, 20" x 9", dial 6", c. 1910, 8 Day, strike (E2-108).*
.... 80.00   100.00

☐ **San Juan,** *weathered oak, wooden dial with white figures on a background of dark brown, fancy brass hands, 20½" x 9½", dial 6", c. 1910, 8 Day, strike (E2-108).*
.... 80.00   100.00

☐ **Tosca,** *solid oak, Flemish finish, wood dial with white Arabic figures painted on a dark blue background, brass hands, pendulum movement, 12½" x 6½", dial 4", c. 1910, 8 Day, strike (E2-108).*
.... 95.00   115.00

☐ **Vega,** *solid oak, Flemish finish, wood dial with white Arabic figures painted on a dark blue background, brass hands, pendulum movement, 13" x 6", dial 4", c. 1910, 8 Day, strike (E2-108).*
.... 95.00   115.00

GRANDFATHER

☐ **Dutch No. 40,** *solid oak, Flemish finish, cast brass hands and numerals, 77½" x 17½", c. 1910, 8 Day, strike, spring (E2-108).*
.... 210.00   240.00

☐ **La Plata,** *weathered oak, brass numerals and hands, 22¾" x 13¾", c. 1910, 8 Day, strike (E2-108).*
.... **110.00   135.00**

☐ **Minas,** *solid oak, Flemish finish, fitted with pendulum movement with brass hands and numerals, 12" x 4½", dial 3", c. 1910, 1 Day (E2-109).*
.... **55.00   70.00**

☐ **Minch,** *solid oak, Flemish finish, fitted with pendulum movement with brass hands and numerals, 12" x 4½", dial 3", c. 1910, 1 Day (E2-109).*
.... **55.00   70.00**

☐ **Dutch No. 45,** *solid oak, Flemish finish, stamped brass hands and numerals, 68½" x 15½", c. 1910, 8 Day, strike, spring (E2-108).*
.... **210.00   240.00**

KITCHEN

☐ **La Lanza,** *weathered oak, brass numerals and hands, 22" x 13½", c. 1910, 8 Day, strike (E2-108).*
.... **110.00   135.00**

☐ **Minho,** *solid oak, Flemish finish, fitted with pendulum movement, with brass hands and numerals, 12" x 4½", dial 3", c. 1910, 1 Day (E2-109).*
.... **55.00   70.00**

☐ **San Benito,** *weathered oak, 21" x 13½", dial 6", c. 1910, 8 Day, strike (E2-109).*
.... **110.00   135.00**

NOVELTY

□ **Santa Clara,** *weathered oak, six-inch dial with brass numerals and hands, 20¼" x 11¼", c. 1910, 8 Day, strike (E2-109).*
. . . . **105.00   130.00**

□ **San Mateo,** *weathered oak, six-inch dial with brass numerals and hands, 20½" x 9½", c. 1910, 8 Day, strike (E2-109).*
. . . . **105.00   130.00**

□ **San Pedro,** *weathered oak, six-inch dial with brass numerals and hands, 19" x 12½", c. 1910, 8 Day, strike (E2-109).*
. . . . **105.00   130.00**

KITCHEN HANGING

□ **Durance Hanging,** *solid oak, Flemish finish, cast brass hands and numerals, 37½" x 15¾", c. 1910, 8 Day (E2-109).*
. . . . **140.00   165.00**

□ **As above,** *8 Day, strike*
. . . . **190.00   220.00**

□ **As above,** *30 Day*
. . . . **210.00   240.00**

□ **Liso,** *solid oak, Flemish finish, wood dial with white figures painted on a dark blue background, lever movement, 8½" x 4½", dial 2", c. 1910, 1 Day (E2-109).*
. . . . **40.00   55.00**

☐ **Loma,** *solid oak, Flemish finish, wood dial with white figures painted on a dark blue background, lever movement, 8½" x 4", dial 2", c. 1910, 1 Day (E2-109).*
.... 40.00   55.00

☐ **Acrobat,** *cast in brass, barbadienne finish, silver and gold finish, bell, height 16¼", dial 4", c. 1900, 8 Day, strike (E2-112).*
.... 175.00   200.00

☐ **Lute,** *solid oak, Flemish finish, wood dial with white figures painted on a dark blue background, lever movement, 9" x 4½", dial 2", c. 1910, 1 Day (E2-109).*
.... 40.00   55.00

OCTAGON, DROP

☐ **Dulce,** *solid oak, Flemish finish, cast brass hands and numerals, 24" x 16", wood dial 12", c. 1910, 8 Day (E2-109).*
.... 165.00   190.00
☐ **As above,** *8 Day, strike*
.... 190.00   220.00

NOVELTY

FANCY

☐ **Acme,** *solid cast brass, hand finished, 2½" enamel dial, c. 1900, 1 Day (E2-111).*
.... 80.00   95.00

Aida

☐ **Aida,** *antique brass, height 12³/₄",*
dial 6", c. 1900, 15 Day (E2-112).
. . . . **105.00**   **125.00**

☐ **Andorra,** *ormolu gold plated case,*
10¹/₄" x 3³/₄", porcelain dial 2", c.
1900 1 Day (E2-113).
. . . . **60.00**   **75.00**

☐ **Bamboo,** *height 8³/₄", c. 1900, 1*
Day (E2-112).
. . . . **80.00**   **100.00**
☐ **As above,** *1 Day, calendar*
. . . . **125.00**   **150.00**

☐ **Banjo,** *silver plated and oxidized,*
height 7", dial 2", c. 1900, 1 Day
(E2-112).
. . . . **70.00**   **85.00**

☐ **Barrel On Skids,** *oak with brass hoops, height 6¾", dial 2½", c. 1900, 1 Day (E2-111).*
.... **40.00   55.00**

☐ **Bouquet,** *gold or silver plated, beveled glass, mirror and cut glass scent bottle, height 8", c. 1900, 1 Day (E2-111).*
.... **125.00   150.00**

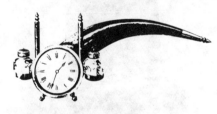

☐ **Buffalo Ink,** *polished horn, brass trimmings, cut glass inks, front glass of best crystal lens, ½" thick, and of high magnifying power, c. 1900, 1 Day (E2-112).*
.... **75.00   90.00**

☐ **Calendar,** *plush, assorted colors, c. 1900, 1 Day, calendar (E2-112).*
.... **125.00   150.00**

☐ **Chatelaine,** *antique brass finish, height 14", dial 6", length over all 21", c. 1900, 15 Day (E2-112).*
.... **175.00   200.00**

☐ **Cigar Lighter,** *c. 1900, 1 Day (E2-111).*
.... **150.00   175.00**

Egyptian

☐ **Egyptian,** *height 8", c. 1900, 1 Day (E2-112).*
.... **75.00**   **90.00**
☐ **As above,** *1 Day, calendar*
.... **105.00**   **125.00**

☐ **Etruscan,** *pottery case, c. 1900, 1 Day (E2-112).*
.... **60.00**   **75.00**
☐ **As above,** *1 Day, alarm*
.... **80.00**   **95.00**

☐ **Flush,** *ormolu gold plated case, 5" x 5", dial 2", c. 1900, 1 Day (E2-113).*
.... **55.00**   **70.00**

☐ **Lighthouse,** *oxidized silver and gilt, cut pinion movement, revolving lanterns, height 12½", dial 2", c. 1900, 1 Day (E2-111).*
.... **175.00**   **200.00**

☐ **Lisbon,** *ormolu gold plated case, 6" x 6½", dial 2", c. 1900, 1 Day (E2-113).*
.... **55.00**   **70.00**

☐ **Mace,** *silver body with gold spikes, c. 1900, 1 Day (E2-112).*
.... **105.00**   **125.00**

☐ **Mandolin,** *black and silver finish, length 23", dial 5", c. 1900, 8 Day (E2-112).*
. . . . **110.00** **135.00**

☐ **Parasol,** *finished in black and gold, height 15", c. 1900, 15 Day (E2-111).*
. . . . **150.00** **175.00**

☐ **Paper Weight,** *watch movement, width 3", c. 1900, 1 Day (E2-112).*
. . . . **45.00** **60.00**

☐ **Racquet,** *gold finish, c. 1900, 1 Day (E2-112).*
. . . . **95.00** **115.00**

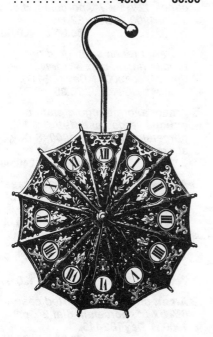

☐ **Sheaf,** *ormolu gold plated case, 7½" x 6", dial 2", c. 1900, 1 Day (E2-113).*
. . . . **75.00** **90.00**

☐ **Stirrup,** *gold and silver finish, height 17", dial 2", c. 1900, 1 Day (E2-112).*
. . . . **70.00** **85.00**

GILT

☐ **Aire,** *ormolu gold plated case, 6"
x 5", dial 2", c. 1900, 1 Day
(E2-113).*
. . . . 60.00   75.00

☐ **Allier,** *ormolu gold plated case,
11½" x 6", porcelain dial 2", c.
1900, 1 Day (E2-114).*
. . . . 70.00   85.00

☐ **Altair,** *ormolu gold plated case,
cast sash, decorated porcelain
panel, 12½" x 7", porcelain dial
3", c. 1900, 8 Day (E2-119).*
. . . . 360.00   400.00

☐ **Alvord,** *French satin gold or
bronze finish, 6" x 4¼", ivorized
dial 2", c. 1900, 1 Day (E2-117).*
. . . . 70.00   85.00

☐ **Amanda,** *ormolu gold plate or
antique verde case, 19¼" x 11",
porcelain dial 4", c. 1900, 8 Day,
strike (E2-119).*
. . . . 210.00   240.00

☐ **Amoret,** *ormolu gold plated case,
6¾" x 3½", porcelain dial 2", c.
1900, 1 Day (E2-116).*
. . . . 40.00   55.00

☐ **Annecy,** *ormolu gold plated case,
10¾" x 6¼", porcelain dial 2", c.
1910, 8 Day (E2-119).*
. . . . 100.00   120.00

☐ **Arcot,** *ormolu gold plated case,
6¾" x 5", porcelain dial 2", c.
1900, 1 Day (E2-116).*
. . . . 70.00   85.00

☐ **Arden,** *French satin gold or bronze finish, 8½" x 4¾", ivorized dial 2", c. 1900, 1 Day (E2-117).*
. . . . 65.00   80.00

☐ **Ardennes,** *ormolu gold plated case, 11½" x 4¼", porcelain dial 2", c. 1900, 1 Day (E2-115).*
. . . . 65.00   80.00

☐ **Ariel,** *ormolu gold plated case, 8" x 4½", porcelain dial 2", c. 1900, 1 Day (E2-114).*
. . . . 75.00   90.00

☐ **Arverne,** *French satin gold finish, 10½" x 7½", ivorized dial 2", c. 1900, 1 Day (E2-115).*
. . . . 70.00   85.00
☐ **As above,** *8 Day*
. . . . 115.00   140.00

☐ **Astoria (Jeweled Watch),** *14K gold plate finish, stem wind and stem set, jeweled front, fitted with folding back as desk ornament, 3¼" x 2¾", white porcelain dial 1¾", c. 1900, 1 Day (E2-119).*
. . . . 65.00   80.00

☐ **Atlas,** *French satin gold or bronze finish, height 9¼", porcelain dial 1¾", c. 1900, 1 Day (E2-117).*
. . . . 75.00   90.00

☐ **Baroda,** *ormolu gold plate, 9¾" x 7", porcelain dial 2", c. 1911, 1 Day (E1-172).*
. . . . 80.00   95.00

☐ **Bellona,** *ormolu gold plated case, 9¾" x 6½", porcelain dial 2", c. 1900, 1 Day (E2-116).*
. . . . 70.00   85.00

☐ **Bellona,** *French satin gold or bronze finish, 9¾" x 6½", ivorized dial 2", c. 1910, 1 Day (E2-120).*
. . . . 60.00   75.00
☐ **As above,** *8 Day*
. . . . 105.00   130.00

☐ **Bermuda,** *ormolu gold plate, 9¾" x 6½", ivorized dial 2", c. 1911, 1 Day (E1-172).*
. . . . 80.00   95.00

☐ **Bucknell,** *ormolu gold plated case, 6½" x 4¼", dial 2", c. 1900, 1 Day (E2-113).*
. . . . 60.00   75.00

☐ **Capel,** *ormolu gold plated case, 6¼" x 5", dial 2", c. 1900, 1 Day (E2-113).*
.... 50.00   65.00

☐ **Celeste,** *ormolu gold plated case, 8¼" x 4", porcelain dial 2", c. 1900, 1 Day (E2-116).*
.... 50.00   65.00

☐ **Clovelly,** *French satin gold or bronze finish, 4¼" x 4¼", ivorized dial 2", c. 1900, 1 Day (E2-117).*
.... 45.00   60.00

☐ **Corolan,** *French satin gold or bronze finish, 8½" x 5", ivorized dial 2", c. 1900, 1 Day (E2-117).*
.... 125.00   150.00
☐ **As above,** *8 Day*
.... 155.00   180.00

☐ **Crescent Stand,** *bronze, nickel or gilt finish, either the Jasper or Astoria will fit this, 7¾" x 6½", base 3½", c. 1900 (E2-119).*
.... 40.00   55.00

☐ **Criterion,** *French satin gold or bronze finish, 14¾" x 6½", ivorized dial 2", c. 1910, 8 Day (E2-120).*
.... 150.00   175.00

☐ **Cupid,** *French satin gold or bronze finish, 12½" x 6", ivorized dial 2", c. 1910, 1 Day (E2-120).*
.... 70.00   85.00
☐ **As above,** *8 Day*
.... 115.00   140.00

☐ **Dalton,** *French satin gold or bronze finish, 10" x 3½", ivorized dial 2", c. 1900, 1 Day (E2-117).*
.... 55.00   70.00

☐ **Daphne,** *ormolu gold plate, 5⅜" x 3¼", white dial 2", c. 1911, 1 Day (E1-172).*
.... 30.00   40.00

☐ **Darien,** *ormolu gold plate, 8½" x 6¾", porcelain dial 2", c. 1920, 1 Day.(E1-176).*
.... 50.00   65.00

☐ **Delano,** *ormolu gold plated case, 8" x 4¾", porcelain dial 2", c. 1910, 1 Day (E2-118).*
. . . . 65.00   80.00

☐ **Delong,** *ormolu gold plate, 5½" x 4½", white dial 2", c. 1911, 1 Day (E1-172).*
. . . . 25.00   35.00

☐ **Devon,** *ormolu gold plate, 5¾" x 4½", porcelain dial 2", c. 1911, 1 Day (E1-172).*
. . . . 60.00   75.00

☐ **Dixon,** *ormolu gold plated case, 9" x 6¾", porcelain dial 2", c. 1900, 1 Day (E2-115).*
. . . . 60.00   75.00

☐ **Dixon,** *ormolu gold plated case, 9" x 6¾", porcelain dial 3", c. 1900, 8 Day (E2-115).*
. . . . 75.00   90.00

☐ **Drew,** *ormolu gold plated case, 7" x 5", porcelain dial 2", c. 1910, 1 Day (E2-118).*
. . . . 75.00   90.00

☐ **Dunstan,** *ormolu gold plate, 10½" x 5¾", porcelain dial 2", c. 1920, 1 Day (E1-176).*
. . . . 80.00   100.00

☐ **Eberle,** *ormolu gold plate, 7¾" x 4½", porcelain dial 2", c. 1920, 1 Day (E1-176).*
. . . . 65.00   80.00

☐ **Eldon,** *ormolu gold plated case, 5½" x 3½", porcelain dial 2", c. 1900, 1 Day (E2-116).*
. . . . 60.00   75.00

☐ **Eldora,** *ormolu gold plated case, 6¾" x 4¾", porcelain dial 2", c. 1900, 1 Day (E2-115).*
. . . . 45.00   60.00

☐ **Falmouth,** *ormolu gold plate, 11½" x 8½", porcelain dial 3", c. 1920, 8 Day (E1-176).*
. . . . **70.00**   **85.00**

☐ **Fenwick,** *ormolu gold plated case, 6¼" x 6", porcelain dial 2", c. 1900, 1 Day (E2-115).*
. . . . **45.00**   **60.00**

☐ **Fleury,** *French satin gold or bronze finish, 5" x 4", ivorized dial 2", c. 1900, 1 Day (E2-117).*
. . . . **45.00**   **65.00**

☐ **Ferney,** *ormolu gold plated case, 5¾" x 5¾", porcelain dial 2", c. 1900, 1 Day (E2-114).*
. . . . **80.00**   **95.00**

☐ **Flores,** *ormolu gold plated case, gilt hands, 15" x 8", porcelain dial 4", c. 1900, 8 Day, strike (E2-119).*
. . . . **155.00**   **180.00**

☐ **Galva,** *ormolu gold plated case, 9" x 5½", porcelain dial 2", c. 1900, 1 Day (E2-114).*
.... **110.00   135.00**

☐ **Follen,** *ormolu gold plated case, 11½" x 7", porcelain dial 3", c. 1900, 8 Day (E2-116).*
.... **105.00   125.00**

☐ **Garland,** *ormolu gold plated case, 9" x 6½", porcelain dial 2", c. 1900, 1 Day (E2-116).*
.... **50.00   65.00**

☐ **Forli,** *ormolu gold plated case, 7½" x 6½", porcelain dial 2", c. 1900, 1 Day (E2-115).*
.... **45.00   60.00**

☐ **Garnet,** *ormolu gold plated case, 6½" x 4½", porcelain dial 2", c. 1900, 1 Day (E2-114).*
.... **55.00   70.00**

☐ **Furness,** *ormolu gold plated case, 11½" x 7", porcelain dial 3", c. 1900, 8 Day (E2-116).*
.... **95.00   115.00**

☐ **Gaudin,** *ormolu gold plated case, 9" x 6", porcelain dial 2", c. 1900, 1 Day (E2-114).*
.... 75.00   90.00

☐ **Hazel,** *ormolu gold plate, 4⅜" x 3¼", white dial 2", c. 1911, 1 Day (E1-172).*
.... 25.00   35.00

☐ **Heath,** *ormolu gold plated case, 6¾" x 5¾", porcelain dial 2", c. 1900, 1 Day (E2-114).*
.... 75.00   90.00

☐ **Isere,** *ormolu gold plated case, visible pendulum, 18¼" x 19¼", porcelain dial with beveled glass 4", c. 1900, 8 Day, strike (E2-119).*
.... 270.00   300.00

☐ **Jasper,** *finished in nickel, bronze or gilt with best French magnifying lens back and front, stem wind and stem set, made with beveled bottom for use as paper weight or may be combined with Dolphin or Crescent stand, 3¼" x 2¾", white porcelain dial 1¾", and 2½" lens, c. 1900, 1 Day (E2-119).*
.... 125.00   150.00

☐ **Kazan,** *ormolu gold plated case, 6¼" x 5½", dial 2", c. 1900, 1 Day (E2-113).*
.... 45.00   60.00

☐ **Lachute,** *ormolu gold plated case, 7" x 4", porcelain dial 2", c. 1900, 1 Day (E2-116).*
.... 45.00   60.00

☐ **Lantier,** *ormolu gold plated case, 6½" x 5¾", porcelain dial 2", c. 1900, 1 Day (E2-116).*
.... 60.00   75.00

☐ **Laveta,** *ormolu gold plated case, 9¾" x 5", porcelain dial 3", c. 1900, 1 Day (E2-114).*
.... 85.00   105.00

☐ **Lannes,** *ormolu gold plated case, 6" x 3½", porcelain dial 2", c. 1900, 1 Day (E2-116).*
.... 50.00   65.00

☐ **Larissa,** *ormolu gold plated case, 7" x 6½", porcelain dial 2", c. 1900, 1 Day (E2-114).*
.... 75.00   90.00

☐ **Lascar,** *French satin gold or bronze finish, 5½" x 4½", ivorized dial 2", c. 1900, 1 Day (E2-117).*
.... 45.00   60.00

☐ **Le Fuel,** *ormolu gold plated case, 12¼" x 7", porcelain dial 3", c. 1900, 8 Day (E2-115).*
.... 105.00   125.00

☐ **Leroy,** *French satin gold or bronze, 3¾" x 2½", ivorized dial 2", c. 1900, 1 Day (E2-117).*
.... 125.00   150.00

☐ **Lescot,** *ormolu gold plated case, 6" x 4¼", porcelain dial 2", c. 1900, 1 Day (E2-114).*
.... 55.00   70.00

☐ **Lescure,** *ormolu gold plated case, 6" x 5¼", dial 2", c. 1900, 1 Day (E2-113).*
.... 50.00   65.00

☐ **Levan,** *ormolu gold plated case, 8¾" x 3½", porcelain dial 2", c. 1900, 1 Day (E2-117).*
.... 45.00　　60.00

☐ **Libitina,** *ormolu gold plated case, cathedral gong, 17¼" x 9¼", porcelain dial with beveled glass 4", c. 1900, 8 Day, strike (E2-119),*
.... 230.00　　260.00

☐ **Libourne,** *ormolu gold plated case, 10½" x 5¼", porcelain dial 3", c. 1900, 8 Day (E2-115).*
.... 95.00　　115.00

☐ **Lillian,** *ormolu gold plated case,. 6¼" x 7", porcelain dial 3", c. 1900, 1 Day (E2-114).*
.... 105.00　　125.00

☐ **Limoges,** *ormolu gold plated case, 5½" x 4¼", dial 2", c. 1900, 1 Day (E2-113).*
.... 45.00　　60.00

☐ **Loire,** *ormolu gold plated case, 6½" x 7", porcelain dial 2", c. 1900, 1 Day (E2-114).*
.... 75.00　　90.00

☐ **Lucile,** *ormolu gold plated case, 9¼" x 5½", porcelain dial 3", c. 1900, 1 Day (E2-114).*
.... 130.00　　155.00

☐ **Maintenon,** *French satin gold or bronze finish, 3½" x 8", ivorized dial 2", c. 1900, 1 Day (E2-117).*
.... 50.00　　65.00
☐ **As above,** *8 Day*
.... 90.00　　110.00

☐ **Mangrove,** *French satin gold finish, 10¼" x 5¼", ivorized dial 2", c. 1900, 1 Day (E2-115).*
.... 55.00　　70.00
☐ **As above,** *8 Day*
.... 90.00　　110.00

☐ **Manila,** *French satin gold or bronze finish, 4" x 3¼", ivorized dial 2", c. 1900, 1 Day (E2-117).*
. . . . **40.00   55.00**

☐ **Mistral,** *French satin gold or bronze finish, height 10¼", porcelain dial 1¾".*
. . . . **60.00   80.00**

☐ **Minot,** *ormolu gold plated case, 9¾" x 6¾", porcelain dial 2", c. 1900, 1 Day (E2-114).*
. . . . **85.00   105.00**

Nana

☐ **Nana,** *ormolu gold plated case, 5½" x 3½", porcelain dial 2", c. 1900, 1 Day (E2-117).*
.... 90.00   110.00

☐ **Napier,** *ormolu gold plated case, 7" x 4½", porcelain dial 2", c. 1910, 1 Day (E2-118).*
.... 55.00   70.00

☐ **Naruna,** *ormolu gold plated case, 6¾" x 5¾", porcelain dial 2", c. 1910, 1 Day (E2-118).*
.... 75.00   90.00

☐ **Nashoba,** *ormolu gold plate, 7" x 4½", dial 2", c. 1920, 1 Day (E1-176).*
.... 40.00   50.00

☐ **Paran,** *ormolu gold plated case, 5½" x 4½", porcelain dial 2", c. 1900, 1 Day (E2-114).*
.... 55.00   70.00

☐ **Pavia,** *French satin gold or bronze finish, 10¼" x 5¼", ivorized dial 2", c. 1910, 1 Day (E2-120).*
.... 70.00   85.00
☐ **As above,** *8 Day*
.... 115.00   140.00

☐ **Pelham,** *ormolu gold plated case, 6½" x 4½", porcelain dial 2", c. 1900, 1 Day (E2-116).*
.... 60.00   75.00

☐ **Perley,** *ormolu gold plated case, 8½" x 5", porcelain dial 2", c. 1900, 1 Day (E2-115).*
.... 50.00   65.00

☐ **Phillipina,** *French satin gold or bronze finish, 4¼" x 3¼", ivorized dial 2", c. 1900, 1 Day (E2-117).*
.... **50.00** **65.00**

☐ **Picton,** *ormolu gold plated case, 7" x 4½", porcelain dial 2", c. 1900, 1 Day (E2-116).*
.... **45.00** **60.00**

☐ **Plevna,** *French satin gold finish, 11¾" x 8½", ivorized dial 2", c. 1900, 1 Day (E2-115).*
.... **70.00** **85.00**
☐ **As above,** *8 Day*
.... **115.00** **140.00**

☐ **Reita,** *ormolu gold plated case, 7" x 4½", porcelain dial 2", c. 1900, 1 Day (E2-115).*
.... **50.00** **65.00**

☐ **Reno,** *ormolu gold plated case, 8" x 4½", porcelain dial 2", c. 1900, 1 Day (E2-116).*
.... **45.00** **60.00**

☐ **Rochelle,** *French satin gold or bronze finish, 11" x 6½", ivorized dial 2", c. 1910, 1 Day (E2-120).*
.... **65.00** **80.00**
☐ **As above,** *8 Day*
.... **105.00** **135.00**

☐ **Samoa,** *French satin gold or bronze finish, 7¼" x 4", ivorized dial 2", c. 1900, 1 Day (E2-117).*
.... **105.00** **135.00**
☐ **As above,** *8 Day*
.... **140.00** **165.00**

☐ **Toltec,** *ormolu gold plated case,
6¼" x 5¼", dial 2", c. 1900, 1
Day (E2-113).*
.... 40.00   50.00

☐ **Trianon,** *French satin gold or
bronze finish, 7½" x 3¾",
ivorized dial 2", c. 1900, 1 Day
(E2-117).*
.... 65.00   80.00

☐ **Tulle,** *ormolu gold plated case,
8" x 3", porcelain dial 2", c.
1900, 1 Day (E2-116).*
.... 65.00   80.00

☐ **Tralee,** *French satin gold or
bronze finish, 4½" x 3", ivorized
dial 2", c. 1900, 1 Day (E2-117).*
.... 45.00   60.00

☐ **Trianon,** *ormolu gold plated case,
7½" x 3¾", porcelain dial 2", c.
1900, 1 Day (E2-113).*
.... 65.00   80.00

☐ **Tyrone,** *French satin gold or
bronze finish, 5¼" x 3¾",
ivorized dial 2", c. 1900, 1 Day
(E2-117).*
.... 50.00   65.00

☐ **Valetta,** *ormolu gold plated case, 10¾" x 4¾", porcelain dial 2", c. 1910, 1 Day (E2-119).*
.... **90.00   110.00**

☐ **Vendome,** *ormolu gold plated case, 6" x 3½", porcelain dial 2", c. 1900, 1 Day (E2-113).*
.... **55.00   70.00**

☐ **Vieta,** *ormolu gold plated case, 6" x 5½", porcelain dial 2", c. 1900, 1 Day (E2-117).*
.... **65.00   80.00**

☐ **Yantus,** *ormolu gold plated case, 6½" x 6¾", porcelain dial 2", c. 1910, 1 Day (E2-118).*
.... **55.00   70.00**

FRENCH GILT

☐ **Arnold,** *French satin gold finish with decorated porcelain panels, 14" x 9", decorated porcelain dial 3", c. 1900, 8 Day, strike (E2-120).*
.... **285.00   325.00**

☐ **Yesner,** *ormolu gold plated case, 9¼" x 6", porcelain dial 2", c. 1910, 1 Day (E2-118).*
.... **80.00   100.00**

☐ **Yuma,** *ormolu gold plated case, 6¼" x 5¼", dial 2", c. 1900, 1 Day (E2-113).*
.... **50.00   65.00**

☐ **Lakeside,** *French satin gold finish with decorated porcelain panels, 18½" x 10¾", decorated porcelain dial 3", c. 1900, 8 Day, strike (E2-120).*
.... **675.00   750.00**

☐ **Lenore,** *French satin gold finish with decorated porcelain panels, 15" x 9", decorated porcelain dial 3", c. 1900, 8 Day, strike (E2-120).*
. . . . **335.00   375.00**

☐ **Larchmont,** *French satin gold finish with decorated porcelain panels, 16" x 9", decorated porcelain dial 3", c. 1900, 8 Day, strike (E2-120).*
. . . . **490.00   550.00**

☐ **Lyons,** *French satin gold finish with decorated porcelain panels, 16½" x 9", decorated porcelain dial 3", c. 1900, 8 Day, strike (E2-120).*
. . . . **450.00   500.00**

☐ **Sicilian,** *French satin gold finish with decorated porcelain panels, 16½" x 8", decorated porcelain dial 3", c. 1900, 8 Day, strike (E2-120).*
. . . . **400.00   450.00**

OFFICE INKS

☐ **Secretary Ink,** *hand chased cast brass stand, with cut glass inks, c. 1900, 1 Day (E2-111).*
.... **105.00**   **125.00**

☐ **Louis Ink,** *solid brass, c. 1900, 1 Day (E2-111).*
.... **310.00**   **350.00**

☐ **The Scribe (Ink Stand),** *brass finish, reversible inks, c. 1900, 1 Day (E2-111).*
.... **310.00**   **350.00**

☐ **Maintenon Ink,** *solid brass, c. 1900, 1 Day (E2-111).*
.... **335.00**   **375.00**

REGULATOR
FIGURE EIGHT

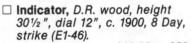

☐ **Indicator,** *D.R. wood, height 30½", dial 12", c. 1900, 8 Day, strike (E1-46).*
.... **310.00   350.00**
☐ **As above,** *8 Day, simple spring*
.... **360.00   400.00**

☐ **8" Saxon,** *rosewood, height 20", dial 8", c. 1900, 8 Day (E2-122).*
.... **245.00   275.00**
☐ **As above,** *8 Day, strike*
.... **270.00   300.00**
☐ **As above,** *8 Day, calendar*
.... **285.00   325.00**
☐ **As above,** *8 Day, stirke, calendar*
.... **310.00   350.00**

☐ **8" Saxon Mosaic,** *wood, height 20", dial 8", c. 1900, 8 Day (E2-122).*
.... **245.00   275.00**
☐ **As above,** *8 Day, strike*
.... **270.00   300.00**
☐ **As above,** *8 Day, calendar*
.... **285.00   325.00**
☐ **As above,** *8 Day, strike, calendar*
.... **310.00   350.00**

☐ **10" Saxon,** *rosewood, height 22", dial 10", c. 1900, 8 Day (E2-122).*
.... **270.00   300.00**
☐ **As above,** *8 Day, strike*
.... **285.00   325.00**

☐ **As above,** *8 Day, calendar*
.... **310.00   350.00**
☐ **As above,** *8 Day, strike, calendar*
.... **335.00   375.00**

☐ **10″ Saxon Mosaic,** *wood, height
22″, dial 10″, c. 1900, 8 Day
(E2-122).*
.... **270.00   300.00**
☐ **As above,** *8 Day, stirke*
.... **285.00   325.00**
☐ **As above,** *8 Day, calendar*
.... **310.00   350.00**
☐ **As above,** *8 Day, strike, calendar*
.... **335.00   375.00**

OCTAGON TOP, LONG DROP

☐ **Erie,** *oak, 33½″ x 18½″, dial 12″,
c. 1920, 8 Day (E1-183).*
.... **245.00   275.00**
☐ **As above,** *8 Day, strike*
.... **270.00   300.00**
☐ **As above,** *8 Day, calendar*
.... **285.00   325.00**

OCTAGON TOP, SHORT DROP
☐ **Blake,** *oak, height 27″, dial 12″,
c. 1900, 8 Day (E1-37).*
.... **195.00   225.00**

☐ **Regulator D.R., Calendar,** *wood,
height 31″, dial 12″, c. 1900, 8
Day (E2-93).*
.... **270.00   300.00**
☐ **As above,** *8 Day, strike*
.... **285.00   325.00**
☐ **As above,** *8 Day, calendar*
.... **310.00   350.00**
☐ **As above,** *8 Day, strike, calendar*
.... **335.00   375.00**

☐ **Drop Octagon No. 2,** *wood, height 24", dial 12", c. 1900, 8 Day (E2-122).*
.... 220.00   250.00
☐ **As above,** *8 Day, strike*
.... 245.00   275.00

☐ **Ventura,** *light or dark wood, height 24¾", dial 12", c. 1900, 8 Day (E1-37).*
.... 195.00   225.00
☐ **As above,** *30 Day*
.... 245.00   275.00

☐ **10" Small Drop Octagon,** *rosewood and zebra, gilt and gilt buttons, height 21", dial 10", c. 1900, 8 Day (E2-122).*
.... 195.00   225.00
☐ **As above,** *8 Day, strike*
.... 220.00   250.00
☐ **As above,** *8 Day, calendar*
.... 245.00   275.00
☐ **As above,** *8 Day, strike, calendar*
.... 270.00   300.00

☐ **10" Small Drop Octagon Gilt,** *rosewood or zebra, c. 1900, 8 Day (E2-122).*
.... 195.00   225.00
☐ **As above,** *8 Day, strike*
.... 220.00   250.00
☐ **As above,** *8 Day, calendar*
.... 245.00   275.00
☐ **As above,** *8 Day, strike, calendar*
.... 270.00   300.00

☐ **12" Drop Octagon,** *R.C. rosewood or zebra, height 24", dial 12", c. 1900, 8 Day (E2-122).*
.... 195.00   225.00
☐ **As above,** *8 Day, strike*
.... 220.00   250.00
☐ **As above,** *8 Day, calendar*
.... 245.00   275.00
☐ **As above,** *8 Day, strike, calendar*
.... 270.00   300.00

☐ **12" Drop Octagon, Calendar,** *rosewood or zebra, height 24", dial 12", c. 1900, 8 Day (E2-122).*
.... 195.00   225.00
☐ **As above,** *8 Day, strike*
.... 220.00   250.00

☐ **As above,** *8 Day, calendar*
.... **245.00   275.00**
☐ **As above,** *8 Day, strike, calendar*
.... **270.00   300.00**

OPEN SWINGING

☐ **12″ Mosaic Drop,** *wood, height
24″, dial 12″, c. 1900, 8 Day
(E2-122).*
.... **195.00   225.00**
☐ **As above,** *8 Day, strike*
.... **220.00   250.00**
☐ **As above,** *8 Day, calendar*
.... **245.00   275.00**
☐ **As above,** *8 Day, strike, calendar*
.... **270.00   300.00**

☐ **Ros Study No. 1,** *oak height 35″,
silver dial and trimmings, c. 1894,
8 Day, strike (E2-124).*
.... **425.00   475.00**

PARLOR SHELF

☐ **Ros Study No. 2,** *oak, height 26",
gilt dial and trimmings, c. 1894, 8
Day, strike (E2-124).*
. . . . **310.00   350.00**

☐ **Champion,** *black walnut, height
25", dial 6", c. 1890, 8 Day, strike
(E2-89).*
. . . . **300.00   340.00**
☐ **As above,** *8 Day, strike, alarm*
. . . . **300.00   350.00**

☐ **Corsair,** *black walnut, metal
ornaments, height 24", dial 6¾",
c. 1890, 8 Day, strike (E2-89).*
. . . . **250.00   280.00**

☐ **Vistula,** *wood, height 23½", dial
6", c. 1900, 8 Day, strike (E2-102).*
. . . . **190.00   220.00**

PARLOR TEAR DROP

☐ **Cuba,** *oak, 25⅞ x 12¾", dial 6",*
c. 1920, 8 Day, strike (E1-183).
. . . . **270.00   300.00**

PARLOR WALL

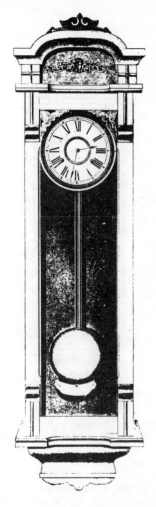

☐ **Columbian,** *oak height 48½",*
dial 8", c. 1894, 30 Daytime
(E2-124).
. . . . **750.00   850.00**

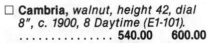

☐ **Cambria,** *walnut, height 42, dial*
8", c. 1900, 8 Daytime (E1-101).
. . . . **540.00   600.00**
☐ **As above,** *8 Day, strike*
. . . . **575.00   650.00**

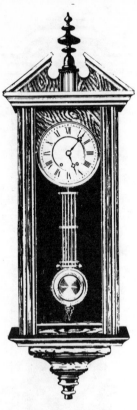

☐ **Fatinitza, Gilt,** *walnut, veneered, ebony and gilt trimmings, height 33", dial 6", c. 1900, 8 Daytime (E1-101).*
.... **490.00**   **550.00**
☐ **As above,** *8 Day, strike*
.... **540.00**   **600.00**

☐ **Faustina, Gilt,** *walnut, veneered, ebony and gilt trimmings, height 33", dial 6", c. 1900, 8 Daytime (E1-101).*
.... **540.00**   **600.00**
☐ **As above,** *8 Day, strike*
.... **575.00**   **650.00**

☐ **Jestla,** *mahogany, 17³/₄" x 7", dial 5", c. 1920, 8 Day, strike (E1-184).*
.... **85.00**   **105.00**

☐ **Madero,** *oak or mahogany, 28³/₄" x 13", dial 8", c. 1920, 8 Day, strike (E1-184).*
☐ **As above,** *oak*
.... **150.00**   **175.00**
☐ **As above,** *mahogany*
.... **225.00**   **250.00**

☐ **Marino,** *oak or mahogany, 16" x 11", dial 8", c. 1920, 8 Day, strike (E1-184).*

☐ **Mimosa,** *oak or mahogany, 26¾" x 10¾", dial 8", c. 1920, 8 Day, strike (E1-184).*
☐ **As above,** *oak*
.... **135.00   160.00**

☐ **Maywood,** *oak, 44½" x 17", dial 8", c. 1900, 8 Daytime (E1-36).*
.... **450.00   500.00**

Mirada

☐ **Mirada,** *oak or mahogany, 28¼"*
x 12", dial 8", c. 1920, 8 Day,
strike (E1-184).
☐ **As above,** *oak*
.... 135.00   160.00
☐ **As above,** *mahogany*
.... 210.00   235.00

☐ **Norseman,** *oak and walnut,*
height 47½", dial 10", c. 1900, 8
Daytime (E1-102).
☐ **As above,** *oak*
.... 575.00   650.00
☐ **As above,** *oak*
.... 625.00   700.00
☐ **As above,** *walnut*
.... 675.00   750.00
☐ **As above,** *walnut*
.... 725.00   800.00

☐ **Referee,** *oak or mahogany, 35½"*
x 16", dial 12", c. 1920 (E1-183).
☐ **As above,** *oak, 8 Daytime*
.... 270.00   300.00
☐ **As above,** *oak, 8 Daytime, strike*
.... 285.00   325.00
☐ **As above,** *oak, 8 Daytime,*
calendar
.... 310.00   350.00
☐ **As above,** *oak, 8 Daytime, strike,*
calendar
.... 335.00   375.00
☐ **As above,** *mahogany, 8 Daytime*
.... 345.00   375.00
☐ **As above,** *mahogany, 8 Daytime,*
strike
.... 360.00   400.00
☐ **As above,** *mahogany, 8 Daytime,*
calendar
.... 385.00   425.00
☐ **As above,** *mahogany, 8 Daytime,*
strike, calendar
.... 410.00   450.00

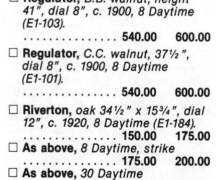

☐ **Regulator,** *B.B. walnut, height 41", dial 8", c. 1900, 8 Daytime (E1-103).*
. . . . 540.00   600.00

☐ **Regulator,** *C.C. walnut, 37½", dial 8", c. 1900, 8 Daytime (E1-101).*
. . . . 540.00   600.00

☐ **Riverton,** *oak 34½" x 15¾", dial 12", c. 1920, 8 Daytime (E1-184).*
. . . . 150.00   175.00

☐ **As above,** *8 Daytime, strike*
. . . . 175.00   200.00

☐ **As above,** *30 Daytime*
. . . . 220.00   250.00

☐ **Saracen,** *mahogany, height 49", dial 10", c. 1900, 8 Daytime (E1-102).*
. . . . 540.00   600.00

☐ **As above,** *8 Day, strike*
. . . . 575.00   650.00

☐ **Solent,** *oak, antique finish, 36¾" x 13½", dial 8", c. 1914, 8 Daytime (E2-123).*
. . . . 310.00   350.00

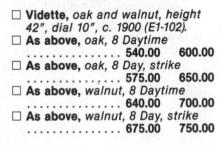

☐ **Vidette,** *oak and walnut, height 42", dial 10", c. 1900 (E1-102).*
☐ **As above,** *oak, 8 Daytime*
. . . . 540.00   600.00
☐ **As above,** *oak, 8 Day, strike*
. . . . 575.00   650.00
☐ **As above,** *walnut, 8 Daytime*
. . . . 640.00   700.00
☐ **As above,** *walnut, 8 Day, strike*
. . . . 675.00   750.00

☐ **Viking,** *oak and walnut, height 44", dial 8", c. 1900 (E1-102).*
☐ **As above,** *oak, 8 Daytime*
. . . . 540.00   600.00
☐ **As above,** *oak, 8 Day, strike*
. . . . 575.00   650.00
☐ **As above,** *walnut, 8 Daytime*
. . . . 640.00   700.00
☐ **As above,** *walnut, 8 Day, strike*
. . . . 675.00   750.00

ROUND TOP, LONG DROP

☐ **Winnipeg,** *walnut, height 35",*
dial 6", c. 1900, 8 Daytime
(E1-102).
.... 540.00   600.00
☐ **As above,** *8 Day, strike*
.... 575.00   650.00

☐ **Barometer Regulator,** *wood,*
height 37", dial 12", c. 1900, 8
Daytime (E2-93).
.... 360.00   400.00
☐ **As above,** *8 Daytime, strike*
.... 400.00   450.00

☐ **Glenor,** *mahogany or oak,*
antique finish, 36½" x 15¼",
dial 12, c. 1914, 8 Daytime,
weight (E2-123).
.... 600.00   675.00

□ **Regulator — Calendar,** *walnut veneer, solid walnut circle, height 32", c. 1900, 8 Daytime, calendar (E1-37).*
.... 310.00   350.00
□ **As above,** *8Day, strike, calendar*
.... 335.00   375.00

□ **Imperial,** *rosewood, height 32½", dial 12", c. 1900, 8 Daytime (E2-93).*
.... 310.00   350.00

□ **Regulator,** *oak, 32¼" x 17¾", dial 12", c. 1920, 8 Daytime (E1-183).*
.... 235.00   265.00
□ **As above,** *8 Daytime, strike*
.... 290.00   330.00
□ **As above,** *8 Daytime, strike, calendar*
.... 335.00   375.00

□ **Regulator,** *walnut veneer, solid walnut circle, height 32", dial 12", c. 1900, 8 Daytime (E1-37).*
.... 270.00   300.00
□ **As above,** *8 Daytime, strike*
.... 285.00   325.00

□ **Regulator — Calendar,** *wood, height 32", dial 12, c. 1900, 8 Daytime (E2-93).*
.... 270.00   300.00
□ **As above,** *8 Daytime, strike*
.... 285.00   325.00
□ **As above,** *8 Daytime, calendar*
.... 310.00   350.00
□ **As above,** *8 Day, strike, calendar*
.... 335.00   375.00

SECONDS BIT
□ **Austrian,** *oak or cherry, 48¾" x 19", dial 10", c. 1900 (E1-36).*
□ **As above,** *oak, 8 Daytime*
.... 360.00   400.00
□ **As above,** *oak, 8 Day, strike*
.... 400.00   450.00
□ **As above,** *oak, 30 Daytime*
.... 450.00   500.00
□ **As above,** *oak, 8 Daytime, weight*
.... 575.00   650.00
□ **As above,** *cherry, 8 Daytime*
.... 610.00   650.00

☐ **As above,** *cherry, 8 Day, strike*
. . . . **650.00   700.00**

☐ **As above,** *cherry, 30 Daytime*
. . . . **700.00   750.00**

☐ **As above,** *cherry, 8 Daytime, weight*
. . . . **825.00   900.00**

☐ **Cimbrian,** *oak, 44" x 17¾", dial 10", c. 1896, 30 Daytime (E2-123).*
. . . . **575.00   650.00**

☐ **As above,** *8 Daytime*
. . . . **540.00   600.00**

☐ **As above,** *8 Daytime, strike*
. . . . **490.00   550.00**

☐ **Elfrida,** *wood, 49" x 19", dial 10", c. 1896, 8 Daytime (E2-123).*
. . . . **650.00   750.00**

☐ **As above,** *8 Daytime, strike*
. . . . **700.00   800.00**

☐ **As above,** *8 Daytime, weight*
. . . . **900.00   1000.00**

☐ **As above,** *30 Day*
. . . . **800.00   900.00**

Enquirer

☐ **Enquirer,** *wood, 50½" x 19", dial 10", c. 1896, 8 Daytime (E2-123).*
. . . . **900.00   1000.00**
☐ **As above,** *8 Daytime, strike*
. . . . **950.00   1050.00**
☐ **As above,** *8 Daytime, weight*
. . . . **1100.00   1200.00**

☐ **Grecian,** *oak, 51" x 20", dial 10", c. 1900, 8 Daytime, weight (E1-36).*
. . . . **750.00   850.00**

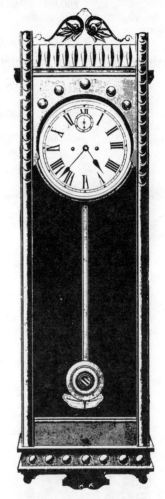

☐ **Hebe,** *oak, height 49", dial 10", c. 1894, 30 Daytime (E2-124).*
. . . . **600.00   700.00**

☐ **Gloriana,** *oak, height 42", dial 10", c. 1894, 30 Daytime (E2-124).*
. . . . **575.00   650.00**

☐ **Office No. 2,** *walnut or mahogany, height 41", dial 12", c. 1900 (E1-102).*
☐ **As above,** *mahogany, 8 Daytime, weight*
. . . . **700.00   800.00**
☐ **As above,** *walnut, 8 daytime, weight*
. . . . **750.00   850.00**

☐ **Prussian,** *oak, 51½" x 19", dial 10", c. 1896, 30 Daytime (E2-123).*
. . . . **575.00   650.00**
☐ **As above,** *8 Daytime*
. . . . **490.00   550.00**

☐ **Rutland,** *oak, 48" x 19½", dial 10", c. 1914, 8 Daytime (E2-123).*
. . . . **450.00   500.00**
☐ **As above,** *8 Daytime, strike*
. . . . **490.00   550.00**
☐ **As above,** *8 Daytime, calendar*
. . . . **540.00   600.00**
☐ **As above,** *8 Daytime, strike, calendar*
. . . . **575.00   650.00**
☐ **As above,** *30 Daytime*
. . . . **540.00   600.00**
☐ **As above,** *30 Day, calendar*
. . . . **800.00   900.00**

☐ **Standing Regulator No. 10,** *oak, walnut, mahogany, height 90", dial 12", c. 1900 (E1-104).*
☐ **As above,** *mahogany, 8 Daytime*
. . . . **2000.00   2400.00**
☐ **As above,** *oak, 8 Daytime*
. . . . **1850.00   2250.00**
☐ **As above,** *walnut, 8 Daytime*
. . . . **2050.00   2450.00**

☐ **Tampico,** *oak, 43" x 15½", dial 12", c. 1914, 8 Daytime (E2-123).*
.... 360.00   400.00

☐ **As above,** *30 Daytime*
.... 400.00   450.00

☐ **Vamoose,** *light wood, height 45", dial 10", c. 1900, 8 Daytime (E1-36).*
.... 285.00   325.00

☐ **As above,** *8 Day, strike*
.... 310.00   350.00

☐ **As above,** *8 Daytime, calendar*
.... 360.00   400.00

☐ **Watchman's Electric Clock,** *walnut, height 64", dial 12", c. 1900, 8 Daytime (E1-102).*
.... 1000.00   1100.00

☐ **Watchman's Electric Clock,** *walnut, height 64", dial 12", register 8", c. 1900 (E2-93).*

☐ **As above,** *Battery*
.... 900.00   1000.00

☐ **As above,** *weight*
.... 1200.00   1300.00

SQUARE TOP

☐ **Emperor,** *oak, height 25½", dial 12", c. 1900, 8 Daytime (E2-122).*
.... 220.00   250.00

☐ **As above,** *8 Daytime, strike*
.... 245.00   275.00

☐ **As above,** *8 Daytime, calendar*
.... 270.00   300.00

☐ **As above,** *8 Daytime, strike, calendar*
.... 285.00   325.00

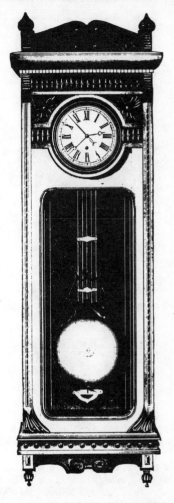

☐ **Emperior Brass Bands,** *oak, height 25½", dial 12", c. 1900, 8 Daytime (E2-122).*
.... 245.00   275.00
☐ **As above,** *8 Daytime, strike*
.... 270.00   300.00
☐ **As above,** *8 Daytime, calendar*
.... 285.00   325.00
☐ **As above,** *8 Daytime, strike, calendar*
.... 310.00   350.00

SWEEP SECOND
☐ **Giant,** *solid oak, Swiss regulator movement, sweep second, 10'3" x 3', dial 12", c. 1900, 8 Day (E1-35).*
.... 2200.00   2400.00

☐ **New York,** *oak, Swiss regulator movement, sweep second, height 7'2", dial 12", c. 1900, 8 Day (E1-35).*
.... 2200.00   2400.00

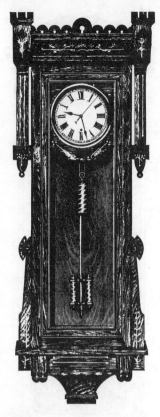

☐ **Regulator No. O,** *black walnut, oak mahogany, 84" x 31", c. 1900 (E1-104).*
☐ **As above,** *blackwalnut, 8 Daytime, weight*
.... 3200.00   3700.00
☐ **As above,** *black walnut, 8 Daytime, strike, weight*
.... 3450.00   3950.00
☐ **As above,** *oak, 8 Daytime, weight*
.... 3000.00   3500.00
☐ **As above,** *oak, 8 Daytime, strike, weight*
.... 3250.00   3750.00
☐ **As above,** *mahogany, 8 Daytime, weight*
.... 3150.00   3650.00
☐ **As above,** *mahogany, 8 Daytime, strike, weight*
.... 3400.00   3900.00

☐ **Regulator No. 00,** *oak or mahogany, wood pendulum rod, polished brass weights, height 63", dial 10", c. 1900 (E1-104).*
☐ **As above,** *oak, 8 Daytime, weight*
.... 2000.00   2200.00
☐ **As above,** *oak, 8 Daytime, sweep seconds*
.... 2250.00   2500.00
☐ **As above,** *mahogany, 8 Daytime, weight*
.... 2150.00   2350.00
☐ **As above,** *mahogany, 8 Daytime, sweep seconds*
.... 2400.00   2650.00

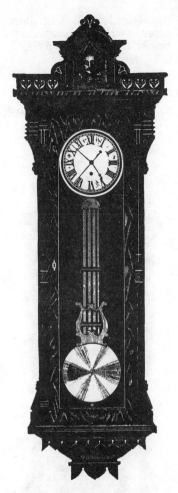

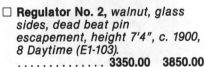

☐ **Regulator No. 2,** *walnut, glass sides, dead beat pin escapement, height 7'4", c. 1900, 8 Daytime (E1-103).*
.... 3350.00   3850.00

☐ **Regulator No. 3,** *walnut, mahogany, ash, glass sides, dead-beat pin escapement, height 7'2", c. 1900 (E1-103).*
☐ **As above,** *mahogany, 8 Daytime*
.... 3350.00   3900.00
☐ **As above,** *walnut, 8 Daytime*
.... 3400.00   3950.00
☐ **As above,** *ash, 8 Daytime*
.... 3450.00   4000.00

□ **Regulator No.8,** *walnut, glass sides, dead-beat escapement, height 10'6", c. 1900, 8 Day (E1-104).*
.... 3000.00   3500.00

□ **As above,** *8 Daytime, sweep*
.... 3500.00   4000.00

□ **Regulator No. 4,** *walnut, glass sides, dead-beat pin escapement, height 10'2½", c. 1900, 8 Daytime (E1-103).*
.... 3500.00   4000.00

□ **Regulator No. 6,** *ebony finish, hardwood polished case, white carvings, finished in gold leaf, glass sides, dead-beat, escapement, height 78", c. 1900, 8 Daytime (E1-104).*
.... 2000.00   2250.00
□ **As above,** *8 Daytime, swiss*
.... 1400.00   1600.00

□ **Regulator No. 9,** *walnut, glass sides, dead-beat pin escapement, c. 1900, 8 Daytime (E1-103).*
.... 3000.00   3500.00

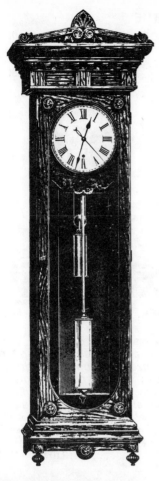

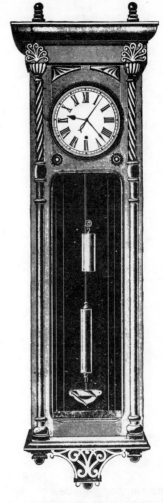

☐ **Regulator No 10,** *oak, walnut, mahogany, height 77½", dial 12", c. 1900 (E1-103).*
☐ **As above,** *walnut, 8 Daytime*
.... 2450.00 2900.00
☐ **As above,** *oak, 8 Daytime*
.... 2250.00 2700.00
☐ **As above,** *mahogany, 8 Daytime*
.... 2400.00 2850.00

☐ **St. Louis,** *oak or cherry, Swiss regulator movement, sweep second, height 6'6", dial 12", c. 1900, 8 Day (E1-35).*
☐ **As above,** *oak*
.... 1900.00 2200.00
☐ **As above,** *cherry*
.... 2150.00 2450.00

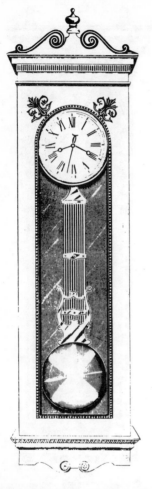

**STATUE
LARGE**

☐ **Aegean,** *black enamel or
Malachite finish, French gilt or
bronze trimmings, cathedral
gong, ivorized porcelain dial,
fancy gilt center or decorated
porcelain dial, Empire sash and
heavy beveled glass, 20" x 12¼",
dial 4", c. 1900, 8 Day, strike
(E2-110).*
. . . . 210.00   240.00

☐ **Thornton,** *hanging, oak or cherry,
Swiss regulator movement,
sweep second, 74" x 22", c. 1900,
8 Day (E1-36).*
☐ **As above,** *oak*
. . . . 1600.00   1800.00
☐ **As above,** *cherry*
. . . . 1850.00   2050.00

☐ **Carthage,** *gilt or bronze, empire sash, ivorized porcelain dial, visible escapement, 20″ x 20″, dial 6″, c. 1900, 8 Day, strike (E2-127).*
.... 275.00   315.00

☐ **Don Juan,** *bronze and silver, visible escapement, height 21″, c. 1900, 8 Day, strike (E1-112).*
.... 450.00   500.00

☐ **Norman,** *gilt or bronze, empire sash, ivorized porcelain dial, visible escapement, 20½″ x 20″, dial 6″, c. 1900, 8 Day, strike (E2-127).*
.... 285.00   325.00

☐ **Philip,** *bronze and silver, visible escapement, height 23″, c. 1900, 8 Day, strike (E1-112).*
.... 375.00   425.00

☐ **Lulli,** *bronze and silver, visible escapement, height 21″, base 17¼″, c. 1900, 8 Day, strike (E1-112).*
.... 375.00   425.00

☐ **Roman,** *gilt or bronze, empire sash, ivorized porcelain dial, visible escapement, 20" x 20", dial 6", c. 1900, 8 Day, strike (E2-127).*
. . . . 275.00   315.00

☐ **Saxon,** *gilt or bronze, empire sash, ivorized porcelain dial, visible escapement, 20" x 20", dial 6", c. 1900, 8 Day, strike (E2-127).*
. . . . 275.00   315.00

☐ **Spartan,** *antique brass or barbadiene, ivorized dial, height 24", dial 4½", c. 1900, 15 Day, strike (E1-101).*
. . . . 750.00   850.00

SMALL

☐ **Benvenuto Cellini,** *gilt or bronze, empire sash, ivorized porcelain dial, visible escapement, 16" x 20", dial 6", c. 1900, 8 Day, strike (E2-127).*
. . . . 255.00   285.00

☐ **Bernard Palissy,** *gilt or bronze, empire sash, ivorized porcelain dial, visible escapement, 16" x 20", dial 6", c. 1900, 8 Day, strike (E2-127).*
. . . . 255.00   285.00

☐ **Brennus,** *bronze or gold finish, with black or colored marbleized base, empire sash, porcelain dial, visible escapement, 16" x 26", dial 6", c. 1900, 8 Day, strike (E1-41).*
. . . . 255.00   285.00

☐ **Carthage,** *bronze and silver, visible escapement, height 19¼", base 17", c. 1900, 8 Day, strike (E1-112).*
. . . . 400.00   450.00

☐ **Clotho,** *gilt or bronze, empire sash, ivorized porcelain dial, visible escapement, 16" x 20", dial 6", c. 1900, 8 Day, strike (E2-126).*
. . . . 245.00   275.00

☐ **Fame,** *gilt or bronze, empire sash, ivorized porcelain dial, visible escapement, 16" x 20", dial 6", c. 1900, 8 Day, strike (E2-127).*
.... 255.00   285.00

☐ **Fisher Boy,** *bronze and silver, visible escapement, height 28", base 17", c. 1900, 8 Day, strike (E1-112).*
.... 490.00   550.00

☐ **Flower Girl,** *gilt or bronze, empire sash, ivorized porcelain dial, visible escapement, 16" x 20", dial 6", c. 1900, 8 Day, strike (E2-126).*
.... 225.00   285.00

☐ **Flute Player,** *gilt or bronze, empire sash, ivorized porcelain*

dial, visible escapement, 16" x 20", dial 6", c. 1900, 8 Day, strike (E2-126).
.... 255.00   285.00

☐ **Horse,** *gilt or bronze, empire sash, ivorized porcelain dial, visible escapement, 16" x 20", dial 6", c. 1900, 8 Day, strike (E2-126).*
.... 255.00   285.00

☐ **Hunter And Dog,** *bronze and silver, visible escapement, height 15½", c. 1900, 8 Day, strike (E1-112).*
.... 425.00   475.00

Infantry

☐ **Infantry,** *bronze and silver, visible escapement, height 20", base 17", c. 1900, 8 Day, strike (E1-112).* 360.00   400.00

☐ **Mignon,** *bronze and silver, visible escapement, height 19¼", base 17", c. 1900, 8 Day, strike (E1-112).* 335.00   375.00

☐ **Ivanhoe,** *gilt or bronze, empire sash, ivorized porcelain dial, visible escapement, 16" x 20", dial 6", c. 1900, 8 Day, strike (E2-127).* 255.00   285.00

☐ **Octavius,** *gilt or bronze, empire sash, ivorized porcelain dial, visible escapement, 16" x 20", dial 6", c. 1900, 8 Day, strike (E2-128).* 255.00   285.00

☐ **Knight,** *gilt or bronze, empire sash, ivorized porcelain dial, visible escapement, 17" x 20", dial 6", c. 1900, 8 Day, strike (E2-127).* 270.00   300.00

☐ **Orpheus,** *satin gold or bronze, with black or green enameled iron base, cathedral gong, empire sash, heavy beveled glass, ivorized porcelain dial with gilt center, or decorated porcelain dial, 16" x 12½", dial 3", c. 1900, 8 Day, strike (E2-110).* 210.00   240.00

☐ **Poetry,** *gilt or bronze, empire sash, ivorized porcelain dial, visible escapement, 16" x 20", dial 6", c. 1900, 8 Day, strike (E2-126).* 265.00   295.00

WATCH

☐ **Rebecca,** *bronze and silver,*
visible escapement, height 19",
base 17", c. 1900, 8 Day, strike
(E1-112).
.... **375.00** **425.00**

☐ **Roman,** *bronze or gold finish,*
with black or colored marbleized
base, empire sash, porcelain
dial, visible escapement, 16" x
20", dial 6", c. 1900, 8 Day, strike
(E1-41).
.... **275.00** **315.00**

☐ **Sir Christopher,** *bronze and*
silver, visible escapement, height
15⅝", base 16¼", c. 1900, 8 Day,
strike (E1-112).
.... **360.00** **400.00**

☐ **Tempest,** *satin gold or bronze,*
cathedral gong, empire sash,
heavy beveled glass, ivorized
porcelain dial with gilt center, or
decorated porcelain dial, 19¼" x
11¼", dial 3", c. 1900, 8 Day, ½
hour strike (E2-110).
.... **210.00** **240.00**

☐ **Sting,** *nickel or silver, size 3", c.*
1900 (E2-111).
.... **70.00** **85.00**

G.B. OWEN

George B. Owen worked for the
Gilbert Clock Company in Winsted as
a business manager for many years.
A case stylist in his own right, Owen
maintained a private business in Connecticut and New York.

CALENDAR

☐ **Round Top Shelf,** *13½" x 10",*
dial 4½", 8 Day, strike
(M429-134).
.... **800.00** **900.00**

J.I. PEATFIELD

CALENDAR

☐ **Calendar Clock,** *(M519-159).*
.... **2500.00** **2800.00**

PRENTISS IMPROVEMENT CLOCK COMPANY

A small eastern firm, Prentiss manufactured calendar clocks. It was one of several companies begun with the idea of producing a new calendar design, distinctive of the particular company. Their movements were usually bought in Connecticut.

CALENDAR

☐ **Empire,** *dial 10", 2 spring, 80 beat pendulum, 8 Day, (E2-87, M513-157).*
.... 1350.00 1800.00
☐ **As above,** *15 Day.*
.... 1440.00 1890.00
☐ **As above,** *30 Day.*
.... 1485.00 1935.00
☐ **As above,** *60 Day.*
.... 1530.00 1980.00
☐ **As above,** *90 Day.*
.... 1620.00 2070.00

☐ **Office Gallery,** *28" x 37", dial 14", 2 spring, 120 beat pendulum, rare, 8 Day (E2-87, M515-157).*
.... 1800.00 1980.00
☐ **As above,** *15 Day.*
.... 1890.00 2070.00
☐ **As above,** *60 Day.*
.... 1980.00 2160.00

☐ **Standard,** *47" x 16", dial 12", 2 spring, 72 beat pendulum, 15 Day (E2-87, M514-157).*
.... 1800.00 2160.00
☐ **As above,** *30 Day.*
.... 1800.00 2160.00
☐ **As above,** *60 Day.*
.... 1890.00 2250.00
☐ **As above,** *90 Day.*
.... 1980.00 2430.00

☐ **Regulator,** *62" x 18", dial 14", 2 spring, 60 beat pendulum, 15 Day (E2-87, M512-156).*
.... 1890.00 2520.00
☐ **As above,** *30 Day.*
.... 2250.00 2500.00
☐ **As above,** *60 Day.*
.... 2520.00 2880.00
☐ **As above,** *90 Day.*
.... 2700.00 3150.00

☐ **Regulator,** *62" x 18", dial 14", 2 spring, beats seconds, 60 Day (E2-86).*
.... 2250.00 2700.00
☐ **As above,** *90 Day.*
.... 2430.00 2880.00

RUSSELL & JONES

The Russell & Jones Clock Company, bought out the Massachusetts business of the famous Terry family. It lasted from 1888, (the time of their takeover) until it failed seven years before the turn of the century.

CALENDAR

☐ **Beacon,** *round nickel, lever, dial 4", 1 Day, alarm, simple calendar (E1-84).*
.... 100.00 125.00

☐ **Beacon,** *round nickel, lever, dial 4", 1 Day, simple calendar (E1-84).*
.... 110.00   135.00

☐ **8" Octagon Top,** *short drop, height 19", spring, 8 Day, simple calendar (E1-88).*
.... 300.00   400.00

☐ **10" Octagon Top,** *short drop, height 21", spring, 8 Day, simple calendar (E1-88).*
.... 350.00   450.00

☐ **12" Octagon Top,** *long drop, height 31", spring, 8 Day, simple calendar (E1-89).*
.... 400.00   500.00

JOSEPH K. SEEM DIAL COMPANY

CALENDAR

☐ **Steeple Shelf,** *E. Ingraham Clock, 20" x 11", spring, 8 Day (M312-102).*
.... 400.00   425.00

☐ **Cottage Shelf,** *Ansonia Clock, 13½" x 10½", dial 5", spring, 1 Day, strike (M313-102).*
.... 450.00   500.00

SEEM CALENDAR

CALENDAR

☐ **Seem Mechanism,** *fitted to Seth Thomas, column flat, top clock, 30 hour strike, weight (M321-104).*
.... 2250.00   2500.00

SESSIONS CLOCK COMPANY

Originally the E.N. Welch Manufacturing Company, William Sessions acquired the firm by buying up stock at a gradual rate, and waiting until the financial difficulties of the former owners became so great they were forced to sell.

A father and son operation, the Sessions Clock Company began manufacturing around the turn of the century. They continued to put out many of the Welch classics, such as the black mantel and oak cased kitchen clock. During the depression the firm suffered difficulties, but succeeded in switching over to a line of popular electric clocks. The company prospered until the end of the 1950's when it was sold to an electronics corporation and subsequently to a metal goods company.

Meanwhile, a descendant of the original Sessions pair succeeded in opening a clock company in legendary Bristol, although he eventually relocated in Farmington.

CALENDAR

☐ **Eclipse Regulator,** *square cornered rectangle with trim, 38" x 17", dial 11", spring, 8 Day, simple calendar (M230-79).*
.... **325.00   400.00**

☐ **Gentry Octagon Top,** *short drop, height 24", dial 12", spring, 8 Day, simple calendar (E1-175).*
.... **325.00   475.00**

☐ **Regulator "E",** *square cornered rectangle with trim, 38½" x 17", dial 12", spring, 8 Day, simple calendar (E1-175).*
.... **400.00   550.00**

☐ **Star Pointer Regulator Octagon Top,** *long drop, height 32", dial 12", spring, 8 Day, simple calendar (E1-176).*
.... **350.00   500.00**

SETH THOMAS CLOCK COMPANY

In the early 1800's Seth Thomas was thought to be conservative and C. Jerome wrote that he did not change his clocks until forced to do so to keep his customers. This probably helped the company weather some of the depressions of the 1800's and resulted in very long runs of production for many models of Seth Thomas clocks. He produced wood works clocks until 1844 or 45, and was probably one of the last major makers to abandon the wood works.

During this period all his labels were of the Plymouth Hollow, Connecticut location, except for the clocks sold through southern outlets that had the following labels: Couch, Stowe and Company, Rocksprings, Tennessee; Reeves and Huson, Fayetteville, North Carolina; Case, Dye, Wadsworth and Company, Savannah, Georgia. These are rare labels much desired by collectors.

Probably prompted by lagging sales after the panic of 1837 and the extensive crop failures of 1835, 1837 and 1838, Chauncey Jerome had his brother, Noble, develop and patent the 30 hour brass movement that could be made much cheaper than wood works, and after 1845 Seth Thomas switched to the brass works.

In 1850 the Seth Thomas factory was reported to have a production of 24,000 clocks annually, with a total value that averaged about $2.50 each.

In 1852 Seth Thomas built a brass rolling mill, which he then incorporated in 1853 as a "joint stock company." That same year, because (or so an old article reported) he was beginning to feel the effects of old age, he incorporated his clock company. His death followed six years later in 1859. Up to this time his company had produced only weight movements in about a half dozen styles, although they had sold a very few of their clocks with brass spring movements purchased from Terry and Andrews. Immediately after his death the company began to put many new models into production.

In 1860 they started the production of small spring driven clocks, and in that year they were reported to have an annual production of 40,000 clocks, with a total value that averaged about $3.00 each. That year they also started the production of some regulators, including the No. 2, which saw a production run of 90 years and is being extensively reproduced at the present time. The production of calendars was started in 1862, and the 1876 Andrews improvement made the Perpetual Calendar such a popular item that by 1888 15 different styles of calendar clocks were offered. The No. 3 Parlor Calendar, introduced in 1868, was produced until 1917, giving it a production run of about 49 years.

In 1865 the Connecticut city name of Plymouth Hollow was changed to Thomaston, and although it was not officially incorporated as such until 1875, all Seth Thomas clock labels immediately showed Thomaston, giving collectors an immediate quick and easy division point in determining the age of all Seth Thomas clocks. In 1865 Seth Thomas became associated with the sales agency, American Clock Company, as was E.N. Welch, Welch Spring and Company, New Haven Clock Company, and Seth Thomas' Sons and Company. Seth Thomas' Sons and Company was incorporated in 1865 to make Marine or Lever movements, and by 1870 was producing 15,887 Marine movements annually, with a total value that averaged about $4.25 each. In 1879 this company was consolidated with Seth Thomas Clock Company. In its 14 years of existence this company made high quality movements and clocks, and the statue clocks made by this company are prized by collectors today.

By 1870 Seth Thomas Company had an annual production of 135,000 clocks, with a total value that averaged about $3.50 each. In 1931 the Seth Thomas Company became a division of General Time Instruments Corporation, later known as General Time Corporation.

By 1932 leadership of Seth Thomas passed out of the Thomas family for the first time, ending a long reign of producing clocks that are probably more prized today than at that time. Few of the clocks produced after this time are desired by collectors. The name "Seth Thomas" is still seen on clocks today, keeping the public aware of the name and perhaps being a part of the reason why some very common clocks with the name Seth Thomas are prized by collectors, and thus command good prices.

This account gives information that allows the general determining of the age of Seth Thomas clocks. Very specific dating of the early models can be accomplished by checking the address of the printer, Elihu Geer of Hartford. This name and the address is usually found in the lower right-hand corner of the label. Unfortunately, this part of the label is usually one of the first parts to wear off. The addresses, and dates at each, for Elihu Greer are:

26½	State Street	1839-1844
26	State Street	1845-1846
1	State Street	1847-1849
10	State Street	1850-1855
16	State Street	1856-1864
18	State Street	1865-?

This printer was used by Seth Thomas until 1863, after which their labels were printed by Francis and Loutrel of New York City. Since Elihu Geer also printed labels for other companies, this table is useful in dating many clocks. The approximate years of production of various case styles of clocks are as follows:

MAJOR YEARS OF PRODUCTION

Steeple	1879-1917
Regulators	1860-1950
No. 1	1860-1890
	Tablet dropped 1879
No. 2	1860-1950
	Seconds Bit adopted 1879, Tablet dropped 1880, being extensively reproduced today.
No. 3	1863-1879
	Original model as 8D Reg.
	1879-1917 As No. 3
	1928-1930 As No. 3
No. 10	1879-1909
No. 12	1880-1911 Mercury pendulum.
No. 14	1880-1911 Mercury pendulum.
No. 15	1880-1911 Mercury pendulum.
Ships Bell	1884-1941
Brass Movement	
Hall Clocks	1888-1911 (in 1902 had 26 models)
Walnut Kitchen	1884-1909
Oak Kitchen	1890-1915
Marble	1887-1895
Black Iron	1892-1895
Black Wood	1890-1917
Porcelain	1898-1917
Tambours	1904-Present (Became popular 1914, and was most popular model 1920's-30's).
Sonora Chimes	After 1914
Banjos	1924-probably late 40's.
Electric	1928-Present
Calendars	1862-1917
No. 1 Office	1863-1884
No. 2 Office	1863-1879
No. 3 Office	1866-1870 or 72
No. 4 Office	1868-1879
No. 1 Parlor	1866-1887
No. 3 Parlor	1868-1917

Seth Thomas Clocks normally have just that on the label, "Seth Thomas," even though the company name was Seth Thomas Company until the incorporation in 1863, and Seth Thomas Clock Company afterwards. Therefore, the other information on the label and the production information above must be used to estimate the age of these clocks.

ALARMS

FANCY

☐ **Advance,** *black adamantine finish, green marbleized top and base mouldings, gold plated feet and ornaments, height 11", dial 4½", c. 1904, 8 Day, alarm (E1-124).*
.... **45.00   60.00**

☐ **As above,** *8 Day, strike, alarm.*
.... **60.00   75.00**

☐ **Elk Lever Alarm,** *nickel dial 4½", c. 1888, 1 Day, alarm (E1-33).*
.... **65.00   80.00**

☐ **Grand,** *metal case and dial, verde antique base, gun metal top and hands, gold dial, silver center and raised black numerals and minute dots, height 10",*

base 7½", gold dial 7", c. 1904, 8
Day, alarm (E1-124).
.... 60.00   75.00

☐ **Lodge Lever,** *nickel frame and
sides, metal case, gold gilt front,
height 7", dial 3", c. 1888, 1 Day
(E1-33).*
.... 65.00   80.00
☐ **As above,** *1 Day, strike.*
.... 85.00   105.00
☐ **As above,** *1 Day, alarm.*
.... 80.00   95.00

☐ **"Nutmeg " Lever,** *brass or nickel,
c. 1880 (E1-55).*
.... 40.00   50.00

☐ **Progress,** *quartered oak and
mahogany, highly finished and
polished, height 12½", dial 4½",
c. 1904, 8 Day, alarm (E1-124).*
.... 40.00   50.00
☐ **As above,** *8 Day, strike, alarm.*
.... 50.00   65.00

☐ **Bee,** *nickel, dial 2", c. 1888, 1
Day (E1-33).*
.... 40.00   50.00
☐ **As above,** *1 Day, alarm.*
.... 50.00   65.00

☐ **Student Lever,** *nickel plated
frame, sides and bell, c. 1888, 1
Day, alarm (E1-33).*
.... 75.00   90.00

ROUND

☐ **Anvil Lever,** *nickel, c. 1888, 1 Day,
alarm (E1-33).*
.... 150.00   175.00

☐ **Echo,** *nickel, dial 4½", c. 1888, 1
Day, alarm (E1-33).*
.... 25.00   35.00
☐ **As above,** *1 Day.*
.... 20.00   30.00

☐ **No. 1,** *nickel or gilt, width 2", c.
1888, 30 hour (E1-33).*
.... 35.00   45.00

☐ **No. 2,** *nickel or gilt, width 2", c.
1888, 30 hour, calendar (E1-33).*
.... 60.00   75.00

CABINET

☐ **Austin,** *oak, metal ornaments at head and base, porcelain dial, height 15½", dial 4½", c. 1890, 8 Day, strike, spring (E1-50).*
.... **175.00   200.00**
☐ **As above,** *walnut, 8 Day, strike, spring.*
.... **200.00   225.00**
☐ **As above,** *cherry, 8 Day, strike, spring.*
.... **200.00   225.00**

☐ **Bee,** *oak, marqueterie panel, height 14", c. 1880, 15 Day, strike (E1-56).*
.... **150.00   175.00**
☐ **As above,** *mahogany, 15 Day, strike.*
.... **175.00   200.00**
☐ **As above,** *walnut, 15 Day, strike.*
.... **175.00   200.00**

☐ **Carson,** *sheet brass case, nickeled body, gold gilt ornaments at head and base, bronzed alligator panel, porcelain dial, French sash with beveled glass, height 14½", dial 4½", c. 1920, 8 Day, strike (E1-139).*
.... **125.00   150.00**

☐ **Cordova,** *mahogany, metal ornaments, old brass finish, porcelain dial, French sash, beveled glass, height 10¾", base 9¾", dial 4", c. 1900, 8 Day, strike (E2-129).*
.... **130.00   155.00**
☐ **As above,** *golden oak.*
.... **155.00   180.00**

☐ **Dallas,** *oak, metal ornaments at base, porcelain dial, height 13", dial 4½", c. 1880, 8 Day, strike, spring (E1-56).*
.... **175.00   200.00**
☐ **As above,** *walnut, 8 Day, strike, spring.*
.... **200.00   225.00**
☐ **As above,** *cherry, 8 Day, strike, spring.*
.... **200.00   225.00**

☐ **Hotel,** *mahogany, height 18", dial 8", c. 1900, 8 Day, strike (E2-129).*
.... **150.00   175.00**
☐ **As above,** *old oak, 8 Day, strike.*
.... **125.00   150.00**

☐ **Kent,** *dark oak, solid sash with beveled glass, height 14½, dial 5", c. 1900, 8 Day, strike (E2-129).*
.... **135.00   160.00**

☐ **Mentone,** *oak, metal ornaments in bronze finish, cream porcelain dial, French sash with beveled glass, height 11¼", base 10", dial 4", 8 Day, strike (E2-136).*
.... 135.00   160.00
☐ **As above,** *mahogany 8 Day, strike.*
.... 160.00   185.00

☐ **Milan,** *oak, cream porcelain dial, French sash, beveled glass, height 10¼", base 9½", dial 4", c. 1900, 8 Day, strike (E2-129).*
.... 135.00   160.00
☐ **As above,** *mahogany, 8 Day, strike.*
.... 160.00   185.00

☐ **Minster,** *oak, height 15½", c. 1880, 15 Day, strike (E1-56).*
.... 160.00   185.00
☐ **As above,** *mahogany, 15 Day, strike.*
.... 185.00   210.00
☐ **As above,** *walnut, 15 Day, strike.*
.... 185.00   210.00

☐ **No. 800,** *walnut case with ash beryl veneers, height 11½", base 13", c. 1920, 8 Day, strike (E1-139).*
.... 125.00   145.00
☐ **As above,** *oak case with French walnut veneers, old oak finish, 8 Day, strike.*
.... 100.00   120.00

☐ **Normandy,** *walnut, height 15", c. 1880, 15 Day, strike (E1-56).*
.... 150.00   175.00
☐ **As above,** *ash, 15 Day, strike.*
.... 175.00   200.00

☐ **Portland,** *walnut, height 17", dial 5", dial 5", c. 1920, 8 Day, strike (E1-139).*
.... 115.00   120.00
☐ **As above,** *oak.*
.... 90.00   100.00

☐ **Selma,** *walnut, height 16½", dial 5", c. 1920, 8 Day, strike (E1-139).*
.... 115.00   120.00
☐ **As above,** *old oak.*
.... 90.00   100.00

☐ **Seville,** *mahogany, metal ornaments in bronze finish, cream porcelain dial, French sash with beveled glass, height 11¼", base 10", dial 4", c. 1910, 8 Day, strike (E2-136).*
.... 160.00   185.00
☐ **As above,** *oak, 8 Day, strike.*
.... 135.00   160.00

CALENDAR

☐ **Dixie Victorian Shelf,** *height 28", dial 8", 8 Day, strike, simple calendar (E2-142).*
.... 575.00   650.00

☐ **Drop Octagon,** *spring, 24" x 16", dial 12", 8 Day, simple calendar (M58-24).*
.... 325.00   425.00

☐ **Empire Shelf,** *Plymouth Hollow label, 30" x 16½", 8 Day, strike (E1-61, M19-12).*
.... 800.00   900.00

☐ **Office No. 3,** *peanut, two springs, 23½" x 11", time dial 5", calendar dial 7", 8 Day (E1-61, M21-13).*

.... **3050.00   3650.00**

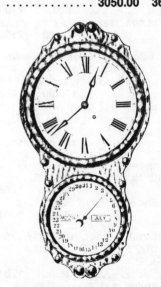

☐ **Office No. 1,** *40" x 19½", time dial 12", calendar dial 14", 8 Day (E1-51, M11-10).*

.... **1600.00   1800.00**

☐ **Office No. 2,** *42½" x 20½", dials 14", 8 Day (E1-52, M14-10).*

.... **1200.00   1500.00**

☐ **Office No. 4,** *spring, 28" x 15", time dial 12", calendar dial 7", 8 Day (E1-51, M23-13).*

.... **950.00   1050.00**

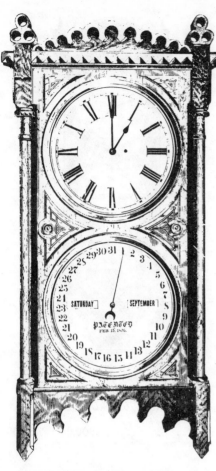

☐ **Office Calendar No. 6,** *spring,*
height 21", dial 10", 8 Day.
. . . . **2200.00   2900.00**

☐ **Office Calendar No. 5,** *50" x 21",*
dials 14", 8 Day (E1-51, M47-21).
. . . . **3000.00   3500.00**

Office Calendar No. 8

☐ **Office Calendar No. 8,** *height 66", dials 14", 8 Day (E1-49, M51-22).*
. . . . 3250.00   3750.00

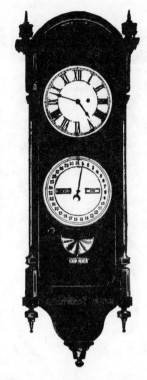

☐ **Office Calendar No. 10,** *height 49", dials 10", 8 Day (E1-49, M53-22).*
. . . . 1800.00   2450.00

☐ **Office Calendar No. 9,** *height 68", dials 14", 8 Day (E1-49, M52-22).*
. . . . 2000.00   2500.00

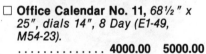

☐ **Office Calendar No. 11,** *68½" x 25", dials 14", 8 Day (E1-49, M54-23).*
.... 4000.00 5000.00

☐ **Office Calendar No. 12,** *48" x 20", dials 10", 8 Day (E1-49, M56-24).*
.... 1800.00 2000.00

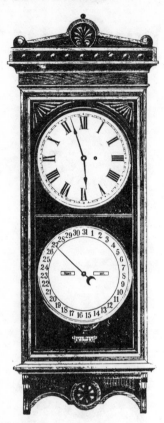

☐ **12″ Octagon Top Short Drop,** *height 23½″, 8 Day, strike, simple calendar (E1-143).*
. . . . **300.00   375.00**

☐ **Office Calendar No. 13,** *height 49″, dials 12″, 8 Day (E1-49, M57-24).*
. . . . **1800.00   2200.00**

☐ **12″ Octagon Top Short Drop,** *height 23½″, 8 Day, strike, simple calendar (E1-32).*
. . . . **325.00   400.00**

No. 6

No. 11

No. 10

☐ **Parlor Calendar No. 6,** *spring, 27" x 15", dials 7½", 8 Day, strike (E1-49, M39-19).*
. . . . **900.00   1000.00**

☐ **Parlor Calendar No. 10,** *36" x 24", dials 10", 8 Day, strike (E1-49, M43-20).*
. . . . **2100.00   2500.00**

☐ **Parlor Calendar No. 11,** *spring, 30" x 16", dials 7½", 8 Day, strike (E1-49, M45-20).*
. . . . **1450.00   1600.00**

☐ **Parlor No. 1,** *new, 33" x 15",*
dials 10", 8 Day, strike (M28-15).
.... **950.00   1050.00**

☐ **Parlor No. 2.**
.... **1000.00   1100.00**

☐ **Parlor No. 3,** *spring, 27" x 14",*
dials 7½", 8 Day, strike (E1-51,
M31-16).
.... **800.00   975.00**

☐ **Parlor No. 4,** *spring, 24" x 15½",*
dials 7½", 8 Day, strike (E1-51,
M33-16).
.... **900.00   1175.00**

☐ **Parlor No. 5,** *spring, 20" x 12¾",*
dials 7½", 8 Day, strike (E1-54,
M36-18).
.... **700.00   800.00**

☐ **Parlor Shelf,** *spring, 29½" x 18",*
dials 7½", 8 Day, strike (M42-19).
.... **1750.00   2000.00**

☐ **Parlor Shelf No. 8.**
.... **1200.00   1400.00**

☐ **Parlor Shelf No. 9.**
.... **1400.00   1600.00**

☐ **8" Round Top Long Drop,** *8 Day,*
strike, simple calendar.
.... **300.00   375.00**

☐ **Shelf Double Dial,** *Plymouth*
Hollow label, rosewood, octagon
dial, openings in door, 30" x
18½", 8 Day, strike (M7-9).
.... **1500.00   1650.00**

CARRIAGE

☐ **Artist Lever,** *nickel plated frame and glass sides, gold gilt handle, c. 1888, 1 Day, alarm (E1-33).*
. . . . 70.00   85.00
☐ **As above,** *1 Day, strike.*
. . . . 75.00   90.00

☐ **Joker Lever,** *nickel frame and glass sides, gold gilt front and handle, dial 3", c. 1888, 1 Day, alarm (E1-33).*
. . . . 70.00   85.00
☐ **As above,** *1 Day, strike.*
. . . . 75.00   90.00

CONNECTICUT SHELF

ARCH TOP

☐ **Arch top,** *wood, height 16", c. 1875, 8 Day, strike, spring (E1-54).*
. . . . 160.00   185.00

☐ **Cincinnati,** *wood, height 17", c. 1875, 8 Day, strike, spring (E1-53).*
. . . . 175.00   200.00

COLUMN

☐ **Chicago,** *wood, height 17", c. 1875, 8 Day, strike, spring (E1-53).*
. . . . 120.00   145.00

☐ **Column,** *wood, height 16", c. 1875, 30 hour, strike, spring (E1-53).*
. . . . 115.00   140.00
☐ **As above,** *8 Day, strike, spring*
. . . . 150.00   175.00

☐ **Column,** *walnut veneer, height 25", c. 1888, 1 Day, strike, weight (E1-27).*
. . . . 130.00   155.00
☐ **As above,** *8 Day, strike, weight*
. . . . 195.00   225.00
☐ **As above,** *rosewood, 1 Day, strike, weight*
. . . . 155.00   180.00
☐ **As above,** *rosewood, 8 Day, strike, weight*
. . . . 210.00   250.00

☐ **Column,** *walnut veneer, polished rosewood shell or gilt columns, height 25", dial 7½", c. 1920, 1 Day, strike, weight (E1-139).*
. . . . 105.00   125.00
☐ **As above,** *8 Day, strike, weight*
. . . . 170.00   195.00

☐ **As above,** *rosewood, 1 Day, strike, weight*
.... **125.00   150.00**

☐ **As above,** *rosewood, 8 Day, strike, weight*
.... **195.00   220.00**

☐ **Rosewood,** *gilt column, rosewood, height 25", c. 1875, 30 hour, strike, weight).*
.... **140.00   165.00**

☐ **As above,** *8 Day, strike, weight*
.... **195.00   225.00**

☐ **Rosewood,** *shell column, wood, height 25", c. 1875, 30 hour, strike, weight (E1-53).*
.... **195.00   225.00**

☐ **As above,** *8 Day, strike, weight*
.... **220.00   250.00**

☐ **St. Louis,** *wood, height 15½", c. 1875, 30 hour, strike, spring (E1-53).*
.... **150.00   175.00**

☐ **As above,** *8 Day, strike, spring*
.... **185.00   215.00**

COTTAGE

☐ **Cottage,** *wood, height 9", c. 1880, 8 Day (E1-55).*
.... **125.00   150.00**

☐ **As above,** *30 hour,*
.... **105.00   125.00**

☐ **Cottage,** *extra, wood, height 15",
c. 1875, 8 Day or 30 hour, strike,
spring (E1-54).*
.... **70.00   85.00**

EMPIRE

☐ **Franklin,** *mahogany, gold gilt
columns, hand carved scroll at
head, cathedral bell, dial 10", c.
1912, 8 Day, strike, weight
(E2-143).*
.... **400.00   450.00**

☐ **Large Rosewood,** *shell column,
rosewood, height 32", c. 1875, 8
Day, strike, weight (E1-53).*
.... **310.00   350.00**

OCTAGON TOP

☐ **Large Rosewood,** *gilt column,
rosewood, height 32", c. 1875, 8
Day, strike, weight (E1-53).*
.... **310.00   350.00**

☐ **Nashville,** *V.P., wood, height 16",
c. 1875, 8 Day, strike, spring
(E1-54).*
.... **125.00   150.00**

☐ **As above,** *30 hour, simple spring*
.... **100.00   120.00**

☐ **Octagon Top,** *wood, height 9", c. 1880, 1 Day (E1-55) (E1-147).*
.... **105.00   125.00**

O.G. AND O.O.G.

☐ **O.G.,** *wood, height 25" and 29½", c. 1894, 1 Day, strike, weight (E1-143).*
.... **130.00   155.00**

☐ **O.G.,** *wood, height 25", c. 1875, 30 hour, strike, weight, Plymouth Hollow (E1-53).*
.... **135.00   160.00**

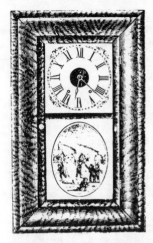

☐ **O.O.G.,** *wood, height 25", c. 1875, 8 Day, strike, weight, Thomaston (E1-53).*
.... **105.00   130.00**

☐ **Round Band,** *wood, height 17", c. 1888, 1 Day, strike, spring (E1-27).*
.... **90.00   110.00**

REPRODUCTIONS

☐ **Continental,** *mahogany case, brass or wood tips, 32" x 17½", dial 10", c. 1910, 8 Day, strike, spring (E2-142).*
.... 220.00   250.00

☐ **Plymouth,** *mahogany, 17" x 9¼", decorated dial 5", c. 1926, 8 Day, strike (E2-141).*
.... 210.00   240.00

☐ **Plymouth,** *mahogany, colored tablet, mahogany tips, 24" x 12", dial 6", c. 1912, 8 Day, strike (E2-133).*
.... 125.00   150.00

☐ **Salem,** *mahogany, 13" x 9¼", decorated dial 5", c. 1926, 8 Day, strike (E2-141).*
.... 105.00   125.00

☐ **Sharon,** *mahogany, 14¼" x 9¼", decorated dial 5", c. 1926, 8 Day, strike (E2-141).*
.... 140.00   165.00

ROUND TOP

☐ **Cabinet,** *wood, height 9½", c. 1880, 8 Day (E1-55).*
.... 125.00   150.00

☐ **As above,** *30 hour, strike*
.... 105.00   130.00

☐ **Chicago,** *V.P., wood, height 17", c. 1875, 8 Day, strike, spring (E1-54).*
.... 105.00   130.00

☐ **Louisville,** *V.P., wood, height 22", c. 1875, 8 Day, strike, spring (E1-54).*
.... 195.00   225.00

☐ **Tudor No. 1,** *wood, height 16", c. 1880, 8 Day, strike, spring (E1-55).*
.... 125.00   150.00

☐ **Tudor No. 3,** *wood, height 12", c. 1880, 8 Day, strike, spring (E1-55).*
.... 125.00   150.00

SPLIT TOP

☐ **Albert,** *wood, height 16½", c. 1894, 1 Day, strike, spring (E1-143).*
.... 70.00   85.00

☐ **As above,** *8 Day, strike, spring*
.... 85.00   105.00

☐ **New Orleans,** *V.P., wood, height 16", c. 1875, 8 Day, strike, spring (E1-54).*
.... 150.00   175.00

☐ **As above,** *30 hour, strike, spring*
.... **125.00** **150.00**

☐ **Victoria,** *wood, height 15½ ", c.
1875, 8 Day or 30 hour, strike,
spring (E1-54).*
.... **70.00** **85.00**

STEEPLE

☐ **Sharp Gothic,** *wood, height 21 ",
c. 1894, 1 Day, strike, spring
(E1-143).*
.... **90.00** **110.00**
☐ **As above,** *8 Day, strike, spring*
.... **120.00** **145.00**

CRYSTAL REGULATORS

☐ **Cupid Empire,** *bronze art
nouveau finish, height 16¾ ", c.
1920, 15 Day (E1-129).*
.... **700.00** **775.00**

☐ **Emperor,** *rich gold and bronze art
nouveau finish, cathedral bell,
height 16¾ ", base 14½ ",
porcelain dial 3", c. 1910, 15 Day,
strike (E2-140).*
.... **575.00** **650.00**

☐ **Empire No. 0,** *polished gold
finish, height 10¾ ", base 6½ ",
c. 1920 (E1-129).*
.... **220.00** **250.00**

☐ **Empire No. 1,** *polished gold
finish, height 11", c. 1920
(E1-127).*
.... **220.00** **250.00**

☐ **Empire No. 2,** *rich gold finish,
height 11¾ ", base 7", c. 1920
(E1-127).*
.... **310.00** **350.00**

☐ **Empire No. 3,** *mahogany and old
oak base and top, height 12¼ ",
base 7", c. 1920 (E1-129).*
.... **325.00** **365.00**

☐ **Empire No. 4,** *bronze top and base, gold body and trimmings, raised gold ornaments, height 11", base 6¼", c. 1920 (E1-127).*
.... **245.00   275.00**

☐ **Empire No. 5,** *bronze top and base, gold body and trimmings, height 14", c. 1920, 8 Day, strike (E1-126).*
.... **400.00   450.00**

☐ **Empire No. 6,** *rich gold finish, height 10½", base 6½", c. 1920 (E1-128).*
.... **220.00   250.00**

☐ **Empire No. 7,** *with bust, rich gold ornaments and polished gold uprights, height 17", base 8½", c. 1920 (E1-128).*
.... **390.00   440.00**

☐ **Empire No. 8,** *bronze top and base, gold body and trimmings, convex front, height 12½", dial 4", c. 1920, 8 Day, strike (E1-128).*
.... **400.00   450.00**

☐ **Empire No. 9,** *rich gold finish, height 13", c. 1920, 8 Day, strike (E1-126).*
.... **400.00   450.00**

☐ **Empire No. 11,** *rich gold with hand burnighing, height 14", c. 1920, 8 Day (E1-127).*
.... **380.00   435.00**

☐ **Empire No. 14,** *ormolu gold (E1-127).*
.... **490.00   550.00**

☐ **Empire No. 15,** *rich gold finish, height 15½", base 8", c. 1920 (E1-127).*
.... **360.00   400.00**

☐ **Empire No. 16,** *rich gold ornaments and polished gold uprights, height 16", base 8", c. 1920 (E1-126).*
.... **625.00   700.00**

☐ **Empire No. 19,** *rich gold and burnished finish, height 15½", c.*

1920, 8 Day (E1-129).
.... **360.00   400.00**

☐ **Empire No. 20,** *rich gold finish, height 14", base 8", c. 1920 (E1-126).*
.... **280.00   320.00**

☐ **Empire No. 22,** *rich gold finish, height 13½", base 7¾", c. 1920 (E1-128).*
.... **250.00   280.00**

☐ **Empire No. 23,** *rich gold finish, porcelain dial, height 11½", concave base 7¼", c. 1920 (E1-126).*
.... **310.00   350.00**

☐ **Empire No. 27,** *rich gold and bronze art nouveau finish, cathedral bell, height 21½", base*

11", porcelain dial 3", c. 1910, 15
Day, strike (E2-140).
.... **775.00   875.00**

☐ **Empire No. 28,** *bronze top and
base, gold body and trimmings,
height 16½", base 10", c. 1920
(E1-129).*
.... **625.00   700.00**

☐ **Empire No. 29,** *bronze top and
base, gold body and trimmings,
height 17", base 8½", decorated
dial 3½", c. 1920, 15 Day (E1-126).*
.... **575.00   650.00**

☐ **Empire No. 30,** *polished gold,
steel cut pinions and springs in
barrels, cut glass top, sides,
columns and and base, height
12¾", base 8", decorated
porcelain dial 4", c. 1920, 15 Day
(E1-129).*
.... **900.00   1000.00**

☐ **Empire No. 31,** *figure and base
bronze, barbedienne finish, body
and trimmings rich gold,
burnished, cut glass columns,
height 25", base 14½", c. 1920
(E1-128).*
.... **725.00   800.00**

☐ **Empire No. 32,** *figure bronze art
nouveau, base barbedienne
finish, body and trimmings rich
gold, burnished, cut glass
columns, height 20", base 14½",
c. 1920 (E1-128).*
.... **725.00   800.00**

☐ **Empire No. 35,** *rich gold finish,
height 10", base 6", c. 1920
(E1-129).*
.... **245.00   275.00**

☐ **Empire No. 41,** *rich gold finish,
decorated dial, height 13½",
base 6", c. 1920 (E1-129).*
.... **425.00   475.00**

☐ **Empire No. 42,** *rich gold finish,
height 8¾", c. 1920, 15 Day,
strike (E1-128).*
.... **310.00   350.00**

☐ **Empire No. 43,** *polished top and
base, rich gold columns, height
9½", c. 1920, 15 Day (E1-127).*
.... **310.00   350.00**

☐ **Empire No. 44,** *polished gold
body, rich gold pillars and top,
height 12¼", c. 1920 (E1-129).*
.... **600.00   675.00**

☐ **Empire No. 45,** *polished top and
base, rich gold columns, height
9½", c. 1920, 15 Day.*
.... **310.00   350.00**

☐ **Empire No. 46,** *polished gold
body, gold pillars and top, sharp
square corners on base and top,
height 12¼", c. 1920 (E1-129).*
.... **600.00   675.00**

☐ **Empire No. 47,** *rich gold
ornaments and polished gold
uprights, height 10", base 6", c.
1920 (E1-129).*
.... **335.00   375.00**

☐ **Empire No. 48,** *polished gold
finish, convex front, height 8¾",
c. 1920 (E1-126).*
.... **360.00   400.00**

☐ **Empire No. 48, extra,** *rich gold
finish, convex front, height 8¾",
c. 1920 (E1-126).*
.... **360.00   400.00**

☐ **Empire No. 49,** *rich gold finish,
convex front, metal columns,
height 9½", base 7", c. 1920
(E1-127).*
.... **400.00   450.00**
☐ **As above,** *cut glass columns*
.... **470.00   530.00**

☐ **Empire No. 60,** *polished gold
finish, convex front, height 11",
c. 1920 (E1-126).*
.... **360.00   400.00**

☐ **Empire No. 60, extra,** *rich gold
finish, convex front, height 11",
c. 1920 (E1-126).*
.... **360.00   400.00**

☐ **Empire No. 63,** *rich gold finish, porcelain dial, height 11", base 7½", c. 1920 (E1-127).*
.... **400.00   450.00**

☐ **Empire No. 64,** *rich gold finish, decorated dial, height 11½", base 9", c. 1920 (E1-126).*
.... **450.00   500.00**

☐ **Empire No. 65,** *polished gold finish, convex front, metal columns, height 11", base 9½", c. 1920 (E1-128).*
.... **575.00   650.00**
☐ **As above,** *cut glass columns*
.... **725.00   800.00**
☐ **As above,** *gold decorated columns*
.... **750.00   850.00**

☐ **Empire No. 67,** *rich gold finish, height 12½", base 9½", c. 1920 (E1-128).*
.... **370.00   420.00**

☐ **Empire No. 100,** *onyx top and base, polished gold body, convex front, height 11", dial 4", c. 1920, 8 Day (E1-128).*
.... **200.00   230.00**

☐ **Empire No. 140,** *onyx top and base, polished gold body, convex front, height 9", c. 1920 (E1-129).*
.... **360.00   400.00**

☐ **Empire No. 148,** *onyx top and base, polished gold body, convex front, height 9", c. 1920, (E1-126).*
.... **425.00   475.00**

☐ **Empire No. 160,** *onyx top and base, polished gold body, convex front, height 11", c. 1920 (E1-126).*
.... **425.00   475.00**

☐ **Empire No. 201,** *polished gold finish, height 10", c. 1920, 8 Day (E1-129).*
.... **190.00   220.00**

☐ **Orchid No. 3,** *polished gold finish, height 10¼", base 6¾", c. 1920 (E1-128).*
.... **270.00   300.00**

☐ **Orchid No. 4,** *polished gold finish, height 10¾", base 6¾", c. 1920 (E1-126).*
.... **280.00   320.00**

☐ **Orchid No. 5,** *c. 1920 (E1-127).*
.... **280.00   320.00**

☐ **Orchid No. 8,** *brass case, gold plated and lacquered, cased in a cylinder cup bell, French sash, convex beveled glass, height 11", base 8", porcelain dial 3½", c. 1920, 15 Day, movement (E1-127).*
.... **220.00   250.00**

☐ **Orchid No. 10,** *metal case, gold plated, burnished and lacquered, rich gold trimmings, cased in a cylinder cup bell, French sash, convex beveled glass, height 18", base 11", porcelain dial 3½", c. 1920, 15 Day, movement (E1-127).*
.... **575.00   650.00**

GALLERY LEVER

☐ **Banner Lever,** *brass, dial 4", c. 1880 (E1-55).*
.... **105.00   125.00**
☐ **As above,** *dial 6"*
.... **125.00   150.00**
☐ **As above,** *dial 8"*
.... **150.00   175.00**

☐ **Brass Lever,** *for locomotives, 6", c. 1880, 1 Day (E1-55).*
.... **105.00   125.00**
☐ **As above,** *8 Day*
.... **125.00   150.00**

☐ **Chronometer Lever,** *brass or nickel plate, dial 3½", c. 1880, 1 Day (E1-55).*
.... **195.00   225.00**
☐ **As above,** *dial 4½", 1 Day*
.... **245.00   275.00**

☐ **Engine Lever,** *brass or nickel, dial 6", c. 1888, 1 Day (E1-33).*
.... **105.00   125.00**
☐ **As above,** *8 Day*
.... **125.00   150.00**

☐ **French Lever,** *rosewood or walnut, jeweled balance, dial 8", c. 1880 (E1-55).*
.... **150.00   175.00**

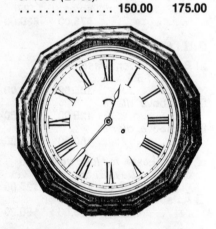

☐ **Lever,** *wood, dial 10", c. 1880 (E1-55).*
.... **150.00   175.00**
☐ **As above,** *dial 12"*
.... **175.00   200.00**
☐ **Ship's Bell Lever,** *nickel, height 10½", dial 6", c. 1888, 1 Day, strike (E1-33).*
.... **310.00   350.00**

GRANDFATHER

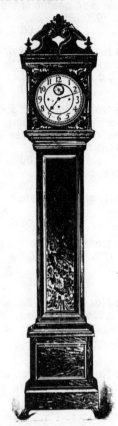

☐ **Hall Clock No. 21,** *oak or old oak veneer, height 94", metal dial 12", c. 1890, 8 Day, strike, weight (E1-47).*
.... **1600.00   1800.00**
☐ **As above,** *mahogany, 8 Day, strike, weight*
.... **1700.00   1900.00**

☐ **Hall Clock No. 22,** *oak, height 98", painted moon face dial 12", c. 1890, 8 Day, strike, weight (E1-47).*
.... 2250.00   2700.00
☐ **As above,** *old oak or mahogany, 8 Day, strike, weight*
.... 2350.00   2800.00

KITCHEN

☐ **Albany,** *walnut, spring wound, height 20", dial 6", c. 1888, 8 Day, strike (E1-29).*
.... 160.00   185.00

☐ **Alton,** *walnut, spring wound, height 19", dial 5", c. 1888, 1 Day, strike (E1-29).*
.... 150.00   175.00

☐ **Athens,** *walnut, spring wound, height 17", dial 6", c. 1888, 1 Day, strike (E1-29).*
.... 100.00   125.00
☐ **As above,** *8 Day, strike*
.... 135.00   160.00

☐ **Atlanta,** *V.P., wood, spring wound, height 19½", c. 1894, 1 Day, strike (E1-143).*
.... 135.00   160.00
☐ **As above,** *8 Day, strike*
.... 105.00   130.00

☐ **Atlas,** *walnut, spring wound, height 22½", c. 1894, 8 Day, strike, weight, calendar (E1-143).*
.... 245.00   275.00
☐ **As above,** *cherry*
.... 245.00   275.00
☐ **As above,** *oak*
.... 220.00   250.00

☐ **Bangor,** *walnut, spring wound, height 20", dial 6", c. 1894, 8 Day, strike (E1-142).*
.... 120.00   145.00
☐ **As above,** *oak*
.... 100.00   120.00

☐ **Boston,** *walnut, spring wound, height 21", dial 6", c. 1890, 8 Day, strike (E1-50).*
.... 195.00   225.00

☐ **Buffalo,** *walnut, brass pillars, spring wound, height 20½", dial 6", c. 1880, 8 Day, strike (E1-56).*
.... 175.00   200.00

☐ **Cairo,** *walnut, spring wound, height 18½", dial 5", c. 1888, 1 Day, strike (E1-29).*
.... 150.00   175.00

☐ **Cambridge,** *old oak, cathedral bell, packed and sold in "assortments" consisting of six clocks, one of each of the six different patterns, Cambridge, New York, Oxford, Yale, Harvard, Cornell, spring wound, height 23", dial 6", c. 1910, 8 Day, strike (E2--131).*
.... 155.00   180.00

☐ **Camden,** *walnut, spring wound, height 22½", dial 6", c. 1888, 8 Day, strike (E1-29).*
.... 150.00   175.00

☐ **Columbus,** *walnut, spring wound, height 24½", dial 6", c. 1880, 8 Day, strike (E1-56).*
.... 195.00   225.00

☐ **Concord,** *walnut, spring wound, height 22½", dial 6", c. 1888, 8 Day, strike (E1-29).*
.... 175.00   200.00

☐ **Cornell,** *old oak, cathedral bell, packed and sold in "assortments" consisting of six clocks, one of each of the six different patterns, college series, spring wound, height 23", dial 6", c. 1910, 8 Day, strike (E2-131).*
.... 155.00   180.00

☐ **Derby,** *walnut, spring wound, height 20", dial 6", c. 1894, 8 Day, strike (E1-142).*
.... 120.00   145.00

☐ **Detroit,** *walnut, spring wound, height 19½", dial 6", c. 1880, 1 Day, strike (E1-56).*
.... 150.00   175.00
☐ **As above,** *8 Day, strike*
.... 175.00   200.00

☐ **Dover,** *oak, spring wound, height 20", dial 6", c. 1894, 8 Day, strike (E1-142).*
.... 100.00   120.00
☐ **As above,** *walnut*
.... 120.00   145.00

☐ **Erie,** *walnut, spring wound, height 19", dial 6", c. 1880, 8 Day, strike (E1-56).*
.... 195.00   225.00

☐ **Harvard,** *old oak, cathedral bell, packed and sold in "assortments" consisting of six clocks, one of each of the six different patterns, college series, spring wound, height 23", dial 6", c. 1910, 8 Day, strike (E2-131).*
.... 155.00   180.00

☐ **Hecla,** *walnut, spring wound, height 22½", dial 6", c. 1894, 8 Day, strike (E1-142).*
.... 145.00   170.00
☐ **As above,** *cherry*
.... 145.00   170.00
☐ **As above,** *oak*
.... 125.00   150.00

☐ **Lafayette,** *walnut, spring wound, height 25½", dial 6", c. 1880, 8 Day, strike (E1-56).*
.... 245.00   275.00

☐ **Lyons,** *walnut, rosewood veneer, spring wound, height 21½", dial 6", c. 1894, 8 Day, strike (E1-143).*
.... 135.00   160.00

☐ **Midland,** *walnut, spring wound, height 22", dial 6", c. 1920, 8 Day, strike (E1-139).*
.... 145.00   170.00

☐ **Newark,** *walnut, spring wound, height 22", dial 6", c. 1888, 8 Day, strike (E1-29).*
.... 175.00   200.00

☐ **New York,** *old oak, cathedral bell, packed and sold in "assortments" consisting of six clocks, one of each of the six different patterns, college series, spring wound, height 23", dial 6", c. 1910, 8 Day, strike (E2-131).*
.... 155.00   180.00

☐ **Norfolk,** *walnut, spring wound, height 19½", dial 6", c. 1880, 1 Day, strike (E1-56).*
.... 125.00   150.00

☐ **As above,** *8 Day, strike*
.... 150.00   175.00

☐ **Ogden,** *walnut, spring wound, height 21½", dial 6", c. 1888, 8 Day, strike (E1-29).*
.... 175.00   200.00

☐ **Omaha,** *walnut, spring wound, height 19", dial 6", c. 1888, 8 Day, strike (E1-29).*
.... 155.00

☐ **As above,** *oak*
.... 105.00   130.00

☐ **Oregon,** *cocobola finish, marqueterie top, spring wound, height 19½", dial 6", c. 1880, 8 Day, strike (E1-56).*
.... 160.00   185.00

☐ **Oxford,** *old oak, cathedral bell, packed and sold in "assortments" consisting of six clocks, one of each of the six different patterns, college series, spring wound, height 23", dial 6", c. 1910, 8 Day, strike (E2-131).*
.... 155.00   180.00

☐ **Peoria,** *walnut, spring wound, height 20", dial 6", c. 1888, 8 Day, strike (E1-29).*
.... 130.00   155.00

☐ **Pittsburgh,** *V.P., wood, spring wound, height 23", c. 1875, 8 Day, strike (E1-54).*
.... 220.00   250.00

☐ **Princeton,** *walnut, spring wound, height 23½", dial 6", c. 1888, 8 Day, strike (E1-29).*
.... 165.00   190.00

☐ **Reno,** *walnut, spring wound, height 19½", dial 6", c. 1888, 8 Day, strike (E1-29).*
.... 175.00   200.00

☐ **Santa Fe,** *walnut, spring wound, height 22½", dial 6", c. 1888, 8 Day, strike (E1-29).*
.... **220.00   250.00**

☐ **St. Paul,** *V.P., wood, spring wound, height 21", c. 1875, 8 Day, strike (E1-54).*
.... **310.00   350.00**

☐ **Summit,** *walnut, spring wound, height 18½", dial 6", c. 1888, 8 Day, strike (E1-29).*
.... **120.00   145.00**

☐ **Tacoma,** *oak, spring wound, dial 6", c. 1920, 8 Day, strike (E1-139).*
.... **105.00   130.00**

☐ **Topeka,** *walnut, spring wound, height 20", dial 6", c. 1888, 8 Day, strike (E1-29).*
.... **130.00   155.00**

☐ **Utica,** *walnut, spring wound, height 22", dial 6", c. 1888, 8 Day, strike (E1-29).*
.... **150.00   175.00**

☐ **Yale,** *old oak, cathedral bell, packed and sold in "assortments" consisting of six clocks, one of each of the six different patterns, college series, spring wound, height 23", dial 6", c. 1910, 8 Day, strike (E2-131).*
.... **155.00   180.00**

SERIES

☐ **Capitol Series,** *The glass tablets on this line show three pictures of the Capitol at Washington, D.C., also three pictures of the White House. The buildings are an exact reproduction of color scheme and the grounds show the green lawns, etc. Cathedral bell, oak only, packed and sold only in assortments, consisting of six clocks, one of each of the six different patterns. Capital no. 1 — 6 shown, spring wound, height 23", dial 6", c. 1910, 8 Day, ½ hour strike (E2-130).*
.... **each 170.00   195.00**

☐ **College Series,** *old oak, cathedral bell, packed and sold in "assortments" consisting of six clocks, one of each of the six different patterns, Cambridge, New York, Oxford, Yale, Harvard, Cornell, spring wound, height 23", dial 6", c. 1910, 8 Day, strike (E2-131).*
.... **each 155.00   180.00**

☐ **Exposition Series,** *golden oak finish, highly embossed, embossed wood, sold in "assortments" of six clocks, two of each of the three different patterns, 6 clocks shown (no names), spring wound, height 25", dial 6", c. 1904, 8 Day, strike (E2-129).*
.... **each 170.00   195.00**

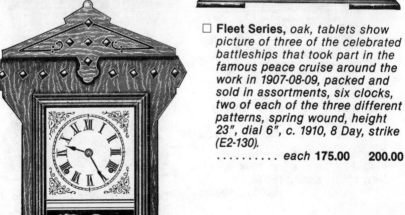

☐ **Fleet Series,** *oak, tablets show picture of three of the celebrated battleships that took part in the famous peace cruise around the work in 1907-08-09, packed and sold in assortments, six clocks, two of each of the three different patterns, spring wound, height 23", dial 6", c. 1910, 8 Day, strike (E2-130).*

. . . . *each* **175.00**   **200.00**

☐ **The Metal Series,** *old oak, metal ornaments, cathedral bell, packed and sold in "assortments" consisting of six clocks, one of each of the six different patterns, metal no. 1 through no. 6, spring wound, height 23", dial 6", c. 1910, 8 Day, strike (E2-131).*
.... *each* 150.00   175.00

TEAR DROP

☐ **Concord,** *walnut, spring wound, height 22½", dial 6", c. 1894, 8 Day, strike, spring (E1-143).*
.... 145.00   170.00

☐ **Tampa,** *walnut, spring wound, height 22", dial 6", c. 1894, 8 Day, strike, spring (E1-143).*
.... 165.00   190.00

MANTEL
BRASS FINISH

☐ **Paris,** *Dull gold plated brass base and feet, verde antique top, gold plated sash and mat and beveled glass, height 8½", base 9", porcelain 3½", c. 1910, 15 Day, strike (E2-138).*
.... 155.00   180.00

BRONZE

☐ **Duchess,** *bronze finish, height 9¾", dial 4½", c. 1910 (E2-137).*
.... 150.00   175.00

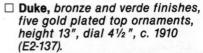

□ **Duke,** *bronze and verde finishes, five gold plated top ornaments, height 13", dial 4½", c. 1910 (E2-137).*
.... **160.00** **185.00**

DECORATED METAL

□ **La Reine,** *bronze finish, French sash and beveled glass, height 13½", decorated dial 3½", c. 1910, 8 Day, strike (E2-137).*
.... **145.00** **170.00**

□ **Louvre,** *metal, porcelain dial, height 11½", base 7½", c. 1910, 8 Day, strike (E2-136).*
.... **230.00** **260.00**

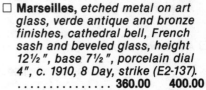

□ **Marseilles,** *etched metal on art glass, verde antique and bronze finishes, cathedral bell, French sash and beveled glass, height 12½", base 7½", porcelain dial 4", c. 1910, 8 Day, strike (E2-137).*
.... **360.00** **400.00**

☐ **Rex,** *brass antique and bronze finish, height 12½", porcelain dial 4½", c. 1910, 8 Day, strike (E2-136).*
.... **175.00   200.00**

☐ **Versailles,** *metal, porcelain dial, height 12½", base 8", c. 1910, 8 Day, strike (E2-136).*
.... **285.00   325.00**

MAHOGANY

☐ **Dundee,** *mahogany, silvered dial, 10¼" x 8¾", minute circle 4½", c. 1912, 8 Day, strike (E2-133).*
.... **65.00   80.00**

☐ **Gothic,** *real bronze case and finish, bronze dial silvered with cut raised numerals and minute dots fastened back of dial, convex beveled glass, height 11¾", base 7¾", dial 5", c. 1904, 15 Day, strike (E1-124).*
.... **95.00   115.00**

☐ **As above,** *height 14", base 9½", dial 6"*
.... **110.00   135.00**

☐ **As above,** *height 18", base 12", dial 8"*
.... **140.00   165.00**

☐ **Leader,** *mahogany, height 10", convex and glass dial 5", c. 1912, 8 Day, strike (E2-133).*
.... **35.00   45.00**

☐ **Perth,** *mahogany, silvered dial, 11¼" x 8¾", minute circle 4½", c. 1912, 8 Day, strike (E2-133).*
.... **65.00   80.00**

☐ **Priscilla,** *mahogany, colored tablet, 13" x 8½", dial 5", c. 1912, Day (E2-133).*
.... **105.00   125.00**

METAL REGENCY

☐ **Blossom,** *rich gold finish, height 13", base 6½", c. 1910, 8 Day, strike (E2-136).*
.... **210.00   240.00**

☐ **Cluny,** *rich gold and bronze art nouveau finish, cathedral bell, height 15½", base 8", porcelain dial 3", c. 1910, 15 Day, strike (E2-140).*
.... **140.00   165.00**

☐ **Dauphin,** *rich gold and bronze art nouveau finish, cathedral bell, height 21", base 12", porcelain dial 3", c. 1910, 15 Day, strike (E2-140).*
.... **170.00   195.00**

☐ **Garnish,** *rich gold and bronze art nouveau finish, cathedral bell, height 12½", base 9", porcelain dial 3", c. 1910, 15 Day, strike (E2-140).*
.... **160.00   185.00**

☐ **Imperial,** *rich gold and bronze art nouveau finish, cathedral bell, height 21", base 12", porcelain dial 3", c. 1910, 15 Day, strike (E2-140).*
.... **375.00   425.00**

☐ **La Fleur,** *rich gold finish, height 14", base 7½", c. 1910, 8 Day, strike (E2-136).*
.... **195.00   220.00**

☐ **La Norma,** *rich gold finish, height 12", base 7", c. 1910, 8 Day, strike (E2-136).*
.... **195.00   220.00**

☐ **Piper,** *rich gold finish, height 9¾", c. 1910, 8 Day, strike (E2-136).*
.... **80.00   95.00**

☐ **Royal,** *rich gold and bronze art nouveau finish, cathedral bell, height 16", base 10", porcelain dial 3", c. 1910, 15 Day, strike (E2-140).*
.... **210.00   240.00**

☐ **Vista,** *rich gold finish, height 12¾", base 8", c. 1910, 8 Day, strike (E2-136).*
.... **310.00   350.00**

ROUND TOP

☐ **Elect,** *metal case and dial, verde antique base, gun metal top and hands, silver center and raised black numerals and minute dots, height 10", base 7½", gold dial 7", c. 1910, 8 Day, strike (E2-138).*
.... **70.00   85.00**

WESTMINSTER CHIME

☐ **Chime Clock No. 71,** *mahogany, silvered dial, 13⅜" x 10½", depth 7¼", c. 1912 (E2-133).*
.... **210.00   240.00**

☐ **Chime Clock No. 72,** *mahogany, silvered dial, 14¾" x 10¼", depth 7¼", c. 1912 (E2-133).*
.... **210.00   240.00**

☐ **Chime Clock No. 75,** *mahogany, cast sash, silvered mat and convex beveled glass, 9¾" x 22½", depth 6⅞", convex silvered dial 6", c. 1912 (E2-133).*
.... **220.00   250.00**

☐ **Chime Clock No. 73,** *mahogany, silvered dial, 13⅞" x 10¾", depth 7⅛", c. 1912 (E2-133).*
.... **270.00   300.00**

☐ **Chime Clock No. 74 (Tambour),** *mahogany, silvered dial, 10" x 20¼", depth 6¾", convex beveled glass dial, cast sash, 6", c. 1912 (E2-133).*
.... **220.00   250.00**

MISSION

☐ **Aztec,** *panel birdseye maple, body dark red oak, visible pendulum, height 17", base 11¾", metal dial 6", c. 1910, 8 Day, strike (E2-130).*
.... **125.00   150.00**

☐ **Onava**, *panel dark olive green oak, body silver gray oak, visible pendulum, height 15¾", base 11½", metal dial 6", c. 1910, 8 Day, strike (E2-130).*
.... **125.00 150.00**

☐ **Zuni**, *panel dark red oak, body weathered oak, height 14½", base 12", metal dial 6", c. 1910, 8 Day, strike (E2-130).*
.... **125.00 150.00**

NOVELTY
ART NOUVEAU

☐ **Abe**, *rich gold, and art nouveau bronze, height 8½", porcelain dial 2", c. 1910, 1 Day (E2-135).*
.... **70.00 85.00**

☐ **Alice**, *rich gold, and art nouveau bronze, height 10", porcelain dial 2", c. 1910, 1 Day (E2-135).*
.... **55.00 70.00**

☐ **Artful**, *rich gold and bronze art nouveau finish, cathedral bell, height 16", base 8", porcelain dial 3", c. 1910, 15 Day, strike (E2-139).*
.... **140.00 165.00**

☐ **Beth**, *rich gold, also art nouveau bronze, height 9½", porcelain dial 2", c. 1910, 1 Day (E2-134).*
.... **60.00 75.00**

☐ **Bungalow**, *rich gold, also art nouveau bronze, height 7¼", porcelain dial 2", c. 1910, 1 Day (E2-134).*
.... **55.00 70.00**

☐ **Cis**, *rich gold, and art nouveau bronze, height 8", porcelain dial 2", c. 1910, 1 Day (E2-135).*
.... **50.00 65.00**

☐ **Colin**, *rich gold, also art nouveau bronze, height 6", porcelain dial 2", c. 1910, 1 Day (E2-134).*
.... **50.00 65.00**

☐ **Colonial**, *rich gold, and art nouveau bronze, height 8¾", porcelain dial 2", c. 1910, 1 Day (E2-135).*
.... **40.00 55.00**

☐ **Corinna**, *rich gold finish, height 5¼", porcelain dial 2", c. 1910, 1 Day (E2-134).*
.... **35.00 45.00**

☐ **Cyril,** *rich gold finish, height 9½", porcelain dial 2", c. 1910, 1 Day (E2-134).*
.... 60.00 75.00

☐ **Dimple,** *rich gold finish, height 8¾", porcelain dial 2", c. 1910, 1 Day (E2-135).*
.... 70.00 85.00

☐ **Dorothy,** *rich gold and bronze art nouveau finish, cathedral bell, height 16", base 9", porcelain dial 3", c. 1910, 15 Day, strike (E2-139).*
.... 135.00 160.00

☐ **Flora,** *rich gold and bronze art nouveau finish, cathedral bell, height 14", base 7", porcelain dial 3", c. 1910, 15 Day, strike (E2-139).*
.... 135.00 160.00

☐ **Florizel,** *rich gold finish, height 8¾", porcelain dial 2", c. 1910, 1 Day (E2-135).*
.... 50.00 65.00

☐ **Floss,** *rich gold, and art nouveau bronze, height 8½", porcelain dial 2", c. 1910, 1 Day (E2-135).*
.... 50.00 65.00

☐ **Fountain,** *rich gold finish, height 8½", porcelain dial 2", c. 1910, 1 Day (E2-135).*
.... 70.00 85.00

☐ **Holly,** *rich gold, porcelain dial 2", height 7½", c. 1910, 1 Day (E2-134).*
.... 50.00 65.00

☐ **Irma,** *rich gold and bronze art nouveau finish, decorated dial, French sash and beveled glass, height 18", base 11", dial 4½", c. 1910, 8 Day, strike (E2-138).*
.... 175.00 200.00

☐ **Isabel,** *rich gold and bronze art nouveau finish, cathedral bell, porcelain dial 3", height 18",* base 11", c. 1910, 15 Day, strike (E2-140).
.... 190.00 220.00

☐ **Jen,** *rich gold, and art nouveau bronze, porcelain dial, height 11", dial 2", c. 1910, 1 Day (E2-135).*
.... 60.00 75.00

☐ **Jess,** *rich gold, also art nouveau bronze, porcelain dial, height 9", dial 2", c. 1910, 1 Day (E2-134).*
.... 60.00 75.00

☐ **Lily,** *Jap bronze with gold panel, imitation porcelain dial, plain beaded sash and plain glass, height 11½" x 8½", c. 1904, 8 Day, strike (E1-124).*
.... 80.00 95.00

☐ **Lola,** *rich gold finish, porcelain dial, height 7¼", dial 2", c. 1910, 1 Day (E2-134).*
.... 45.00 60.00

☐ **Lucerne,** *rich gold and bronze art nouveau finish, cathedral bell, porcelain dial, height 15½", base 9", dial 3", c. 1910, 15 Day, strike (E2-139).*
.... 145.00 170.00

☐ **Lucrece,** *rich gold and bronze art nouveau finish, cathedral bell, porcelain dial, height 15½", base 9", dial 3", c. 1910, 15 Day, strike (E2-139).*
.... 135.00 160.00

☐ **Mignon,** *rich gold and bronze art nouveau finish, cathedral bell, porcelain dial, height 15" x 8", dial 3", c. 1910, 15 Day, strike (E2-139).*
.... 135.00 160.00

☐ **Nan,** *rich gold finish, porcelain dial, height 7¼", dial 2", c. 1910, 1 Day (E2-134).*
.... 45.00 60.00

☐ **Natty,** *rich gold finish, porcelain dial, height 6½", dial 2", c. 1910, 1 Day (E2-134).*
.... 35.00 45.00

☐ **Orleans,** *rich gold and bronze art nouveau finish, cathedral bell, porcelain dial, height 14½", base 9½", dial 3", c. 1910, 15 Day, strike (E2-139).*
.... **125.00   150.00**

☐ **Paddock,** *rich gold, also art nouveau bronze, porcelain dial, height 7½", dial 2", c. 1910, 1 Day (E2-134).*
.... **50.00   65.00**

☐ **Poppy,** *rich gold and bronze art nouveau finish, cathedral bell, porcelain dial, height 19", base 9", c. 1910, 15 Day, strike (E2-139).*
.... **140.00   165.00**

☐ **Roselle,** *rich gold and bronze art nouveau finish, cathedral bell, porcelain dial, height 15", base 9", dial 3", c. 1910, 15 Day, strike (E2-139).*
.... **175.00   200.00**

☐ **Serenade,** *rich gold and nart nouveau bronze, porcelain dial, height 8½", dial 2", c. 1910, 1*

Day (E2-135).
.... **60.00   75.00**

☐ **Thistle,** *rich gold, cathedral bell, decorated porcelain dial, French sash and beveled glass, height 14½", base 7", dial 3½", c. 1910, 8 Day, strike (E2-138).*
.... **145.00   170.00**

☐ **Tick Tick,** *rich gold and art nouveau bronze, porcelain dial, height 6½", dial 2", c. 1910, 1 Day (E2-135).*
.... **50.00   65.00**

☐ **Tristan,** *rich gold and bronze art nouveau finish, cathedral bell, porcelain dial, height 12", base 8½", dial 3", c. 1910, 15 Day, strike (E2-139).*
.... **150.00   175.00**

☐ **Vanity,** *rich gold, and art nouveau bronze, porcelain dial, height 12½", dial 2", c. 1910, 1 Day (E2-135).*
.... **60.00   75.00**

CHINA

☐ **Tile Clock,** *art tile in dark olive, brown, light blue and canary, gilt hands, lever, 6" square, c. 1904, 1 Day (E1-124).*
.... **70.00   85.00**

GILT

☐ **Ada,** *Rich gold finish, porcelain dial, height 4", dial 2", c. 1910, 1 Day (E2-134).*
. . . . 55.00   70.00

☐ **Bona,** *rich gold finish, porcelain dial, height 5¾", dial 2", c. 1910, 1 Day (E2-134).*
. . . . 80.00   100.00

☐ **Bouquet,** *rich gold finish, porcelain dial, height 7", dial 2", c. 1910, 1 Day (E2-135).*
. . . . 40.00   50.00

☐ **Cherubs,** *rich gold finish, porcelain dial, height 5¾", dial 2", c. 1910, 1 Day (E2-134).*
. . . . 70.00   85.00

☐ **Elephant,** *rich gold finish, porcelain dial, height 5", dial 2", c. 1910, 1 Day (E2-135).*
. . . . 45.00   60.00

☐ **Dido,** *rich gold finish, porcelain dial, height 5¾", dial 2", c. 1910, 1 Day (E2-134).*
. . . . 35.00   45.00

☐ **Dorrit,** *rich gold finish, porcelain dial, height 5", dial 2", c. 1910, 1 Day (E2-135).*
. . . . 70.00   85.00

☐ **Eagle,** *rich gold finish, porcelain dial, height 7", dial 2", c. 1910, 1 Day (E2-135).*
. . . . 40.00   55.00

☐ **Goethe,** *bronze top and base, rich gold pillars and center, porcelain dial, height 8", dial 2", c. 1910, 1 Day (E2-134).*
. . . . 80.00   95.00

☐ **Jacket,** *bronze, also yellow, porcelain dial, height 3", dial 2", c. 1910, 1 Day (E2-135).*
. . . . 45.00   60.00

☐ **Mozart,** *bronze top and base, rich gold pillars and center, porcelain dial, height 8", dial 2", c. 1910, 1 Day (E2-134).*
. . . . 80.00   95.00

☐ **Schiller,** *bronze top and base, rich gold pillars and center, porcelain dial, height 8", dial 2", c. 1910, 1 Day (E2-134).*
. . . . 80.00   95.00

☐ **School Days,** *rich gold, also gold clock with bronze girl, porcelain dial, height 7½", dial 2", c. 1910, 1 Day (E2-135).*
. . . . 45.00   60.00

☐ **School Girl,** *rich gold, also gold clock with bronze girl, porcelain dial, height 5", dial 2", c. 1910, 1 Day (E2-135).*
. . . . 40.00   50.00

☐ **Shakespeare,** *bronze top and base, rich gold pillars and center, porcelain dial, height 8", dial 2", c. 1910, 1 Day (E2-134).*
. . . . 80.00   95.00

☐ **Turk,** *metal, light blue or pink, enameled and gilt case, height 7", base 4¼", c. 1904, 1 Day (E1-124).*
.... **40.00   50.00**

☐ **Veva,** *rich gold finish, porcelain dial, height 8½", dial 2", c. 1910, 1 Day (E2-135).*
.... **50.00   65.0C**

☐ **Wagner,** *bronze top and base, rich gold pillars and center, porcelain dial, height 8", dial 2", c. 1910, 1 Day (E2-134).*
.... **80.00   95.00**

IRON

☐ **Arab,** *metal, light blue or pink, enameled and gilt case, lever, height 6½", base 5¼", c. 1904, 1 Day (E1-124).*
.... **40.00   50.00**

☐ **Kaffir,** *metal, light blue or pink, enameled and gilt case, lever, height 8", base 5", c. 1904, 1 Day (E1-124).*
.... **60.00   75.00**

☐ **Malay,** *metal, light blue or pink, enameled and gilt case, lever, height 6", base 4¾", c. 1904, 1 Day (E1-124).*
.... **40.00   50.00**

WALL

☐ **Lusitania Hanging Clock,** *rich gold highly burnished, fitted with a fine lever time movement, 11 jewels, compensating balance, porcelain dial, French sash and convex beveled glass, 20" x 9½", dial 4¼", c. 1904, 8 Day (E1-124).*
.... **125.00   150.00**

FIGURE EIGHT

☐ **Signet,** *walnut, height 23", dial 10", c. 1890, 8 Day (E1-52).*

OCTAGON TOP, LONG DROP

☐ **Globe,** *old oak, veneer polished, height 31", dial 12", c. 1890, Day (E1-50).*
.... 285.00   325.00
☐ **As above,** *8 Day, strike.*
.... 310.00   350.00
☐ **As above,** *walnut, 8 Day.*
.... 335.00   375.00
☐ **As above,** *walnut, 8 Day, strike.*
.... 360.00   400.00
☐ **As above,** *rosewood, 8 Day.*
.... 335.00   375.00
☐ **As above,** *rosewood, 8 Day, strike.*
.... 360.00   400.00

OCTAGON TOP, SHORT DROP

☐ **Office No. 2,** *walnut, height 26", dial 12", c. 1890, 8 Day, strike, spring, (E1-50).*
.... 270.00   300.00

☐ **As above,** *8 Day, strike, spring.*
.... **285.00   325.00**

☐ **Office No. 3,** *walnut veneer or rosewood, height 21½", dial 10", c. 1890, 8 Day, strike, spring (E1-50).*
.... **345.00   275.00**

OPEN SWINGING

☐ **10" Drop Octagon,** *gilt, wood, height 21½", dial 10", c. 1888, 8 Day, spring (E1-32).*

☐ **12" Drop Octagon,** *wood, height 23½", c. 1894, 8 Day, spring (E1-143).*
.... **195.00   225.00**

☐ **As above,** *8 Day, strike, spring.*
.... **220.00   250.00**

☐ **As above,** *8 Day, calendar, spring.*
.... **245.00   275.00**

☐ **As above,** *8 Day, simple calendar, spring.*
.... **270.00   300.00**

☐ **Jupiter,** *oak, moon face, height 59", dial 12", c. 1890, 8 Day, strike (E1-52).*
.... **1350.00   1500.00**

☐ **As above,** *mahogany, 8 Day, strike.*
.... **1500.00   1650.00**

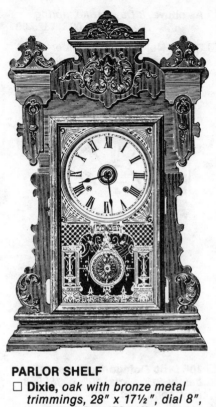

☐ **Lunar,** *oak, moon face, height 41", dial 12", c. 1890, 8 Day, strike (E1-52).*
.... 2250.00   2500.00
☐ **As above,** *mahogany, 8 Day, strike.*
.... 2400.00   2650.00

PARLOR SHELF
☐ **Dixie,** *oak with bronze metal trimmings, 28" x 17½", dial 8", c. 1910, 8 Day (E2-142).*
.... 350.00   400.00
☐ **As above,** *8 Day, strike.*
.... 375.00   425.00
☐ **As above,** *8 Day, calendar.*
.... 400.00   450.00
☐ **As above,** *8 Day, simple calendar.*
.... 425.00   475.00

☐ **Garfield,** *oak, brass weights, wooden rod, height 29", dial 8", c. 1920, 8 Day, strike, weight (E1-139).*
.... 650.00   750.00
☐ **As above,** *cherry, 8 Day, strike, weight.*
.... 750.00   850.00

☐ **As above,** *walnut, 8 Day, strike, weight.*
.... **725.00   825.00**

☐ **Greek,** *oak, height 24", dial 6", c. 1890, 8 Day, strike, spring (E1-50).*
.... **220.00   250.00**

☐ **As above,** *mahogany, 8 Day, strike, spring.*
.... **270.00   300.00**

☐ **As above,** *walnut, 8 Day, strike, spring.*
.... **295.00   325.00**

☐ **Lincoln,** *V.P. walnut, height 27", dial 8", c. 1920, 8 Day, strike, weight (E1-139).*
.... **550.00   600.00**

☐ **As above,** *oak, 8 Day, strike, weight.*
.... **530.00   570.00**

☐ **Rome,** *walnut, height 20½", dial 6", c. 1920, 8 Day, strike (E1-139).*
.... **135.00   160.00**

☐ **As above,** *oak.*
.... **105.00   125.00**

☐ **Yorktown,** *mahogany case, hand carved columns, feet and ornament, cathedral bell, height 36", base 18", dial 10", c. 1910, 8 Day (E2-128).*
.... **335.00   375.00**

PARLOR WALL

☐ **Flora,** *mahogany, case hand carved, height 38", dial 8", c. 1890, 8 Day, strike, weight (E1-52).*
.... **875.00   975.00**

☐ **As above,** *oak, 8 Day, strike, weight.*
.... **800.00   900.00**

☐ **As above,** *cherry, 8 Day, strike, weight.*
.... **950.00   1050.00**

☐ **As above,** *walnut, 8 Day, strike, weight.*
.... **900.00   1000.00**

☐ **March,** *oak, height 46", dial 8½", 1890, 8 Day, strike, spring (E1-47).*
.... **1050.00   1300.00**

☐ **As above,** *walnut.*
.... **1150.00   1400.00**

☐ **As above,** *cherry.*
.... **1200.00   1450.00**

☐ **Panama,** *oak, height 30", dial 6",*
c. 1912, 8 Day, strike, spring
(E2-143).
.... 575.00   650.00
☐ **As above,** *walnut.*
.... 675.00   750.00
☐ **As above,** *cherry.*
.... 750.00   800.00

PARLOR WALL CHIME

☐ **Chime Clock No. 101,** *mahogany,*
silvered dial, 28" x 13", depth
7½", dial 8½", c. 1912 (E2-133).
.... 190.00   220.00

☐ **Chime Clock No. 103,** *mahogany,*
dull rubbed finish, hand-painted
dial in antique finish with
ornamental corners in colors,
fine crotch mahogany panel in
lower door, 31" x 12", depth 8",
dial 8", c. 1912 (E2-133).
.... 310.00   350.00

☐ **Chime Clock No. 102,** *mahogany,*
silvered dial, 31" x 13", depth
7½", dial 8", c. 1912 (E2-133).
.... 240.00   270.00

PRECISION

☐ **Precision Clock,** *metal case,*
dead beat escapement, height
62", dial 14", c. 1890, 32 Day
(E1-47).
.... 7500.00 10000.00
☐ **As above,** *8 Day, gravity.*
.... 7500.00 10000.00

ROUND TOP, SHORT DROP

☐ **Brighton,** *mahogany, height 22¼", dial 12", c. 1910, 8 Day, strike, spring (E2-142).*
.... 210.00   240.00

☐ **Office No. 1,** *walnut, height 25", dial 12", c. 1890, 8 Day, spring (E1-50).*
.... 270.00   300.00

☐ **As above,** *8 Day, strike, spring.*
.... 285.00   325.00

☐ **Rio,** *mahogany veneer, polished, height 25¼", dial 12", c. 1910, 8 Day, strike, spring, (E2-142).*
.... 245.00   275.00

SECONDS BIT

☐ **Queene Anne,** *walnut, height 36", dial 8½", c. 1890, 8 Day, spring (E1-52).*
.... 600.00   650.00

☐ **As above,** *walnut, 8 Day, strike, spring.*
.... 650.00   700.00

☐ **As above,** *oak, 8 Day, spring.*
.... 400.00   450.00

☐ **As above,** *oak, 8 Day, strike, spring.*
.... 450.00   500.00

☐ **As above,** *cherry, 8 Day, spring.*
.... 650.00   700.00

☐ **As above,** *cherry, 8 Day, strike, spring.*
.... 700.00   750.00

☐ **Regulator No. 2,** *walnut and oak veneer, polished movement 2½" x 4½", lantern pinions Graham pallets, brass covered zinc ball and wood rod, 80 beats to the minute, movement has retaining power, height 24", dial 12", c. 1888, 8 Day, weight (E1-26).*
.... 540.00   600.00

☐ **Regulator No. 3,** *walnut, height 14", dial 14", c. 1890, 8 Day, weight (E1-52).*
.... 900.00   1150.00

☐ **As above,** *8 Day, strike, weight.*
.... 1000.00   1250.00

☐ **Regulator No. 4,** *walnut, height 47", dial 7", c. 1890, 8 Day, weight (E1-50).*
.... 1250.00   1500.00

☐ **Regulator No. 5,** *walnut, height 50", porcelain dial 7½", c. 1890, 8 Day, weight (E1-50).*
.... 1250.00   1500.00

☐ **Regulator No. 6,** *oak, 80 beats to the minute, retaining power, Graham pallets, lantern pinions, brass covered zinc ball, wood rods, height 49", dial 10", c. 1888, 8 Day, weight (E1-24).*
.... 1000.00   1200.00

☐ **As above,** *cherry, 8 Day, weight.*
.... 1250.00   1450.00

☐ **As above,** *walnut, 8 Day, weight.*
.... 1200.00   1400.00

☐ **Regulator No. 7,** *oak, height 45",
dial 12", 8 Day, weight.*
. . . . 1250.00   1500.00
☐ **As above,** *cherry.*
. . . . 1500.00   1750.00
☐ **As above,** *walnut.*
. . . . 1450.00   1700.00
☐ **Regulator No. 8,** *oak, polished
movement cut steel pinions,
Graham pallets, wood rod, brass
ball, retaining power, 68 beats to
the minute, height 56", dial 14",
c. 1888, 8 Day, weight (E1-24).*
. . . . 1200.00   1400.00

☐ **As above,** *cherry, 8 Day, weight.*
. . . . 1350.00   1550.00
☐ **As above,** *walnut, 8 Day, weight.*
. . . . 1300.00   1500.00

☐ **Regulator No. 11,** *golden oak,
Graham dead-beat escapement
and maintaining power, beats
seconds, height 56", dial 12", c.
1900, 8 Day, weight (E2-144).*
. . . . 1250.00   1450.00
☐ **As above,** *mahogany, 8 Day,
weight.*
. . . . 1350.00   1550.00

☐ **Regulator No. 15,** *walnut,
mercury pendulum, independent
second, beats seconds, height
100", dial 14", c. 1890, 8 Day,
weight (E1-47).*
. . . . 3000.00   3500.00

☐ **Regulator No. 17,** *oak or old oak,
beats seconds, height 68", dial
14", c. 1890, 8 Day, weight.*
. . . . 1400.00   1600.00
☐ **As above,** *cherry.*
. . . . 1550.00   1750.00
☐ **As above,** *walnut.*
. . . . 1500.00   1700.00

☐ **Regulator No. 18,** *walnut veneer,
beats seconds, brass weights,
wood rod, Graham pallets,
lantern pinions and retaining
power, height 54", dial 14", c.
1888, 8 Day, weight (E1-24).*
. . . . 1600.00   1800.00

☐ **Regulator No. 19,** *old oak, height
48½", dial 14", c. 1912, 8 Day,
weight (E2-143).*
. . . . 1300.00   1500.00
☐ **As above,** *mahogany.*
. . . . 1400.00   1600.00

☐ **Regulator No. 20,** *cherry,
mahogany and old oak, large
movement, wood rod, brass
covered zinc ball, Graham dead-
beat escapement and
maintaining power, the round top
and two side pieces can be
removed if a plain top case is*

desired, beats seconds, height 62", dial 14", c. 1900, 8 Day, weight (E2-144).
.... **1500.00 1750.00**

☐ **Regulator No. 31,** *walnut, cherry, oak or old oak, beats seconds, height 68", dial 18", c. 1890, 8 Day, weight (E1-47).*
.... **1600.00 1800.00**

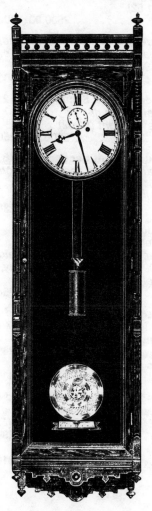

☐ **Regulator No. 32,** *old oak, Graham dead-beat escapement and maintaining power, beats seconds, height 68", dial 12", c. 1900, 8 Day, weight (E2-144).*
.... **1800.00 2000.00**

☐ **Regulator No. 63,** *mahogany or golden oak, Graham dead-beat escapement, brass covered zinc ball, wood rod, beats seconds, height 76", dial 14", c. 1900, 8 Day, weight (E2-143).*
.... **2000.00 2250.00**
☐ **As above,** *8 Day, spring.*
.... **225.00 275.00**

SQUARE TOP

Litchfield

☐ **Litchfield,** *mahogany finish, Graham dead-beat escapement, gold leaf border on upper and lower glasses, height 31", dial 12", c. 1910, 30 Day (E2-142).* **400.00 450.00**

☐ **Regulator No. 25,** *Flemish oak, height 32", dial 12", c. 1910, 8 Day, weight (E2-142).* **750.00 850.00**

STORE

☐ **Office No. 6,** *old oak finish, height 36", dial 12", c. 1910, 8 Day, spring (E2-142).* **245.00 275.00**

☐ **30 Day Office,** *large double spring time movement, with Graham dead-beat escapement, oak, height 42", dial 12", c. 1910 (E2-142).* **270.00 300.00**

SWEEP SECONDS

☐ **Sweep Second No. 10,** *walnut, height 72", c. 1890, 8 Day, weight (E1-52).* **2500.00 3000.00**

☐ **Sweep Second No. 11,** *walnut, beats seconds, height 96", c. 1890, 8 Day, weight (E1-52).* **2500.00 3000.00**

☐ **Independent Seconds No. 12,** *walnut, height 72", c. 1890, 8 Day, weight (E1-52).* **2000.00 2500.00**

☐ **Independent Seconds No. 13,** *walnut, beats seconds, height 96", c. 1890, 8 Day, weight (E1-52).* **2100.00 2300.00**

☐ **Regulator No. 14,** *walnut, mercury pendulum, beats seconds, sweep second, height 100", dial 14", c. 1890, 8 Day, weight (E1-47).* **3000.00 3500.00**

☐ **Regulator No. 16,** *oak or old oak, height 75", dial 12", c. 1890, 8 Day, weight (E1-47).* **2500.00 2800.00**

☐ **As above,** *walnut* **2700.00 3000.00**

☐ **Regulator No. 19,** *oak or old oak, beats seconds, height 75", dial 12", c. 1890, 8 Day, weight (E1-47).* **2600.00 2900.00**

☐ **As above,** *walnut* **2800.00 3100.00**

☐ **As above,** *mahogany*
.... 2450.00   2700.00

STATUE
LARGE

☐ **Regulator No. 60,** *oak, Graham escapement, beats seconds, height 58½", dial 14", c. 1912, 8 Day, weight (E2-143).*
.... 2600.00   3000.00

☐ **As above,** *mahogany*
.... 2800.00   3200.00

☐ **Regulator No. 62,** *oak, Graham pallets, retaining power, beats seconds, height 60", dial 14", c. 1912, 8 Day, weight (E2-143).*
.... 2250.00   2500.00

☐ **Frolic,** *bronze and verde antique finishes, height 23", base 9¼", porcelain dial 4½", c. 1910, 8 Day, strike (E2-137).*
.... 150.00   175.00

☐ **Huntress,** *Seth Thomas' Sons And Company 20" strikes hour and half hour, French bronze, verde antique, light verde, c. 1875, 15 Day (E1-59).*
.... 375.00   425.00

LARGE, ART NOUVEAU

☐ **Creation,** *rich gold and bronze art nouveau finish, cathedral bell, height 18", base 14", porcelain dial 3", c. 1910, 15 Day, strike (E2-139).*
.... 270.00   300.00

☐ **Toiler,** *bronze and brass antique finishes, height 27", base 9¼", porcelain dial 4¼", c. 1910, 8 Day, strike (E2-137).*
.... 140.00   165.00

☐ **Victory,** *Syrian bronze finish, French sash and beveled glass, height 22", decorated porcelain dial 4", c. 1904, 8 Day, strike (E1-124).*
.... 220.00   250.00

☐ **Whistling Boy,** *Syrian bronze finish, French sash and beveled glass, height 21", decorated porcelain dial 4", c. 1904, 8 Day, strike (E1-124).*
.... 220.00   250.00

☐ **Folly,** *bronze art nouveau finish, French sash and beveled glass, height 21½", base 9", porcelain dial 4", c. 1910, 15 Day, strike (E2-138).*
.... 210.00   240.00

☐ **Gaiety,** *rich gold and bronze art nouveau finishes, cathedral bell, height 22½", base 14", porcelain dial 3", c. 1910, 15 Day, strike (E2-139).*
. . . . 230.00   260.00

☐ **Innocence,** *bronze art nouveau finish, cathedral bell, French sash and beveled glass, height 21", base 21", porcelain dial 4", c. 1910, 8 Day, strike (E2-137).*
. . . . 310.00   350.00

☐ **Inspiration,** *bronze art nouveau finish, cathedral bell, French sash and beveled glass, height 21", base 21", porcelain dial 4", c. 1910, 8 Day, strike (E2-137).*
. . . . 285.00   325.00

☐ **Inspiration And Innocence,** *bronze art nouveau finish, cathedral bell, French sash and beveled glass, height 21", base 26", porcelain dial 4", c. 1910, 8 Day, strike (E2-137).*
. . . . 360.00   400.00

☐ **Jeannette,** *rich gold and bronze art nouveau finish, cathedral bell, height 20", base 8½", porcelain dial 3", c. 1910, 15 Day, strike (E2-140).*
. . . . 175.00   200.00

☐ **Josephine,** *bronze art nouveau finish, French sash and beveled glass, height 21", base 12½", porcelain dial 4", c. 1910, 8 Day, strike (E2-138).*
. . . . 190.00   220.00

☐ **Mercedes,** *bronze art nouveau finish, French sash and beveled glass, height 26", base 15", porcelain dial 4", c. 1910, 8 Day, strike (E2-138).*
. . . . 210.00   240.00

☐ **Tanya,** *bronze art nouveau finish, French sash, beveled glass, height 25", base 10", porcelain dial 4", c. 1910, 8 Day, strike (E2-138).*
. . . . 210.00   240.00

☐ **Valentine,** *bronze finish with verde ball, French sash, beveled glass, height 22½", base 14", porcelain dial 4", c. 1910, 15 Day, strike (E2-138).*
. . . . 210.00   240.00

☐ **Vivien,** *rich gold and bronze art nouveau finish, cathedral bell, height 27½", base 16½", porcelain dial 3", c. 1910, 15 Day, strike (E2-140).*
. . . . 490.00   550.00

SMALL

☐ **Leisure,** *Seth Thomas' Sons And Company 18" strikes, quarter and half hours, French bronze, verde antique, light verde, c. 1875, 15 Day (E1-59).*
. . . . 285.00   325.00

☐ **Rebecca At The Well,** *bronze art nouveau finish, cathedral bell, French sash and beveled glass, height 15½", base 15", porcelain dial 4", c. 1910, 8 Day, strike (E2-137).*
. . . . 335.00   375.00

SMALL, ART NOUVEAU

☐ **Nymph,** *rich gold and bronze art nouveau finish, cathedral bell, height 18", base 9½", porcelain dial 3", c. 1910, 15 Day, strike (E2-140).*

.... 140.00   165.00

STREET

☐ **Two Dial Post Clock,** *iron column and iron head, height 13', dial 10", 40", c. 1910 (E2-128).*

.... 1500.00   2000.00

☐ **Four Dial Post Clock,** *iron dials with black or gilt numerals, height to center of dial 13', base of column 36", 24" square, dial 3", c. 1910 (E2-128).*

.... 2500.00   3000.00

NOTE: *These two clocks represent typical examples of street clocks which were made in many styles and decorations. Most of the eight day movements have been replaced by electric movements and for a collector the electric movement decreases the value. Because they are rare and varied each clock must be judged on its merits and a guide to value is hard to determine.*

SOUTHERN CALENDAR CLOCK COMPANY

One of the better known calendar clock manufacturing outfits, the Southern Calendar Clock Company was based in St. Louis, Missouri, although they bought their clock movements from Connecticut firms.

CALENDAR

☐ **Fashion Model 1,** *28½" x 15½", dials 7", spring, 8 Day, strike, alarm (M330-107).*
.... 900.00   1075.00

☐ **Fashion Model 2,** *short pendulum, 21" x 15", dials 7½", spring, 8 Day, strike (M331-107).*
.... 1250.00   1450.00

☐ **Fashion Model 3,** *short pendulum, 32" x 16", dials 7½", spring, 8 Day, strike (M342-110).*
.... 1650.00   1975.00

☐ **Fashion Model 4,** *short pendulum, 32" x 16", dials 7½", spring, 8 Day, strike (M343-110).*
.... 1600.00   2000.00

☐ **Fashion Model 5,** *long pendulum, 32" x 16½", dials 7½", spring, 8 Day, strike (M353-133).*
.... 1850.00   2250.00

☐ **Fashion Model 6,** *long pendulum, 32" x 16½", dials 7½", spring, 8 Day, strike (M354-113).*
.... 2000.00   2450.00

☐ **Fashion Model 7,** *long pendulum, 32½" x 16½", dials 7½", spring, 8 Day, strike (M359-115).*
.... 1900.00   2325.00

☐ **Fashion Model 8,** *long pendulum, 32½" x 16½", dials 7½", spring, 8 Day, strike (M360-115).*
.... 1850.00   2375.00

☐ **Fashion Model 9,** *short pendulum, 32" x 17", dials 7", spring, 8 Day, strike (M364-116).*
.... 1500.00   1675.00

SOUTHERN CLOCK COMPANY

CALENDAR

☐ **O.G.,** *25¾" x 15¼", dials 8", spring, 8 Day, strike, simple calendar (M468-144).*
.... 350.00   425.00

STANDARD CALENDAR CLOCK CO.—O.G. CLOCK CO.

CALENDAR

☐ **O.G. Standard Calendar Clock Co.,** *made by New Haven Clock Co., 25¾" x 15½", spring, 8 Day, strike, simple calendar (M385-122).*
.... 245.00   275.00

☐ **O.G. Clock Co.,** *made by New Haven Clock Co., 26" x 15½", spring, 8 Day, strike (M387-122).*
.... 300.00   400.00

TERRY CLOCK COMPANY

Eli Terry, born at East Windsor in Connecticut, showed a mechanical inclination early in life. Inspired by Eli Whitney, inventor of the cotton gin, Terry is credited as the father of mass clock mechanization. Seth Thomas was his assistant at one time, as was Silas Hoadley.

In a mill by the Naugatuck river, he created a shelf clock design, that virtually displaced the longcase model and was more popular than either the wall or standing clock variations. Terry is also responsible for the start of Bristol's reputation as a clock making center of the state of Connecticut. Terry's patent, was of course widely imitated, and Terry despite his efforts was not successful in inhibiting patent reproductions. Seth Thomas, his former partner, discontinued licensing and fee paying for the privilege of the original design. A lawsuit followed where the issue was not resolved in Terry's favor, further opening the doors for shelf clock imitators to proceed without censor.

Terry's sons Eli Jr., Silas and Samuel followed him into the business, as did his grandsons, Cornelius, Solon, and Simeon. As mentioned earlier the firm passed into the hands of Russell & Jones, near the end of the century, ending the Terry family's tradition of almost a century's worth of expertise, pioneering, and enterprise within the horological field.

CALENDAR

□ **Octagon Wall,** *short drop, reverse O.G. moulding on case, 22¼" x 16", dial 11", spring, 8 Day, simple calendar (M233-80).*
. . . . **500.00   750.00**

□ **Octagon Wall,** *short drop, height 22¾", dial 9", spring, 8 Day, simple calendar (M235-80).*
. . . . **400.00   475.00**

CONNECTICUT SHELF

CHAPEL

□ **No.160,** *bronze, height 13", dial 4", spring, pendulum, 8 Day, strike.*
. . . . **200.00   250.00**

□ **No.120,** *bronze, height 9½", dial 3½", 1 Day, spring, pendulum.*
. . . . **125.00   150.00**

☐ **No.121**, *bronze, height 9½ ", dial 3½ ", 1 Day, spring, pendulum, alarm.*
.... 135.00   160.00

☐ **No.22**, *walnut, height 10½ ", dial 4", 1 Day, spring, pendulum.*
.... 180.00   200.00

☐ **No.23**, *walnut, height 10½ ", dial 4", 1 Day, spring, pendulum, alarm.*
.... 200.00   220.00

☐ **No.24**, *walnut, height 10½ ", dial 4", 1 Day, spring, pendulum, strike.*
.... 230.00   250.00

☐ **No.25**, *walnut, height 10½ ", dial 4", 8 Day, spring, pendulum.*
.... 230.00   250.00

☐ **No.26**, *walnut, height 10½ ", dial 4", 8 Day, spring, pendulum, strike.*
.... 270.00   290.00

COLUMN

☐ **Rose Column**, *wood, 22½ " x 15", dial 8", 1 Day, weight, pendulum, strike.*
.... 150.00   165.00

☐ **Rose Column**, *wood, 22½ " x 15", dial 8", 8 Day, weight, pendulum, strike.*
.... 200.00   225.00

COTTAGE

☐ **Cottage**, *wood, height 11", dial 5", 1 Day, spring, pendulum.*
.... 120.00   150.00

☐ **Cottage**, *wood, height 11", dial 5", 1 Day, spring pendulum, alarm.*
.... 130.00   160.00

GOTHIC AND MANTEL

☐ **No.43**, *Gothic black and gilt iron, height 13", dial 5", 1 Day, spring, pendulum.*
.... 180.00   200.00

☐ **No.44**, *Gothic black and gilt iron, height 13", dial 5", 1 Day, spring, pendulum, alarm.*
.... 200.00   225.00

☐ **No.45,** *Gothic black and gilt iron, height 13", dial 5", 8 Day, spring, pendulum.*
.... 180.00   200.00

☐ **No.46,** *Gothic black and gilt iron, height 13", dial 5", 8 Day, spring, pendulum, alarm.*
.... 200.00   225.00

☐ **No,47,** *Gothic black and gilt iron, height 13", dial 5", 8 Day, pendulum, strike.*
.... 240.00   260.00

☐ **No.48,** *Gothic black and gilt iron, height 13", dial 5", 8 Day, pendulum, strike, alarm.*
.... 250.00   275.00

☐ **No.110,** *Mantel bronze, height 7½", dial 2½", 1 Day, spring, pendulum.*
.... 130.00   150.00

☐ **No.111,** *Mantel bronze, height 7½", dial 2½", 1 Day, spring, pendulum, alarm.*
.... 130.00   150.00

NOVELTY

☐ **No.140, Boy and Dog,** *bronze, height 11½", dial 3", 1 Day, spring, pendulum.*
.... 130.00   150.00

☐ **No.141, Boy and Dog,** *bronze, height 11½", dial 3", 1 Day, spring, pendulum, alarm.*
.... 140.00   160.0(

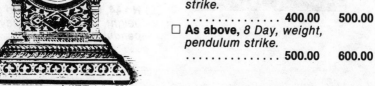

☐ **No.150, Alhambra,** *bronze, height 10", dial 4", 1 Day, spring, pendulum, strike.*
.... 255.00   275.00

O.G., O.O.G. AND REVERSED O.G.

☐ **Reversed O.G.,** *wood, 1 Day, spring pendulum.*
.... 110.00   120.00

☐ **As above,** *spring pendulum, alarm.*
.... 120.00   130.00

☐ **As above,** *spring pendulum, strike.*
.... 130.00   150.00

☐ **As above,** *8 Day, spring pendulum, strike.*
.... 130.00   150.00

☐ **O.G. No.2,** *wood, 18" x 11½", dial 6", 1 Day, weight, pendulum strike.*
.... 400.00   500.00

☐ **O.G.,** *wood, 18" x 11½", dial 6", 8 Day, weight, pendulum strike.*
.... 500.00   600.00

☐ **O.O.G.,** *wood, 18" x 11½", dial 6", 1 Day, weight, pendulum strike.*
.... 400.00   500.00

☐ **As above,** *8 Day, weight, pendulum strike.*
.... 500.00   600.00

ROUND TOP

☐ **No.1,** *plain black iron, height 6",
dial 2½", c. 1873, 1 Day, spring
pendulum.*
. . . . 100.00   120.00

☐ **No.2,** *black and gilt iron, height
6", dial 2½", c. 1873, 1 Day,
spring pendulum.*
. . . . 110.00   130.00

☐ **No.7,** *plain black iron, height 8",
dial 3½", c. 1873, 1 Day, spring
pendulum.*
. . . . 100.00   120.00

☐ **No.8,** *black and gilt iron, height
8", dial 3½", c. 1873, 1 Day,
spring pendulum.*
. . . . 110.00   130.00

☐ **No.10,** *plain black iron, height 8",
dial 3½", c. 1873, 1 Day, spring
pendulum, strike.*
. . . . 110.00   130.00

☐ **No.11,** *black and gilt iron, height
8", dial 3½", c. 1873, 1 Day,
spring pendulum, strike.*
. . . . 120.00   140.00

☐ **No.13,** *plain black iron, height 8",
dial 3½", c. 1873, 1 Day, spring
pendulum, alarm.*
. . . . 110.00   130.00

☐ **No.14,** *black and gilt iron, height
8", dial 3½", c. 1873, 1 Day,
spring pendulum, alarm.*
. . . . 120.00   130.00

☐ **No.16,** *plain black iron, height 8",
dial 3½", c. 1873, 1 Day, spring
alarm, strike.*
. . . . 130.00   150.00

☐ **No.17,** *black and gilt iron, height
8", dial 3½", c. 1873, 1 Day,
spring pendulum, strike, alarm.*
. . . . 140.00   160.00

☐ **No.20,** *plain black iron, height 6",
dial 2½", c. 1873, 1 Day, spring
pendulum, alarm.*
. . . . 110.00   130.00

☐ **No.21,** *black and gilt iron, height
6", dial 2½", c. 1873, 1 Day,
spring pendulum, alarm.*
. . . . 120.00   140.00

☐ **No.27,** *plain black iron, height 9",
dial 4", c. 1873, 8 Day, spring
pendulum.*
. . . . 110.00   130.00

☐ **No.28,** *black and gilt iron, height
9", dial 4", c. 1873, 8 Day, spring
pendulum*
. . . . 120.00   140.00

☐ **No.30,** *plain black iron, height 9", dial 4", c. 1873, 8 Day, spring pendulum, strike.*
. . . . **120.00   140.00**

☐ **No.31,** *black and gilt iron, height 9", dial 4", c. 1873, 8 Day, spring pendulum, strike.*
. . . . **130.00   150.00**

☐ **No.33,** *plain black iron, height 9", dial 4", c. 1873, 8 Day, spring, alarm.*
. . . . **110.00   130.00**

☐ **No.34,** *black and gilt iron, height 9", dial 4", c. 1873, 8 Day, spring pendulum, strike, alarm.*
. . . . **120.00   140.00**

☐ **No.36,** *plain black iron, height 9", dial 4", c. 1873, 8 Day, spring, alarm, strike.*
. . . . **130.00   150.00**

☐ **No.37,** *black and gilt iron, height 9", dial 4", c. 1873, 8 Day, spring pendulum, alarm, strike.*
. . . . **140.00   160.00**

☐ **No.130,** *plain black iron, height 11", dial 5", c. 1873, 8 Day, spring pendulum, strike.*
. . . . **180.00   200.00**

☐ **No.131,** *black and gilt iron, height 11", dial 5", c. 1873, 8 Day, spring pendulum, strike.*
. . . . **200.00   220.00**

☐ **No.133,** *plain black iron, height 11", dial 5", c. 1873, 8 Day, spring pendulum, calendar.*
. . . . **350.00   400.00**

☐ **No.134,** *black and gilt iron, height 11", dial 5", c. 1873, 8 Day, spring pendulum, calendar.*
. . . . **350.00   400.00**

☐ **No.136,** *plain black iron, height 11", dial 5", c. 1873, 8 Day, spring pendulum, strike, calendar.*
. . . . **500.00   600.00**

☐ **No.137,** *black and gilt iron, height 11", dial 5", c. 1873, 8 Day, spring pendulum, strike, calendar.*
. . . . **500.00   600.00**

REGULATOR

OCTAGON TOP SHORT DROP — ROUND TOP SHORT DROP

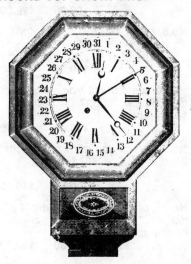

☐ **O.G. Octagon Top,** *wood,*
23" x 15½", dial 12", 1 Day,
spring pendulum.
.... 325.00   350.00
☐ **As above,** *1 Day, spring*
pendulum, strike.
.... 350.00   375.00
☐ **As above,** *1 Day, spring*
pendulum, calendar.
.... 375.00   400.00
☐ **As above,** *1 Day, spring*
pendulum, strike, calendar.
.... 400.00   425.00

☐ **Octagon Top,** *black and gilt iron,*
height 21", dial 12", 8 Day,
spring, ½ second, pendulum.
.... 450.00   500.00
☐ **As above,** *8 Day, spring,*
½ second, pendulum, strike.
.... 500.00   550.00

☐ **No.50,** *round top drop, black and*
gilt iron, height 19", dial 8",
8 Day, spring pendulum.
.... 450.00   500.00

☐ **No.51,** *round top drop, black and*
gilt iron, height 19", dial 8",
8 Day, spring pendulum, strike.
.... 475.00   525.00

☐ **No.60,** *octagon top drop, black*
and gilt iron, height 19", dial 8",
8 Day, spring pendulum that
beats ½ seconds.
.... 450.00   500.00

☐ **No.61,** *Octagon top drop, black*
and gilt iron, height 19", dial 8",
8 Day, spring pendulum that
beats ½ seconds, strike.
.... 475.00   525.00

☐ **No.70,** *round top mantel, black*
and gilt iron, height 19", dial 8",
8 Day, spring pendulum that
beats ½ seconds.
.... 450.00   500.00

☐ **No.71,** *Round Top Mantle, black*
and gilt iron, height 19", dial 8",
spring pendulum that beats
½ seconds, strike.
.... 475.00   525.00

WALTHAM — 1900's WEIGHT BANJOS

These clocks are priced according to the definition of "retail value" as given in the front of this book. However, in this case, there have been many transactions ABOVE this so-called top price. The reasons are simple. The seller may not always make it very clear that these are 1900's production clocks. Waltham and many other manufacturers produced both weight and spring banjos that more or less resembled Willard and Howard banjos. "Willard Clock" and "Banjo Clock" were used as synonyms in some of the advertising, and some sellers today use these terms in the same way but do not always so indicate to an eager buyer.

Some buyers will pay well above the retail value of these banjos because they intend to resell at a much higher price after some modifications. These modifications usually consist of a nameless dial, usually appearing quite old, and marriages with other movements if the clock has a lever or electric movement.

Some buyers are so eager to add a banjo to their collection that the seller of a 1934 Waltham, or other modern versions, has only to imply that it is old, and while maintaining an air of ignorance as to its origin, let the dreams of the buyer persuade him to pay an exorbitant price.

Some sellers have found great profit in replacing electric movements in modern banjos with old pendulum movements. The same has been done with some lever movements. Weight movements have been and are today being reproduced, and sometimes appear in the larger banjos.

"Caveat Emptor" — let the buyer beware. Remember that between the two World Wars, almost all major producers had in their lines banjo clocks. Waltham stated in their advertising that, while they reproduced the Willard Clock "in its general lines", they "added much to the symmetry and beauty of design". All of these banjos are collectible and will add to any collection if original and identifiable. Approach an unmarked, unidentifiable banjo with caution, especially if the seller "believes it could be by a well-known maker". The results of a "May and December marriage" of a modern case to an old works will not add greatly to your collection. For further discussion of the fakes who misrepresent these fine clocks, read the section in this book on Replicas, Reproductions and Fakes.

THE SCIENTIFICALLY BUILT CLOCK BANJOS

☐ **No.1500,** *antique mahogany, torus molding, ornament, 41" x 10½", deep 4", 8 Day, weight.*
.... **2500.00   3000.00**
☐ **As above,** *walnut.*
.... **2700.00   3200.00**

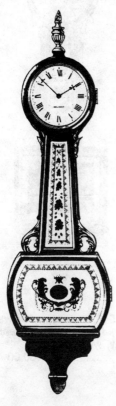

☐ **No.1525,** *mahogany, gold leaf front, acorn base, Waltham design glasses, 40½" x 10½", deep 4", 8 Day, weight.*
.... **4000.00   5000.00**

☐ **No.1505,** *antique mahogany, carved top and side ornaments, Waltham design glasses, 41½" x 10½", deep 4", 8 Day, weight.*
.... **3500.00   4500.00**

☐ **No.1540,** *mahogany or walnut ivory, red or green crackle flat moulding, brass eagle and side rails, 40½" x 10½", deep 4", 8 Day, weight.*

.... 2500.00   3500.00

☐ **No.1543,** *mahogany or walnut carved, gilded rope and balls, 40½" x 10½", deep 4", 8 Day, weight.*

.... 2500.00   3000.00

☐ **No.1546,** *mahogany or walnut inlay, 40½" x 10½", deep 4", 8 Day, weight.*

.... 2500.00   3500.00

☐ **No.1550,** *mahogany, walnut or crackle, 21" x 5¼", deep 2", 7 jewel spring, 8 Day.*
.... 250.00   350.00

☐ **No.1554,** *mahogany or walnut, torus molding, 21" x 5¼", deep 2", 8 Day, spring.*
.... 250.00   350.00

☐ **No.1553,** *mahogany or walnut, torus molding, 21" x 5½", deep 2", 8 Day, spring.*
.... 250.00   350.00

☐ **No.1555,** *mahogany, gold leaf front, 21" x 5¼", deep 2", 8 Day, spring.*
.... 2250.00   2500.00

LIBRARY CLOCKS

This unusually attractive clock is available in mahogany, walnut or black finish.

☐ **No.1425,** *7 jewel, mahogany,*
13¼" x 9¾", deep 1⅛".
.... 50.00   75.00

☐ **No.1426,** *7 jewel, walnut,*
13¼" x 9¾", deep 1⅛".
.... 50.00   75.00

☐ **No.1427,** *7 jewel, black finish,*
13¼" x 9¾", deep 1⅛".
.... 50.00   75.00

☐ **No.1428,** *17 jewel, mahogany,*
13¼" x 9¾", deep 1⅛".
.... 125.00   150.00

☐ **No.1429,** *15 jewel, walnut,*
13¼" x 9¾", deep 1⅛".
.... 125.00   150.00

☐ **No.1430,** *15 jewel, black finish,*
13¼" x 9¾", deep 1⅛".
.... 125.00   150.00

☐ **No.1470,** *an adaptation of the*
quaint colonial clock, exclusive
Waltham design, gilded eagle,
hand painted glasses, carved
base reminiscent of the early
American period. Brass
ornaments, gilt rope, solid
mahogany, ivory dial with black
figures, 14½"x 5¼", 7 jewel.
.... 650.00   900.00

☐ **As above,** *No.1471, 15 jewel.*
.... 800.00 1000.00

☐ **No.1467,** *antique gilt modernistic*
type, 15½" x 13", deep 1½",
7 jewel.
.... 60.00   90.00

☐ **As above,** *No.1468, 15 jewel.*
.... 120.00   150.00

☐ **No.8514,** *mahogany only, brass*
trimmings, hand painted panel
glasses, 12" x 5¾", 7 jewel.
.... 675.00   925.00

☐ **No.8516,** *solid bronze, natural finish, art deco, 11¾" x 13½", deep 1½", 15 jewel.*
. . . . **350.00   400.00**

☐ **As above,** *No.8517, 15 jewel, verde finish.*
. . . . **350.00   400.00**

☐ **No.8518,** *solid bronze, natural finish, art deco, 11" x 11½", deep 1⅝", 15 jewel.*
. . . . **350.00   400.00**

☐ **No.8525,** *Waltham Chronometer, lever escapement, winding indicator movement adjusted to changes in temperature and isochronism, enclosed in a dust and weather proof case suspended on gimbals in solid mahogany box, 15 jewel.*
. . . . **300.00   350.00**

W. A. TERRY — ANSONIA

CALENDAR

☐ **Round Wall,** *short drop, 25½" x 16", dial 11", 8 Day, strike (M243-84).*
. . . . **750.00   850.00**

☐ **Shelf Clock,** *Ansonia Brass and Copper Co., Ansonia, Ct., 32¾" x 16", dial 11", 8 Day, strike (M242-83).*
. . . . **1000.00   1100.00**

W. A. TERRY — ATKINS

CALENDAR

☐ **Italian Type Shelf,** *18" x 11", spring, 8 Day, strike (M237-81).*
. . . . **1000.00   1200.00**

WATERBURY CLOCK COMPANY

A major producer of clocks in its time, Waterbury began production of a cheap watch towards the end of the 19th century, and continued up until the present.

The company originated through a brass producing firm, and was connected with Chauncey Jerome for a time. There was a place for brass in the clock manufacturing world, and Waterbury was quick to make that lucrative connection.

The company styled its own clocks, the most notable examples being the round top, and octagon drop regulators. The company also sold substantial numbers of its own movements.

Waterbury and all other clock companies for that matter, issued a catalogue to their dealers every year or so. It pictured and described the clocks they offered, along with prices, terms, etc. The dealers or wholesalers, depending on their size and other factors, selected the clocks they wanted to offer for sale from the Waterbury line. These clocks were usually combined with clocks from other companies and then pictured in their general catalogue. This is why some old catalogues show many pictures of several clocks of different manufacturers. Waterbury clocks are relatively easy to distinguish, as some were made only for a short time, although others ran as long as ten to forty years.

ALARM CALENDAR

☐ **Index nickel,** *lever, dial 3¾",*
1 Day, simple calendar (E1-34).
. . . . **75.00   120.00**

☐ **Kremlin Nickel,** *lever, dial 3¾", 1 Day, simple calendar (E1-34).*
. . . . **75.00   120.00**

☐ **Monitor Nickel,** *lever, dial 3¾", 1 Day, simple calendar (E1-34).*
. . . . **75.00   120.00**

☐ **Sentry,** *Lever, dial 5", 1 Day, simple calendar (E1-34).*
. . . . **80.00   125.00**
NOTE: The above alarm type calendars were available in hammered or fancy ornamented, or brass or nickel cases.

ALARM ROUND

☐ **Caliph,** *nickel, brass recessed backs, brass winding and setting parts, dial 3¾", c. 1888, 1 Day (E1-34).*
. . . . **25.00   35.00**

☐ **Envoy,** *nickel, brass recessed backs, brass winding and setting parts, dial 3¾", c. 1888, 1 Day, (E1-34).*
. . . . **25.00   35.00**

☐ **Index,** *calendar, nickel, brass recessed backs, brass winding and setting parts, dial 3¾", c. 1888, 1 Day, calendar (E1-34).*
. . . . **60.00   75.00**

☐ **Moslem Nickel,** *lever, dial 3¾", 1 Day, simple calendar (E1-34).*
. . . . **75.00   120.00**

☐ **Knight,** *nickel, dial 5", c. 1888, 1 Day, alarm (E1-34).*
.... 30.00   40.00

☐ **Kremlin,** *nickel, brass recessed backs, brass winding and setting parts, dial 3¾", c. 1888, 1 Day, calendar, alarm (E1-34).*
.... 60.00   75.00

☐ **Monitor,** *calendar, nickel, brass recessed backs, brass winding and setting parts, dial 3¾", c. 1888, 1 Day, calendar, alarm (E1-34).*
.... 60.00   75.00

☐ **Moslem,** *nickel, brass recessed backs, brass winding and setting parts, dial 3¾", c. 1888, 1 Day, calendar (E1-34).*
.... 60.00   75.00

☐ **Sentry,** *nickel, dial 5", c. 1888, 1 Day, calendar, alarm (E1-34).*
.... 40.00   50.00

☐ **Sunrise,** *nickel, brass recessed backs, brass winding and setting parts, dial 3¾", 1 Day, c. 1888, alarm (E1-34).*
.... 30.00   40.00

☐ **Turk,** *nickel, dial 4½", c. 1888, 1 Day, alarm (E1-34).*
.... 40.00   55.00

CABINET

☐ **Cabinet E,** *walnut, height 16", porcelain dial, c. 1888, 8 Day, strike(E1-32).*
.... 110.00   135.00
☐ **As above,** *ash.*
.... 135.00   160.00

☐ **As above,** *cherry.*
.... **110.00   135.00**

☐ **Cabinet F,** *walnut, height 19½",
porcelain dial, c. 1888,
8 Day, strike (E1-23).*
.... **125.00   150.00**

☐ **As above,** *ash.*
.... **150.00   175.00**

☐ **As above,** *cherry.*
.... **125.00   150.00**

CALENDAR

☐ **Andes Figure 8,** *height 24", dial
12", 8 Day, strike, simple
calendar (E1-183).*
.... **300.00   400.00**

☐ **Antique Drop, Octagon Top,**
*short drop, spring, 22½" x 14½",
dial 10", spring, 8 Day, strike,
simple calendar (E1-25, M301-99).*
.... **375.00   450.00**

☐ **Arion Octagon Top 10",** *short
drop, 22½" x 15", spring, 8 Day,
strike, simple calendar (E1-183,
M300-99).*
.... **275.00   325.00**

☐ **Arion Octagon Top 12",** *short
drop, height 24", 8 Day, strike,
simple calendar (E1-183).*
.... **300.00   375.00**

☐ **Bahia Mosaic Figure 8,** *height
22", dial 10", spring, 8 Day,
strike, simple calendar (E1-149).*
.... **375.00   425.00**

☐ **Belden Victorian Shelf,**
*22" x 15", dial 5", spring, 8 Day,
strike, simple calendar (M295-98).*
.... **225.00   275.00**

☐ **Box Regulator No.2,** *oak, height
38½", dial 12", 8 Day, strike,
simple calendar (E1-184).*
.... **350.00   450.00**

☐ **Box Regulator No.4,** *mahogany,
height 38½", dial 12", 8 Day,
strike, simple calendar (E1-184).*
.... **350.00   450.00**

☐ **Dabney Shelf,** *height 22", dial 6",
with thermometer and barometer,
8 Day, strike, simple calendar
(M306-100).*
.... **225.00   275.00**

☐ **Double Dial Shelf No.40?,**
*23½" x 14½", dials 6", spring,
8 Day (M279-94).*
.... **750.00   850.00**

☐ **Double Dial Shelf No.40,**
*24" x 14½", dials 6", spring,
8 Day, strike (E1-151, M285-95).*
.... **750.00   850.00**

□ **Double Dial Shelf No.43,** *height 28¼", dials 8", spring, 8 Day, strike (E1-98, M283-95).*
. . . . **700.00   900.00**

□ **Double Dial Wall No.25,** *double weight dead beat, retaining power, 49½" x 19¼", dials 10", seconds bit, 8 Day (E1-98, M270-92).*
. . . . **1900.00   2100.00**

□ **Double Dial Wall No.26,** *double weight dead beat, retaining power, height 46", dials 9", seconds bit, 8 Day (E1-153).*
. . . . **1900.00   2150.00**

□ **Double Dial Wall No.27,** *44¾" x 14½", dials 10", spring, 8 Day (E1-150, M271-92).*
. . . . **1400.00   1600.00**

□ **Double Dial Shelf No.44,** *24" x 14½", dials 6", spring, 8 Day, strike (E1-151, M284-95).*
. . . . **650.00   750.00**

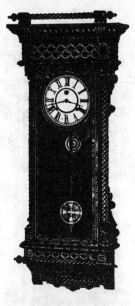

□ **Double Dial Wall No.30,** *height 40¼", dials 9", spring, 8 Day (E1-151).*
.... **1800.00   2000.00**

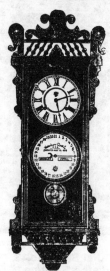

□ **Double Dial Wall No.28,** *41" x 15", dials 8", spring, 8 Day (E1-151, M272-92).*
.... **1800.00   2000.00**

□ **No.31,** *not pictured.*
.... **1900.00   2100.00**

☐ **Double Dial Shelf No.33,**
*39" x 15", dials 8", spring, 8 Day
(E1-98, M274-93).*
.... 900.00   1100.00

☐ **Double Dial Shelf No.34,**
*29" x 15¾", spring, 11" time and
10" calendar dials, 8 Day
(M277-93).*
.... 1100.00   1250.00

☐ **Double Dial Shelf No. 36,**
*28" x 15", dials 6", spring,
8 Day (E1-151, M275-93).*
.... 900.00   1000.00

☐ **Double Dial Shelf No.38,** *height
28", dials 6", spring, 8 Day
(E1-151).*
.... 1800.00   2000.00

☐ **No.39,** *not pictured.*
.... 1700.00   1900.00

☐ **Felix Shelf,** *height 22", dial 6",
spring, 8 Day, simple calendar
(M304-100).*
.... 225.00   275.00

☐ **Gibson Victorian Shelf,**
*24" x 15", dial 5", with
thermometer and barometer,
spring, 8 Day, strike, simple
calendar (M296-98).*
.... 225.00   250.00

☐ **Glenwood Figure 8,** *height 25½",
dial 12", 8 Day, strike, simple
calendar (E1-100).*
.... 450.00   550.00

☐ **Heron Octagon Top,** *long drop,
height 32", dial 12", 8 Day,
strike, simple calendar (E1-183).*
.... 350.00   425.00

☐ **Joliet Roller Type Wall,** *spring,
8 Day (M309-101).*
.... 1500.00   1750.00

☐ **Natchez Wall,** *40" x 13¾", dial
8", spring, 8 Day, simple
calendar (E1-97, M303-100).*
.... 600.00   675.00

☐ **Octagon Lever Wall 8",** *spring,
8 Day, simple calendar (E1-27).*
.... 250.00   300.00

☐ **Octagon Lever Wall 8",** *spring,
1 Day, simple calendar
(M307-101).*
.... 225.00   275.00

☐ **Octagon Lever Wall 10",** *spring,
1 Day, simple calendar (E1-27).*
.... 250.00   300.00

☐ **Octagon Lever Wall 10",** *spring,
8 Day, simple calendar (E1-27).*
.... 275.00   350.00

☐ **Octagon Lever Wall 12",** *spring,
8 Day, simple calendar (E1-27).*
.... 300.00   375.00

☐ **Octagon Top 12",** *short drop,
height 24", spring, 8 Day, strike,
simple calendar (E1-183).*
.... 300.00   375.00

☐ **Octagon Top 8″**, *short drop, height 19″, spring, 8 Day, strike, simple calendar (E1-25).*
.... 250.00   300.00

☐ **Octagon Top 10″**, *short drop, 22½″ x 15″, spring, 8 Day, strike, simple calendar (E1-149).*
.... 275.00   325.00

☐ **Octagon Top 10″**, *"Zebra Case" short drop, height 21″, spring, 8 Day, strike, simple calendar (E1-32).*
.... 275.00   325.00

☐ **Octagon Top 10″**, *gilt case, short drop, height 21″, spring, 8 Day, strike, simple calendar (E1-32).*
.... 275.00   325.00

☐ **Octagon Top 12″**, *short drop, height 24″, spring, 8 Day, strike, simple calendar (M299-99).*
.... 325.00   375.00

☐ **Ontario Victorian Shelf,** *28½″ x 17½″, dials 7″, spring, 8 Day, strike, simple calendar (M293-97).*
.... 325.00   375.00

☐ **Oswego Double Dial Shelf,** *28″ x 17½″, dials 7″, spring, 8 Day, strike (M287-96).*
.... 550.00   650.00

☐ **Paris Parlor Shelf,** *23″ x 13″, dial 5″, spring, 8 Day, strike, simple calendar (M297-98).*
.... 300.00   400.00

☐ **Pelican Box Regulator,** *height 37½″, dial 12″, 8 Day, strike, simple calendar (E1-184).*
.... 350.00   450.00

☐ **Peoria Roller Type Wall,** *spring, 8 Day, not pictured.*
.... 1600.00   1850.00

☐ **Regent Octagon Top,** *long drop, height 32″, dial 12″, spring, 8 Day, strike, simple calendar (E1-100).*
.... 400.00   500.00

☐ **Rochester Victorian Shelf,** *27″ x 17½″, dial 7″, spring, 8 Day, strike, simple calendar (M289-96).*
.... 300.00   375.00

☐ **Selborne Victorian Shelf,** *height 23″, dial 6″, 8 Day, strike, simple calendar (E1-28).*
.... 200.00   300.00

☐ **Springfield Wall Regulator,** *40½″ x 13¾″, dial 8″, spring, 8 Day, strike, simple calendar (E1-96, M302-100).*
.... 600.00   675.00

☐ **Victorian Kitchen Shelf,** *spring, dial 5″, with thermometer and barometer, 8 Day, strike, simple calendar (M294-97).*
.... 225.00   250.00

☐ **Walton Wall Regulator,** *41″ x 15¼″, dial 10″, 8 Day, strike, simple calendar (E1-96).*
.... 500.00   600.00

CARRIAGE

☐ **Compass,** *nickel, dial 3½",*
c. 1888, 1 Day, strike (E1-34).
. . . . 105.00   125.00

☐ **Magnet,** *nickel, dial 3½", c. 1888,*
1 Day, alarm (E1-34).
. . . . 95.00   115.00
As above *1 Day, alarm,*
sweep sec.
. . . . 105.00   130.00

☐ **Passenger,** *nickel, dial 3½",*
c. 1888, 1 Day, alarm (E1-34).
. . . . 80.00   95.00

☐ **Tourist,** *nickel, dial 3½", c. 1888,*
1 Day, alarm (E1-34).
. . . . 80.00   95.00
☐ **As above,** *1 Day, strike.*
. . . . 85.00   105.00
☐ **Traveler,** *nickel, dial 2¼",*
c. 1888, 1 Day, alarm (E1-34).
. . . . 100.00   120.00
☐ **As above,** *1 Day, alarm, sweep*
sec.
. . . . 110.00   135.00

☐ **Voyager,** *nickel, dial 2¼",*
c. 1888, 1 Day, strike (E1-34).
. . . . 105.00   130.00

CONNECTICUT SHELF

COTTAGE

☐ **Cottage Extra,** *polished wood,*
height 12¾", c. 1888, 1 Day,
strike, spring (E1-27).
. . . . 70.00   85.00
☐ **As above,** *8 Day, strike, spring*
. . . . 100.00   120.00

☐ **Cottage No. 2,** *polished wood,*
height 12", c. 1888, 1 Day, spring
(E1-27).
. . . . 60.00   75.00
☐ **As above,** *1 Day, strike, spring*
. . . . 80.00   100.00

☐ **Tick Tack,** *imitation mahogany,*
height 11", c. 1888, 1 Day, spring
(E1-27).
. . . . 55.00   70.00

CONNECTICUIT SHELF O.G.

☐ **O.G.,** *weight, polished wood, height 26", dial 8", c. 1888, 1 Day, strike (E1-27).*
.... 130.00   155.00

☐ **As above,** *8 Day, strike*
.... 175.00   200.00

CRYSTAL REGULATORS

☐ **Aubert,** *rich gold plated or Syrian bronze, visible escapement, cast gilt bezel, beveled glass front, sides and back, 13⅜" x 6¼", ivory dial 4½", c. 1910, 8 Day, strike (E1-130).*
.... 270.00   310.00

☐ **Aude,** *rich gold plated, ivory center, visible escapement, cast gilt bezel, beveled glass front, sides and back, 10⅛" x 7¾", ivory dial 4¼", c. 1910, 8 Day, strike (E1-130).*
.... 270.00   315.00

☐ **Bordeaux,** *rich gold plated, ivory center, visible escapement, cast gilt bezel, beveled glass front, sides and back, 18¼" x 8⅝", ivory dial 4½", c. 1910, 8 Day, strike (E1-131).*
.... 515.00   575.00

☐ **Brest,** *rich gold plated, ivory center, visible escapement, cast gilt bezel, beveled glass front, sides and back, 9¼" x 5¾", ivory dial 3½", c. 1910, 8 Day, strike (E1-132).*
.... 145.00   170.00

☐ **Brittany,** *rich gold plated, ivory center, visible escapement, cast gilt bezel, beveled glass front, sides and back, 11⅞" x 7", ivory dial 4½", c. 1910, 8 Day, strike (E1-130).*
.... 335.00   375.00

☐ **Caen,** *rich gold plated, ivory center, visible escapement, cast gilt bezel, beveled glass front, sides and back, 9⅞" x 7", ivory dial 4¼", c. 1910, 8 Day, strike (E1-132).*
.... 205.00   235.00

☐ **Calais,** *rich gold plated, ivory center, visible escapement, cast gilt bezel, beveled glass front, sides and back, 11⅞" x 7", ivory dial 4¼", c. 1910, 8 Day, strike (E1-131).*
.... 400.00   450.00

☐ **Cantal,** *rich gold plated, ivory center, visible escapement, cast gilt bezel, beveled glass front, sides and back, 10⅜" x 6⅝", ivory dial 4¼", c. 1910, 8 Day, strike (E1-131).*
.... 310.00   350.00

☐ **Charente,** *rich gold plated, ivory center, visible escapement, cast gilt bezel, beveled glass front, sides and back, 11⅜" x 8⅛", ivory dial 4½", c. 1910, 8 Day, strike (E1-130).*

. . . . 340.00   380.00

☐ **Dieppe,** *rich gold plated, ivory center, visible escapement, cast gilt bezel, beveled glass front, sides and back, 10⅝" x 7⅝", ivory dial 4½", c. 1910, 8 Day, strike (E1-132).*

. . . . 255.00   285.00

☐ **Dijon,** *rich gold plated, ivory center, visible escapement, cast gilt bezel, beveled glass front, sides and back, 13⅛" x 9", ivory dial 3½", c. 1910, 8 Day, strike (E1-131).*

. . . . 490.00   550.00

☐ **Flanders,** *rich gold plated, polished mahogany lower part of base and lower part of top, ivory center, visible escapement, cast gilt bezel, beveled glass front, sides and back, 12⅛" x 6⅝", ivory dial 4¼", c. 1910, 8 Day, strike (E1-132).*

. . . . 270.00   310.00

☐ **Gard,** *rich gold plated, green onyx base and top, ivory center, visible escapement, cast gilt bezel, beveled glass front, sides and back, 16" x 7½", ivory dial 4½", c. 1910, 8 Day, strike (E1-131).*

. . . . 540.00   600.00

☐ **Gers,** *rich gold plated, green onyx base and top, ivory center, visible escapement, cast gilt bezel, beveled glass front, sides and back, 11¼" x 7⅝", ivory dial 4½", c. 1910, 8 Day, strike (E1-131).*

. . . . 450.00   500.00

☐ **Gironde,** *rich gold plated, green onyx base and top, ivory center,*

visible escapement, cast gilt bezel, beveled glass front, sides and back, 12¾" x 7¾", ivory dial 4½", c. 1910, 8 Day, strike (E1-131).

. . . . 500.00   560.00

☐ **Granville,** *rich gold plated, ivory center, visible escapament, cast gilt bezel, beveled glass front, sides and back, 10⅞" x 6¾", ivory dial 4½", c. 1910, 8 Day, strike (E1-132).*

. . . . 205.00   235.00

☐ **Landes,** *rich gold plated, polished mahogany columns, ivory center, visible escapement, cast gilt bezel, beveled glass front, sides and back, 10⅝" x 7⅞", ivory dial 4¼", c. 1910, 8 Day, strike (E1-130).*

. . . . 285.00   325.00

☐ **Marseilles,** *rich gold plated, ivory center, visible escapement, cast gilt bezel, beveled glass front, sides and back, 16" x 6¼", ivory dial 4½", c. 1910, 8 Day, strike (E1-130).*

. . . . 275.00   315.00

☐ **Mogul,** *rich gold plated, ivory center, visible escapement, cast gilt bezel, beveled glass front, sides and back, 15⅛" x 7", ivory dial 3½", c. 1910, 8 Day, strike (E1-130).*

.... 460.00   520.00

☐ **Morlaix,** *rich gold plated, ivory center, visible escapement, cast gilt bezel, beveled glass front, sides and back, 9⅛" x 5¾", ivory dial 3½", c. 1910, 8 Day, strike (E1-132).*

.... 165.00   190.00

☐ **Navaree,** *rich gold plated, ivory center, visible escapement, cast gilt bezel, beveled glass front, sides and back, 8⅞" x 6½", ivory dial 3½", c. 1910, 8 Day, strike (E1-132).*

.... 195.00   225.00

☐ **Orleans,** *rich gold plated or Syrian bronze, ivory center, visible escapement, cast gilt bezel, beveled glass front, sides and back, 14¾" x 7", ivory dial 3½", c. 1910, 8 Day, strike (E1-130).*

.... 450.00   500.00

☐ **Orne,** *rich gold plated, cut glass columns, ivory center, visible escapement, cast gilt bezel, beveled glass front, sides and back, 13⅛" x 9", ivory dial 3½", c. 1910, 8 Day, strike (E1-131).*

.... 750.00   850.00

☐ **Ostend,** *rich gold plated, ivory center, visible escapement, cast gilt bezel, beveled glass front, sides and back, 9⅞" x 6⅛", ivory dial 4¼", c. 1910, 8 Day, strike (E1-132).*

.... 155.00   180.00

☐ **Paris,** *rich gold plated, polished mahogany base and top, ivory center, visible escapement, cast gilt bezel, beveled glass front, sides and back, 19" x 13¼",*

ivory dial 4½", c. 1910, 8 Day, strike (E1-131).

.... 875.00   975.00

☐ **Rennes,** *rich gold plated, ivory center, visible escapement, cast gilt bezel, beveled glass front, sides and back, 13½" x 8¼", ivory dial 3½", c. 1910, 8 Day, strike (E1-132).*

.... 540.00   600.00

☐ **Riviera,** *rich gold plated or Syrian bronze, ivory center, visible escapement, cast gilt bezel, beveled glass front, sides and back, 11½" x 7½", ivory dial 4½", c. 1910, 8 Day, strike (E1-130).*

.... 310.00   350.00

☐ **Savoy,** *rich gold plated, ivory center, visible escapement, cast gilt bezel, beveled glass front, sides and back, 10⅝" x 7", ivory dial 3½", c. 1910, 8 Day, strike (E1-132).*

.... 295.00   335.00

☐ **Sevres,** *rich gold plated, ivory center, visible escapement, cast gilt bezel, beveled glass front, sides and back, 14½" x 10", ivory dial 4½", c. 1910, 8 Day, strike (E1-131).*
. . . . 575.00   650.00

☐ **Tarn,** *rich gold plated, ivory center, visible escapement, cast gilt bezel, beveled glass front, sides and back, 10⅜" x 7", ivory dial 4¼", c. 1910, 8 Day, strike (E1-130).*
. . . . 285.00   325.00

☐ **Toulon,** *rich gold plated, ivory center, visible escapement, cast gilt bezel, beveled glass front, sides and back, 10⅝" x 7", ivory dial 4½", c. 1910, 8 Day, strike (E1-132).*
. . . . 170.00   195.00

☐ **Vannes,** *rich gold plated, ivory center, visible escapement, cast gilt bezel, beveled glass front, sides and back, 10⅝" x 6⅛", ivory dial 4¼", c. 1910, 8 Day, strike (E1-132).*
. . . . 160.00   185.00

☐ **Vendee,** *rich gold plated, polished mahogany columns, base and top, ivory center, visible escapement, cast gilt bezel, beveled glass front, sides and back, 11¾" x 8¼", ivory dial 4¼", c. 1910, 8 Day, strike (E1-130).*
. . . . 285.00   325.00

GALLERY LEVER

☐ **R.C. Octagon Lever,** *mahogany, spring, c. 1888, 1 Day, 4" (E1-27).*
. . . . 80.00   95.00
☐ **As above,** *1 Day, 6".*
. . . . 90.00   110.00
☐ **As above,** *1 Day, 8".*
. . . . 105.00   125.00
☐ **As above,** *1 Day, 10".*
. . . . 115.00   140.00
☐ **As above,** *8 Day, 6".*
. . . . 125.00   150.00
☐ **As above,** *8 Day, 8".*
. . . . 135.00   160.00
☐ **R.C. Octagon Lever,** *rosewood, spring, c. 1888, 1 Day, 4" (E1-27).*
. . . . 100.00   115.00
☐ **As above,** *1 Day, 6".*
. . . . 110.00   130.00
☐ **As above,** *1 Day, 8".*
. . . . 125.00   150.00
☐ **As above,** *1 Day, 10".*
. . . . 135.00   160.00
☐ **As above,** *8 Day, 6".*
. . . . 145.00   170.00
☐ **As above,** *8 Day, 8".*
. . . . 155.00   180.00

GRANDFATHER

☐ **Hall Clock,** *mahogany case, 7'7½" x 23½", 12" gilt and silver plated dial, 8 Day, strike (E2-174).*
.... 2000.00   2250.00

c. 1915, 8 Day, strike, weight (E1-96).
.... 1980.00   2200.00
☐ **As above,** *mahogany.*
.... 2080.00   2300.00

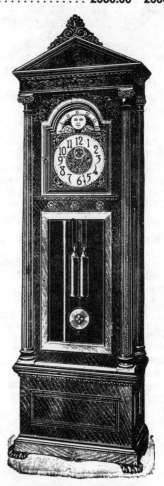

☐ **Hall Clock No.72,** *quartered oak, beveled plate glass panel, moon's phases, brass weights, beats seconds, dead-beat escapement, retaining power, solid polished movement frames, 99" x 25", dial 12",*

☐ **Hall Clock No.77,** *quartered oak, gilt ornaments, beveled plate glass panel, moon's phases, brass weights, beats seconds, dead-beat escapement, retaining power, solid polished movement frames, 96" x 29½", dial 12", c. 1915, 8 Day, weight (E1-96).*
.... 3375.00   3750.00

KITCHEN

☐ **Albany,** *walnut, height 24", dial 6", c. 1888, 8 Day, strike (E1-28).*
. . . . 135.00   160.00

☐ **Antrim,** *walnut, height 20¾", dial 6", c. 1888, 1 Day, strike (E1-27).*
. . . . 115.00   140.00

☐ **Arcade,** *walnut, height 24", dial 6", c. 1888, 8 Day, strike (E1-31).*
. . . . 125.00   150.00

☐ **Auburn,** *ash, height 19½", dial 6", c. 1888, 8 Day, strike (E1-31).*
. . . . 130.00   155.00

☐ **Belmont,** *walnut, height 22¼", dial 6", c. 1888, 1 Day, strike (E1-27).*
. . . . 115.00   140.00

☐ **Borden,** *walnut, height 21½", dial 6", c. 1888, 8 Day, strike (E1-31).*
. . . . 125.00   150.00

☐ **Branford,** *oak, height 17¼", dial 6", c. 1888, 8 Day, strike (E1-31).*
. . . . 100.00   120.00

☐ **Clyde,** *walnut, height 21¾", dial 6", c. 1888, 1 Day, strike (E1-27).*
. . . . 115.00   140.00

☐ **Corona,** *walnut, height 17¼", dial 5", c. 1888, 1 Day, strike (E1-27).*
. . . . 110.00   135.00

☐ **Corning,** *walnut, height 22", dial 6", c. 1888, 8 Day, strike (E1-28).*
. . . . 130.00   155.00

☐ **Dayton,** *walnut, height 21", dial 6", c. 1888, 8 Day, strike (E1-31).*
. . . . 130.00   155.00

☐ **Delhi,** *walnut, height 22¼", dial 6", c. 1888, 8 Day, strike (E1-28).*
. . . . 125.00   150.00

☐ **Dunbar,** *walnut, height 21", dial 6", c. 1888, 8 Day, strike (E1-28).*
. . . . 130.00   155.00

☐ **Dunkirk,** *walnut, height 22⅞", dial 6", c. 1888, 8 Day, strike (E1-28).*
. . . . 130.00   155.00

☐ **Elmira,** *walnut, height 22⅜", dial 6", c. 1888, 8 Day, strike (E1-28).*
. . . . 130.00   155.00

☐ **Essex,** *ash with walnut trimmings, height 19", dial 6", c. 1888, 8 Day, strike (E1-31).*
. . . . 125.00   150.00

☐ **Fonda,** *walnut, height 21¾", dial 6", c. 1888, 8 Day, strike (E1-28).*
. . . . 125.00   150.00

☐ **Foster,** *walnut, height 25", dial 6", c. 1888, 8 Day, strike (E1-28).*
. . . . 130.00   155.00

□ **Granville,** *walnut, height 22½",
dial 6", c. 1888, 8 Day, strike
(E1-31).*
.... **120.00   145.00**

□ **Harding,** *walnut, height 21½",
dial 6", c. 1888, 1 Day, strike
(E1-27).*
.... **115.00   140.00**

□ **Highland,** *walnut, height 24½",
dial 6", c. 1888, 8 Day, strike
(E1-31).*
.... **125.00   150.00**

□ **Homer,** *walnut, height 22", dial
6", c. 1888, 8 Day, strike (E1-31).*
.... **125.00   150.00**

□ **Jenner,** *walnut, height 21¾", dial
6", c. 1888, 8 Day, strike (E1-28).*
.... **125.00   150.00**

□ **Kimble,** *walnut, height 20¾",
dial 6", c. 1888, 8 Day, strike
(E1-31).*
.... **125.00   150.00**

□ **Gibson Calendar,** *oak, with
thermometer and barometer,
height 24", dial 6", 8 Day, strike
(E2-160).*
.... **200.00   225.00**
□ **As above,** *8 Day, gong.*
.... **225.00   250.00**

□ **Gibson Calendar,** *walnut, with
thermometer and barometer,
height 24", dial 6", 8 Day, strike
(E2-160).*
.... **225.00   250.00**
□ **As above,** *8 Day, gong.*
.... **250.00   275.00**

□ **Gilford,** *walnut, height 20", dial
6", c. 1888, 1 Day, strike (E1-27).*
.... **110.00   135.00**

□ **Graham,** *walnut, height 21⅝",
dial 6", c. 1888, 8 Day, strike
(E1-31).*
.... **130.00   155.00**

□ **Knox,** *walnut, height 22¼", dial
6", c. 1888, 1 Day, strike (E1-27).*
.... **115.00   140.00**

☐ **Lodi,** *walnut, height 21⅜", dial 6", c. 1888, 8 Day, strike (E1-28).* 110.00   135.00

☐ **Lyons,** *walnut, height 21⅞", dial 6", c. 1888, 8 Day, strike (E1-28).* 110.00   135.00

☐ **Malvern,** *walnut, height 19½", dial 6", c. 1888, 1 Day, strike (E1-27).* 115.00   140.00

☐ **Medina,** *walnut, height 22", dial 6", c. 1888, 8 Day, strike (E1-28).* 125.00   150.00

☐ **Merwin,** *walnut, height 24", dial 6", c. 1888, 8 Day, strike (E1-31).* 125.00   150.00

☐ **Middlesex,** *ash with walnut trimmings, height 21", dial 6", c. 1888, 8 Day, strike (E1-31).* 135.00   160.00

☐ **Morris,** *walnut, height 20⅛, dial 6", c. 1888, 8 Day, strike (E1-31).* 115.00   140.00

☐ **Napier Extra,** *oak, with thermometer and barometer, height 24", dial 6", c. 1888, 8 Day, strike (E1-31).* 150.00   175.00

☐ **As above,** *walnut* 175.00   200.00

☐ **Paris,** *walnut, height 24", dial 6", c. 1888, 8 Day, strike (E1-28).* 195.00   225.00

☐ **Rondo,** *walnut, height 24", dial 6", c. 1888, 8 Day, strike (E1-31).* 125.00   150.00

☐ **Seaford,** *walnut, height 21⅛", dial 6", c. 1888, 8 Day, strike (E1-28).* 130.00   155.00

☐ **Selborne,** *walnut, height 22⅞", dial 6", c. 1888, 8 Day, strike (E1-28).* 120.00   145.00

☐ **Sussex,** *walnut, height 22¼", dial 6", c. 1888, 8 Day, strike (E1-31).* 125.00   150.00

☐ **Ventnor,** *walnut, height 21¾", dial 6", c. 1888, 8 Day, strike (E1-28).* 130.00   155.00

☐ **Vernon,** *walnut, height 17⅜", dial 6", c. 1888, 1 Day, strike, (E1-27).* 110.00   135.00

WALL

☐ **Cato,** *walnut, with thermometer and barometer, height 27", dial 6", 8 Day, strike (E2-163).* 335.00   375.00

☐ **As above,** *8 Day, strike, calendar.* 385.00   425.00

☐ **As above,** *8 Day, strike,*
.... 285.00   325.00
☐ **As above,** *8 Day, strike, calendar.*
.... 335.00   375.00

☐ **Climax,** *walnut, with
thermometer and barometer,
height 26⅝", dial (rococo) 6",
8 Day, strike (E2-163).*
.... 320.00   350.00
☐ **As above,** *8 Day, strike, calendar.*
.... 360.00   400.00

☐ **Climax,** *oak, with thermometer
and barometer, height 26⅝", dial
(rococo) 6", 8 Day, strike (E2-163).*
.... 270.00   300.00
☐ **As above,** *8 Day, strike, calendar.*
.... 310.00   350.00

☐ **Havana,** *walnut, height 29¾",
dial (rococo) 6", 8 Day, strike
(E2-163).*
.... 320.00   350.00
☐ **As above,** *oak.*
.... 270.00   300.00

☐ **Lawrence,** *walnut, height 29",
dial 6", c. 1888, 8 Day (E1-32).*
.... 310.00   350.00

☐ **Olive,** *walnut, height 18¼", dial
6", c. 1915, 8 Day, strike (E2-163).*
.... 155.00   175.00

☐ **Orange,** *walnut, height 18¼",
dial 6", c. 1915, 8 Day, strike
(E2-163).*
.... 155.00   175.00

☐ **Orrin,** *walnut, height 18¼", dial
6", c. 1915, 8 Day, strike (E2-163).*
.... 155.00   175.00
☐ **As above,** *oak.*
.... 105.00   125.00

MANTEL METAL REGENCY

☐ **Cadosia,** *rich Roman gold plated, ivory center, visible escapement, rococo cast gilt sash and bezel, beveled glass, 12" x 7⅛", ivory dial 4½", c. 1900, 8 Day, strike (E1-110).*
.... **110.00   135.00**

☐ **Carlisle,** *rich Roman gold plated, ivory center, visible escapement, rococo cast gilt sash and bezel, beveled glass, 13" x 8⅞", ivory dial, c. 1900, 8 Day, strike (E1-110).*
.... **230.00   260.00**

☐ **Nantes,** *rich Roman gold plated, ivory center, visible escapement, rococo cast gilt sash and bezel, beveled glass, 15½" x 9⅜", ivory dial, c. 1900, 8 Day, strike (E1-110).*
.... **360.00   400.00**

☐ **Sartoris,** *rich Roman gold plated, decorated porcelain panel, ivory center, visible escapement, rococo cast gilt sash and bezel, beveled glass, 14" x 7¼", ivory dial, c. 1900, 8 Day, strike (E1-117).*
.... **310.00   350.00**

☐ **Seine,** *rich Roman gold plated or golden bronze, ivory center, visible escapement, rococo cast gilt sash and bezel, beveled glass, 13½" x 9⅛", ivory dial, c. 1900, 8 Day, strike (E1-117).*
.... **105.00   130.00**

☐ **Valhalla,** *Japanese or Syrian Bronze, ivory center, visible escapement, rococo cast gilt sash and bezel, beveled glass, 12¼" x 8⅛", ivory dial, c. 1900, 8 Day, strike (E1-117).*
.... **200.00   250.00**

☐ **Valiant,** *Japanese or Syrian bronze, ivory center, rococo cast gilt sash and bezel, beveled glass, 18" x 10⅞", ivory dial, c. 1900, 8 Day, strike (E1-117).*
.... **245.00   275.00**

☐ **Vancouver,** *Japanese or Syrian bronze, ivory center, visible escapement, rococo cast gilt sash and bezel, beveled glass, 17¼" x 11¼", ivory dial, c. 1900, 8 Day, strike (E1-117).*
.... **195.00   225.00**

☐ **Varick,** *Japanese or Syrian bronze, ivory center, visible escapement, rococo cast gilt sash and bezel, beveled glass, 14⅝" x 11½", ivory dial 4½", c. 1900, 8 Day, strike (E1-109).*
.... **135.00   160.00**

☐ **Vicksburg,** *Japanese or Syrian bronze, ivory center, rococo cast gilt sash and bezel, beveled glass, 12½" x 8½", ivory dial, c. 1900, 8 Day, strike (E1-117).*
.... 105.00 130.00

☐ **Winner,** *bronze or nickel, 9" x 6⅜", c. 1900, 1 Day, alarm (E1-117).*
.... 40.00 55.00

MISSION

☐ **Den No.4,** *dark oak, height 17½" x 12", dial 12, c. 1900, 8 Day (E2-163).*
.... 105.00 125.00
☐ **As above,** *8 Day, strike.*
.... 125.00 150.00

☐ **Den No.5,** *dark oak, height 27½" x 14½", dial 12", 8 Day (E2-163).*
.... 125.00 150.00
☐ **As above,** *8 Day, strike.*
.... 150.00 175.00

NOVELTY

ART NOUVEAU

☐ **Acme,** *rich Roman gold plated, ivory center, rococo cast gilt sash and bezel, beveled glass, 7½" x 6⅝", ivory dial 4½", c. 1900, 8 Day, strike (E1-110).*
.... 60.00 75.00

☐ **Den No.3,** *dark oak, height 26⅜" x 13", dial 10", 8 Day (E2-163).*
.... 95.00 115.00
☐ **As above,** *8 Day, strike.*
.... 110.00 135.00

☐ **Mercury,** *rich Roman gold plated, ivory center, rococo cast gilt sash and bezel, beveled glass, 8" x 7", ivory dial, c. 1900, 8 Day, strike (E1-110).*
. . . . **90.00   110.00**

☐ **Rajah,** *rich Roman gold plated or Syrian bronze, ivory center, rococo cast gilt sash and bezel, beveled glass, 12⅜" x 8½", ivory dial, c. 1900, 8 Day, strike (E1-110).*
. . . . **145.00   160.00**

☐ **Sardis,** *rich Roman gold plated, ivory center, rococo cast gilt sash and bezel, beveled glass, 11" x 6½", ivory dial 4½", c. 1900, 8 Day, strike (E1-110).*
. . . . **125.00   150.00**

☐ **Art,** *rich Roman gold plated, ivory center, rococo cast gilt sash and bezel, beveled glass, ivory dial, c. 1900, 1 Day (E1-110).*
. . . . **70.00   65.00**

☐ **Canoga,** *rich Roman gold plated or Syrian bronze, ivory center, visible escapement, rococo cast gilt sash and bezel, beveled glass, 13½" x 9", ivory dial 4½", c. 1900, 8 Day, strike (E1-110).*
. . . . **125.00   150.00**

☐ **Castalia,** *rich Roman gold plated, ivory center, visible escapement, rococo cast gilt sash and bezel, beveled glass, 12" x 7¾", ivory dial 4½", c. 1900, 8 Day, strike (E1-110).*
. . . . **145.00   160.00**

☐ **Ino,** *rich Roman gold plated, ivory center, rococo cast gilt sash and bezel, beveled glass, 11" x 6½", ivory dial, c. 1900, 8 Day, strike (E1-110).*
. . . . **125.00   150.00**

☐ **Surprise,** *rich Roman gold plated, ivory center, visible escapement, rococo cast gilt sash and bezel, beveled glass, 7½" x 6⅝", ivory dial 4½", c. 1900, 8 Day, strike (E1-110).*
. . . . **60.00   75.00**

IRON

□ **Stunner,** *bronze, long alarm with intermissions, height 9¾", dial 4½", c. 1900, 1 Day, alarm (E1-117).*

. . . . **40.00**   **55.00**

REGULATOR

FIGURE 8

□ **Bahia,** *mosaic, height 22", dial 10", 8 Day (E2-163).*

. . . . **270.00**   **300.00**

□ **As above,** *8 Day, strike.*

. . . . **285.00**   **325.00**

□ **As above,** *8 Day, calendar.*

. . . . **310.00**   **350.00**

□ **As above,** *8 Day, strike, calendar.*

. . . . **335.00**   **375.00**

□ **Bahia,** *rosewood veneered, height 22", dial 10", 8 Day (E2-163).*

. . . . **270.00**   **300.00**

□ **As above,** *8 Day, strike.*

. . . . **285.00**   **325.00**

□ **As above,** *8 Day, calendar.*

. . . . **310.00**   **350.00**

□ **As above,** *8 Day, strike, calendar.*

. . . . **335.00**   **375.00**

OCTAGON TOP, LONG DROP

□ **Regent Calendar,** *rosewood, height 32", dial 12", c. 1910, 8 Day (E1-100).*

. . . . **335.00**   **375.00**

□ **As above,** *8 Day, strike.*

. . . . **360.00**   **400.00**

☐ **Regent,** *wood, height 32", dial 12, c. 1888, 8 Day, sp. (E1-23).*
.... **285.00   325.00**
☐ **As above,** *8 Day, strike, sp.*
.... **310.00   350.00**
☐ **As above,** *8 Day, calendar, sp.*
.... **335.00   375.00**
☐ **As above,** *8 Day, strike, calendar, sp.*
.... **360.00   400.00**

☐ **Regent,** *rosewood, height 32", dial 12", c. 1910, 8 Day (E1-100).*
.... **335.00   375.00**
☐ **As above,** *8 Day, strike.*
.... **375.00   425.00**

OCTAGON TOP, SHORT DROP

☐ **10 Inch Heron,** *oak, height 30", dial 10", 8 Day (E2-162).*
.... **220.00   250.00**
☐ **As above,** *8 Day, strike.*
.... **245.00   275.00**
☐ **As above,** *8 Day, calendar.*
.... **270.00   300.00**

☐ **Digby,** *oak, height 27", dial 12", 8 Day (E2-162).*
.... **220.00   250.00**
☐ **As above,** *8 Day, strike.*
.... **245.00   275.00**
☐ **As above,** *8 Day, calendar.*
.... **270.00   300.00**
☐ **As above,** *8 Day, strike, calendar.*
.... **285.00   325.00**

☐ **8 Inch Drop Octagon,** *oak, height 19", dial 8", 8 Day (E2-162).*
.... **150.00   175.00**
☐ **As above,** *8 Day, strike.*
.... **175.00   200.00**
☐ **As above,** *8 Day, calendar.*
.... **195.00   225.00**
☐ **As above,** *8 Day, strike, calendar.*
.... **220.00   250.00**
☐ **As above,** *rosewood, 8 Day.*
.... **200.00   225.00**
☐ **As above,** *8 Day, strike.*
.... **225.00   250.00**

☐ **8 Inch Yeddo,** *rosewood veneered, brass trimmings, height 19", dial 8", 8 Day (E2-162).*
.... 150.00   175.00
☐ **As above,** *8 Day, strike.*
.... 175.00   200.00
☐ **As above,** *8 Day, calendar.*
.... 195.00   225.00
☐ **As above,** *8 Day, strike, calendar.*
.... 220.00   250.00

☐ **10 Inch Arion,** *oak, height 22",dial 10", 8 Day (E2-162).*
.... 175.00   200.00
☐ **As above,** *8 Day, strike.*
.... 195.00   225.00
☐ **As above,** *8 Day, calendar.*
.... 220.00   250.00
☐ **As above,** *8 Day, strike, calendar.*
.... 245.00   275.00

☐ **10 Inch Drop Octagon,** *oak, height 22", dial 10", 8 Day (E2-162).*
.... 175.00   200.00
☐ **As above,** *8 Day, strike.*
.... 195.00   225.00
☐ **As above,** *8 Day, calendar.*
.... 220.00   250.00
☐ **As above,** *8 Day, strike, calendar.*
.... 245.00   275.00
☐ **As above,** *rosewood, 8 Day.*
.... 225.00   250.00
☐ **As above,** *8 Day, strike.*
.... 245.00   275.00
☐ **As above,** *8 Day, calendar.*
.... 270.00   300.00
☐ **As above,** *8 Day, strike, calendar.*
.... 295.00   325.00

☐ **10 Inch Yeddo,** *rosewood veneered, brass trimmings, height 22", dial 10", 8 Day (E2-162).*
.... 175.00   200.00
☐ **As above,** *8 Day, strike.*
.... 195.00   225.00

☐ **As above,** *8 Day, calendar.*
.... 220.00   250.00
☐ **As above,** *8 Day, strike, calendar.*
.... 245.00   275.00

☐ **12 Inch Arion,** *oak, height 24", dial 12", 8 Day (E2-162).*
.... 195.00   225.00
☐ **As above,** *8 Day, strike.*
.... 220.00   250.00
☐ **As above,** *8 Day, calendar.*
.... 245.00   275.00
☐ **As above,** *8 Day, strike, calendar.*
.... 270.00   300.00
☐ **As above,** *mahogany finish, 8 Day.*
.... 225.00   255.00
☐ **As above,** *8 Day, strike.*
.... 250.00   280.00
☐ **As above,** *8 Day, calendar.*
.... 275.00   305.00
☐ **As above,** *8 Day, strike, calendar.*
.... 300.00   330.00

☐ **12 Inch Drop Octagon,** *oak, height 24", dial 12", 8 Day (E2-162).*
.... 195.00   225.00
☐ **As above,** *8 Day, strike.*
.... 220.00   250.00
☐ **As above,** *8 Day, calendar.*
.... 245.00   275.00
☐ **As above,** *8 Day, strike, calendar.*
.... 270.00   300.00
☐ **As above,** *rosewood veneered, 8 Day.*
.... 245.00   275.00
☐ **As above,** *8 Day, strike.*
.... 270.00   300.00
☐ **As above,** *8 Day, calendar.*
.... 295.00   325.00
☐ **As above,** *8 Day, strike, calendar.*
.... 320.00   350.00

☐ **12 Inch Yeddo,** *rosewood veneered, brass trimmings, height 24", dial 12", 8 Day (E2-162).*

.... 195.00   225.00

☐ **As above,** *8 Day, strike.*

.... 220.00   250.00

☐ **As above,** *8 Day, calendar.*

.... 245.00   275.00

☐ **As above,** *8 Day, strike, calendar.*

.... 270.00   300.00

OPEN SWINGING

☐ **Alabama,** *oak, 38¾" x 17¼", dial 8" porcelain, c. 1915, 8 Day, strike, weight (E1-99).*

.... 800.00   900.00

☐ **As above,** *mahogany.*

.... 900.00   1000.00

☐ **Study No.10,** *oak, glass sides, cast bell, height 26⅝", dial 8", 8 Day, weight (E2-163).*

.... 450.00   550.00

☐ **As above,** *cherry.*

.... 550.00   650.00

☐ **Study No.3,** *oak, 27¼" x 14", dial 8" porcelain, 8 Day, strike, weight (E1-99).*

.... 490.00   550.00

☐ **Study No.4,** *oak, 35¼" x 15¼", dial 8" porcelain, c. 1915, 8 Day, strike, weight (E1-99).*

.... 675.00   750.00

PARLOR SHELF

☐ **Buffalo Calendar,** *walnut, height 26⅞", dial 8", 8 Day (E2-160).*
. . . . **270.00   300.00**
☐ **As above,** *8 Day, strike.*
. . . . **285.00   325.00**
☐ **As above,** *8 Day, calendar.*
. . . . **310.00   350.00**
☐ **As above,** *8 Day, strike, calendar.*
. . . . **335.00   375.00**

☐ **Elberon,** *walnut, height 32¾", dial 8", c. 1888, 8 Day, strike (E1-32).*
. . . . **310.00   350.00**

PARLOR WALL

☐ **Aurora,** *oak, 42¼" x 17¼", dial 8", 8 Day (E2-161).*
. . . . **490.00   550.00**
☐ **As above,** *8 Day, strike.*
. . . . **540.00   600.00**

☐ **Berlin,** *walnut, height 46", dial 10", c. 1910, 8 Day, weight (E1-98).*
. . . . **800.00   1050.00**

☐ **Breton,** *oak, glass sides, 44¼" x 14⅛", dial 8", c. 1915, 8 Day (E1-97).*
. . . . **540.00   600.00**
☐ **As above,** *8 Day, strike*
. . . . **625.00   700.00**
☐ **As above,** *mahogany, 8 Day*
. . . . **615.00   675.00**
☐ **As above,** *mahogany, 8 Day, strike*
. . . . **700.00   775.00**

☐ **Cairo,** *oak, 43" x 17⅞", dial 10", c. 1915, 8 Day (E1-96).*
. . . . **450.00   500.00**
☐ **As above,** *8 Day, strike*
. . . . **490.00   550.00**
☐ **As above,** *walnut, 8 Day*
. . . . **550.00   600.00**
☐ **As above,** *walnut, 8 Day, strike*
. . . . **590.00   650.00**
☐ **As above,** *mahogany, 8 Day*
. . . . **525.00   575.00**
☐ **As above,** *mahogany, 8 Day, strike*
. . . . **565.00   625.00**

☐ **Cambridge,** *oak, 50⅝" x 20¼", dial 12", c. 1915, 8 Day (E1-99).*
. . . . **490.00   550.00**
☐ **As above,** *8 Day, strike*
. . . . **540.00   600.00**
☐ **As above,** *30 Day*
. . . . **575.00   650.00**
☐ **As above,** *walnut, 8 Day*
. . . . **590.00   650.00**
☐ **As above,** *walnut, 8 Day, strike*
. . . . **640.00   700.00**
☐ **As above,** *walnut, 30 Day*
. . . . **675.00   750.00**

☐ **Camden,** *walnut, height 46", dial 10", c. 1910, 8 Day, weight (E1-100).*
. . . . **900.00   1000.00**

☐ **Carleton,** *walnut, height 42", dial 8", 8 Day (E1-26).*
. . . . **450.00   500.00**
☐ **As above,** *8 Day, strike*
. . . . **490.00   550.00**

☐ **Eton,** *oak, 39¼″ x 15″, dial 8″, c. 1915, 8 Day (E1-97).*
.... 400.00   450.00
☐ **As above,** *8 Day, strike*
.... 490.00   550.00
☐ **As above,** *walnut, 8 Day*
.... 500.00   550.00
☐ **As above,** *walnut, 8 Day, strike*
.... 590.00   650.00

☐ **Fostoria,** *oak, 40¾″ x 16¼″, dial 12″, c. 1893, 8 Day (E2-163).*
.... 360.00   400.00
☐ **As above,** *8 Day, strike.*
.... 400.00   450.00
☐ **As above,** *30 Day, sec. hand.*
.... 450.00   500.00
☐ **As above,** *walnut, 8 Day*
.... 460.00   500.00
☐ **As above,** *8 Day, strike.*
.... 500.00   550.00
☐ **As above,** *30 Day, sec. hand.*
.... 550.00   600.00

☐ **Freeport,** *oak, 45″ x 18⅛″, dial 10″, 8 Day (E2-161).*
.... 490.00   550.00
☐ **As above,** *8 Day, strike.*
.... 515.00   575.00
☐ **As above,** *30 Day, sec. hand.*
.... 540.00   600.00
☐ **As above,** *walnut, 8 Day.*
.... 590.00   650.00
☐ **As above,** *8 Day, strike.*
.... 615.00   675.00
☐ **As above,** *30 Day, sec. hand.*
.... 640.00   700.00

☐ **Kingston,** *walnut, height 37″, dial 8″, c. 1910, 8 Day (E1-100).*
.... 450.00   500.00
☐ **As above,** *8 Day, strike.*
.... 490.00   550.00

☐ **Leipsic,** *oak, 48″ x 17¾″, dial 8″ porcelain, c. 1915, 8 Day, strike (E1-99).*
.... 540.00   600.00
☐ **As above,** *30 Day.*
.... 625.00   700.00
☐ **As above,** *walnut, 8 Day, strike.*
.... 640.00   700.00
☐ **As above,** *30 Day.*
.... 725.00   800.00

☐ **Nassau,** *oak, 45″ x 18⅛″, dial 10″, c. 1915, 8 Day, strike spring (E1-96).*
.... 360.00   400.00
☐ **As above,** *30 Day.*
.... 400.00   450.00

☐ **Natchez,** *oak, 40⅛″ x 13¾″, dial 8″, c. 1915, 8 Day (E1-97).*
.... 400.00   450.00
☐ **As above,** *8 Day, strike.*
.... 450.00   500.00
☐ **As above,** *8 Day, calendar.*
.... 540.00   600.00
☐ **As above,** *8 Day, strike, calendar.*
.... 575.00   650.00
☐ **As above,** *mahogany, 8 Day.*
.... 475.00   525.00
☐ **As above,** *8 Day, strike.*
.... 525.00   575.00
☐ **As above,** *8 Day, calendar.*
.... 615.00   675.00
☐ **As above,** *8 Day, strike, calendar.*
.... 650.00   725.00

☐ **Nelson,** *oak, 50⅝″ x 14¾″, dial 8″, c. 1915, 8 Day (E1-99).*
.... 490.00   550.00
☐ **As above,** *8 Day, strike.*
.... 575.00   650.00
☐ **As above,** *mahogany, 8 Day.*
.... 565.00   625.00
☐ **As above,** *8 Day, strike.*
.... 650.00   725.00

☐ **Montreal,** *walnut, height 37½″, c. 1910, dial 8″, 8 Day (E1-100).*
.... 725.00   800.00
☐ **As above,** *8 Day, strike.*
.... 750.00   850.00

☐ **Ontario,** *walnut, height 40″, dial 8″, c. 1910, 8 Day (E1-100).*
.... 540.00   600.00
☐ **As above,** *8 Day, strike*
.... 575.00   650.00

☐ **Ottawa,** *walnut, height 32″, dial 6″, c. 1888, 8 Day (E1-32).*
.... 360.00   400.00

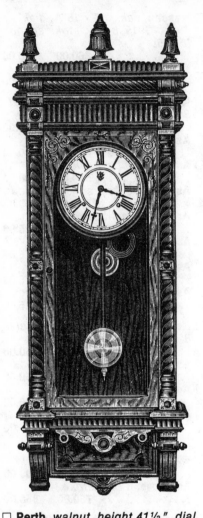

☐ **Perth**, *walnut, height 41½", dial 8", 8 Day (E2-161).*
. . . . 825.00   900.00
☐ **As above**, *8 Day, strike.*
. . . . 850.00   950.00
☐ **As above**, *cherry, 8 Day.*
. . . . 875.00   950.00
☐ **As above**, *oak, 8 Day*
. . . . 725.00   800.00
☐ **As above**, *oak, 8 Day, strtike*
. . . . 750.00   850.00

☐ **Pictou**, *oak, 50¾" x 16⅜", dial 10", c. 1915, 8 Day (E1-99).*
. . . . 490.00   550.00
☐ **As above**, *8 Day, strike.*
. . . . 540.00   600.00
☐ **As above**, *mahogany, 8 Day.*
. . . . 565.00   625.00
☐ **As above**, *8 Day, strike.*
. . . . 615.00   675.00

☐ **Pontiac**, *walnut, height 43", dial 8", 8 Day (E1-26).*
. . . . 540.00   600.00
☐ **As above**, *8 Day, strike.*
. . . . 575.00   650.00

☐ **Prescott**, *walnut, height 32", dial 6", c. 1888, 8 Day (E1-32).*
. . . . 360.00   400.00

☐ **Quebec**, *walnut, height 42", dial 8", c. 1910, 8 Day, weight (E1-98).*
. . . . 725.00   800.00
☐ **As above**, *8 Day, strike, weight.*
. . . . 800.00   900.00

☐ **Regulator No.4**, *walnut, height 51", dial 10", dead beat escapement, retaining power, c. 1888, 8 Day, weight (E1-23).*
. . . . 975.00   1225.00
☐ **As above**, *ash.*
. . . . 1025.00   1275.00
☐ **As above**, *mahogany.*
. . . . 950.00   1200.00

☐ **Springfield**, *oak, 39⅜" x 16½", dial 8", c. 1915, 8 Day (E1-96).*
. . . . 360.00   400.00
☐ **As above**, *8 Day, strike.*
. . . . 400.00   450.00
☐ **As above**, *8 Day, calendar.*
. . . . 490.00   550.00
☐ **As above**, *8 Day, strike, calendar.*
. . . . 540.00   600.00

☐ **Stafford**, *ash, height 35", dial 8", c. 1888, 8 Day, sp. (E1-23).*
. . . . 435.00   475.00
☐ **As above**, *8 Day, strike, sp.*
. . . . 475.00   525.00
☐ **As above**, *walnut, 8 Day, sp.*
. . . . 360.00   400.00
☐ **As above**, *8 Day, strike, sp.*
. . . . 400.00   450.00

☐ **Toronto,** *walnut, height 45", dial 8", c. 1910, 8 Day, sp. (E1-98).*
.... 800.00   900.00
☐ **As above,** *8 Day, strike, sp.*
.... 900.00   1000.00

☐ **Walton,** *oak, 41" x 15¼", dial 10", c. 1915, 8 Day (E1-96).*
.... 310.00   350.00
☐ **As above,** *8 Day, strike.*
.... 360.00   400.00
☐ **As above,** *8 Day, calendar.*
.... 400.00   450.00

☐ **Yarmouth,** *oak, height 30", dial 6", rococo, c. 1915, 8 Day (E1-97).*
.... 400.00   450.00
☐ **As above,** *8 Day, strike.*
.... 450.00   500.00

ROUND TOP, LONG DROP

☐ **Regulator,** *oak, dead beat escapement, retaining power, solid movement frame, height 41", dial 18", 8 Day, weight (E2-163).*
.... 1000.00   1250.00

☐ **Regulator No.2,** *wood, height 36½", dial 12", dead beat escapement, retaining power, c. 1888, 8 Day, weight (E1-23).*
.... 725.00   800.00

ROUND TOP, SHORT DROP

☐ **Andes,** *oak, height 24", dial 12", 8 Day (E1-162).*
.... 175.00   200.00
☐ **As above,** *8 Day, strike.*
.... 195.00   225.00
☐ **As above,** *8 Day, calendar.*
.... 220.00   250.00
☐ **As above,** *8 Day, strike, calendar.*
.... 245.00   275.00

☐ **English Drop No.2,** *veneered, inlaid, height 27¾", dial 12", 8 Day (E2-161).*
.... 310.00   350.00
☐ **As above,** *8 Day, strike.*
.... 335.00   375.00
☐ **As above,** *8 Day, calendar.*
.... 360.00   400.00
☐ **As above,** *8 Day, strike, calendar.*
.... 375.00   425.00

☐ **Glenwood, Calendar,** *rosewood, height 25½", dial 12", c. 1910, 8 Day (E1-100).*
.... 360.00   400.00
☐ **As above,** *8 Day, strike.*
.... 400.00   450.00

SECONDS BIT

☐ **Round Head Drop,** *oak, height 24", dial 12", 8 Day (E2-162).*
.... 195.00   225.00
☐ **As above,** *8 Day, strike.*
.... 220.00   250.00
☐ **As above,** *8 Day, calendar.*
.... 245.00   275.00
☐ **As above,** *8 Day, strike, calendar.*
.... 270.00   300.00

☐ **Regulator No.3,** *walnut, brass weights, dead beat escapement, retaining power, solid movement frames, height 46", dial 9", (E2-161).*
.... 1050.00   1250.00

☐ **Kendall,** *oak, height 52", dial 10", 30 Day (E2-161).*
.... 800.00   900.00

☐ **As above,** *walnut.*
.... 1000.00   1200.00

☐ **Regulator,** *walnut, cabinet finish, glass sides, dead beat escapement, retaining power, beats seconds, height 87", silver dial 10", c. 1890, 8 Day, weight (E2-173).*
.... 2025.00   2250.00

☐ **As above,** *8 Day, weight, strike.*
.... 2070.00   2300.00

☐ **Regulator No.3,** *walnut, height 46", dial 9", dead beat escapement, c. 1888, 8 Day, weight (E1-23).*
.... 950.00   1050.00

☐ **As above,** *ash.*
.... 1000.00   1100.00

☐ **As above,** *mahogany.*
.... 900.00   1000.00

☐ **Regulator No.6,** *walnut, height 87", dial 10", beats seconds, dead beat escapement, retaining power, c. 1888, 8 Day, weight (E1-23).*
.... 2025.00   2250.00

☐ **Regulator No.11,** *oak, glass sides, brass weights, dead beat escapement, retaining power, solid polished movement frames, height 52¼", dial 10", 8 Day, weight (E2-161).*
.... 900.00   1150.00

☐ **As above,** *cherry.*
.... 1150.00   1400.00

☐ **As above,** *walnut.*
.... 1100.00   1350.00

☐ **Regulator No.14,** *walnut, beats seconds, dead beat escapement, retaining power, height 72", dial 12", c. 1888, 8 Day, weight (E1-23).*
.... 1300.00   1600.00

☐ **Regulator No.19,** *oak, dead beat escapement, retaining power, solid polished movement frames, 50" x 19½", dial 12", 8 Day, weight (E2-161).*
.... 850.00   950.00

☐ **Waterbury Regulator No.2,** *rosewood, height 36½", dial 12", c. 1910, 8 Day, weight (E1-100).*
. . . . 675.00   750.00

SWEEP SECONDS

☐ **Jewelers' Regulator No.60,** *quartered oak, cabinet finish, glass sides, brass weights, sweep seconds, dead beat escapement, retaining power, 79½" x 26", porcelain dial 12", 8 Day, weight (E2-175).*
. . . . 3375.00   3750.00

☐ **As above,** *walnut.*
. . . . 3575.00   3975.00

☐ **Jewelers' Standing Regulator No.61,** *quartered oak, dead beat pin escapement, sweep second, retaining power, brass weight, Swiss pattern movement, 96¼" x 28⅞", porcelain dial 12", 8 Day, weight (E2-175).*
. . . . 3600.00   4000.00

☐ **As above,** *walnut.*
. . . . 3800.00   4200.00

☐ **Jewelers' Regulator No.65,** *fine quartered oak, sweep seconds, dead beat escapement, retaining power, 81" x 24", dial 12", 8 Day, weight (E2-175).*
. . . . 3375.00   3750.00

☐ **As above,** *walnut.*
. . . . 3575.00   3950.00

☐ **Regulator No.7,** *walnut, glass sides, sweep seconds, dead beat escapement, retaining power, height 82", porcelain dial 12", 8 Day, weight (E1-23).*
. . . . 3600.00   4000.00

☐ **As above,** *cherry.*
. . . . 3700.00   4100.00

☐ **Regulator No.7,** *quartered oak, brass weights, dead beat escapement, sweep second, retaining power, glass sides, 82" x 25½", porcelain dial 12", c. 1915, 8 Day, weight (E1-97).*
. . . . 3600.00   4000.00

☐ **Regulator No.15,** *walnut, glass sides, dead beat pin escapement, sweep second, retaining power, height 91", porcelain dial 12", c. 1888, 8 Day, weight (E1-23).*
. . . . 3700.00   4100.00

☐ **As above,** *cherry.*
. . . . 3850.00   4250.00

☐ **As above,** *antique oak.*
. . . . 3600.00   4000.00

☐ **Regulator No.61,** *quartered oak, brass weights, dead beat escapement, sweep second, retaining power, 96¼" x 28⅝", porcelain dial 12", c. 1915, 8 Day, weight (E1-97).*
.... 3600.00   4000.00
☐ **As above,** *walnut.*
.... 3800.00   4200.00

☐ **Regulator No.70,** *quartered oak, polished finish, dead beat escapement, sweep second, retaining power, 82" x 26¼", porcelain dial 12", 8 Day, weight (E2-175).*
.... 3375.00   3750.00
☐ **As above,** *mahogany.*
.... 3525.00   3900.00

☐ **Regulator No.71,** *quartered oak, brass weights, dead beat escapement, sweep seconds, retaining power, 96¼" x 28", porcelain dial 12", c. 1915, 8 Day, weight (E1-97).*
.... 3600.00   4000.00
☐ **As above,** *mahogany.*
.... 3750.00   4150.00

☐ **Walnut, Regulator No.9,** *walnut, pin escapement, sweep second, height 88", dial 12", 8 Day, c. 1910, weight (E1-98).*
.... 3600.00   4000.00

☐ **Walnut Regulator No.10,** *walnut, pin escapement, sweep second, height 85", dial 12", c. 1910, 8 Day, weight (E1-98).*
.... 3375.00   3750.00

STATUE
LARGE
☐ **Cavalier,** *rich Roman gold plated, ivory center, visible escapement, rococo cast gilt sash and bezel, beveled glass, 22¼" x 17¼", ivory dial 4½", c. 1900, 8 Day, strike (E1-109).*
.... 375.00   425.00

☐ **Crusader,** *rich Roman gold plated, ivory center, visible escapement, rococo cast gilt sash and bezel, beveled glass, 27¼" x 17¾", ivory dial 4½", c. 1900, 8 Day, strike (E1-109).*
.... 450.00   500.00

☐ **Verndale,** *Japanese or Syrian bronze, ivory center, rococo cast gilt sash and bezel, beveled glass, 21" x 23", ivory dial, c. 1900, 8 Day, strike (E1-117).*
.... 490.00   550.00

SMALL
☐ **Valencia,** *Japanese or Syrian bronze, ivory center, visible escapement, rococo cast gilt sash and bezel, beveled glass, 12½" x 12½", ivory dial, c. 1900, 8 Day, strike (E1-117).*
.... 175.00   200.00

Vassar, *Japanese or Syrian bronze, ivory center, visible escapement, rococo cast gilt sash and bezel, beveled glass, 16⅞" x 16¼", ivory dial 4½", c. 1900, 8 Day, strike (E1-109).*
.... 310.00   350.00

Venango, *Japanese or Syrian bronze, ivory center, visible escapement, rococo cast gilt sash and bezel, beveled glass, 15½" x 19¾", ivory dial 4½", c. 1900, 8 Day, strike (E1-109).*
.... 450.00   500.00

Verona, *Japanese or Syrian bronze, ivory center, visible escapement, rococo cast gilt sash and bezel, beveled glass, 13½" x 12", ivory dial, c. 1900, 8 Day, strike (E1-110).*
.... 310.00   350.00

Viborg, *Japanese or Syrian bronze, ivory center, visible escapement, rococo cast gilt sash and bezel, beveled glass, 12½" x 14", ivory dial 4½", c. 1900, 8 Day, strike (E1-109).*
.... 190.00   220.00

Vilna, *Japanese or Syrian bronze, ivory center, visible escapement, rococo cast gilt sash and bezel, beveled glass, 19⅜" x 19¾",*

ivory dial 4½", c. 1900, 8 Day, strike (E1-109).
.... 285.00   325.00

Vineland, *Japanese or Syrian bronze, ivory center, visible escapement, rococo cast gilt sash and bezel, beveled glass, 16⅞" x 20", ivory dial 4½", c. 1900, 8 Day, strike (E1-109).*
.... 450.00   500.00

Volga, *Japanese or Syrian bronze, ivory center, visible escapement, rococo cast gilt sash and bezel, beveled glass, 19⅜" x 19¾", ivory dial 4½", c. 1900, 8 Day, strike (E1-109).*
.... 270.00   300.00

Voltaire, *Japanese or Syrian bronze, ivory center, visible escapement, rococo cast gilt sash and bezel, beveled glass, 12¼" x 14¾", ivory dial, c. 1900, 8 Day, strike (E1-117).*
.... 190.00   220.00

THE E.N. WELCH MANUFACTURING COMPANY

Elisha Niles Welch is the founding father of this famous company, which continues today under the name of *The Sessions Clock Company.* With his father, Elisha ran an iron foundry in Bristol, selling the valuable weights and sometimes bells, to clock makers. By 1834 Welch was in the clock business himself, with partner Thomas Barnes.

The partnership changed hands a few times with Welch emerging on top. It is important to note that Welch's business was primarily concerned with the manufacture of metals for clocks and clock movements.

The company subsidized Welch, Spring and Company, producing a high quality grade of clocks even for Bristol. Eventually E.N. Welch Manufacturing Company absorbed the entire firm. Elisha's son James suffered financial difficulties, and the firm was taken over by Sessions, as has been previously noted.

ALARM
FANCY

☐ **Fairy Queen,** *nickel, height 4¾", dial 2½", c. 1875, 1 Day, lever (E1-62).*
.... **25.00**   **35.00**

☐ **Fairy Queen,** *nickel, height 5", dial 2½", c. 1875, 1 Day, Alarm, lever (E1-62).*
.... **30.00**   **40.00**

ROUND

☐ **Boom,** *nickel, height 5¾", dial 3", c. 1875, 1 Day, Lever (E1-62).*
.... **20.00**   **30.00**

☐ **Brilliant,** *nickel, height 5¾", dial 3½", c. 1890, 1 Day, alarm (E1-66).*
.... **30.00**   **40.00**

☐ **Charmer,** *nickel, height 5¼", dial 4", 8 Day, calendar, lever (E1-62).*
.... **60.00**   **75.00**

☐ **Daybreak,** *hammered brass, height 5¾", dial 3½", c. 1890, 1 Day, alarm (E1-66).*
.... **30.00**   **40.00**

☐ **The Little Chick,** *nickel, dial 2½", c. 1890, 1 Day, strike (E1-67).*
.... **45.00**   **60.00**
☐ **As above,** *1 Day, alarm*
.... **45.00**   **60.00**
☐ **As above,** *1 Day*
.... **40.00**   **50.00**

☐ **Morning Glory,** *nickel, height 7", dial 5", c. 1890, 1 Day, alarm (E1-67).*
.... **35.00**   **45.00**

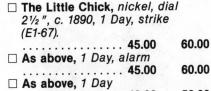

☐ **Nelson,** *nickel, height 5¾", dial 4", c. 1890, 1 Day (E1-66).*
.... **20.00**   **30.00**
☐ **As above,** *1 Day, alarm*
.... **25.00**   **35.00**

CABINET

☐ **Cabinets No. 1 Series,** *oak, (6) 3 different patterns, 2 of each pattern, turnback movement, height 16½", dial 5", c. 1890, 8 Day, strike (E1-72).*
.... *each* **85.00**   **105.00**

☐ **Cabinet K (61 to 65),** *wood, height 17", dial 5", c. 1900, 8 Day, strike (E1-68).*
.... *each* **115.00**   **140.00**

☐ **Martini,** *oak, turnback movement, height 16½", dial 5", c. 1890, 8 Day, strike (E1-72).*
.... **85.00**   **105.00**

☐ **Rubini,** *oak, turnback movement, height 16½", dial 5", c. 1890, 8 Day, strike (E1-72).*
. . . . 85.00   105.00

☐ **Spontini,** *oak, turnback movement, height 16½", dial 5", c. 1890, 8 Day, strike (E1-72).*
. . . . 85.00   105.00

CALENDAR

☐ **Axtell Octagon,** *short drop, 25" x 18", dial 12", 8 Day, strike, simple calendar (E1-72).*
. . . . 300.00   350.00

☐ **Dodecagon (12 Sided),** *lever, seconds bit, gallery clock, dial 10", 1 Day, strike, simple calendar (E1-22, M214-73).*
. . . . 175.00   250.00

☐ **No. 1 Drop Octagon,** *spring 24½", dial 12", 8 Day, simple calendar (E1-72).*
. . . . 300.00   350.00

☐ **Eclipse Regulator,** *spring, 35" x 15", dial 7", 8 Day, simple calendar (M207-72).*
. . . . 500.00   600.00

☐ **Eclipse Regulator,** *spring, 39" x 15", dial 7", 8 Day, strike, simple calendar (M206-72).*
. . . . 500.00   600.00

☐ **Eclipse Regulator,** *long drop octagon, spring, 33" x 17", dial 11", 8 Day, simple calendar (M210-73).*
. . . . 425.00   475.00

☐ **Gentry Octagon Top,** *short drop, 26", dial 12", 8 Day, strike, simple calendar (E1-69).*
. . . . 325.00   375.00

☐ **Globe Kitchen,** *spring, 23" x 15", dial 6", 8 Day, strike, simple calendar (E1-142).*
. . . . 200.00   250.00

☐ **8" Miniature Octagon Top,** *short drop, 18½", dial 8", 8 Day, simple calendar (E1-72).*
. . . . 300.00   350.00

☐ **Octagon,** *short drop, spring 24" x 16½", dial 12", 8 Day, strike, simple calendar (E1-21, M212-73).*
.... 350.00   375.00

☐ **Octagon,** *short drop, spring, 24" x 17", dial 11", 8 Day, strike, simple calendar (M208-72).*
.... 350.00   425.00

☐ **Patchen Octagon Top,** *short drop, 26", dial 12", 8 Day, strike, simple calendar (E1-69).*
.... 300.00   350.00

☐ **Press Kitchen Extra,** *spring, thermometer and barometer, 23" x 15", dial 6", 8 Day, strike, simple calendar (E1-142).*
.... 225.00   275.00

☐ **Press Kitchen,** *spring, 23" x 15", dial 6", 8 Day, strike, simple calendar (E1-142).*
.... 200.00   250.00

☐ **Ruddygore Victorian Kitchen,** *spring 24", dial 6", 8 Day, strike, simple calendar (E1-163).*
.... 450.00   500.00

☐ **Star Pointer Octagon Top,** *long drop, 32½", dial 12", 8 Day, simple calendar (E1-69).*
.... 400.00   450.00

☐ **St. Clair Octagon Top,** *long drop, spring 32½", dial 12", 8 Day, simple calendar (E1-69).*
.... 400.00   450.00

☐ **Victorian Kitchen,** *spring, 24" x 13", dial 5", 8 Day, strike, simple calendar (M213-73).*
.... 300.00   375.00

CALENDAR
WELCH, SPRING AND COMPANY

☐ **Arditi Shelf DD,** *height 27", dial 8", 8 Day, strike (E1-163).*
.... 300.00   400.00

☐ **Auber,** *spring, height 36½", dials 10", 8 Day, strike (E1-21, M196A-69).*
.... **2100.00   2350.00**

☐ **Auber,** *strap brass movement, V calendar mechanism, height 42", dials 12", 8 Day, strike (E1-21, M196-69).*
.... **2000.00   2350.00**

☐ **Damrosch Double Dial Wall Regulator,** *height 41", dials 8" (E1-163).*
.... **2500.00   3000.00**

☐ **Double Dial Shelf,** *spring, 30" x 20", dial 7", 8 Day, strike (M192-68).*
.... **2050.00   2500.00**

☐ **Italian Shelf No. 1,** *spring, dials 7", 8 Day (M190A-67).*
.... **700.00   800.00**

☐ **Italian-Type Shelf,** *spring, V calendar mechanism, 17" x 19½", 4½" time and 5" calendar dial, 8 Day, strike (M185-66).*
.... **800.00   1000.00**

☐ **Italian-Type Shelf,** *spring, V Calendar Mechanism, 19½" x 12", dial 6½", 8 Day, strike (M186-66).*
.... **700.00   800.00**

☐ **Italian-Type Shelf,** *spring, Y calendar, 21" x 11½", dial 5", 8 Day, strike (M184-66).*
.... **900.00   1050.00**

☐ **Regulator Calendar No. 3,** *double weight retaining power, V calendar mechanism, 52", dial 10", 8 Day (E1-22, M200-70).*
.... **4200.00   4750.00**

☐ **Regulator Calendar No. 3 Mantel,** *double weight, 45", dial 10", 8 Day (M202-71).*
.... **3400.00   3800.00**

☐ **Regulator Calendar No. 5,** *spring, 41", 8" time and 8½" calendar dial, 30 Day (E1-22, M204-71).*
.... **2900.00   3150.00**

☐ **Round Head Calendar No. 4,** *spring, 32" x 16", 11½" time and 7" calendar dial, 8 Day (E1-22, M203-71).*
.... **1100.00   1450.00**

☐ **Round Head Regulator No. 1,** *double weight retaining power, V calendar mechanism, 1 second pendulum, 18" time and 12" calendar dial, 8 Day (E1-22, M198-70).*
.... **2000.00   2400.00**

☐ **Round Head Regulator No. 2,** *double weight retaining power, V calendar mechanism, 34", 12" time and 8" calendar dial, 8 Day (E1-22, M199-70).*
.... **1800.00   2000.00**

☐ **Shelf No. 1,** *spring, 32" x 20", dial 7" 8 Day, strike (M191-68).*
.... **2000.00   2575.00**

☐ **Wagner Hanging,** *spring, height 32½", dial 7", 8 Day, strike (E1-21, M194-69).*
.... **2100.00   2550.00**

☐ **Wagner Mantel,** *spring, height 26", dial 7", 8 Day, strike (E1-21, M195-69).*
.... **1900.00 2100.00**

CARRIAGE

☐ **Furore,** *nickel, height 3½", c. 1890, 1 Day (E1-67).*
.... **35.00 45.00**

☐ **Little Lord Fauntleroy,** *nickel, height 2½", c. 1890, 1 Day (E1-67).*
.... **35.00 45.00**

☐ **The Lurline,** *nickel frame, sides and top glass, height 5½", dial 2½", c. 1890, 1 Day, alarm (E1-67).*
.... **100.00 120.00**

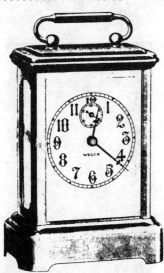

☐ **The Outing,** *nickel, front and sides glass, 5", c. 1890, 1 Day (E1-67).*
.... **80.00 100.00**

CONNECTICUT SHELF
BEEHIVE

☐ **Round Gothic,** *wood, height 19", c. 1875, 1 Day, strike, spring (E1-16).*
.... **100.00 120.00**

COLUMN

☐ **Arch Column,** *rosewood, rose and gilt pillars, height 17", c. 1875, 8 Day, strike, spring (E1-20).*
.... **170.00 195.00**

Column

☐ **Column**, *mahogany case, shell/gilt column, height 25", dial 8", c. 1875, 1 Day, strike, weight (E1-63).*
. . . . **105.00   125.00**

☐ **As above**, *8 Day, strike, weight*
. . . . **160.00   175.00**

☐ **As above**, *rosewood, height 2", dial 8", 1 Day, strike, weight*
. . . . **105.00   125.00**

☐ **As above**, *rosewood, 8 Day, strike, weight*
. . . . **105.00   125.00**

COTTAGE

☐ **Cottage**, *wood, height 11" to 13", c. 1875, 1 Day, spring (E1-16).*
. . . . **65.00   80.00**

☐ **As above**, *1 Day, strike*
. . . . **80.00   100.00**

☐ **Cottage-Extra**, *height 11", c. 1875, 1 Day, spring (E1-16).*
. . . . **65.00   80.00**

☐ **As above**, *height 13", 1 Day, strike*
. . . . **80.00   100.00**

☐ **As above**, *height 13", 8 Day, strike*
. . . . **110.00   135.00**

☐ **Cottage No. 1**, *wood, height 13", dial 6", c. 1875 1 Day (E1-63).*
. . . . **55.00   70.00**

☐ **Cottage No. 2**, *wood, height 12", dial 6", c. 1875 1 Day, spring (E1-63).*
. . . . **60.00   75.00**

EMPIRE

☐ **Extra Column**, *wood, height 33", c. 1875, 8 Day, strike, weight (E1-20).*
. . . . **310.00   350.00**

OCTAGON TOP

☐ **Aimee**, *wood, height 10¾", c. 1875, 1 Day, spring (E1-16).*
. . . . **80.00   95.00**

☐ **Empress,** *wood, height 16", c. 1875, 1 Day, strike, spring (E1-16).*
.... **75.00   90.00**
☐ **As above,** *8 Day, strike*
.... **105.00   125.00**

☐ **Empress, V.P.,** *wood, height 17", c. 1875, 1 Day, strike, spring (E1-16).*
.... **80.00   100.00**
☐ **As above,** *8 Day, strike*
.... **125.00   150.00**

☐ **Seguin,** *wood, height 10¾", c. 1875, 1 Day, spring (E1-16).*
.... **80.00   95.00**

O.G. AND O.O.G.

☐ **O.G. Nos. 1 And 2,** *wood, height 26", dial 8", c. 1875, 1 Day, strike (E1-63).*
.... **130.00   155.00**

☐ **O.G. And O.O.G.,** *mahogany, height 29", c. 1875, 8 Day, strike, weight (E1-20).*
.... **195.00   225.00**
☐ **As above,** *rosewood, 8 Day, strike, weight*
.... **195.00   225.00**
☐ **As above,** *zebra, 8 Day, strike, weight*
.... **205.00   235.00**

☐ **O.O.G.,** *wood, height 18", c. 1875, 1 Day, strike, spring (E1-20).*
.... **130.00   155.00**
☐ **As above,** *8 Day, strike, spring*
.... **145.00   170.00**

☐ **O.O.G.,** *wood, height 18", dial 6", c. 1875, 1 Day, strike, spring (E1-63).*
.... **140.00   165.00**
☐ **As above,** *8 Day, strike, spring*
.... **195.00   225.00**

☐ **O.O.G.,** *wood, height 26", dial 8", c. 1875, 1 Day, strike, weight (E1-63).*
.... **135.00   160.00**

ROUND TOP

☐ **Italian No. 1,** *wood, height 18½", c. 1875, 8 Day, strike, spring (E1-16).*
.... **150.00   175.00**

☐ **Italian No. 2, V.P.,** *wood, height 16", c. 1875, 8 Day, strike, spring (E1-16).*
.... **115.00   145.00**

☐ **Italian No. 2,** *wood, height 16", c. 1875, 8 Day, strike, spring (E1-16).*
.... **140.00   165.00**

☐ **Italian No. 3, V.P.,** *wood, height 14", c. 1875, 1 Day, strike, spring (E1-16).*
. . . . **110.00   135.00**

SPLIT TOP

☐ **Peerless, V.P.,** *wood, height 17½", dial 6", c. 1875, 1 Day, strike, spring (E1-62).*
. . . . **75.00   90.00**
☐ **As above,** *8 Day, strike, spring*
. . . . **105.00   125.00**

STEEPLE
☐ **Sharp Gothic, V.P.,** *wood, height 20", dial 6", c. 1875, 1 Day, strike, spring (E1-62).*
. . . . **80.00   100.00**
☐ **As above,** *8 Day, strike*
. . . . **110.00   135.00**

☐ **Sharp Gothic,** *wood, height 20", c. 1875, 1 Day, strike, spring, (E1-16).*
. . . . **100.00   120.00**

☐ **Small Gothic,** *wood, height 14½", c. 1875, 1 Day, spring (E1-16).*
. . . . **90.00   110.00**
☐ **As above,** *8 Day, strike*
. . . . **100.00   120.00**

GALLERY, LEVER

☐ **Carved And Gilt Gallery,** *metal, height 12", c. 1875, 8 Day (E1-20).*
. . . . **245.00   275.00**

☐ **Nickel Lever,** *3", c. 1875 1 Day, strike (E1-16).*
. . . . **45.00   60.00**
☐ **As above,** *3", 8 Day, strike*
. . . . **60.00   75.00**

☐ **As above,** *6", 1 Day, strike*
.... 75.00   90.00
☐ **As above,** *6", 8 Day, strike*
.... 90.00   110.00
☐ **As above,** *8", 1 Day, strike*
.... 90.00   110.00
☐ **As above,** *8", 8 Day, strike*
.... 110.00   135.00

☐ **Round Corner Octagon Lever,** *wood, 4", c. 1875, 8 Day, strike (E1-16).*
.... 40.00   50.00
☐ **As above,** *6"*
.... 55.00   70.00
☐ **As above,** *8"*
.... 75.00   90.00
☐ **As above,** *12"*
.... 80.00   100.00

KITCHEN

☐ **Agnesi,** *oak, the Bassos series, height 23", dial 6", spring wound, 8 Day, strike, c. 1890 (E1-73).*
.... 150.00   170.00
☐ **As above,** *walnut*
.... 175.00   195.00

☐ **Albani,** *oak, the Contraltos series, height 22", dial 6", spring wound, 8 Day, strike, c. 1890 (E1-73).*
.... 140.00   160.00
☐ **As above,** *walnut*
.... 165.00   185.00

☐ **Booth,** *oak, Actors series, height 23", dial 6", spring wound, 8 Day, strike, c. 1890 (E1-72).*
.... 150.00   170.00

☐ **Cary,** *oak, the Contraltos series, height 22", dial 6", spring wound, 8 Day, strike, c. 1890 (E1-73).*
.... 140.00   160.00
☐ **As above,** *walnut*
.... 165.00   185.00

☐ **Dewey,** *oak, height 24", dial 6", spring wound, 8 Day, strike, c. 1900 (E1-69).*
.... 250.00   275.00

☐ **Dolaro,** *walnut, height 23", dial 6", spring wound, 8 Day, strike, c. 1890 (E1-65).*
.... 185.00   205.00

☐ **Falka,** *walnut, height 23¼", dial 6", spring wound, 8 Day, strike, c. 1890 (E1-65).*
.... 200.00   225.00

☐ **Fannie Rice,** *oak, Prima Donnas series, height 23", dial 6", spring wound, 8 Day, strike, c. 1890 (E1-73).*
.... 150.00   170.00
☐ **As above,** *walnut*
.... 175.00   195.00

☐ **Foli,** *oak, the Bassos series, height 23", dial 6", spring wound, 8 Day, strike, c. 1890 (E1-73).*
.... 150.00   170.00
☐ **As above,** *walnut*
.... 175.00   195.00

☐ **Hal Pointer,** *oak, height 23", dial 6", spring wound, 8 Day, strike, c. 1890 (E1-72).*
.... 150.00   170.00

☐ **Hatton,** *walnut, height 23", dial 6", spring wound, 8 Day, strike, c. 1890 (E1-65).*
.... 185.00   205.00

☐ **Irving,** *oak, Actors series, height 23", dial 6", spring wound, 8 Day, strike, c. 1890 (E1-72).*
.... 150.00   170.00

☐ **Jansen,** *walnut, height 22", dial 6", spring wound, 1 Day, strike, c. 1890 (E1-65).*
.... 200.00   225.00

☐ **Lee,** *oak, height 24", dial 6", spring wound, 8 Day, strike, c. 1900 (E1-69).*
.... 250.00   275.00

☐ **Lillian Russell,** *oak, Prima Donnas series, height 23", dial 6", spring wound, 8 Day, strike, c. 1890 (E1-72).*
.... 150.00   170.00

☐ **As above,** *walnut*
.... 175.00   195.00

☐ **Litta,** *walnut, height 23", dial 6", spring wound, 8 Day, strike, c. 1890 (E1-65).*
.... 185.00   205.00

☐ **Louise Montague,** *oak, Prima Donnas series, height 23", dial 6", spring wound, 8 Day, strike, c. 1890 (E1-72).*
.... 150.00   170.00

☐ **As above,** *walnut*
.... 175.00   195.00

☐ **The Maine,** *oak, height 24", dial 6", spring wound, 8 Day, strike, c. 1900 (E1-69).*
.... 250.00   275.00

☐ **Marie Tempest,** *oak, Prima Donnas series, height 23", dial 6", spring wound, 8 Day, strike, c. 1890 (E1-73).*
.... 150.00   170.00

☐ **As above,** *walnut*
.... 175.00   195.00

☐ **Marion Manola,** *oak, Prima Donnas series, height 23", spring wound, dial 6", 8 Day, strike, c. 1890 (E1-72).*
.... 150.00   170.00

☐ **As above,** *walnut*
.... 175.00   195.00

☐ **Materna,** *walnut, height 23", dial 6", spring wound, 8 Day, strike, c. 1890 (E1-65).*
.... 185.00   205.00

☐ **Nanon,** *walnut, height 21½", dial 6", spring wound, 8 Day, strike, c. 1890 (E1-65).*
.... 200.00   225.00

☐ **Pauline Hall,** *oak, Prima Donnas series, height 23", dial 6", spring wound, 8 Day, strike, c. 1890 (E1-73).*
.... 150.00   170.00

☐ **As above,** *walnut*
.... 175.00   195.00

☐ **Roze,** *walnut, height 21", dial 6", spring wound, 8 Day, strike, c. 1890 (E1-65).*
.... 175.00   200.00

☐ **Sampson,** *oak, height 24", dial 6", spring wound, 8 Day, strike, c. 1900 (E1-69).*
.... 250.00   275.00

☐ **Scalchi,** *oak, the Contraltos series, height 22", dial 6", spring wound, 8 Day, strike, c. 1890 (E1-73).*
.... 140.00   160.00

☐ **As above,** *walnut*
.... 165.00   185.00

☐ **Schley,** *oak, height 24", dial 6", spring wound, 8 Day, strike, c. 1900 (E1-69).*
.... 250.00   270.00

☐ **Thursby,** *walnut, height 23", dial 6", spring wound, 1 Day, strike, c. 1890 (E1-65).*
.... 175.00   200.00

☐ **Wheeler,** *oak, height 24", dial 6", spring wound, 8 Day, strike, c. 1900 (E1-69).*
. . . . 250.00   275.00

☐ **Whitney,** *oak, the Bassos series, height 23", dial 6", spring wound, 8 Day, strike, c. 1890 (E1-73).*
. . . . 150.00   175.00

☐ **As above,** *walnut*
. . . . 175.00   195.00

SERIES

☐ **The Actors Series (6),** *oak, 2 patterns, 3 of each pattern, turnback movement, Booth, Irving, height 23", dial 6", c. 1890, 8 Day, strike (E1-72).*
. . . . *each* 150.00   170.00

☐ **Assortment A. (1 to 6),** *oak, height 22¾", dial 6", 8 Day, strike, c. 1900 (E1-68).*
. . . . 140.00   160.00

☐ **As above,** *walnut*
. . . . 165.00   185.00

☐ **Assortment B. (7 to 12),** *oak, height 23", dial 6", 8 Day, strike, c. 1900 (E1-68).*
. . . . *each* 150.00   170.00

☐ **As above,** *walnut*
. . . . *each* 175.00   195.00

☐ **Assortment C. (13 to 18),** *oak, height 23", dial 6", 8 Day, strike, c. 1900 (E1-68).*
. . . . *each* 150.00   170.00

☐ **As above,** *walnut*
. . . . *each* 175.00   195.00

☐ **Assortment D. (19 to 24),** *oak, height 23¼", dial 6", 8 Day, strike, c. 1900 (E1-69).*
. . . . *each* 140.00   170.00

☐ **The Bassos Series,** *oak, 3 different patterns, 1 walnut and 1 oak of each pattern, Whitney, Foli, Agnesi, turnback movement, height 23", dial 6", 8 Day, strike, c. 1890 (E1-73).*
.... *each* **150.00   170.00**

☐ **As above,** *walnut*
.... *each* **175.00   195.00**

☐ **The Contraltos Series,** *oak, 3 different patterns, 1 walnut and 1 oak of each pattern, Cary, Scalchi, Albani, turnback movement, height 22", dial 6", 8 Day, strike, c. 1890 (E1-73).*
.... *each* **140.00   160.00**

☐ **As above,** *walnut*
.... *each* **165.00   185.00**

☐ **The Prima Donnas Series,** *oak, 6 different patterns, 3 walnut and 3 oak, Marie Tempest, Pauline Hall, Fannie Rice, Marion Manola, Louise Montague, Lillian Russell, turnback movement, height 23", dial 6", 8 Day, strike, c. 1890 (E1-73).*
.... *each* **150.00   170.00**

☐ **As above,** *walnut*
.... *each* **175.00   195.00**

TEAR DROP

☐ **Parepa, V.P.,** *spring, height 22", dial 6", 8 Day, strike, c. 1890 (E1-65).*
.... **350.00   450.00**

☐ **Parisian,** *walnut, height 24", dial 6", 8 Day, strike, c. 1890 (E1-65).*
.... **275.00   325.00**

☐ **Texas,** *walnut, height 23", dial 6", 8 Day, strike, c. 1890 (E1-65).*
.... **275.00   325.00**

MANTEL

BLACK IRON

☐ **Cremona,** *black enameled iron, bronze feet and side ornaments, mouldings marbleized, gilt or white dials, regular sash and glass, 10¾" x 16½", dial 5", c. 1890 (E1-71).*
.... **105.00   125.00**

☐ **Maritana,** *black enameled iron, bronze feet and side ornaments, gilt mouldings, gilt or white dials, with regular sash and glass, 12½" x 11", dial 5", c. 1890 (E1-70).*
.... **175.00   200.00**

☐ **Oberon,** *black enameled iron, bronze feet and side ornaments, mouldings marbleized, gilt or white dials, regular sash and glass, 12½" x 11", dial 5", c. 1890, 8 Day, strike (E1-70).*
. . . . **175.00   200.00**

☐ **Tuba,** *black enameled iron, bronzed columns, gilt or white dials, with regular sash and glass, 10½" x 12", dial 5", c. 1890, 8 Day, strike (E1-71).*
. . . . **90.00   110.00**

BLACK WOOD
☐ **Bellini,** *black enameled wood, bronze feet and side ornaments, panels marbleized, white or gilt dials, regular sash and glass, 11" x 16", dial 5", c. 1890, 8 Day, strike (E1-71).*
. . . . **75.00   90.00**

☐ **Camilla Urso,** *black enameled wood, bronze feet and side ornaments, mouldings and panels marbleized, white or gilt dials, regular sash and glass, 11" x 16½", dial 5", c. 1890, 8 Day, strike (E1-70).*
. . . . **85.00   105.00**

☐ **Del Puente,** *black enameled wood, bronze feet and side ornaments, mouldings marbleized, white, black or gilt dials, regular sash and glass, c. 1890, 8 Day, strike (E1-73).*
. . . . **85.00   105.00**

☐ **De Murska,** *black enameled wood, bronze feet and side ornaments, mouldings marbleized, white, black or gilt dials, regular sash and glass, 11" x 17", dial 5", c. 1890, 8 Day, strike (E1-73).*
. . . . **90.00   110.00**

☐ **Kodak,** *black enameled wood, bronze feet and side ornaments, mouldings marbleized, white, black or gilt dials, regular sash and glass, 11" x 16½", dial 5", c. 1890, 8 Day, strike (E1-71).*
. . . . **85.00   105.00**

☐ **La Favorita,** *black enameled wood, bronze feet and side ornaments, columns marbleized, white or gilt dials, with regular sash and glass, 11" x 15½", dial 5", c. 1890, 8 Day, strike (E1-70).*
. . . . **85.00   105.00**

NOVELTY
FANCY
☐ **The Escalop,** *nickel, height 4", c. 1890, 1 Day (E1-67).*
. . . . **20.00   30.00**

☐ **The Jewel,** *cut glass case in crystal (white), amber and sapphire, height 3½", porcelain dial 2½", c. 1890, 1 Day (E1-67).*
.... 30.00   40.00

IRON

☐ **Chalet,** *gilt or nickel, diamond pin escapement, solid steel pinion movement, height 9", dial 3", c. 1875, 8 Day, pendulum (E1-62).*
.... 65.00   80.00

☐ **Egypt,** *gilt or nickel, height 7¾", dial 3", c. 1875, 1 Day, lever (E1-62).*
.... 60.00   75.00

☐ **Fire Bug,** *nickel, lamp lights automatically at the hour for alarm, height 8", dial 3", c. 1875, 1 Day, alarm, lever (E1-62).*
.... 80.00   100.00

☐ **Galaxy,** *gilt or nickel, height 7¾", dial 3", c. 1875, 1 Day, lever (E1-62).*
.... 50.00   65.00

☐ **Good Luck,** *gilt or nickel, height 6", dial 3", c. 1875, 1 Day, lever (E1-62).*
.... 40.00   50.00

☐ **La Banniere,** *gilt or nickel, height 9", dial 3", c. 1875, 1 Day, lever (E1-62).*
.... 80.00   100.00

☐ **La Belle,** *gilt or nickel, height 6", dial 3", c. 1875, 1 Day, lever (E1-62).*
.... 45.00   60.00

☐ **La Reine,** *gilt or nickel, height 8¼", dial 3", c. 1875, 1 Day, lever (E1-62).*
.... 80.00   95.00
☐ **As above,** *8 Day, pendulum*
.... 85.00   105.00

☐ **Le Prince,** *gilt or nickel, height 8", dial 3", c. 1875, 1 Day, lever (E1-62).*
.... 65.00   80.00

☐ **Le Roi,** *gilt or nickel, height 6½", dial 3", c. 1875, 1 Day, lever (E1-62).*
.... 50.00   65.00

☐ **L'Imperial,** *gilt or nickel, height 9¼", dial 3", c. 1875, 1 Day, lever (E1-62).*
.... 80.00   100.00
☐ **As above,** *8 Day, pendulum*
.... 90.00   110.00

PATTI MOVEMENTS

☐ **Cary, V.P.,** *height 20", wood dial 5", c. 1875, 8 Day, strike, spring (E1-63).*
. . . . 750.00   850.00

☐ **Eveline,** *oak, height 17½", dial 5", c. 1890, 8 Day, strike (E1-65).*
. . . . 675.00   750.00

☐ **As above,** *mahogany*
. . . . 725.00   800.00

☐ **Gerster, V.P.,** *wood, height 18½", dial 5", c. 1875, 8 Day, strike, spring (E1-63).*
. . . . 750.00   850.00

☐ **Nilsson,** *polished mahogany, cathedral bell, height 22", dial 6", c. 1890, 8 Day, strike (E1-65).*
. . . . 800.00   900.00

☐ **As above,** *walnut*
. . . . 850.00   950.00

☐ **Parepa, V.P.,** *height 22", wood dial 6", c. 1875, 8 Day, strike, spring (E1-63).*
. . . . 360.00   400.00

☐ **Patti, V.P.,** *wood, height 18½", dial 5", c. 1875, 8 Day, strike, spring (E1-63).*
. . . . 725.00   800.00

☐ **Patti No. 2, V.P.,** *wood, height 10¼", dial 3", c. 1875, 8 Day, spring (E1-63).*
. . . . 1665.00   1850.00

☐ **Scalchi,** *walnut, height 19½", dial 5", c. 1890, 8 Day, strike (E1-65).*
. . . . 725.00   800.00

☐ **Victoria,** *ebony, plain or gilded front, hand painted, height 13½", dial 4", c. 1890, 8 Day, strike (E1-65).*
. . . . 725.00   800.00

REGULATOR
FIGURE "8"

☐ **Alexis No. 1,** *wood, height 26", dial 12", c. 1875, 8 Day, spring (E1-63).*
. . . . 270.00   300.00

☐ **As above,** *8 Day, strike, spring*
. . . . 285.00   325.00

☐ **As above,** *30 Day, duplex*
. . . . 310.00   350.00

☐ **Alexis No. 2,** *wood, height 22", dial 10", c. 1875, 8 Day, spring (E1-63).*
. . . . 270.00   300.00

☐ **As above,** *8 Day, strike, spring*
. . . . 285.00   325.00

☐ **Ionic,** *wood, height 22", c. 1875, 8 Day, spring (E1-20).*
. . . . 270.00   300.00

☐ **As above,** *8 Day, strike, spring*
. . . . 285.00   325.00

☐ **Regulator,** *wood, height 2'9", dial 12", c. 1875 (E1-20).*
. . . . 1125.00   1250.00

OCTAGON TOP, LONG DROP

☐ **St. Clair Calendar,** *oak, height 32½", dial 12", c. 1900, 8 Day (E1-69).*
. . . . 270.00   300.00
☐ **As above,** *8 Day, strike*
. . . . 285.00   325.00
☐ **As above,** *8 Day, calendar*
. . . . 310.00   350.00
☐ **As above,** *8 Day, strike, calendar*
. . . . 335.00   375.00

☐ **Star Pointer Calendar,** *oak, height 32½", dial 12", c. 1900, 8 Day (E1-69).*
. . . . 270.00   300.00
☐ **As above,** *8 Day, strike*
. . . . 285.00   325.00
☐ **As above,** *8 Day, calendar*
. . . . 310.00   350.00
☐ **As above,** *8 Day, strike, calendar*
. . . . 335.00   375.00

☐ **Verdi,** *wood, height 31", dial 12", c. 1875 8 Day, strike (E1-63).*
. . . . 310.00   350.00

OCTAGON TOP, SHORT DROP

☐ **Axtell,** *drop octagon, rosewood finish, height 25", dial 12", c. 1890, 8 Day, spring (E1-72).*
. . . . 195.00   225.00
☐ **As above,** *8 Day, strike, spring*
. . . . 220.00   250.00
☐ **As above,** *8 Day, calendar, spring*
. . . . 245.00   275.00
☐ **As above,** *8 Day, strike, calendar, spring*
. . . . 270.00   300.00

☐ **8" Inch Drop Octagon,** *rosewood, height 18¾", dial 8", c. 1890, 8 Day (E1-72).*
. . . . 150.00   175.00
☐ **As above,** *8 Day, strike*
. . . . 175.00   200.00
☐ **As above,** *8 Day, calendar*
. . . . 195.00   225.00
☐ **As above,** *8 Day, strike, calendar*
. . . . 270.00   300.00
☐ **As above,** *zebra, 8 Day*
. . . . 170.00   195.00
☐ **As above,** *zebra, 8 Day, strike*
. . . . 195.00   220.00
☐ **As above,** *zebra, 8 Day, calendar*
. . . . 205.00   245.00
☐ **As above,** *zebra, 8 Day, strike, calendar*
. . . . 290.00   320.00

☐ **Drop Octagon,** *wood, height 25", dial 12", c. 1875, 8 Day, spring (E1-20).*
. . . . 310.00   350.00
☐ **As above,** *8 Day, strike, spring*
. . . . 360.00   400.00

☐ **Drop Octagon, R.C.,** *wood, height 25", dial 12", c. 1875, 8 Day, spring (E1-63).*
. . . . 195.00   225.00
☐ **As above,** *8 Day, strike, spring*
. . . . 220.00   250.00

☐ **Drop Octagon No. 1,** *rosewood, spring, height 24½", dial 12", c. 1890, 8 Day (E1-72).*
. . . . 195.00   225.00
☐ **As above,** *8 Day, strike*
. . . . 220.00   250.00

☐ **Drop Octagon No. 2,** *wood, height 25", dial 12", c. 1875, 8 Day, spring (E1-63).*
.... **220.00   250.00**
☐ **As above,** *8 Day, strike, spring*
.... **245.00   275.00**

☐ **Gentry Calendar,** *oak, height 26", dial 12", c. 1900, 8 Day (E1-69).*
.... **195.00   225.00**
☐ **As above,** *8 Day, strike*
.... **220.00   250.00**
☐ **As above,** *8 Day, calendar*
.... **245.00   275.00**
☐ **As above,** *8 Day, strike, calendar*
.... **270.00   300.00**

☐ **Patchen Calendar,** *oak, height 26", dial 12", c. 1900, 8 Day (E1-69).*
.... **195.00   225.00**
☐ **As above,** *8 Day, strike*
.... **220.00   250.00**
☐ **As above,** *8 Day, strike, calendar*
.... **270.00   300.00**
☐ **As above,** *8 Day calendar*
.... **245.00   275.00**

PARLOR SHELF

☐ **Lucca, V.P.,** *wood, height 24", dial 6", c. 1890, 8 Day, strike (E1-65).*
.... **540.00   600.00**

PARLOR WALL

☐ **Italian Hanging, V.P.,** *wood, height 28", dial 7", c. 1875, 8 Day, strike (E1-63).*
.... **1260.00   1400.00**

☐ **Meyerbeer,** *walnut, height 40", dial 8", c. 1890, 8 Day, spring (E1-66).*
.... **640.00   700.00**
☐ **As above,** *8 Day, calendar, spring*
.... **725.00   800.00**
☐ **As above,** *8 Day, strike, spring*
.... **825.00   900.00**
☐ **As above,** *8 Day, strike, spring, calendar*
.... **900.00   1000.00**
☐ **As above,** *oak, 8 Day, spring*
.... **540.00   600.00**
☐ **As above,** *oak, 8 Day, calendar, spring*
.... **625.00   700.00**
☐ **As above,** *8 Day, strike, spring*
.... **725.00   800.00**
☐ **As above,** *8 Day, strike, calendar, spring*
.... **800.00   900.00**

☐ **Regulator G.,** *mahogany, hanging, height 51½", dial 10", c. 1890, 8 Day, weight.*
.... **1215.00   1350.00**
☐ **As above,** *walnut*
.... **1240.00   1375.00**
☐ **As above,** *ash*
.... **1265.00   1400.00**

☐ **Regulator H.,** *mahogany, hanging, height 38", dial 8", c. 1890, 8 Day, spring (E1-64).*
.... 490.00   550.00
☐ **As above,** *8 Day, strike, spring*
.... 540.00   600.00
☐ **As above,** *8 Day, calendar, spring*
.... 625.00   700.00
☐ **As above,** *8 Day, strike, calendar, spring*
.... 675.00   750.00
☐ **As above,** *walnut, 8 Day, spring*
.... 515.00   575.00
☐ **As above,** *walnut, 8 Day, strike, spring*
.... 565.00   625.00
☐ **As above,** *walnut, 8 Day, calendar, spring*
.... 650.00   725.00
☐ **As above,** *walnut, 8 Day, strike, calendar, spring*
.... 700.00   775.00
☐ **As above,** *ash, 8 Day, spring*
.... 540.00   600.00
☐ **As above,** *ash, 8 Day, strike, spring*
.... 590.00   650.00
☐ **As above,** *ash, 8 Day, calendar, spring*
.... 675.00   750.00

☐ **Regulator No. 6,** *wood, height 41", dial 8", c. 1875, 8 Day, weight (E1-63).*
.... 360.00   400.00

ROUND TOP, LONG DROP

☐ **Regulator No. 3,** *wood, height 35", dial 12", c. 1890, 8 Day, weight (E1-65).*
.... 575.00   650.00

ROUND TOP, SHORT DROP
☐ **Round Head,** *wood, height 26", dial 12", c. 1875, 8 Day, spring (E1-63).*
.... 270.00   300.00
☐ **As above,** *8 Day, strike, spring*
.... 310.00   350.00

☐ **Round Top Drop,** *wood, height 24", c. 1875, 8 Day, spring.*
.... 270.00   300.00
☐ **As above,** *8 Day, strike, spring*
.... 285.00   325.00

SECONDS BIT
☐ **Regulator No. 2,** *wood, height 53", dial 18", c. 1890, 8 Day, weight (E1-64).*
.... 900.00   1000.00

☐ **Regulator No. 11,** *oak, seconds pendulum, 60" x 18", dial 10", c. 1890, 30 Day (E1-67).*
.... **1000.00   1175.00**

☐ **As above,** *mahogany*
.... **1150.00   1325.00**

☐ **As above,** *walnut*
.... **1200.00   1375.00**

☐ **Regulator No. 12,** *oak, seconds pendulum, 66" x 22½", dial 12", c. 1890, 30 Day (E1-67).*
.... **1530.00   1700.00**

☐ **As above,** *mahogany*
.... **1680.00   1850.00**

☐ **As above,** *walnut*
.... **1730.00   1900.00**

☐ **Regulator E.,** *mahogany, hanging, height 56", dial 10", c. 1890, 8 Day, weight (E1-64).*
.... **1350.00   1500.00**

☐ **As above,** *walnut*
.... **1400.00   1550.00**

☐ **As above,** *ash*
.... **1450.00   1600.00**

☐ **Regulator F.,** *mahogany, hanging, height 56", dial 10", c. 1890, 8 Day, weight (E1-64).*
.... **1250.00   1500.00**

☐ **As above,** *ash*
.... **1350.00   1600.00**

☐ **As above,** *walnut*
.... **1300.00   1550.00**

SWEEP SECOND

☐ **Regulator A.,** *oak, three cell mercurial compensating pendulum, dead beat pin escapement, jeweled movement, 108" x 32½", depth 12½", porcelain dial with sweep seconds 12", c. 1890, 8 Day, weight (E1-67).*
.... **3375.00   3750.00**

☐ **As above,** *mahogany*
.... **3525.00   3900.00**

☐ **As above,** *walnut*
.... **3575.00   3950.00**

☐ **Regulator B.,** *standing, oak, metal compensating pendulum, dead beat pin escapement, jeweled movement, sweep second, 108" x 32½", depth 12½", porcelain dial 12", c. 1890, 8 Day, weight (E1-64).*
.... **3150.00   3500.00**

☐ **As above,** *mahogany*
.... **3300.00   3750.00**

☐ **As above,** *walnut*
.... **3350.00   3700.00**

☐ **Regulator C.,** *oak, three cell mercurial compensating pendulum, dead beat pin escapement, jeweled movement, sweep second, 90" x 26", depth 10", c. 1890, 8 Day, weight (E1-67).*
.... **3150.00   3500.00**

☐ **As above,** *mahogany*
.... **3300.00   3750.00**

☐ **As above,** *walnut*
.... **3350.00   3700.00**

☐ **Regulator D.,** *hanging, mahogany, sweep second, with metal compensating pendulum, height 51½", dial 10", c. 1890, 8 Day, weight (E1-64).*
.... 3240.00   3600.00
☐ **As above,** *ash*
.... 3490.00   3850.00
☐ **As above,** *walnut*
.... 3440.00   3800.00

☐ **Regulator (I) Eye,** *hanging, mahogany, sweep second, 62" x 16¾", dial 10", c. 1890, 8 Day, weight (E1-64).*
.... 1000.00   1700.00
☐ **As above,** *walnut*
.... 1200.00   1900.00
☐ **As above,** *ash*
.... 1250.00   1950.00

☐ **Regulator (J) Jay,** *hanging, mahogany, sweep second, 62" x 14", dial 10", c. 1890, 8 Day, weight (E1-64).*
.... 1100.00   1800.00
☐ **As above,** *walnut*
.... 1300.00   2000.00
☐ **As above,** *ash*
.... 1350.00   2050.00

☐ **Regulator No. 7,** *wood, sweep secondhand, height 47", dial 8", c. 1890, 8 Day, weight (E1-64).*
.... 2250.00   2500.00

☐ **Regulator No. 8,** *walnut, brass weights, sweep second hand, pendulum beats seconds, dead beat escapement, 66" x 19", porcelain dial 9", c. 1890, 8 Day, weight (E1-66).*
.... 1250.00   1550.00

ROTARY

☐ **Brown's Rotary,** *brass or nickel, c. 1875, 1 Day, spring (E1-16).*
.... 325.00   375.00

WATCHES

☐ **Bicycle,** *nickel, luminous dial, watch and holder, c. 1890 (E1-66).*
.... **125.00   150.00**

Back

☐ **The Columbian,** *nickel or gilt, height 4½", length 4", c. 1890, 1 Day (E1-66).*
.... **310.00   350.00**

Front

TEMPUS VITAM REGIT

THE NATIONAL ASSOCIATION OF
WATCH AND CLOCK COLLECTORS, INC.
BOX 33, 514 POPLAR STREET, COLUMBIA, PA 17512

This non-profit, scientific and educational corporation was founded in 1943 to bring together people who are interested in timekeeping in any form or phase. More than 33,000 members now enjoy its benefits. The Headquarters, Museum and Library are located in the Borough of Columbia on the eastern bank of the Susquehanna River within historic Lancaster County, Pennsylvania, where a continuing heritage of clock and watchmaking spans two and one-quarter centuries.

Some of the tangible benefits of membership are the Association's publications. The bi-monthly **Bulletin** is the world's leading publication devoted to timekeeping. It contains papers written by members on technical and historic aspects of horology. Through its "Answer Box" column it also provides the member with an opportunity to direct his "knotty" horological problems to a panel of fifty volunteer authorities from around the world, many of whom are authors of definitive works in their respective areas of interest. Reviews help the collector keep abreast with the ever growing number of horological publications. Activities of the more than 100 Chapters located around the world are also included as are listings of stolen items. The **Mart,** also bi-monthly, is an informal medium in which members may list items that they wish to buy, trade, or sell. Like the **Bulletin,** its circulation exceeds 33,000. Other publications include the **Roster of Members,** a listing of books available through the Association's Lending Library, and occasional papers meriting separate publication.

Another benefit of membership is the use of the Nation's largest collection of books devoted to timekeeping. A number of the titles are duplicated in the Lending Library and may be borrowed through the mail for merely the cost of postage and, on occasion, insurance. The Library is under the supervision of a professional librarian who will also help a member in his research. A visitor can study the various horological periodicals of many sister horological associations around the world. The serious researcher may also examine rare and early works concerning horology. The Nation's only computerized Horological Data Bank is at the member's disposal as are thousands of American patents dealing with timekeeping.

Free admission to the NAWCC Museum in Columbia for both the member and his immediate family is yet another benefit. The Museum offers a rare opportunity to examine a collection of watches, clocks, tools, and other related items which range from the primitive to the modern. The "how and why" of timekeeping is emphasized throughout whether the display be of early non-mechanical timepieces or of the highly sophisticated "Atomic Clock." Movements of wood, iron, and brass are displayed for study. Many of the items exhibited are becoming increasingly rare and beyond the reach of many private collectors. Two special exhibitions are mounted each year: a three-month winter exhibition and a six-month summer exhibition. Items included in the special exhibitions are drawn from the collections of members, friends, and other museums.

Membership in the National Association also makes one eligible for membership in one or more of the more than 100 Chapters located in the United States, Australia, Canada, England, and Japan. It also makes one eligible to register for the regularly scheduled regional and national meetings each year. Chapter, regional, and national meetings usually consist of seminars, exhibits, and an opportunity to improve the member's own collection through trading, buying, or selling to other members. Finally, membership can enable a person to form lasting friendships with some of the finest people in the world: timekeeper enthusiasts!

For a brochure and membership application write to the Administrator, N.A.W.C.C., Box 033, Columbia, PA 17512.

for more information . . .

PRICE GUIDE SERIES

American Silver & Silver Plate

Today's silver market offers excellent opportunities *to gain big profits* — if you are well informed. *Over 15,000 current market values* are listed for 19th and 20th century American made Sterling. Coin and Silverplated flatware and holloware. Special souvenir spoon section. *ILLUSTRATED.*
$9.95-2nd Edition, 576 pgs., 5⅜" x 8", paperback, Order #: 184-5

Antique Clocks

A pictorial price reference for all types of American made clocks. Detailed listings insure positive identification. Includes company histories. *ILLUSTRATED.*
$9.95-1st Edition, 576 pgs., 5⅜" x 8", paperback, Order #: 364-3

Antique & Modern Firearms

This unique book is an encyclopedia of gun lore featuring over *21,000 listings with histories* of American and foreign manufacturers *plus a special section on collector cartridges values.* *ILLUSTRATED.*
$9.95-3rd Edition, 544 pgs., 5⅜" x 8", paperback, Order #: 363-5

Antiques & Other Collectibles

Introduces TODAY'S world of antiques with *over 100,000 current market values* for the most complete listing of antiques and collectibles IN PRINT! In this *new — 832 PAGE edition, many new categories have been added to keep fully up-to-date with the latest collecting trends.* *ILLUSTRATED.*
$9.95-4th Edition, 832 pgs., 5⅜" x 8", paperback, Order #: 374-0

Antique Jewelry

Over *8,200 current collector values* for the most extensive listing of antique jewelry ever published, Georgian, Victorian, Art Nouveau, Art Deco. *Plus a special full color gem identification guide.* *ILLUSTRATED.*
$9.95-2nd Edition, 672 pgs., 5⅜" x 8", paperback, Order #: 354-6

Bottles Old & New

Over *22,000 current buying and selling prices* of both common and rare collectible bottles . . . ale, soda, bitters, flasks, medicine, perfume, poison, milk and more. *Plus expanded sections on Avon and Jim Beam. ILLUSTRATED.*
$9.95-6th Edition, 672 pgs., 5⅜" x 8", paperback, Order #: 350-3

Collector Cars

Over *36,000 actual current prices* for 4000 models of antique and classic automobiles — U.S. and foreign. Complete with engine specifications. *Special sections on auto memorabilia values and restoration techniques. ILLUSTRATED.*
$9.95-4th Edition, 544 pgs., 5⅜" x 8", paperback, Order #: 357-0

Collector Handguns

Over *15,000 current values* for antique and modern handguns. Plus the most up-to-date listing of current production handguns. *ILLUSTRATED.*
$9.95-1st Edition, 544 pgs., 5⅜" x 8", paperback, Order #: 367-8

Collector Knives

Over *13,000 buying and selling prices* on U.S. and foreign pocket and sheath knives. *Special sections on bicentennial, commemorative, limited edition, and handmade knives.* By J. Parker & B. Voyles. *ILLUSTRATED.*
$9.95-5th Edition, 704 pgs., 5⅜" x 8", paperback, Order #: 324-4

Collector Plates

Destined to become the ''PLATE COLLECTORS' BIBLE.'' This unique price guide offers the most comprehensive listing of collector plate values — *in Print! Special information includes: company histories; artist backgrounds; and helpful tips on buying, selling and storing a collection.* *ILLUSTRATED.*
$9.95-1st Edition, 672 pgs., 5⅜" x 8", paperback, Order #: 349-X

PUBLISHED BY: *THE HOUSE OF COLLECTIBLES, INC.*
1900 PREMIER ROW, ORLANDO, FL 32809 PHONE: (305) 857-9095

PRICE GUIDE SERIES

Collector Prints

Over **14,750 detailed listings** representing over 400 of the most famous collector print artists from Audubon and Currier & Ives, to modern day artists. **Special feature includes gallery/artist reference chart.** *ILLUSTRATED.*
$9.95-4th Edition, 544 pgs., 5⅜" x 8", paperback, Order #: 189-6

Comic & Science Fiction Books

Over **31,000 listings with current values** for comic and science fiction publications **from 1903-to-date. Special sections on Tarzan, Big Little Books, Science Fiction publications and paperbacks.** *ILLUSTRATED.*
$9.95-6th Edition, 544 pgs., 5⅜" x 8", paperback, Order #: 353-8

Glassware

Over **25,000 listings** for all types of American made glassware, pressed and pattern, depression, cut, carnival and more. *ILLUSTRATED.*
$9.95-1st Edition, 544 pgs., 5⅜" x 8", paperback, Order #: 125-X

Hummel Figurines & Plates

The most complete guide ever published on every type of Hummel — including the most recent trademarks and size variations, with **4,500 up-to-date prices. Plus tips on buying, selling and investing.** *ILLUSTRATED.*
$9.95-3rd Edition, 448 pgs., 5⅜" x 8", paperback, Order #: 325-X

Kitchen Collectibles

This beautiful pictorial guide has over **1,100 illustrations** - truly a MASTERPIECE of reference. This first really complete *History of America in the Kitchen* describes hundreds of implements and lists their current market values. *ILLUSTRATED.*
$9.95-1st Edition, 544 pgs., 5⅜" x 8", paperback, Order #: 371-6

Military Collectibles

This detailed historical reference price guide covers the largest accumulation of military objects — 15th century-to-date — listing over **12,000 accurate prices. Special expanded Samuri sword and headdress sections.** *ILLUSTRATED.*
$9.95-2nd Edition, 576 pgs., 5⅜" x 8", paperback, Order #: 191-8

Music Machines

Virtually every music related collectible is included in this guide — over **11,000 current prices. 78 recordings, mechanical musical machines, and instruments.** *ILLUSTRATED.*
$9.95-2nd Edition, 544 pgs., 5⅜" x 8", paperback, Order #: 187-X

Old Books & Autographs

Descriptions of the finest literary collectibles available, with over **11,000 prices for all types of books:** Americana, bibles, medicine, cookbooks and more. **Plus an updated autograph section.** *ILLUSTRATED.*
$9.95-4th Edition, 512 pgs., 5⅜" x 8", paperback, Order #: 351-1

Oriental Collectibles

Over **15,000 detailed listings and values** for all types of Chinese & Japanese collectibles, pottery, rugs, statues, porcelain, cloisonne, metalware. *ILLUSTRATED.*
$9.95-1st Edition, 544 pgs., 5⅜" x 8", paperback, Order #: 375-9

Paper Collectibles

Old Checks, Invoices, Books, Magazines, Newspapers, Ticket Stubs and even Matchbooks — any paper items that reflects America's past — are gaining collector value. This book contains **over 25,000 current values** and descriptions for all types of paper collectibles. *ILLUSTRATED.*
$9.95-2nd Edition, 608 pgs., 5⅜" x 8", paperback, Order #: 186-1

Pottery & Porcelain

Over **10,000 current prices and listings** of fine pottery and porcelain, plus an extensive Lenox china section. **Special sections on identifying china trademarks and company histories.** *ILLUSTRATED.*
$9.95-2nd Edition, 576 pgs., 5⅜" x 8", paperback, Order #: 188-8

PUBLISHED BY: *THE HOUSE OF COLLECTIBLES, INC.*
1900 PREMIER ROW, ORLANDO, FL 32809   PHONE: (305) 857-9095

PRICE GUIDE SERIES

Records

Over **31,000 current prices** of collectible singles, EPs, albums, plus 20,000 memorable song titles recorded by over 1100 artists. **Rare biographies and photos are provided for many well known artists.** ILLUSTRATED.
$9.95-4th Edition, 544 pgs., 5⅜" x 8", paperback, Order #: 356-2

Royal Doulton

This authoritative guide to Royal Doulton porcelains contains over **3,500 detailed listings** on figurines, plates and Toby jugs. Includes tips on buying, selling and displaying. **Plus an exclusive numerical reference index.** ILLUSTRATED.
$9.95-2nd Edition, 544 pgs., 5⅜" x 8", paperback, Order #: 355-4

Wicker

You could be sitting on a **fortune!** Decorators and collectors are driving wicker values to unbelievable highs! This pictorial price guide **positively identifies all types** of Victorian, Turn of the century and Art Deco wicker furniture. **A special illustrated section on wicker repair is included.** ILLUSTRATED.
$9.95-1st Edition, 416 pgs., 5⅜" x 8", paperback, Order #: 348-1

Encyclopedia Of Antiques

The House of Collectibles, the world's largest publisher of collector price guides opens its vast archives of knowledge to the public in an easy to use volume that ranks as an **absolute must** for the library of every collector and investor. A total of more than **10,000 definitions, explanations, consise factual summeries of names, dates, histories, confusing terminology** . . . for every popular field of collecting. **An exclusive appendix** includes many trademark and pattern charts as well as a catagorized list of museums and reference publications.
$9.95-1st Edition, 672 pgs., 5⅜" x 8", paperback, Order # 365-1

Buying & Selling Guide To Antiques

Covers every phase of collecting from beginning a collection to its ultimate sale . . . examines in detail the collecting potential of over **200 different catagories** of items in all price ranges — from razors to Rembrant paintings. Learn how the collectibles market operates, which factors determine the value of a collectors item. **Special features include a dealer directory, a condition grading report, list of museums and reference publications, plus a discussion of buying and selling techniques.** ILLUSTRATED.
$9.95-1st Edition, 608 pgs., 5⅜" x 8", paperback, Order #: 369-4

MINI PRICE GUIDE SERIES

Antiques & Flea Markets

Discover the fun and profit of collecting antiques with this handy pocket reference to **over 15,000 types of collectibles**. Avoid counterfeits and learn the secrets to successful buying and selling. ILLUSTRATED.
$2.50-1st Edition, 240 pgs., 4" x 5½", paperback, Order #: 308-2

Antique Jewelry

A handy-pocket sized up-date to the larger Official Price Guide to Antique Jewelry, lists **thousands of values** for bracelets, brooches, chains, earrings, necklaces and more. **Special sections on gold, silver and diamond identification.**
$2.95-1st Edition, 240 pgs., 4" x 5½", paperback, Order #: 373-2

Baseball Cards

This guide lists **over 70,000 current market values** for baseball cards – Bowman, Burger King, Donruss, Fleer, O-Pee-Chee and Topps. ILLUSTRATED.
$2.95-3rd Edition, 288 pgs., 4" x 5½", paperback, Order #: 376-7

PUBLISHED BY: **THE HOUSE OF COLLECTIBLES, INC.**
1900 PREMIER ROW, ORLANDO, FL 32809   PHONE: (305) 857-9095

MINI PRICE GUIDE SERIES

Beer Cans
The first pocket-sized guide to list *thousands of values* for cone and flat top beer cans produced since the mid 1930's. Each listing is graphically detailed for positive identification.
$2.95-1st Edition, 240 pgs., 4″ x 5½″, paperback, Order #: 377-5

Comic Books
Young and Old are collecting old comic books for fun *and Profit!* This handy ''pocket-sized'' price guide lists current market values and detailed descriptions for the most sought-after ''collectible'' comic books. *Buying, selling and storing tips are provided for the beginning collector.* *ILLUSTRATED.*
$2.50-1st Edition, 240 pgs., 4″ x 5½″, paperback, Order #: 345-7

Dolls
Doll collecting is one of America's favorite hobbies and this guide lists *over 3,000 actual market values* for all the manufacturers! Kewpies, Howdy Doody, Shirley Temple, GI Joe plus comprehensive listings of Barbies. *ILLUSTRATED.*
$2.95-1st Edition, 240 pgs., 4″ x 5½″, paperback, Order #: 316-3

O.J. Simpson Football Cards
The world famous O.J. Simpson highlights this comprehensive guide to football card values. *Over 21,000 current collector prices* are listed for: Topps, Bowman, Fleer, Philadelphia and O-Pee-Chee. *Includes a full color O.J. SIMPSON limited edition collector card. ILLUSTRATED.*
$2.50-2nd Edition, 256 pgs., 4″ x 5½″, paperback, Order #: 323-6

Hummels
How much are your Hummels worth? You can become an expert on these lovely figurines with this guide, *FULLY ILLUSTRATED,* with a handy numerical index that puts descriptions and *3,000 market prices* at your fingertips. Learn why the slightest variation could mean hundreds in value.
$2.95-1st Edition, 240 pgs., 4″ x 5½″, paperback, Order #:318-X

Paperbacks & Magazines
Old discarded paperbacks and magazines could be worth 50-100 times their original cover price. Learn how to identify them. *Thousands* of descriptions and prices show which issues are rare. *ILLUSTRATED.*
$2.50-1st Edition, 240 pgs., 4″ x 5½″, paperback, Order #: 315-5

Pocket Knives
This mid-season up-date to the larger *Official Price Guide to Collector Knives* lists *over 4,000 collector values* for Case, Kabar, Cattaraugus, Remington, Winchester and more. *Special sections on buying and selling plus a list of limited edition pocket knives.*
$2.95-1st Edition, 240 pgs., 4″ x 5½″, paperback, Order #: 372-4

Scouting Collectibles
Discover the colorful history behind scouting, relive childhood memories and profit from those old family heirlooms. *Thousands of prices* are listed for all types of Boy and Girl Scout memorabilia. *ILLUSTRATED.*
$2.50-1st Edition, 240 pgs., 4″ x 5½″, paperback, Order #: 314-7

Star Trek / Star Wars
The most startling phenomena in decades! Star Trek and Star Wars fans have created a space age world of collectibles. *Thousands of current values* for book, posters, photos, costumes, models, jewelry and more . . . *plus tips on buying, selling and trading.ILLUSTRATED.*
$2.95-1st Edition, 240 pgs., 4″ x 5½″, paperback, Order #: 319-8

Toys
Kids from eight to eighty enjoy collecting toys and this comprehensive guide has them all! Trains, trucks, comic and movie character, space toys, boats and **MORE.** *Over 8,000 current market values* of toys, old and new, plus investment tips and histories. *ILLUSTRATED.*
$2.95-1st Edition, 240 pgs., 4″ x 5½″, paperback, Order #: 317-1

PUBLISHED BY: *THE HOUSE OF COLLECTIBLES, INC.*
1900 PREMIER ROW, ORLANDO, FL 32809   PHONE: (305) 857-9095